Property of

Julia Nelson 1933
&
Sheldon Nelson

Julia Nelson
1934

Judy Foster

Julia Nelson

NEW
HIGH SCHOOL ALGEBRA

BY

WEBSTER WELLS, S.B.
AUTHOR OF A SERIES OF TEXTS ON MATHEMATICS

AND

WALTER W. HART, A.B.
ASSISTANT PROFESSOR OF MATHEMATICS, UNIVERSITY OF WISCONSIN
COURSE FOR THE TRAINING OF TEACHERS

D. C. HEATH & CO., PUBLISHERS
BOSTON   NEW YORK   CHICAGO

COPYRIGHT, 1912,
BY D. C. HEATH & CO.

3 A 2

This book may be had
with answers or *without answers*
at the same price.

Answer books, bound in paper, may be
obtained free of charge by *teachers*.

PRINTED IN U.S.A.

PREFACE

This text contains sufficient material for the customary three semester courses in algebra, and will be found to meet adequately the varied college entrance requirements. The first part of the text is identical with the corresponding part of the authors' First Year Algebra. Attention is directed to the following features of the text:

By changing the traditional order of topics, some of the confusing difficulties of algebra are postponed until the third semester. Note the omission from Chapter VIII of certain types of factoring and of the generalized forms of even the simple types. These topics are gathered together in Chapter XVI, where they form a desirable review and extension of Chapter VIII. Obviously this chapter may be taken immediately after Chapter VIII if desired. Note also that Chapter XIV contains only so much of evolution and radicals as is required in the solution of quadratic equations. The subjects exponents and radicals are treated toward the end of the course. These chapters also may be taken in their traditional order, before quadratics, if desired. Note also that Chapter II contains only addition and multiplication of signed numbers, leaving subtraction and division until a later time. Note finally the Chapter XXVI containing supplementary topics. Many teachers will wish to use some of these topics in connection with earlier chapters.

In the early part of the text especially, each topic taken up is used in the solution of equations. (See §§ 9, 10, 12, 41, 51, 60, 107, etc.) In this manner the study of the topics is made purposeful and the equation receives desirable emphasis.

Problems are introduced at short intervals. Informational, geometric, and physics problems are used, as well as other valuable types. New types are introduced gradually, are

iii

taught with extreme care, appearing first in classified lists and thereafter in miscellaneous lists. Experimental verification is suggested for some of the facts from geometry and physics that are used. (See Exercises 7, 25, 28, 39, 49, 106; §§ 13, 142, 143, 190, etc.)

The abstract drill examples are simple rather than complex, are graded with extreme care, and are sufficient in quantity to meet the needs of the average class.

Mechanical processes like "transposition" and "clearing of fractions" are not introduced until the student is familiar with the underlying principles. In this manner thoughtful solution of exercises by the student is made habitual.

Efficiency in arithmetic is maintained and increased by the use of fractional and decimal coefficients, by requiring evaluation of expressions, and by expressing quadratic surds in their approximate decimal form. (See in this connection Chapters XIV, XV, and XXI.)

Formulæ are introduced as one of the most practical uses of algebra. (See §§ 17 and 146.) Other applications of algebra are found in §§ 44, 84, 143, 150, 190.

The data for informational problems are, in the main, of permanent rather than temporary interest, and of general rather than local interest.

Graphical representation and graphical methods are introduced from the secondary school point of view. They are viewed as a means of instruction rather than an end. The data for statistical graphs contain only two, or at most three, significant figures.

CONTENTS

		PAGE
I.	LITERAL NUMBERS	2
II.	POSITIVE AND NEGATIVE NUMBERS	23
	Addition of Positive and Negative Numbers	27
	Multiplication of Positive and Negative Numbers	30
III.	ADDITION AND SUBTRACTION OF ALGEBRAIC EXPRESSIONS	34
	Addition of Monomials	35
	Addition of Polynomials	38
	Subtraction	41
	Subtraction of Positive and Negative Numbers	43
	Subtraction of Polynomials	45
IV.	PARENTHESES	55
	Removal of Parentheses	55
	Introduction of Parentheses	59
V.	MULTIPLICATION	65
	Multiplication of Monomials	67
	Multiplication of Polynomials by Monomials	70
	Multiplication of a Polynomial by a Polynomial	72
VI.	DIVISION	85
	Division of Monomials by Monomials	88
	Division of Polynomials by Monomials	90
	Division of Polynomials by Polynomials	91
VII.	SIMPLE EQUATIONS	96
	Properties of Equations	97
VIII.	SPECIAL PRODUCTS AND FACTORING	110
	Quadratic Equations by Factoring	147

CONTENTS

		PAGE
IX.	HIGHEST COMMON FACTOR AND LOWEST COMMON MULTIPLE	154
	Highest Common Factor	155
	Lowest Common Multiple	157
X.	FRACTIONS	160
	Reduction of Fractions	160
	Addition and Subtraction of Fractions	169
	Multiplication of Fractions	175
	Division of Fractions	178
	Complex Fractions	182
XI.	SIMPLE EQUATIONS (*Continued*)	185
	Fractional Equations	185
	Solution of Literal Equations	200
XII.	GRAPHICAL REPRESENTATION	206
XIII.	SIMULTANEOUS LINEAR EQUATIONS	221
	Literal Simultaneous Equations	239
	Equations containing Three Variables	241
XIV.	SQUARE ROOT AND QUADRATIC SURDS	244
	Quadratic Surds	252
XV.	QUADRATIC EQUATIONS	254
	Complete Quadratic Equations	258
	Imaginary Roots in a Quadratic Equation	275
XVI.	SPECIAL PRODUCTS AND FACTORING (ADVANCED TOPICS)	280
	Remainder Theorem	289
	Synthetic Division	290
	Factor Theorem	292
XVII.	QUADRATIC EQUATIONS HAVING TWO VARIABLES	297
	Graphical Solution	297
XVIII.	SIMULTANEOUS EQUATIONS	304
	Involving Quadratics	304

CONTENTS

		PAGE
XIX.	THE THEORY OF QUADRATIC EQUATIONS	315
XX.	EXPONENTS	320
XXI.	RADICALS	330
	Imaginary Numbers	343
	Irrational Equations	346
XXII.	LOGARITHMS	350
XXIII.	PROGRESSIONS	367
	Arithmetic Progression	367
	Geometric Progression	375
XXIV.	THE BINOMIAL THEOREM	382
XXV.	RATIO, PROPORTION, AND VARIATION	386
XXVI.	SUPPLEMENTARY TOPICS	400
	Cube Root	400
	Detached Coefficients	405
	Divisibility of $a^n \pm b^n$	406
	Highest Common Factor by Division	406
	Proof of the Binomial Theorem	410
	Indeterminate Forms	411
	Graphical Solution of Higher Equations	415
	Determinants	417
INDEX		421

ALGEBRA

INTRODUCTION

ALGEBRA is like arithmetic in some respects. Arithmetic consists of the study of addition, subtraction, multiplication, and division of some kinds of numbers, and of the application of this knowledge to some of the common problems of daily life and of business. Algebra continues this study of numbers. In arithmetic, numbers are represented by the digits 1, 2, 3, etc.; sometimes also, they are represented by letters, as, for example, in interest problems, where the principal is represented by P, the rate per cent by R, and the interest by I. These letters make it possible to abbreviate rules; thus, the rule "the interest for one year equals the principal multiplied by the rate per cent," may be expressed by the letters as follows:

$$I = P \times \frac{R}{100}.$$

In algebra, letters are regularly employed to represent numbers. Some new kinds of numbers and many new mathematical ideas are studied, and, as in arithmetic, some of the uses of this knowledge are illustrated.

Algebra has a very long history. A little was known about it centuries before the Christian Era. The oldest mathematical book which we have, written by an Egyptian named Ahmes, contains some problems similar to those found in our algebras. Ahmes lived before 1700 B.C. Knowledge of algebra grew very slowly indeed for many centuries; in fact it was not until the sixteenth century that algebra assumed the form which it has to-day, and since then many discoveries and improvements in it have been made. Many of the wisest mathematicians of former days contributed to this growth. Thanks to their combined achievements and ingenuity, it is now possible for any boy or girl in the first year of high school to get a much broader view of the elementary part of the subject than many of these men had.

Scattered through the text, will be found historical notes calling attention to some of the epoch-making innovations in the development of algebra, together with the name and time of the man making the step forward.

I. LITERAL NUMBER

1. In arithmetic, numbers are represented by the *digits* 1, 2, 3, 4, 5, 6, 7, 8, 9, and 0, and combinations of them. In Algebra, numbers are also represented by letters. Numbers represented by letters are called **Literal Numbers.** The following examples illustrate the use of letters as numbers.

EXAMPLE 1. If a boy saves 5 cents per day, how much does he save:

   (*a*) in 3 days?   (*b*) in 5 days?
    (*c*) in any number of days?

This last result may be expressed by saying, "as many cents as are obtained by finding the product of the number of days and 5."

In algebra, it may be expressed thus:

Let n = the number of days.
Then, $5 \times n$ = the number of cents saved.
 So, if n is 6, $5 \times n$ is 5×6 or 30;
  if n is 8, $5 \times n$ is 5×8 or 40.

EXAMPLE 2. How many inches are there:

  (*a*) in 9 feet?   (*b*) in any number of feet?

Let x = the number of feet.
Then, $12\,x$ = the number of inches in x feet.
 $12\,x$ is read "twelve x."

LITERAL NUMBER

2. Sign of Multiplication. The symbol, ×, is used to indicate multiplication in algebra as well as in arithmetic; it is read "*times*" or "*multiplied by.*" A dot, ·, placed above the line, is also used as a sign of multiplication, and generally even the dot is omitted, so that $12 \times m$ may be written $12 \cdot m$ or $12\,m$. $a \times b$ may be written $a \cdot b$ or ab, and is read "*a b.*"

HISTORICAL NOTE. — The symbol, ×, was first used by an Englishman, Oughtred, about 1631. The symbol, ·, was introduced by Leibnitz in 1693. Multiplication was indicated as early as the thirteenth century, in Hindu and Italian books, by simply writing the factors side by side. This method was forgotten for a time, and was reintroduced by German algebraists during the fifteenth century.

3. The result obtained by multiplying two or more numbers together is called the **Product,** and the numbers are called the **Factors** of the product.

EXERCISE 1

1. What does $10\,d$ mean? $5\,r$? $6\,s$?

2. How much is $10\,d$, when d is 2? 3? 5? 6?

3. How much is $7\,r$, when r is 4? 6? 12? $\frac{5}{7}$?

Another way of expressing this example is to say: "what is the value of $7\,r$ when r is 4?"

4. Find the value of $8\,a$ when a is 5; 15; 2.5; $\frac{3}{4}$.

5. Find the value of $9\,W$ when W is 8; 12; $\frac{4}{3}$.

6. If a equals the number of inches in the line AB, what does $3\,a$ equal? Illustrate it.

    A———a———B

7. If b represents the number of square feet in a rectangle, what does $2\,b$ represent? $\frac{2}{3}b$? $6\,b$?

8. If a man earns $3 per day, what will he earn in 6 days? in 20 days? in n days?

9 If a book costs 75¢, what will three of them cost? x of them? How much is $75x$¢, when x is 4?

10 If a train travels at the rate of 25 miles per hour, how far will it go in 3 hours? in 5 hours? in x hours?

11. One cubic foot of water weighs 62.5 pounds. How much do x cubic feet weigh? How many pounds are $62.5x$ pounds when x is 4? 5? 10?

12. If a farm consists of 85 acres, valued at A dollars per acre, what is the value of the farm? What is it when A is 75?

13. If a man receives y dollars per week, how much will he receive in a year? Find the amount if y is 22.

14. If each of 35 persons contributes s dollars to the expense of an excursion, what is the total expense? Find it when s is 5; 6.

15. If n represents a number, what will represent a number 3 times as large? 5 times? $2\frac{1}{2}$ times? Find the value of each of these when n is 2; 6; 10.

4. The symbols ( ) are called *parentheses*. In mathematics, they mean that the numbers within are to be combined as the signs indicate, and that the result is to be treated as a whole.

Thus, $(3 \times 5) - (7 + 3)$ means: multiply 3 by 5; add 7 and 3; subtract the second result from the first.

5. An Important Multiplication Law. When several numbers are to be multiplied together, the product may be found by multiplying the first factor by the second, that result by the third, and so on.

EXAMPLE 1. $2 \times 3 \times 4 \times 5 = (2 \times 3) \times 4 \times 5 = 6 \times 4 \times 5$
$= (6 \times 4) \times 5 = 24 \times 5 = 120.$

EXAMPLE 2. If a square contains $4a$ square feet, find the area of a square 5 times as large.

SOLUTION: 1. The area is $5 \times 4\,a$ square feet or $(5 \times 4) \times a = 20 \times a = 20\,a$ sq. ft.

2. This result is true for any value of a;
if $\qquad a = 3,\ 4\,a = 12,$
and $\qquad 5 \times 4\,a = 5 \times 12 = 60;$
also $\qquad 20\,a = 20 \times 3 = 60.$

The fact that the result is 60 in both cases shows that the solution is probably correct.

EXERCISE 2

Find, as in Examples 1 and 2, the results in the following examples, and test the results as in 2 for some particular value of the literal number:

1. $6 \times 8\,a.$
2. $7 \times 10\,b.$
3. $9 \times 8\,n.$
4. $9 \times 17\,z.$
5. $3 \times \frac{1}{6}\,m.$
6. $5 \times \frac{3}{5}\,k.$
7. $8 \times \frac{7}{8}\,t.$
8. $12 \times \frac{2}{3}\,x.$

9. If one number is represented by $2\,b$, what will represent a number 3 times as large? one third as large?

10. If John is 4 times as old as James, and if James is $2\,y$ years of age, how old is John? Find both ages if y is 3.

11. If the volume of a sphere is $163\,t$ cubic inches, what is the volume of a sphere 3 times as large?

12. If the interest on a sum of a money is $25\,r$ dollars for one year, what is the interest for 4 years? 3 years? 6 years?

13. There are three numbers of which the first is 4 times the second, and the third is 3 times the first. Represent the second number by s, and find the others. Find their values when the number s is 5.

14. There are three numbers of which the second is 8 times the first, and the third is 4 times the second. Let f represent the first, and then represent the others.

15. The value of A's property is 5 times that of B's, and the value of C's property is 4 times that of A's. Represent the number of dollars B possesses by b, and then represent the number of dollars owned by A and C.

6. An Important Division Law.

Since $2 \times 3a = 6a$, then $6a \div 2 = 3a$.
Similarly, $40x \div 5 = 8x$, since $5 \cdot 8x = 40x$.

Rule. — To divide the product of an arithmetical number and a literal number by an arithmetical number:

1. Find the quotient of the arithmetical numbers.
2. Multiply the quotient of step 1 by the literal number.

EXERCISE 3

1. Divide each of the following numbers by 5:
    (a) $25t$.   (b) $30x$.   (c) $45rs$.   (d) $75y$.

2. Divide each of the following numbers by 3:
    (a) $6r$.   (b) $30c$.   (c) $42d$.   (d) $54e$.

3. Divide each of the numbers in Example 2 by 2.

4. What part of $36w$ is:
    (a) $3w$?   (b) $4w$?   (c) $6w$?   (d) $1w$?

5. What part of $44x$ is:
    (a) $11x$?   (b) $4x$?   (c) $22x$?   (d) $1x$?

Find the following quotients:

6. $39y \div 3$.
7. $96f \div 12$.
8. $81x \div 9$.
9. $49b \div 49$.
10. $120t \div 120$.
11. $45r \div 9$.
12. $63s \div 63$.
13. $72t \div 72$.
14. $25x \div 25$.

HISTORICAL NOTE. — The symbol, $\div$, was introduced by John Pell who lived during the seventeenth century.

7. Use of Literal Numbers in Solving Problems.
Literal numbers aid in solving certain kinds of problems.

EXAMPLE. How long will it take a bricklayer to lay 38,500 bricks if he can lay 3500 in one day?

LITERAL NUMBER

ARITHMETICAL SOLUTION

Since he can lay 3500 bricks in one day, then in the unknown number of days he can lay 3500 times that number of bricks. Since this must be 38,500, according to the statement of the problem, then the number of days must be $\frac{1}{3500}$ of 38,500 or 11.

ALGEBRAIC SOLUTION

Let $n =$ the unknown number of days.
Then, $3500\, n =$ the number of bricks laid in these days,
and $38,500 =$ the number of bricks to be laid.
So, $3500\, n = 38,500$.

Since one n is $\frac{1}{3500}$ of $3500\, n$, divide these two equal numbers by 3500.
Then, $n = 11$.

TEST: 11 is correct, for $3500 \times 11 = 38,500$.

8. The mathematical statement $3500\, n = 38,500$ is called an **Equation**. The literal number in the equation is called the **Unknown Number**.

An **Equation** expresses the equality of two numbers.

The numbers on the right of the equality sign form the **Right Member** of the equation, and the ones on the left, the **Left Member**.

An equation implies a question: "for what value of the unknown number is the equality true?"

For example, in the equation of § 7, n can have only one value, — the one found, 11; thus, n cannot be 10, for 3500×10 is 35,000, and not 38,500.

Finding the value of the unknown is called **Solving the Equation**.

HISTORICAL NOTE. — The equation is implied in Ahmes' book. To indicate the unknown number, he used a word *hau* corresponding to our word *heap*. Diophantus, a Greek mathematician of the fourth century, used for the unknown the last letter, *s*, of the word for number; Vieta, a French mathematician of the sixteenth century, used the vowels, A, E, I, O, U and Y; Harriot, an English mathematician of about the same

ALGEBRA

time, also used the vowels but wrote them with small letters; Descartes, a French mathematician of the same period, used the last letters of the alphabet, x, y, and z.

9. In solving the equation in § 7, two equal numbers were divided by the same number. It is clear that if equal numbers are divided by equal numbers, the quotients are equal.

This fact is used in algebra in the following form:

Rule. — Both members of an equation may be divided by the same number without destroying the equality.

EXAMPLE. Solve the equation:
$$36\,k = 468.$$

SOLUTION: 1. Since k is $\frac{1}{36}$ of $36\,k$, divide both members of the equation by 36.

2. $\qquad\qquad k = \frac{468}{36}$ \hfill (Rule § 9)
3. $\qquad\qquad\quad = 13.$

EXERCISE 4

Solve the following equations:

1. $7\,p = 238.$
2. $8\,n = 608.$
3. $9\,x = 423.$
4. $6\,A = 312.$
5. $15\,x = 240.$
6. $27\,y = 351.$
7. $2\,x = 161.$
8. $5\,v = 218.$
9. $8\,m = 1864.$
10. $10\,w = 2345.$

The arithmetical solution of the following examples is easy. Their algebraic solution leads to the simplest form of equation. Give the algebraic solution.

11. What number multiplied by 13 equals 221?

12. The product of a certain number and 17 equals 408; find the number.

13. A farm consisting of 43 acres is offered for sale at the price $3655. What is the average price per acre?

14. What number multiplied by 3.7 equals 8.51?

LITERAL NUMBER

15. If the total expense for a picnic for a party of 18 boys and girls is $5.94, how much must each one contribute?

16. A man is compelled to make a journey of 126 miles in his automobile over a poor road in 7 hours; how many miles must he average per hour?

17. The fastest train on the Pennsylvania Railroad between St. Louis and New York makes the trip in 24 hours; if the distance is 1052.4 miles, what is the average rate per hour?

10. A second rule used in solving equations is:

Rule.— Both members of an equation may be multiplied by the same number without destroying the equality.

This fact may be illustrated by the scales. Suppose that the sugar S balances the weight W; if the weight is doubled, then the weight of sugar must also be doubled in order to keep the balance.

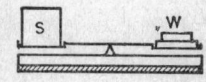

EXAMPLE 1. The circumference of one of the large redwood trees of California is 70 feet. Find its diameter. (The circumference of a circle is twenty-two sevenths of its diameter.)

SOLUTION: 1. Let d = the number of feet in the diameter.

2. Then, $\frac{22}{7}d = 70$, the number of feet in the circumference.

3. Multiply both members of the equation by 7.

Then, $\overset{1}{7} \cdot \frac{22}{7}d = 7 \cdot 70,$ (§ 10)

or $22\,d = 490.$

4. Divide both members of the equation by 22.

Then, $d = \frac{490}{22} = 22\frac{3}{11},$ or 22.2+ feet.

CHECK: Does $\frac{22}{7}$ of $22\frac{3}{11} = 70$?

$$\frac{22}{7} \times 22\frac{3}{11} = \frac{\overset{2}{\cancel{22}}}{\cancel{7}} \times \frac{\overset{35}{\cancel{245}}}{\cancel{11}} = 70.$$

ALGEBRA

EXAMPLE 2. Solve the equation $\frac{5}{8}x = 142$.

SOLUTION: 1. $\frac{5}{8}x = 142$.

2. Multiply both members of the equation by **8**.

Then, $\overset{1}{\cancel{8}} \cdot \frac{5}{\cancel{8}} x = 8 \cdot 142,$ (Rule, § 10)

or $5x = 1136.$

3. Divide both members of the equation of step 2 by **5**.

Then, $x = \overset{227.2}{\cancel{1136}/\cancel{5}} = 227.2.$ (Rule, § 9)

CHECK: Does $\frac{5}{8} \times \overset{28.4}{\cancel{227.2}} = 5 \times 28.4 = 142.0$? Yes.

EXERCISE 5

Solve the following equations and problems:

1. $8a = 280$.
2. $15y = 345$.
3. $27c = 1242$.
4. $76m = 1444$.
5. $27.5x = 277.75$.
6. $\frac{3}{5}x = 81$.
7. $\frac{4}{3}y = 188$.
8. $\frac{3}{7}z = 96$.
9. $\frac{11}{4}t = 429$.
10. $\frac{5}{9}r = 200$.

11. Three tenths of the cost of a certain automobile is $210. Find the cost of the automobile.

12. The selling price of a certain book is $\frac{5}{4}$ of its cost. Find its cost if it sells for $1.50.

13. Five eighths of a certain number is 95. Find the number.

14. Thirteen ninths of a certain number is 143. Find the number.

15. Two fifths of the area of Lake Michigan is 9200 square miles. Find the area of Lake Michigan.

16. Three eighths of the cost of the Suez Canal was $37,500,000. Find the cost of the canal.

LITERAL NUMBER

17. Seven twenty-fifths of the distance from New York to San Francisco is 910 miles. Find the distance from New York to San Francisco.

18. Many metal articles, like a brass candlestick, are made by pouring melted metal into a mold. The piece taken from the mold is called a casting.

In making a brass casting, $\frac{3}{200}$ of the metal is lost in the melting. How much brass must be melted to make a casting which will weigh 72 pounds? (Find the second decimal.)

19. Cottonseed meal is used as a fertilizer on farms. It contains about 7% of nitrogen, a necessary plant food. How many pounds of cottonseed meal must a farmer purchase who wishes to distribute 15 pounds of nitrogen over an acre of ground?

20. Tobacco stems also are used as a fertilizer. They contain about 8% of potash, another necessary plant food. How many pounds of tobacco stems must a farmer purchase who wishes to obtain 12 pounds of potash?

11. Addition and Subtraction of Numbers having a Common Factor.

A number which is a factor of two or more numbers is called a **Common Factor** of these numbers.

> Thus, 3 is a common factor of 6 and 9.
> a is a common factor of $4a$ and $7a$.
> 5 is a common factor of 3×5 and 2×5.

A short method of adding numbers which have a common factor is illustrated in the following examples.

HISTORICAL NOTE. — The symbol, $+$, was first used in print by a German mathematician, Widmann, in 1489. The origin of the symbol is much in doubt. Italian writers of this period used the symbol $\bar{p}$, the first letter of the Latin word *plus*. One explanation given for the sign, $+$, is that it comes from an inverted t, $\mathbf{\imath}$. The Latin word, *et*, means *and*, and in place of it this inverted t was often used. It is easy to see how the symbol $+$ may have been derived from the symbol, $\mathbf{\imath}$.

ALGEBRA

EXERCISE 6

1. 3 times 7 plus 2 times 7 is 5 times 7

   $3 \times 7 \quad + \quad 2 \times 7 \;=\; 5 \times 7$
   for $\quad\;\; 21 \quad + \quad\;\; 14 \;=\;\;\; 35.$

2. $(12 \times 9)+(8 \times 9) = 20 \times 9 = ?$
3. $(8 \times 4)+(7 \times 4) = (?) \times 4 = ?$
4. $(5 \times 7)+(6 \times 7)+(9 \times 7) = (?) \times 7 = ?$
5. 6 times $n + 4$ times $n = (?)$ times n?
6. $6x + 4x = (?)x$?
7. $7a + 3a = ?$
8. $11y + 8y + 5y = ?$
9. $12v + 6v + 3v = ?$
10. $2r + 3r + 5r + 10r = ?$
11. $(5 \times 4)-(2 \times 4) = 3 \times 4 = 12$, for $20 - 8 = 12$.
12. $(10 \times 7)-(4 \times 7) = (?) \times 7 = ?$
13. $(12 \times 8)-(5 \times 8) = (?) \times 8 = ?$
14. $9x - 5x = (?)x$?
15. $16b - 5b = ?$
16. $20y - 10y = ?$
17. $4m + 6m - 2m = ?$
18. $13t - 5t + 9t - 4t = ?$
19. $12A + 6A - 2A + 5A = ?$
20. $8r + 13r - 11r + 5r = ?$

21. One number is four times another. Represent the smaller by s. Then represent the larger and find their sum.

22. One number is $\frac{2}{3}$ as great as another. Let b equal the larger. Represent the smaller and find their sum.

23. One number is 5 times as large as another. Let s equal the smaller. Represent the larger and then find their difference.

24. The base of a rectangle is three times the altitude. Represent the altitude by a; then represent the base. Find also the perimeter.

(The perimeter is the sum of the lengths of the sides.)

25. What is the perimeter of a triangle if one of its sides is $2t$ inches, if the second side is three times as long as the first and the third side is $2\frac{1}{2}$ times as long as the first?

LITERAL NUMBER

26. How many inches in n feet? in n yards? in n yards $+ n$ feet $+ n$ inches?

27. How many cents in x nickels? in x dimes? in x dimes $+ x$ nickels $+ x$ cents?

Simplify the following:

28. $2c + \frac{1}{2}c$. **30.** $5x + \frac{2}{7}x$. **32.** $2b + .25b$. **34.** $\frac{1}{2}x + \frac{1}{6}x$.

29. $3c + \frac{2}{3}c$. **31.** $3c + .2c$. **33.** $4m + .15m$. **35.** $\frac{2}{3}y + \frac{1}{2}y$.

12. Addition of Literal Numbers used in Equations.

EXAMPLE 1. The sum of two numbers is 91. The greater number is 12 times the smaller. Find the numbers.

SOLUTION: 1. Let $\quad s =$ the smaller number.

2. Then, $\quad 12s =$ the larger number.

3. Then, $\quad s + 12s = 91$, since the sum of the numbers is 91.

4. Adding, $\quad 13s = 91$.

5. Dividing, $\quad s = 7$.

CHECK: If the smaller number is 7, the larger must be 84 and their sum is 91.

EXERCISE 7

Solve and check the following equations:

1. $3a + 4a = 42$.

2. $4m + 5m = 108$.

3. $7b - b = 66$.

4. $3x + 7x = 120$.

5. $11y - 2y = 81$.

6. $6z + 5z = 99$.

7. $3x + 11x + 12x = 130$.

8. $15t + 8t - 3t = 20$.

9. $7r - 5r + 6r = 4$.

10. $18w - 7w + 9w = 65$.

11. $22x + 13x - 6x = 116$.

12. $16y - 3y + 4y = 102$.

13. The greater of two numbers is four times the smaller. The sum of the numbers is 60. Find the numbers.

14. If five times a certain number is increased by three times the same number, the result is 168. Find the number.

15. Divide $56 between A and B so that A shall receive seven times as much as B.

16. A, B, and C together have $96. B has twice as much as C, and A has as much as B and C together. How much has each?

17. A man had $4195. After spending a certain sum, he found that he had left four times as much as he had spent. How much did he spend?

18. The sum of three numbers is 120. The second is five times the first, and the third is nine times the first. Find the numbers.

19. The sum of three numbers is 360. The second is fourteen times the first, and the third is the sum of the other two. Find the numbers.

20. Three men are asked to contribute to a fund. The first agrees to give twice as much as the second, and the third to give twice as much as the first. How much must each contribute to make a total of $525?

21. The perimeter of the triangle ABC is 240 inches. Find the lengths of its sides.

22. The perimeter of a rectangle is 132 inches. The base is double the altitude. Find the dimensions of the rectangle.

23. The length of the fence about a rectangular field is 320 rods. If the long dimension is three times the short dimension, find the length of each.

24. The perimeter of the quadrilateral $ABCD$ is 220 inches. The side CD is twice as long as the side AB; the side AD is three times as long; the side BC equals the sum of the sides AD and CD. Find the length of each side.

25. The shortest distance by railroad from New York to Chicago is 10 times the distance from New York to Philadelphia. The sum of the two distances is 990 miles. Find the distance from New York to Chicago and to Philadelphia.

LITERAL NUMBER

PROBLEMS ABOUT ANGLES

13. When two lines meet they form an **Angle** (∠).
The angle *ABC* is a **Right Angle**.

Angles are measured by a *unit* called a **Degree** (°).
A right angle contains 90°.

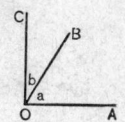

Two angles whose sum is a right angle are **Complementary Angles**; each of the angles is called the **Complement** of the other. The angles *AOB* and *BOC* are complementary; hence $a + b = 90$.

EXERCISE 8

1. How many degrees are there in one half of a right angle? one third?

2. What is the complement of 30°? 40°? 70°? a°? x°?

3. Are angles of 25° and 55° complementary? Why?

4. If the angles $3x$ and $7x$ are complementary, what is their sum? Form an equation and determine x. What are the angles?

5. Determine the angles $5a$ and $4a$ if they are complementary.

6. What angle is double its complement? (Let c equal the number of degrees in the complement; form an equation.)

7. What angle is three times its complement?

8. What angle is five times its complement?

A **Straight Angle** equals two right angles.

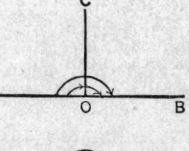

What kind of angles are the angles *AOC* and *BOC*? How many degrees in their sum?
How many degrees in ∠ *AOB*? How many degrees in a straight angle?

9. Find each angle in the adjoining figure.

10. There are three angles whose sum is 180°. The second is double the first, and the third is the sum of the other two. Draw a figure to illustrate this problem. Find the angles.

Two angles whose sum is a straight angle are called **Supplementary Angles**; each of them is called the **Supplement** of the other.

11. What is the supplement of 50°? 90°? 100°? x°? $2a$°?

12. The angles $5x$ and $7x$ are supplementary. How many degrees are there in each?

13. Find the angle which is four times its supplement.

14. Find the angle which is five times its supplement.

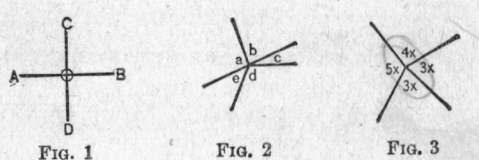

Fig. 1   Fig. 2   Fig. 3

The sum of all the angles around a point is 4 right angles or 360°.

Thus. $a + b + c + d + e = 360$.

15. Find each of the angles in Figure 3.

16. There are four angles whose sum is the total angle around a point. The first angle contains a°; each of the others is double the preceding. Draw a figure to illustrate this problem. How many degrees are there in each angle?

17. There are four angles whose sum is the total angle around a point. The second angle is one half of the first; the third angle is three halves of the first; and the fourth angle is four times the third. Find the angles.

LITERAL NUMBER

If the angles of triangle *ABC* are torn off and placed side by side, their sum is found to be 180°.

Draw a triangle with a ruler, and see if you find this to be true.

From this we conclude that the sum of the angles of a triangle is 180°.

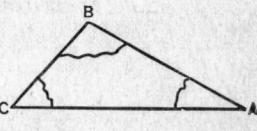

18. The second angle of a triangle is double the first, and the third angle is six times the first. How many degrees are there in each?

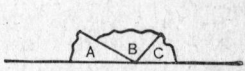

19. Find the angles of a triangle when two of the angles are equal and the third is equal to the sum of the other two.

20. Find the angles of a triangle if the first is 4 times the second, and the third is 7 times the second.

DEFINITIONS

14. An **Algebraic Expression**, or simply an **Expression**, is a number expressed in algebraic symbols; as,

$$2, \; ab, \; 2x - 3zy, \; \frac{r}{s}.$$

The **Numerical Value** of an expression is found by substituting particular values for the literal numbers, and performing the *indicated* operations.

ab indicates that a is to be multiplied by b.

$\frac{r}{s}$ *indicates* that r is to be divided by s.

$2x - 3yz$ *indicates* that 3 times the product of y and z is to be subtracted from 2 times x.

15. If the same number is used as a factor one or more times to form a product, the result is called a **Power** of the number.

The number itself is called the **Base**.

An integer written at the right of and above the base, to

ALGEBRA

indicate the number of times the base is used as a factor, is called an **Exponent**. Thus,

a^2, read "*a square*" or "*a second power*," means $a \times a$;
a^3, read "*a cube*" or "*a third power*," means $a \times a \times a$;
a^4, read "*a fourth*" or "*a fourth power*" means $a \times a \times a \times a$.

If no exponent is written, the exponent 1 is understood.

HISTORICAL NOTE. — Mathematicians sought suitable symbols for the powers of a number for a long time. At first words were used for them. Our "*a square*" and "*a cube*" owe their introduction to Greek mathematicians who called the second power by a word which means the square, and the third power by one which means the cube. Herigone, a French mathematician of the early part of the seventeenth century, wrote $a2$, $a3$, $a4$, etc., and finally Descartes, in 1637, introduced the present symbols. The word, *power*, comes from a Latin word, *potentia*, which corresponds to the Greek word used for the second power. The word, *exponent*, was introduced by Stifel about 1553.

16. The **Fundamental Operations** are addition, subtraction, multiplication, and division. Indicated operations are to be performed in the following order: first, all multiplications and divisions in their order from left to right; then all additions and subtractions from left to right.

EXAMPLE. Find the numerical value of the expression,

$$4\,ab + \frac{6\,c}{b} - d^3,$$

when $a = 4,\ b = 3,\ c = 5,\ d = 2.$

SOLUTION: Substituting,

$$4\,ab + \frac{6\,c}{b} - d^3 = 4 \cdot 4 \cdot 3 + \frac{6 \cdot 5}{3} - 2^3 = 4 \cdot 4 \cdot 3 + \frac{6 \cdot 5}{3} - 2 \cdot 2 \cdot 2$$
$$= 48 + 10 - 8 = 50.$$

EXERCISE 9

Find the numerical value of the following expressions when
$a = 2,\ b = 5,\ c = 3,\ d = 4,\ m = 4,\ n = 3.$

1. $3\,a + 5\,b.$
2. $4\,c - 2\,d.$
3. $5\,m + 3\,n.$
4. $a^2 + c^2.$
5. $b^2 - d^2.$
6. $a^3 + n^3.$

7. $2c^2 - 3b.$

8. $\dfrac{2d}{m} + \dfrac{3c}{n}.$

9. $3ab + 2c - 4d.$

10. $5b + 6m - n^2.$

11. $\dfrac{a}{b} + \dfrac{c}{d} + \dfrac{n}{m}.$

12. $2a^2 - 3a + 1.$

13. $m^2 - mn + n^2.$

14. $a^3 + 3a^2b + 3ab^2.$

15. $\dfrac{2a + 4c - 3d}{m+n}.$

16. $c^a + b^a.$

Write in symbols the following and find their **value:**

17. The sum of a and b; c and d; m and n.

18. The difference between a and b; c and d.
   (The difference between a and b is $b - a$.)

19. The product of a and b; c and d; m and n.

20. The quotient of a and b; c and d; m and n.

21. a increased by $2b$; c increased by $3d$.

22. The square of m increased by the square of n.

23. The cube of b decreased by the cube of m.

24. 10 more than $3a$; 5 less than $4b$.

25. 3 more than the quotient of m divided by d.

26. 4 less than the product of a and c.

27. The sum of the squares of a and b.

FORMULÆ

17. When a rule of computation is expressed by means of algebraic symbols, the result is called a **Formula**.

EXAMPLE 1. Find the formula for the area of a rectangle.

SOLUTION: The area equals the product of the base and altitude.

Let a = the number of units in the altitude.

Let b = the number of units in the base.

Let A = the number of square units in the area;

then, $$A = ab.$$

ALGEBRA

The following examples show how to use a formula.

Example 2. Find the area of a rectangle whose altitude is 8 inches and whose base is 15 inches.

Solution: 1. Use the formula $A = ab$.
2.   Substitute 8 for a, and 15 for b.
Then, $A = 8 \times 15$ or 120.

Example 3. Find the altitude of a rectangle whose base is 75 feet and whose area is 675 square feet.

Solution: 1. Substitute in the formula $A = ab$.
$$A = 675; \; b = 75.$$
2. Then, $675 = a \times 75,$
or $675 = 75\, a.$
3. Divide both members by 75: $9 = a$.

Example 4. Find the base of a rectangle whose altitude is 11 inches and whose area is 385 square inches.

Solution: 1. Substitute in the formula $A = ab$.
2. $A = 385; \; a = 11.$
Then, $385 = 11 \times b.$
3. Divide both members by 11: $\frac{385}{11} = b$,
or $b = 35.$

Rule. — To solve a problem by a formula:

1. For the known letters in the formula substitute their values.
2. Perform all of the indicated operations.
3. If an equation is formed, solve for the unknown letter, if possible.

EXERCISE 10

1. The figure $XYZW$ is a **Parallelogram** (▱). Find a formula for determining its area.

(a) Let b and a equal the units in the base and the altitude, and A the square units in the area.

(b) How does $XYZW$ compare in area with $FGHK$?

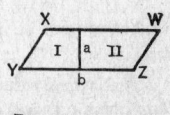

(c) What is $FGHK$? What is its base? altitude? area?

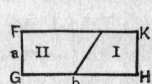

(d) What then is the area of $XYZW$?

LITERAL NUMBER

(e) Make a rule for finding the area of a parallelogram.

(f) Expressed as a formula, this rule is
$$A = a \cdot b$$

(g) Find A when $a = 12$ and $b = 20$.

(h) Find A when $a = 15$ and $b = 25$.

(i) Find a when $A = 500$ and $b = 40$.

(j) Find a when $A = 600$ and $b = 25$.

(k) Find b when $A = 750$ and $a = 15$.

(l) Find b when $A = 960$ and $a = 32$.

2. The figure XYZ is a **Triangle** ($\triangle XYZ$).

Find a formula for determining its area.

(a) Let b, a, and A represent the units in the base, altitude, and area respectively.

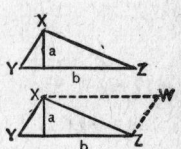

(b) What is the figure $XYZW$? what is its base? altitude? area?

(c) What part of $\square XYZW$ is $\triangle XYZ$?

(d) What then is the area of $\triangle XYZ$?

(e) Make a rule for finding the area of a triangle.

(f) Expressed as a formula, this rule is,
$$A = \frac{1}{2}ab.$$

(g) Find A when $a = 10$ and $b = 17$.

(h) Find A when $a = 20$ and $b = 30$.

(i) Find b when $A = 260$ and $a = 40$.

(j) Find a when $A = 1200$ and $b = 60$.

3. The figure of the rectangular solid has the dimensions indicated.

Find a formula for determining its volume.

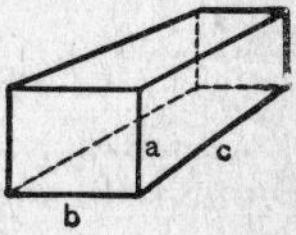

Let V represent the number of units in the volume.
The volume equals the product of the three dimensions.

(a) Express this rule as a formula.

(b) Find V when $a = 3$, $b = 5$, $c = 8$.

(c) Find V when $a = 6$, $b = 9$, $c = 7$.

(d) Find c when $V = 240$, $a = 6$, and $b = 5$.

4. The figure $XYZW$ is a **Pyramid.**

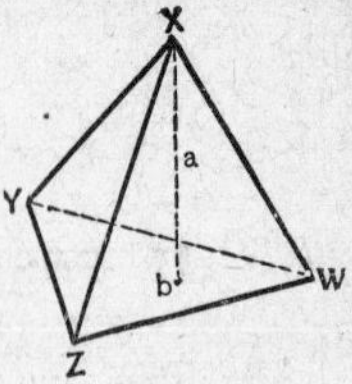

Its volume equals one third of the product of its base and altitude.

(a) Express this rule as a formula, letting V equal the number of units in the volume.
(b) Find V when $a = 18$, $b = 15$.
(c) Find b when $V = 160$, $a = 24$.
(d) Find a when $V = 900$, $b = 30$.

5. The formula for the circumference of a circle is:
$$C = 2\pi R,$$
where $C =$ the number of units in the circumference,
where $R =$ the number of units in the radius,
where $\pi = 3.1416$ (π is read "pi").

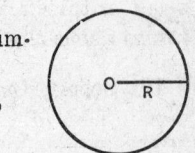

(a) Express this rule in words.
(b) Find, by the formula, C when R is 10 inches.
(c) Find, by the formula, R when C is 628.32 inches.

6. The formula for the area of a circle is:
$$A = \pi R^2.$$

(a) Express this rule in words.
(b) Find, by the formula, A when R is 10 inches.
(c) Find, by the formula, A when R is 5 feet.

7. The numbers s, v, t, and g are connected by the formula:
$$s = vt + \frac{1}{2}gt^2;$$
find s when $v = 50$, $t = 3$, $g = 32.16$.

8. From the formula $E = \dfrac{wv^2}{2g}$, find E when $w = 75$, $v = 50$, $g = 32.16$. (Carry the result to one decimal place.)

9. From the formula $V = \frac{4}{3}\pi R^3$, find V when R is 3.

10. From the formula $S = 4\pi R^2$, find S when $R = 5$.

II. POSITIVE AND NEGATIVE NUMBERS

18. The first numbers studied in arithmetic are the integers, such as, 1, 4, 15, etc.; the next are the common fractions, such as, $\frac{1}{2}$, $\frac{1}{3}$, $\frac{2}{5}$, $\frac{7}{9}$, etc. and the decimals, such as, 2.03, 4.6, etc. The literal numbers in the first chapter represented only these same arithmetical numbers. One of the most distinctive things about algebra is its use of certain other numbers.

19. Opposite Quantities. Suppose that the temperature at a certain hour of the day was 73°, and that there was a change of 5°. To determine the new temperature, it would be necessary to know whether the change was a *rise* of 5° or the *opposite*, a *fall* of 5°.

Suppose that a person was known to weigh 85 pounds, and that during a certain time there was a change in his weight of 5 pounds. To determine his new weight, it is necessary to know whether the change was an *increase* of 5 pounds or the *opposite*, a *decrease* of 5 pounds.

These are two illustrations of opposite quantities. Many concrete quantities exist in two such opposite states.

EXERCISE 11

Tell the opposite of each of the following:

1. Sailing 35 miles north.
2. Sailing 25 miles east.
3. Receiving $30.
4. Gaining $5.
5. Moving 5 steps forward.
6. Depositing $15 in a bank.
7. Rise of 10° in temperature.
8. Walking 5 rods to the right.
9. Increasing weight by 5 pounds.
10. Adding 7.

ALGEBRA

11. What is the total result if any one of the changes in Examples 1 to 10 is followed by a second change of *opposite kind* and *of like amount*?

12. What is the total result of two transactions, one giving a gain of $50, and one a loss of $25?

What single change will produce the same result as the two changes indicated in the following examples?

13. If a ship sails first 6° north and then 2° south?

14. If a ship sails first 8° east and then 10° west?

15. If a boy, becoming ill, loses 10 pounds, and then gains 8 pounds?

16. If the temperature first rises 12°, and then falls 15°?

17. If a man first deposits $100 in a bank and then withdraws $125 from his account?

18. A vessel sails from the equator due north 28°, and then due south 57°. What is her latitude at the end of the voyage?

20. In Example 10, Exercise 11, the opposite of adding 7 is subtracting 7. Addition is always indicated by the sign +, and subtraction by the sign −. These same signs are used to distinguish between opposite quantities. A quantity preceded by the + sign is called a **Positive Quantity**, and one preceded by the − sign is called a **Negative Quantity**. Quantities preceded by the signs plus and minus are called **Signed Quantities**.

EXERCISE 12

The following are naturally considered positive quantities. What are the corresponding negative quantities?

1. Sailing east.
2. Sailing north.
3. Right direction.
4. Increasing.
5. Rising temperature.
6. Forward.
7. Upward.
8. Deposits.

POSITIVE AND NEGATIVE NUMBERS

9. Assets.   **10.** Profits.   **11.** Above zero.   **12.** Time A.D.

13. At 7 A.M. the temperature is $-13°$; at noon it is 8° warmer, and at 6 P.M. it is 5° colder than at noon. Required the temperature at noon and at 6 P.M.

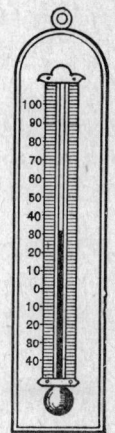

14. At 7 A.M. the temperature is $+6°$; at noon it is 14° colder, and at 6 P.M. it is 2° colder than at noon. Required the temperature at noon and at 6 P.M.

15. At 7 A.M. the temperature is $-7°$, and at noon $+9°$. How many degrees warmer is it at noon than at 7 A.M.?

16. The temperature at 6 A.M. is $-14°$; during the morning it grows warmer at the rate of 3° per hour. Required the temperature at 9 A.M. and at 10 A.M.

17. The positive quantities in this set indicate rise in temperature. What single change will produce the same result?

(a) $+12°$ and $+10°$.

SOLUTION: 1. A 12° rise followed by a 10° rise gives a total of 22° rise.
2. This may also be expressed thus:
$$(+12°)+(+10°)=+22°.$$

(b) $+9°$ and $-5°$.   (c) $-4°$ and $-5°$.   (d) $+7°$ and $-9°$.

18. In this set the positive quantities refer to gains in financial transactions. What is the equivalent single change?

(a) $+\$15, +\$25, -\$30$.

SOLUTION: 1. A gain of $15 followed by a gain of $25 gives a gain of $40; followed by a loss of $30 gives a total result of $10 gain.
2. Expressed in symbols thus:
$$(+\$15)+(+\$25)+(-\$30)=(+\$40)+(-\$30)=+\$10.$$

(b) $+\$20, +\$30, -\$50$.   (c) $-\$45, +\$50, -\$10$.
(d) $+\$35, -\$20, -\$25$.   (e) $+\$14, -\$20, +\$19$

In the following problems, select and mark the positive and negative quantities. Find the total result as in the preceding problems and express it as a signed number.

19. A man's income during the year is $1500, and his expenses are $1300. Find the result at the end of the year.

20. A man's monthly account book shows the items: salary $150, rent $40, food $50, insurance $25, interest on savings $15. Find the result at the end of the month.

21. Positive and Negative Numbers. The preceding exercises show that positive and negative quantities exist. In dealing with these quantities, positive and negative numbers are necessary.

Starting with an arithmetical number like 3, a new number called **Negative 3** is made; 3 is then called **Positive 3**. These two numbers are opposites and have the power of destroying each other when added, just as do opposite quantities which are equal in amount. Positive 3 is written, $+3$; negative 3 is written, -3. The arithmetical number 3 is called the **Absolute Value** of $+3$ and -3.

The negative number must always have its sign written before it; the positive number is often written without its sign.

HISTORICAL NOTE. — Hindu mathematicians, who knew about positive and negative numbers long before European mathematicians, in referring to them, used words which correspond to our words for assets and debits. They also were acquainted with the illustration of such numbers by means of the opposite directions on a straight line. To indicate that a number was a negative number, they placed a dot over it. European mathematicians did not arrive at an equal understanding of positive and negative numbers until the sixteenth century.

EXERCISE 13

1. Read the following numbers, write each in symbols, and tell the absolute value of each:

(a) positive nine; (b) negative seven;
(c) positive four; (d) negative three fourths;
(e) negative five sixths;
(f) negative three and three tenths.

2. Read the following numbers and tell the absolute value of each:

(a) $+6$; (b) -2; (c) -5;
(d) $-\frac{2}{3}$; (e) $+\frac{3}{8}$; (f) -2.98;
(g) $+3.41$; (h) -45.087; (i) -102.34.

22. Addition of Positive and Negative Numbers. The rules for addition of signed numbers are suggested by the following problems:

1. Find the sum of $+5$ and $+3$.

Just as $5 gain plus $3 gain gives $8 gain, similarly

$$(+5)+(+3)=+8.$$

2. Find the sum of -5 and -3.

Just as $5 loss plus $3 loss gives $8 loss, similarly

$$(-5)+(-3)=-8.$$

3. Find the sum of $+5$ and -3.

Just as $5 gain plus $3 loss gives $2 gain, similarly

$$(+5)+(-3)=+2.$$

4. Find the sum of -5 and $+3$.

Just as $5 loss plus $3 gain gives $2 loss, similarly

$$(-5)+(+3)=-2.$$

Rule.—1. To add two positive numbers, add their absolute values (§ 21), and prefix the plus sign to the result.

2. To add two negative numbers, add their absolute values and prefix the minus sign to the result.

3. To add a positive and a negative number, find the difference of their absolute values, and prefix to the result the sign of the number having the greater absolute value.

EXERCISE 14

1. Find the sum of $+10$ and -3.

SOLUTION: Use Rule 3. Subtract 3 from 10; prefix + sign.
$$(+10)+(-3)=+7.$$

2. Find the sum of -12 and $+6$.

SOLUTION: Use Rule 3. Subtract 6 from 12; prefix − sign.
$$(-12)+(+6)=-6.$$

3. Find the sum of -9 and -5.

SOLUTION: Use Rule 2. Add 9 and 5; prefix − sign.
$$(-9)+(-5)=-14.$$

4. To each of the numbers:
$$+6,\ +9,\ +14,\ +5,\ +18,\ +3,$$
(a) add -4;   (b) add -12;   (c) add -15.

5. To each of the numbers:
$$-5,\ -15,\ -2,\ -10,\ -16,\ -20,$$
(a) add $+6$;   (b) add $+15$;   (c) add $+12$;
(d) add -5;   (e) add -6;   (f) add -7.

6. To each of the numbers:
$$-36,\ +48,\ -17,\ -25,\ +24,\ +29,$$
(a) add $+9$;   (b) add -8;   (c) add -7

Find the sum:

7.	8.	9.	10.	11.
$+124$	-15.2	-1.35	$+2.10$	-10.3
$-\ 36$	$+\ 9.1$	-1.63	-1.43	$+\ 3.3$

12. $+\ 9$ Here 9 must be taken from 17. It is necessary to be-
-17 come expert in subtracting the upper number from the
$-\ 8$ lower.

13.	14.	15.	16.	17.	18.
-11	$+17$	-28	$+\ 72$	$+\ 65$	-59
$+43$	-42	$+44$	-109	-247	$+78$

POSITIVE AND NEGATIVE NUMBERS

19. $+6$
-2
$+4$
-5

HINT: There are two ways of doing this example. Either add in order from bottom to top, or from top to bottom; or, add first all of the positive numbers and all of the negative numbers separately, and then combine the results.

20.	21.	22.	23.	24.	25.
$+4$	-7	$+15$	-5	$+16$	-10
-6	-5	-12	-14	-11	$+13$
-2	$+9$	$+6$	$+11$	-7	-14
$+5$	-1	$+6$	$+3$	$+22$	$+7$
-3	$+8$	-9	-8	-9	-3

Find the sum:

26. $-\frac{3}{4}$, $+\frac{1}{2}$.   28. $-\frac{5}{3}$, $-\frac{1}{6}$.   30. $+2\frac{1}{2}$, $-1\frac{3}{4}$.

27. $-\frac{3}{5}$, $-\frac{9}{10}$.   29. $-\frac{9}{8}$, $+\frac{8}{7}$.   31. $-3\frac{1}{3}$, $+2\frac{2}{3}$.

32. Demosthenes was born in the year -385, and died at the age of 63. What was the year of his death?

33. Pythagoras was born in the year -580, and lived to the age of 79 years. What was the year of his death?

34. At the beginning of the month the number of pupils in a schoolroom is 53; 3 pupils enter during the month and 5 leave school. How many pupils are there in the room at the end of the month?

35. A principal of a school finds that his six algebra classes have the enrollment indicated in line 2. He decides to make the changes indicated in line 3.

Classes	1	2	3	4	5	6
Members	29	15	22	28	18	14
Changes	-8	$+6$	-1	-7	$+3$	$+7$

(a) Tell what each of the changes in line 3 means.
(b) Find the result in the class membership.
(c) How can he check his work from line 3?

23. From the examples in Exercise 14 it is clear that adding a negative number has the same effect as subtracting the positive number of equal absolute value.

Thus, $\qquad (+12)+(-5)=12-5=7.$
$\qquad\qquad (-10)+(-5)=-10-5=-15.$

24. It is convenient to picture the positive numbers thus:

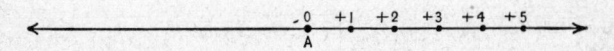

$$\begin{array}{c}\underset{A}{0}\quad +1\quad +2\quad +3\quad +4\quad +5\end{array}$$

where $+1$ is placed at any distance from the point A, $+2$ twice as far, etc. In this sense, the positive numbers form a *scale* extending to the right. Any number precedes all larger numbers on this scale; thus, 3 precedes 4, 5, 6, etc.

Since $(-3)+(+3)=0$, it is natural to think of -3 as being 3 less than zero; and, similarly, of -4 as being 4 less than zero.

It is natural to think of the negative numbers as arranged on the left.

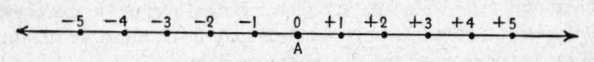

$$-5\quad -4\quad -3\quad -2\quad -1\quad \underset{A}{0}\quad +1\quad +2\quad +3\quad +4\quad +5$$

Thus, the positive and negative numbers together form a *complete scale* extending in both directions from zero.

Starting on the left, any negative number precedes the positive numbers and *may be thought of as being less than the positive numbers.*

MULTIPLICATION OF POSITIVE AND NEGATIVE NUMBERS

25. The terms **Multiplier, Multiplicand,** and **Product** have the same meaning in algebra as in arithmetic.

The rules for multiplication of signed numbers are suggested by the following problems. In these problems, read the sign, × "multiplied by."

POSITIVE AND NEGATIVE NUMBERS

1. Find the product of $+4$ and $+3$.

Since positive numbers are like arithmetical numbers,
$$(+4) \times (+3) = +12.$$

2. Find the product of -4 and $+3$.

In arithmetic, to multiply by 3 means to add the multiplicand three times. If this is done in this problem,
$$(-4) \times (+3) = (-4) + (-4) + (-4) = -12.$$

3. Find the product of $+4$ and -3.

In arithmetic, $4 \times 3 = 3 \times 4$, since each equals 12. The order of the factors may be changed. If it is assumed that the same law holds in algebra,

$(+4) \times (-3)$ should equal $(-3) \times (+4)$ or, -12, by problem 2.
Then, $\quad\quad\quad\quad (+4) \times (-3) = -12.$

To multiply a number by a negative number seems to be accomplished by multiplying it by the absolute value of the multiplier and changing the sign of the product.

4. Find the product of -4 and -3.

The multiplier is a negative number. If the suggestion from problem 3 is followed, the result in this problem may be obtained by multiplying (-4) by 3 and changing the sign of the product.

$(-4) \times 3 = -12.$ Changing the sign of -12 gives $+12$.
Therefore, $\quad\quad\quad\quad (-4) \times (-3) = +12.$

Gathering together the results of problems 1, 2, 3, and 4:

1. $(+4) \times (+3) = +12.$ 3. $(+4) \times (-3) = -12.$
2. $(-4) \times (+3) = -12.$ 4. $(-4) \times (-3) = +12.$

Rule. — To multiply one signed number by another:

1. Find the product of their absolute values. (See all four above.)

2. Make the product *positive* if the multiplicand and multiplier have *like* signs. (See **1** and **4** above.)

3. Make the product *negative* if the multiplicand and multiplier have *unlike* signs. (See **2** and **3** above.)

ALGEBRA

EXERCISE 15

1. Multiply the numbers:

$$+5, +6, +8, +7, +9, +12,$$

(a) by $+4$; (b) by -3; (c) -8; (d) by -9.

2. Multiply the numbers:

$$-6, -10, -8, -7, -15, -12,$$

(a) by $+4$; (b) by -9; (c) by -6; (d) by $+7$.

3. Multiply the numbers:

$$+11, -9, +14, +12, -25, -15,$$

(a) by -6; (b) by $+7$; (c) by -8; (d) by -10.

Find the products of the following factors:

4. $-9, -11$.   **8.** $-13, +8$.   **12.** $+\frac{1}{2}, -\frac{1}{3}$.

5. $-7, +12$.   **9.** $-9, +12$.   **13.** $-\frac{1}{4}, +\frac{1}{5}$.

6. $+9, -20$.   **10.** $-11, -20$.   **14.** $-\frac{2}{5}, -\frac{1}{2}$.

7. $+6, -13$.   **11.** $+9, -16$.

15. Find the product of $-2, +3, -4$.

$$(-2) \cdot (+3) = -6; \quad (-6) \cdot (-4) = +24.$$

16. $-1, +3, -2$.   **20.** $-6, -3, -4$.

17. $+3, -4, -5$.   **21.** $-7, +2, -5$.

18. $-6, -2, -5$.   **22.** $-9, +5, -4$.

19. $+5, -8, -3$.   **23.** $+10, -7, +6$.

24. If the number of negative factors is even, what is the sign of the product?

25. If the number of negative factors is odd, what is the sign of the product?

26. Powers of Positive and Negative Numbers.

$$(+2)^2 = (+2)(+2) = +4. \qquad (\S\ 15)$$
$$(+2)^3 = (+2)(+2)(+2) = +8.$$
$$(+2)^4 = (+2)(+2)(+2)(+2) = +16.$$

It is clear that every power of a positive number is positive.

POSITIVE AND NEGATIVE NUMBERS

$$(-2)^2 = (-2)(-2) = +4.$$
$$(-2)^3 = (-2)(-2)(-2) = -8.$$
$$(-2)^4 = (-2)(-2)(-2)(-2) = +16.$$
$$(-2)^5 = (-2)(-2)(-2)(-2)(-2) = -32.$$

It is clear that every *even* power of a negative number is *positive* and every *odd* power is *negative*.

EXERCISE 16

Find the values of the following powers:

1. $(-3)^2$.
2. $(-3)^5$.
3. $(+4)^3$.
4. $(-1)^5$.
5. $(-5)^3$.
6. $(-2)^6$.
7. $(-4)^4$.
8. $(+1)^6$.
9. $(-3)^4$.
10. $(-5)^2$.
11. $(-6)^3$.
12. $(-1)^6$.

13. Find the value of $ax^2 + bx + c$
when $\qquad a = 1,\ b = 2,\ c = -3,\ x = -2.$
$$ax^2 + bx + c = 1 \cdot (-2)^2 + (+2)(-2) + (-3)$$
$$= +4 - 4 - 3 = -3.$$

In the following examples, let $a = +1$, $b = -2$, $c = +3$, and $x = -2$. Find the values of the expressions:

14. $3ab$.
15. ab^2.
16. $5bx^2$.
17. $-11bcx$.
18. $bc + ax$.
19. $a^2b + ab^2$.
20. $bx^2 - cx^2$.
21. $ax^3 - bx^3$.
22. $ab^3 + bc^3$.
23. $b^3 + x^3$.
24. $a^4 - x^4$.
25. $a^4b^3 - a^3c$.

III. ADDITION AND SUBTRACTION OF ALGEBRAIC EXPRESSIONS

DEFINITIONS

27. A **Monomial** or **Term** is an expression whose parts are not separated by the signs + or —. Thus,

$2x^2$, $-3ab$, and $+5$ are the *terms* of the expression $2x^2 - 3ab + 5$.

In an expression, a term whose sign is plus may be called a *positive term*, and one whose sign is minus, a *negative term*, as the terms $2x^2$, and $-3ab$, respectively, although the algebraic value of the term depends upon the values of its literal factors.

28. If two or more numbers are multiplied together, each of them, or the product of any number of them, is called a **Factor** of the product.

Thus, a, b, c, ab, ac, and bc are factors of the product abc.

29. Any factor of the product is called the **Coefficient** of the product of the remaining factors.

Thus, in $2ab$, 2 is the coefficient of ab, $2a$ of b, a of $2b$, etc.

30. If one factor of a product is expressed in *numerals* and the other factor is expressed in *letters*, the former is called the **Numerical Coefficient** of the latter.

Thus, in $2ab$, 2 is the numerical coefficient of ab.

If no numerical coefficient is expressed, the coefficient 1 is understood; thus, a is the same as $1a$.

31. By § 25, $(-3) \times a = -3a$; that is, $-3a$ is the product of -3 and a. Then -3 is the numerical coefficient of a in $-3a$.

Thus, in a negative term, the numerical coefficient includes the sign.

ADDITION AND SUBTRACTION

32. Terms which are alike in their literal parts are called **Like** or **Similar Terms**; as, $2\,x^2y$ and $-7\,x^2y$.

Terms which are not alike in their literal parts are called **Unlike** or **Dissimilar Terms**; as, $2\,x^2$ and $7\,xy^2$.

Sometimes unlike terms may be *like with respect to one or more letters*. Thus, $2\,axy$ and $3\,bxy$ are like with respect to xy.

EXERCISE 17

1. Tell all of the factors of the monomial $+6\,xy$.
2. What is the numerical coefficient of the monomial $-6\,xy$?
3. In 2, what is the coefficient of y? of x? of xy? of $6\,x$?
4. Select the sets of like terms:

    (a) $+2\,xy^2,\ -3\,xy^2$. (b) $+7\,m,\ -6\,n$.
    (c) $+5\,abc,\ -6\,ab^2c$. (d) $-8\,ab,\ +9\,ab$.

33. The result obtained by adding two or more numbers is called the **Sum**.

ADDITION OF MONOMIALS

34. Addition of Like Terms. In paragraph 11, it was found that $6\,n + 4\,n = 10\,n$. $6\,n$ and $4\,n$ are *like* terms since they have the common factor n (§ 11). The coefficients of n are 6 and 4, and their sum is the coefficient, 10, of the result.

Rule. — To add two or more like terms:

1. Multiply their common factor by the sum of its coefficients.

EXAMPLE 1. Find the sum of $5\,x^2$ and $3\,x^2$.

SOLUTION: 1. The common factor in $5\,x^2$ and $3\,x^2$ is x^2. The coefficients are 5 and 3; their sum is 8.

2. Hence, $5\,x^2 + 3\,x^2 = 8\,x^2$.

CHECK: Let $x = -2$. $5\,x^2 = 5 \cdot (-2)^2 = 5 \cdot 4 = 20$, $3\,x^2 = 3 \cdot 4 = 12$, and $20 + 12 = 32$. Also, $8\,x^2 = 8 \cdot 4 = 32$.

EXAMPLE 2. Find the sum of $-5\,x^2y$ and $+3\,x^2y$.

SOLUTION: $-5\,x^2y + 3\,x^2y = [(-5) + (+3)]\,x^2y = -2\,x^2y$.

ALGEBRA

CHECK: Let $x = 1$ and $y = 1$. Then, $-5x^2y = -5 \cdot 1 \cdot 1 = -5$, $+3x^2y = +3 \cdot 1 \cdot 1 = +3$, and $(-5) + (+3) = -2$. Also, $-2x^2y = (-2) \cdot 1 \cdot 1 = -2$.

EXAMPLE 3. Find the sum of 16×19 and 14×19.

SOLUTION: 1. The common factor is 19; its coefficients are 16 and 14.
2. $16 \times 19 + 14 \times 19 = (16 + 14) \times 19 = 30 \times 19 = 570$.

EXERCISE 18

Find the sum in each of the following:

1. $5A$ and $-12A$.
2. $11p$ and $-6p$.
3. $-7m$ and $-8m$.
4. $-4n$ and $-9n$.
5. $+15E$ and $-11E$.
6. $-5ab$ and $+13ab$.
7. $-13r^2s$ and $+36r^2s$.
8. $-17x^2$ and $-15x^2$.
9. xyz and $-9xyz$.
10. $8x^3y^2$ and $-29x^3y^2$.
11. $-bc$ and $+6bc$.
12. 12×16 and 8×16.
13. 21×17 and 9×17.
14. 13×23 and 7×23.

15.	16.	17.	18.	19.
$+7a$	$+15xy$	$+12r^2s$	$-2xy^2$	$+5m$
$+9a$	$-4xy$	$-3r^2s$	$-9xy^2$	$-15m$

20.
$-7a$
$+9a$
$+8a$
$-3a$
$+7a$

HINT. Add first the positive terms, getting $+17a$; then the negative, getting $-10a$; then add these results, getting $+7a$. All should be done mentally.

21.	22.	23.	24.	25.
$15m$	$-13x^2$	$+8ab$	$16xyz$	$21ab^2c$
$-2m$	$+2x^2$	$-7ab$	$-4xyz$	$-6ab^2c$
$-5m$	$-7x^2$	$-5ab$	$-6xyz$	$-17ab^2c$
$+3m$	$+3x^2$	$+3ab$	$+3xyz$	$+ab^2c$

ADDITION AND SUBTRACTION

26. Find the sum of $9\,a^3$, $-7\,a^3$, and $+8\,a^3$.

SOLUTION: $9\,a^3 + (-7\,a^3) + 8\,a^3 = 9\,a^3 - 7\,a^3 + 8\,a^3 = 10\,a^3$.

NOTE. This illustrates another arrangement of an addition example. The terms are first connected by the $+$ sign. Then $+(-7\,a^3)$ is written as $-7\,a^3$, since adding a negative number is the same as subtracting the positive number of equal absolute value. (§ 21.)

Add, as in Example 26, the following:

27. $7\,ab$, $-3\,ab$, and $+9\,ab$.   **29.** $12\,y$, $-7\,y$, $+9\,y$, and $-8\,y$.

28. $9\,r^3$, $-6\,r^3$, $+3\,r^3$, and $10\,r^3$.   **30.** $15\,z$, $+9\,z$, $-11\,z$, and $-8\,z$.

31. Find the sum of $12\,a$, $-5\,x$, $-3\,y^2$, $-5\,a$, and $8\,x$.

SOLUTION: $\quad 12\,a + (-5\,x) + (-3\,y^2) + (-5\,a) + (8\,x)$
$= 12\,a - 5\,x - 3\,y^2 - 5\,a + 8\,x.$
$= 7\,a + 3\,x - 3\,y^2.$

In this Example, $12\,a$ and $-5\,a$ give $7\,a$; $-5\,x$ and $+8\,x$ give $+3\,x$; there is no term to combine with $-3\,y^2$. Only the like terms may be combined.

Add, as in Example 31, the following:

32. $8\,ab$, $-9\,cd$, $-6\,ab$, and $+4\,cd$.

33. $6\,x^2$, $-10\,z^2$, $2\,y^2$, $4\,z^2$, $-9\,y^2$, and $-3\,x^2$.

34. $12\,r^2$, $-3\,r$, $-8\,s$, $-5\,r$, $+3\,s$, $-7\,r^2$, and $11\,s$.

35. $10\,c$, $-4\,d$, $-3\,k$, $+9\,c$, $-4\,k$, $+5\,d$, $-6\,k$, and $-2\,c$.

36. $11\,m^3$, $-8\,n^2$, $+6\,l$, $-5\,n^2$, $+3\,m^3$, and $-8\,l$.

Simplify the following:

37. $5\,a - 8\,a + 10\,a - 12\,a$.

38. $-3\,x^2 + 6\,x^2 + x^2 - 11\,x^2 + x^2$.

39. $4\,r^2s - 7\,r^2s + 5\,r^2s - 6\,r^2s$.

40. $-8\,m^2n - 3\,m^2n + 2\,m^2n - 9\,m^2n$.

41. $6\,c + 11\,d - 4\,d - 5\,c - 2\,c$.

42. $2\,x^2 - 3\,x - 4\,x - 5\,x^2 + 8\,x$.

43. $9\,r^3 + 2\,r^2 - 3\,r^3 - 4\,r^2$.

44. $\tfrac{1}{2}a + \tfrac{1}{3}a - \tfrac{1}{6}a$.

45. $-\tfrac{1}{4}mn + \tfrac{1}{8}mn + \tfrac{1}{2}mn$.

46. $-\tfrac{2}{3}r^2s^2 + \tfrac{1}{6}r^2s^2 - \tfrac{1}{2}r^2s^2$.

47. $\tfrac{3}{7}xy - \tfrac{1}{14}xy - \tfrac{1}{2}xy$.

48. $\tfrac{1}{5}y^3 + \tfrac{3}{10}y^3 - y^3 + \tfrac{1}{2}y^3$.

49. $2.5\,xy - .3\,xy + 1.2\,xy$.

50. $-3.05\,a + 4.4\,a - 1.3\,a$.

DEFINITIONS

35. A **Polynomial** is an algebraic expression consisting of two or more terms: as, $a + b$, or $2x^2 - 3xy + 5y^2$.

A **Binomial** is a polynomial of two terms: as, $a + b$.

A **Trinomial** is a polynomial of three terms.

ADDITION OF POLYNOMIALS

36. Addition of polynomials is similar to addition of denominate numbers in arithmetic.

EXAMPLE 1. Find the sum of 3 yd. 2 ft. and 6 in. and 5 yd. 1 ft. and 4 in.

SOLUTION:
$$\begin{array}{l} 3 \text{ yd.} + 2 \text{ ft.} + 6 \text{ in.} \\ 5 \text{ yd.} + 1 \text{ ft.} + 4 \text{ in.} \\ \hline 8 \text{ yd.} + 3 \text{ ft.} + 10 \text{ in.} \end{array}$$

EXAMPLE 2. Find the sum of $2a + 3b + 5c$ and $4a + b + 2c$

SOLUTION:
$$\begin{array}{l} 2a + 3b + 5c \\ 4a + b + 2c \\ \hline 6a + 4b + 7c \end{array}$$

Rule. — To add two polynomials:

1. Rewrite the polynomials, if necessary, so that like terms are in the same vertical column.

2. Add the columns of like terms.

3. Write the results of step 2 with their proper signs for the sum.

EXAMPLE 1. Find the sum of $6a - 7x^2$, $3x^2 - 2a + 3y^2$, and $2x^2 - a - mn$.

SOLUTION:
$$\begin{array}{l} 6a - 7x^2 \\ -2a + 3x^2 + 3y^2 \\ -a + 2x^2 - mn \\ \hline 3a - 2x^2 + 3y^2 - mn \end{array}$$

ADDITION AND SUBTRACTION

Check: Letting $a = 2$, $x = 1$, $y = 1$, $m = 2$, $n = 1$:

$6a - 7x^2 = 12 - 7 = 5$; $-2a + 3x^2 + 3y^2 = -4 + 3 + 3 = +2$;

$-a + 2x^2 - mn = -2 + 2 - 2 = -2$;

and the sum of these values of the polynomials is $5 + 2 - 2$ or 5.

The value of the sum of the polynomials,

$3a - 2x^2 + 3y^2 - mn$ is $6 - 2 + 3 - 2$ or 5.

Since the two values are equal, the solution is probably correct. This is called **checking by substitution**.

Another method of checking is to add carefully in the opposite direction, as in arithmetic.

EXAMPLE 2. Find the sum of $x^3 - y^3 + 3xy^2 - 3x^2y$, $2x^3 + 3xy^2 + y^3$, and $2x^2y - 4xy^2$. Check for $x = 1$, $y = 1$.

SOLUTION: 1.

$$\begin{array}{r} x^3 - 3x^2y + 3xy^2 - y^3 = 1 - 3 + 3 - 1 = 0 \\ 2x^3 + 3xy^2 + y^3 = 2 + 3 + 1 = 6 \\ + 2x^2y - 4xy^2 = 2 - 4 = -2 \\ \hline 3x^3 - x^2y + 2xy^2 +4 \end{array}$$

Also, $3x^3 - x^2y + 2xy^2 = 3 - 1 + 2 = +4$. The solution is correct.

37. In Example 2 of this last paragraph, notice that the three polynomials have been rearranged. The term containing the highest power of x is placed first; then the term having the next lower power of x, and so on. The term $-y^3$, not containing any x, is thought of as containing the lowest power of x in this expression. The polynomials are arranged in **Descending Powers** of x.

These polynomials are arranged also in **Ascending Powers** of y. The exponents of y in the terms increase from left to right.

In all examples in addition, subtraction, multiplication, and division of polynomials, it is advisable to arrange the polynomials, if necessary, according to ascending or descending powers of one of the letters when writing them preparatory to solving the example. When the polynomials are so arranged, there is less likelihood of making some error in the solution, comparison and checking of results is facilitated, and the **final solution has a more workmanlike and finished appearance.**

EXERCISE 19

Find the sums in the following:

1.
$$7A - 3B$$
$$-9A + 2B$$
$$+3A - B$$

2.
$$-6t^2 + 5n^3$$
$$+12t^2 - 13n^3$$
$$-8t^2 + 14n^3$$

3.
$$-16am + 14bn$$
$$6am - 5bn$$
$$9am - 5bn$$

4.
$$a^2 - 2ab + b^2$$
$$a^2 + 4ab - 2b^2$$
$$-2a^2 - 2ab$$

5.
$$7r^3 \qquad - 6rs^2$$
$$ + 6r^2s \qquad - 10$$
$$-11r^3 - 5r^2s + 15rs^2$$

6.
$$3x^3 - 5x^2y + 2xy^2 - 4y^3$$
$$+ 6x^2y \qquad\quad + 5y^3$$
$$-5x^3 \qquad\quad - 7xy^2$$

7.
$$-7m^3 \qquad\qquad + 5mn^2$$
$$- 6m^2n - 13mn^2 + 2n^3$$
$$+ 4m^2n + 3mn^2$$

NOTE. In Examples 5 and 7, blank spaces are left when the first polynomial is written for powers which are not present in the polynomial.

8. $3a - 4b + 6c$ and $5a + 7b - 3c$.

9. $4k - 7 + 3m$, $5k + 2 - 4m$, and $3k - 2$.

10. $2a + 8b - 5c$, $-3b - 3c + 7d$, and $+6c - 4a + 2d$.

11. $12r + 6s - 9t$, $8r - 9s + 11t$, and $15r + 7s - 6t$.

12. $x^2 + 2xy + y^2$, $x^2 - 2xy + y^2$, and $-2x^2 - 2y^2 + 10xy$.

13. $4m^2 - 4mn + n^2$, $m^2 + 4mn + 4n^2$, and $-5m^2 + 5n^2$.

14. $a^3 + 3a^2b + 3ab^2 + b^3$ and $a^3 - 3a^2b + 3ab^2 - b^3$.

15. $3x^2 + 9xy - 4y^2$, $-2xy - 5x^2 - 10y^2$, and $7y^2 - 6xy + 8x^2$.

16. $15a^3 - 6 + 4a + 16a^2$ and $-2 - 13a + 8a^2 - 3a^3$.

17. $x^5 + x^2y^3 + x^3y^2 + x^4y + xy^4 + y^5$ and $x^5 - x^4y + xy^4 + x^3y^2 - y^5$.

18. $12x^3 - 4x + 3$, $-8x + 6 + 15x^3 + 2x^2$, and $-16 + 6x - 8x^3 - 11x$.

ADDITION AND SUBTRACTION

19. $9A^3 + 3AB^2 - B^3$, $-2A^2B + 5AB^2 + 7B^3$, and $-6A^3 + 13A^2B$.

20. $\frac{1}{2}a + \frac{1}{3}b - \frac{1}{5}c$ and $\frac{1}{4}a - \frac{1}{6}b + \frac{1}{10}c$.

21. $\frac{2}{3}m - \frac{3}{5}n + r$, $-\frac{1}{3}m + \frac{3}{10}n - \frac{1}{2}r$, and $2m + \frac{1}{10}n - \frac{1}{2}r$.

22. $3a - \frac{1}{2}b - \frac{9}{14}c$ and $-\frac{3}{4}a - \frac{1}{6}b + \frac{5}{7}c$.

23. $2.3A - 6.02B + 3.5C$ and $-1.6A - 4.38B - 2C$.

24. $2.25x^2 - 3.5xy + 4y^2$ and $-1.5x^2 + 2.75xy - 3.2y^2$.

25. $3m - 1.3n + 4$ and $.5m + 2n - 1.6$.

26. $2a^2 - 5ab - b^2$, $7a^2 + 3ab - 9b^2$, and $-4a^2 - 6ab + 8b^2$.

27. $4x - 3x^2 - 11 + 5x^3$, $12x^2 - 7 - 8x^3 - 15x$, and $14 + 6x^3 + 10x - 9x^2$.

28. $x^3 - 3xy^2 - 2x^2y$, $3x^2y - 5y^3 - 4xy^2$, $5xy^2 - 6y^3 - 7x^3$, and $8y^3 + 7x^3 - 9x^2y$.

29. $15a^3 - 2 - 9a^2 - 3a$, $13a - 5a^2 - 6 - 7a^3$, $8 + 4a - 8a^3 - 7a^2$, and $16a^2 + 3a^3 - 10a - 2$.

30. $12a^3 - x^3 + 4ax^2 - 5a^2x$, $18x^3 - 2a^2x - 3a^3 - 13ax^2$, $15a^2x + 11x^3 - 17a^3 + 3ax^2$, and $6ax^2 - 8a^2x - 7x^3 + 9a^3$.

SUBTRACTION

38. **Subtraction** is the process of finding what number must be added to one given number to produce another given number.

Thus, subtracting 3 from 8 determines the number which must be added to 3 to give 8; and subtracting a from b determines the number which must be added to a to give b.

The number subtracted is called the **Subtrahend**.

The number from which the subtrahend is subtracted is called the **Minuend**.

The result is called the **Remainder** or **Difference**.

ALGEBRA

EXERCISE 20

What must be added to the first number to give the second?

1. 4, 12.
2. 11, 15.
3. 12, 18.
4. $3a, 5a$.
5. $4m, 7m$.
6. $8m, 15m$.
7. $13c, 21c$.
8. $25b, 30b$.
9. $16x, 22x$.

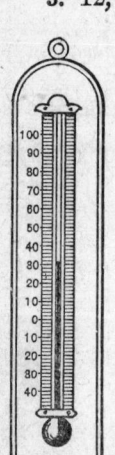

How much must the temperature rise to change:

10. $+2°$ into $+10°$?
11. $+3°$ into $+12°$?
12. $-8°$ into $-3°$?
13. $-6°$ into $-2°$?
14. $-3°$ into $+2°$?
15. $-6°$ into $+4°$?
16. $-5°$ into $+7°$?
17. $-2°$ into $+9°$?

Find the number to be added:

18. $(+3) + ? = +8$.
19. $(-3) + ? = 0$.
20. $(-3) + ? = +2$.
21. $(-3) + ? = +4$.
22. $(-4) + ? = +6$.
23. $(-5) + ? = +3$.
24. $(-8) + ? = -2$.
25. $(-6) + ? = +6$.

How much must the temperature fall to change:

26. $+2°$ into $0°$?
27. $+2°$ into $-3°$?
28. $+4°$ into $-6°$?
29. $+3°$ into $-5°$?
30. $+8°$ into $-3°$?
31. $-2°$ into $-8°$?
32. $+10°$ into $-3°$?
33. $0°$ into $-8°$?

Find the number to be added:

34. $(+3) + ? = 0$.
35. $(+3) + ? = -2$.
36. $(+4) + ? = -7$.
37. $(+5) + ? = -6$.
38. $(+2) + ? = -5$.
39. $(+1) + ? = -7$.
40. $(+7) + ? = -2$.
41. $(-5) + ? = -7$.
42. $(-4) + ? = -8$.
43. $(-1) + ? = -9$.
44. $(-2) + ? = -10$.
45. $(-3) + ? = -12$.

39. Subtraction of Positive and Negative Numbers.

The rule for subtraction of signed numbers is suggested by the following problems:	(A) SIGNS AS GIVEN; SUBTRACT	(B) SIGNS CHANGED; ADD
1. Subtract $+2$ from $+6$. This means: $(+2) + ? = +6$. Result, $+4$. Hence, $(+6) - (+2) = +4$.	$+6$ $+2$ $+4$	$+6$ -2 $+4$
2. Subtract -2 from $+6$. This means: $(-2) + ? = +6$. Result, $+8$. Hence, $(+6) - (-2) = +8$.	$+6$ -2 $+8$	$+6$ $+2$ $+8$
3. Subtract $+2$ from -6. This means: $(+2) + ? = -6$. Result, -8. Hence, $(-6) - (+2) = -8$.	-6 $+2$ -8	-6 -2 -8
4. Subtract -2 from -6. This means: $(-2) + ? = -6$. Result, -4. Hence, $(-6) - (-2) = -4$.	-6 -2 -4	-6 $+2$ -4

In the column *A* on the right, the problem is arranged as usual for a subtraction problem, with the result as it was obtained in the solution on the left; in the column *B* on the right, *the sign of the subtrahend has been changed* from + to —, or from — to +. Notice that the correct result is then obtained by *adding*. Hence,

Rule. — To subtract one number from another, change the sign of the subtrahend and add it to the minuend.

HISTORICAL NOTE. — The symbol, —, like the symbol, +, first appeared in print in a mathematical book by Widmann in 1489. The Italian and French mathematicians of the same period used the symbol, ṁ, derived from the first letter of the Latin word *minus*.

ALGEBRA

EXERCISE 21

1. Subtract -6 from -15.

SOLUTION: -15 Imagine the sign of the subtrahend changed to
           $-\ 6$ $+$ and then add by the rule in § 22. Do not
           $-\ 9$ change the sign on the paper.

2. Find the remainders:

$+13$	$+9$	$+8$	-11	-14	-16	$-\ 8$	-12
$+\ 4$	-5	$+3$	$+\ 2$	$-\ 6$	$+\ 3$	$+10$	$+\ 9$

3.

-29	-34	$+26$	-45	$+37$	-19	-35	$+57$
$+\ 7$	$-\ 6$	$-\ 5$	$+\ 9$	$+\ 8$	$+\ 6$	$+15$	$+13$

4. From each of the minuends of Example 3, subtract -11.

5. From each of the minuends of Example 3, subtract $+12$.

6. From each of the minuends of Example 3, subtract -14.

7. The minimum temperature on a certain day in Chicago was -14 and the maximum was -3. What was the range of temperature?

8. The Roman nation lived under a republican form of government from the year -509 to the year -31; for how many years did the republic last?

9. Was subtraction always possible in arithmetic?

10. Is subtraction always possible in algebra? Why?

11. Find the remainders:

$+15\,a$	$-12\,x$	$-\ 7\,m$	$+14\,n^2$	$+27\,rt$	$-32\,xyz$
$-\ 6\,a$	$+18\,x$	$+15\,m$	$-\ 8\,n^2$	$+34\,rt$	$+18\,xyz$

12.

$-16\,r^2s$	$+33\,xy^2$	$-26\,m^3$	$-43\,n^2$	$-45\,xy$
$-19\,r^2s$	$-15\,xy^2$	$-47\,m^3$	$-17\,n^2$	$+13\,xy$

Subtract:

13. $-xy$ from $+xy$.

14. $-15\,a^3$ from $-46\,a^3$.

15. $21\,abc$ from $-39\,abc$.

16. $-45\,ax^4$ from $+19\,ax^4$

ADDITION AND SUBTRACTION

17. Subtract $-31\,a^2b$ from $-8\,a^2b$.

18. Subtract $19\,rs$ from $-6\,rs$.

19. Take $8\,a$ from $-12\,a$.

20. From $-3\,m^2$ take $4\,m^2$.

21. Take $19\,a$ from $-23\,a$.

22. Take $-16\,n^5x$ from $-27\,n^3x$.

SUBTRACTION OF POLYNOMIALS

40. Rule. — To subtract one polynomial from another:

1. Rewrite the minuend, if necessary, in descending **powers of** some one letter.

2. Write below it the subtrahend, having like terms in the same vertical column.

3. Imagine the signs of the terms of the subtrahend changed, and add the resulting terms to those of the minuend.

EXAMPLE. Subtract $7\,ab^2 - 9\,a^2b + 8\,b^3$ from $-2\,a^2b + 4\,ab^2 + 5\,a^3$.

SOLUTION: 1. Arrange according to descending powers of a.
Minuend: $\quad 5\,a^3 - 2\,a^2b + 4\,ab^2$
Subtrahend: $\quad\;\; -9\,a^2b + 7\,ab^2 + 8\,b^3\quad$ Change signs mentally; add.
Remainder: $\quad \overline{5\,a^3 + 7\,a^2b - 3\,ab^2 - 8\,b^3}$
CHECK: The sum of the subtrahend and remainder is the minuend.

EXERCISE 22

Subtract; check each in some way:

1.
$12\,a^2 - 9\,a - 7$
$\underline{\;8\,a^2 - 6\,a + 13\;}$

2.
$5\,a - 8\,x + 2\,y$
$\underline{-3\,a + 7\,x - 3\,y}$

3.
$17\,m - 12\,n + 6\,p$
$\underline{20\,m - 16\,n - 5\,p}$

4.
$3\,a + 7\,b - c$
$\underline{2\,a + 4\,b - c}$

5.
$2\,ab + 5\,bc - 3\,ac$
$\underline{-ab + 11\,bc - 4\,ac}$

6.
$x^2 + 13\,x - 11$
$\underline{-3\,x^2 + 6\,x - 5}$

ALGEBRA

7.
$10\,r^3 \qquad\quad +6\,rs$
$\underline{3\,r^3 - 2\,r^2s + 8\,rs}$

9.
$a^3 + 3\,a^2b \qquad + 2\,b^3$
$\underline{a^3 - 3\,a^2b + ab^2 - \ b^3}$

11.
$x^2 - 2\,xy + y^2$
$\underline{x^2 + 2\,xy + y^2}$

8.
$5\,x^2 - 6\,x$
$\underline{x^3 + 2\,x^2 \qquad - 5}$

10.
$x^5 \qquad\qquad +y^5$
$\underline{x^5 - x^4y + xy^4 + y^5}$

12.
$x^3 + x^2y + xy^2 + y^3$
$\underline{x^3 - x^2y + xy^2 - y^3}$

13. From $5\,a - 3\,b + 4\,c$ subtract $5\,a + 3\,b - 4\,c$.

14. From $-2\,m^2 - 4\,mn + 9\,n^2$ subtract $8\,m^2 - 7\,mn + 14\,n^2$

15. From $ab + bc + ac$ subtract $ab - bc + ac$.

16. From $4\,x^3 - 9\,x^2 - 11\,x + 18$ subtract $3\,x^3 - 8\,x^2 - 17\,x + 25$

17. From $-3\,y + 8\,x - 4\,z$ subtract $-z + 11\,x - 6\,y$.

18. From $8\,A + 2\,B - 7\,C$ subtract $8\,A - 2\,B + 7\,C$.

19. Subtract $2\,x^3 - 7 - 4\,x - 6\,x^2$ from $5\,x^2 - 12 + 9\,x^3 - 2\,x$.

20. From $x^2 - 2\,xy + y^2$ subtract $x^2 - 2\,xy - y^2$.

21. Take $7\,b - 9\,c - 2\,d$ from $6\,a - 5\,b + 12\,c$.

22. Take $12\,a^3 + 4\,a - 9$ from $3\,a^3 + 8\,a^2 - 6$.

23. Subtract $1 + a^3 - a - a^2$ from $3\,a - 3\,a^2 + 1 - a^3$.

24. From $10\,x^3 - 21\,x^2 - 11\,x$ take $-15\,x^2 - 20\,x + 12$.

25. From $17\,a^3 - 12\,ab^2 + 5\,b^3$ take $8\,a^3 - 3\,a^2b + 13\,b^3$.

26. Take $6\,c - 5\,d - 9\,b - 4\,a$ from $-10\,b - 2\,c + 3\,a - 9\,d$.

27. Subtract $4 - 3\,x - x^2 + 8\,x^3 + 10\,x^4$ from $9 - 7\,x + 6\,x^2 - 12\,x^3 + 5\,x^4$.

28. From $7\,a - 11\,a^3 - 8 + 6\,a^5$ subtract $16\,a^2 - 9 + 2\,a^5 + 15\,a - 10\,a^4$.

29. From $x^5 + 3\,x^4y - x^3y^2 + 5\,x^2y^3 - 4\,xy^4$ subtract $8\,x^4y - 7\,x^3y^2 - 6\,x^2y^3 + 11\,xy^4 - y^5$.

30. Subtract
$7\,n^2 - 5 - 20\,n^3 + 13\,n$ from $-9 - 14\,n^2 + 16\,n + 5\,n^3$.

ADDITION AND SUBTRACTION

31. Subtract
$-x^3 + 3x^2y - 3xy^2 + y^3$ from $x^3 - 2x^2y - 2xy^2 + y^3$.

32. Subtract $-2x^2 - 13 + 41x^3$ from $x + 15x^3 - 18$.

33. Subtract $\frac{1}{2}m - \frac{1}{3}n + \frac{2}{7}p$ from $\frac{3}{4}m + \frac{2}{3}n + \frac{3}{14}p$.

34. Subtract $\frac{5}{6}a - \frac{1}{12}b + \frac{3}{10}c$ from $2a - \frac{1}{2}b - \frac{2}{5}c$.

35. Subtract $-\frac{3}{5}v + \frac{1}{6}w - \frac{3}{7}x$ from $\frac{2}{15}v + \frac{2}{3}w - \frac{3}{14}x$.

36. By how much does $81b^2 + 4a^2 - 36ab$ exceed $-30ab + 9a^2 + 25b^2$?

37. By how much does $-5c + 12a - 8b$ exceed $7a - 9c - b$?

38. By how much does 0 exceed $-3a + 2b - c$?

39. By how much does 1 exceed $-5a - 4b + 6$?

40. From $a^2 - 2ab + b^2$ subtract the sum of $-a^2 + 2ab - b^2$ and $-2a^2 + 2b^2$.

HINT: The last two expressions are both to be subtracted; they are therefore subtrahends and should have their signs changed. Write down the minuend, and, below it, the two subtrahends with their signs changed; then add, thus doing the whole example at one operation.

41. From the sum of $3a^2 - 2ab + b^2$ and $5a^2 - 8ab + 6b^2$ take $6a^2 - 4ab - 3b^2$.

42. From $9x^2 - 8x + x^3$ take the sum of $5 - x^2 + x$ and $6x^3 - 7x - 4$.

43. From the sum of $x + y - 7z$ and $+4x - 9y$ take the sum of $9x - 2y + z$ and $-5x + 6y - 7z$.

44. From the sum of $2a + 3b - 4d$ and $2b - 4c + 3d$ take the sum of $4a - 4b - 3c + 2d$ and $3a + 2c$.

45. Subtract $.5x + .25y - 1.2z$ from $3x - 1.75y + .8z$.

41. Addition and Subtraction used in Equations. There are two more important rules used in solving equations. They will be illustrated by the scales. Review §§ 9 and 10.

Suppose that the sugar S exactly balances the weight W on the scales in the figure. If a 3-lb. weight be added to the right scalepan, and 3 lb. of sugar to the left scalepan, then the scales will still balance.

Similarly, if any number of pounds of weight be removed from the right scalepan and an equal weight of sugar from the left scalepan, then the scales will still balance.

These facts illustrate the rules:

Rule.—1. The same number may be added to both members of an equation without destroying the equality.

2. The same number may be subtracted from both members of an equation without destroying the equality.

EXAMPLE 1. Solve the equation $x - 3 = 7$.

SOLUTION: 1. $x - 3$ is 3 less than x; if 3 is added to $x - 3$, the sum is therefore x. Add 3 to both members of the equation in order to keep them equal.

2. Adding 3 to both members, $x - 3 + 3 = 7 + 3$,
3. or $x = 10$.

CHECK: Does $10 - 3 = 7$? Yes.

EXAMPLE 2. Solve the equation $18x - 5 = 3x + 55$.

SOLUTION: 1. $\qquad 18x - 5 = 3x + 55$.

2. Adding 5 to both members of the equation,
$$18x = 3x + 60.$$

3. Subtracting $3x$ from both members of the equation,
$$15x = 60.$$

4. Dividing both members of the equation by 15,
$$x = 4.$$

CHECK: Substitute 4 in equation 1; does $18 \times 4 - 5 = 3 \times 4 + 55$? does $72 - 5 = 12 + 55$? Yes.

42. In order to abbreviate the explanation of the solutions of equations, symbols A, S, M, and D will be used.

Thus: A_3 will mean "add 3 to both members of the equation."

S_{2n} will mean "subtract $2n$ from both members of the equation."

ADDITION AND SUBTRACTION

M_{-3} will mean "multiply both members of the equation by -3."

D_7 will mean "divide both members of the equation by 7."

These symbols will be used in the text from now on.

Pupils will find them helpful when solving equations.

EXERCISE 23

Tell what the following symbols mean:

1. A_2.
2. S_{-3}.
3. M_{5x}.
4. A_{-8y}.
5. D_{-4}.
6. M_{-1}.
7. A_{2c}.
8. D_{34}.
9. S_{7r}.
10. M_{-5}.

11. Solve the equation $24 - 11 m = 6 - 8 m$.

SOLUTION: 1. $\qquad 24 - 11 m = 6 - 8 m$.
2. A_{8m}: $\qquad 24 - 3 m = 6$. (Rule 1, § 41)
3. S_{24}: $\qquad -3 m = -18$. (Rule 2, § 41)
4. M_{-1}: $\qquad +3 m = +18$. (Rule, § 10)
5. D_3: $\qquad m = 6$. (Rule, § 9)

CHECK: Substitute 6 in the given equation.

Does $24 - 11 \times 6 = 6 - 8 \times 6$? does $24 - 66 = 6 - 48$? does $-42 = -42$? Yes.

NOTE 1. In step 2, "A_{8m}" means "add $8m$ to both members of the previous equation"; the result will be equation 2. In step 4, "M_{-1}" means "multiply both members of the previous equation by -1"; the result will be equation 4.

NOTE 2. Whenever the coefficient of the unknown is negative, as in step 3, multiply both members by -1 so as to make it positive.

Solve the following equations and test the result:

12. $x + 3 = 12$.
13. $y + 7 = 15$.
14. $m - 2 = 9$.
15. $2 m + 5 = 11$.
16. $3 a + 7 = 19$.
17. $5 c - 2 = 23$.
18. $4 t - 7 = 21$.
19. $3 k = 8 + k$.
20. $6 x = x + 45$.
21. $7 y = 3 y + 12$.
22. $6 z = 63 - 3 z$.
23. $10 r = 80 - 6 r$.
24. $2 s = 99 - 9 s$.
25. $3 a = 120 - 7 a$.

ALGEBRA

        $5 - 15x$ 34. $-2x + 5 = -15$.

        $= 6 + 3r$.   35. $-5y + 9 = -21$.

        $9 = 37 - x$.   36. $-11z + 10 = 4 - 8z$

29. $5t - 8 = 28 + 2t$.   37. $16r - 1 = 4r + 5$.

30. $6w - 11 = 88 - 3w$.   38. $17t - 7 = 1 - 7t$.

31. $15k - 13 = 9k + 17$.   39. $11m + 6 = -9m + 18$.

32. $4b + 15 = 35 - b$.   40. $13p - 9 = -2p + 36$.

33. $3c - 6 = c + 14$.   41. $19r + 11 = 7r + 13$.

43. In order to solve problems, it is necessary to translate the statements which give the conditions of the problem into algebraic symbols.

EXAMPLE. One number exceeds another number by 18. The product of the smaller number and 3 equals the larger number. Find the numbers.

SOLUTION: 1. Let $s =$ the smaller number.
2. Then $s + 18 =$ the larger number,
3. and $3s =$ the product of the smaller and 3.
4. $\therefore 3s = s + 18$, since the product must equal the larger number.
5. S_s: $2s = 18$.
6. D_2: $s = 9$.

CHECK: The smaller is 9; the larger 27; and $3 \times 9 = 27$.

NOTE. The symbol, $\therefore$, means "therefore."

Rule. — To solve a problem by means of an equation:

1. Represent one of the unknown numbers by some letter.

2. Represent the other unknown numbers by means of this same letter, using relations given in the problem.

3. From the conditions of the problem form an equation between the numbers; solve the equation.

4. Check the result by comparison with the statements of the problem.

ADDITION AND SUBTRACTION

EXERCISE 24

1. What number increased by 11 equals 19?

2. There are two numbers of which the larger is 5 times the smaller. The difference between the numbers is 24. Find the numbers.

3. One number exceeds another by 54. The larger number is 7 times the smaller. Find the numbers.

4. Five times a certain number exceeds 8 by 37. Find the number.

5. If 12 times a certain number is diminished by 3, the result is the same as if 4 times the number is increased by 5. Find the number.

6. 15 exceeds twice a certain number by the same amount that 3 times the number exceeds 10. Find the number.

7. The age of John is double that of his brother James. What are their ages if equal results are obtained by subtracting 5 years from John's age, and adding 10 to James' age.

8. The age of A is twice that of B, and the age of C equals the sum of the ages of A and B. The sum of the ages of A and C exceeds the age of B by 40 years. Find their ages.

9. One angle is four times as large as a second angle; if their sum is increased by 5°, the result is one straight angle. (See § 13.) Find the angles.

10. A farmer wishes to inclose a rectangular field for a pasture, making it 15 rods wide. He wants to make it as long as possible, using 172 rods of wire fencing, which he has on hand. How long can he make it?

11. If six times the area of Lake Superior, the largest freshwater lake, be decreased by 12,000 square miles, the result equals the area of the Caspian Sea, the largest salt-water lake, 180,000 square miles. Find the area of Lake Superior.

ALGEBRA

12. If twice the height of Mt. McKinley, the highest mountain in North America, be decreased by 11,798 feet, the result equals the height of Mt. Everest, the highest mountain in Asia, 29,002 feet. Find the height of Mt. McKinley.

13. The longest river in the world is the combined Mississippi-Missouri and the next longest is the Nile. Twice the length of the Nile diminished by 2800 miles equals the length of the Mississippi; the length of the Mississippi is 700 miles more than that of the Nile. Find the length of each river.

14. The highest velocity of wind recorded in the United States up to January 1, 1910 exceeded 25 times the lowest average velocity at any point in the United States by 2 miles per hour; the highest velocity exceeds the lowest by 98 miles. Find the highest and lowest velocity.

15. In the United States, the lowest average annual precipitation, rain and snow, is at Yuma, Arizona; and the highest is at Mobile, Alabama. The precipitation in inches at Mobile is 20 times that at Yuma; the sum of the two precipitations is 65.1 inches. Find the precipitation at each place.

44. Percentage and Interest Problems. Many of the problems involving percentage and interest may be expressed and solved by algebraic methods.

EXERCISE 25

Percentage Problems

1. What does 4 % mean? 5 %? r %? m %?

2. What is 4 % of 500? 6 % of 250?

3. Express decimally 4 % of p; 6 % of b; 15 % of c.

4. If the cost of an article is c dollars, and the rate of gain is 25 %, what is the gain? what is the selling price? ($c + .25\,c = ?$.)

5. Find the cost of an article sold for $165 if the gain is 10 %. ($c + .10\,c = 165$.)

ADDITION AND SUBTRACTION

6. A grocer wishes to make 25 % on some canned goods. At what price must he buy them so as to be able to sell the goods at $1.25 per dozen?

7. A man wishes to sell hats at $3.50 each. At what price must he buy them so as to make 12 % upon the cost?

8. A real estate agent knows that he can sell a certain lot for $3270. At what price must he buy the lot from the present owner in order that he may make a profit of 9 %?

Interest Problems

9. What is the simple interest on $200 at 6 % for 1 year? for 2 years? for t years?

10. What is the simple interest on R dollars at 6 % for 1 year? for 2 years? for t years?

11. What is the simple interest on $200 at r % for 1 year? for 4 years? for t years?

12. What is the simple interest on P dollars at r % for 1 year? for 3 years? for t years?

13. If I represents the number of dollars interest on P dollars invested at r % for t years, it may be expressed by the formula: $I = \dfrac{Prt}{100}$. Express this formula in words.

Solve the following problems by substituting in this formula:

14. If a man receives $1150 income from $3500 which has been invested for 4 years and 6 months, what rate of interest has he received?

SOLUTION: 1. Let r = the rate per cent.
2. $P = 3500$; $I = 1150$; $t = 4\frac{1}{2}$.
3. $\therefore 1150 = \overset{35}{\cancel{3500}} \cdot \dfrac{r}{\cancel{100}} \cdot 4\frac{1}{2}$. (Since $I = P \cdot \dfrac{r}{100} \cdot t$.)

$\therefore 1150 = \frac{9}{2} \cdot 35 \cdot r$.
$1150 = \frac{315}{2} r$.

4. M$_2$: $2300 = 315\, r$.
5. D$_{315}$: $r = 7.3 + \%$.

15. What principal must be invested at 4 % to yield an income of $1500 per year?

16. For what length of time must $4000 be invested at 5 % simple interest to yield $750 interest?

17. What rate of simple interest has been earned on an investment of $2500, if the income is $1000 in 10 years?

Amount in Interest Problems

18. The sum of the principal and interest is the amount. Indicate the amount at the end of one year if P dollars are invested at 4 %. $(P + .04\,P = 1.04\,P.)$

Similarly at 6 %; at 7 %.

19. What is the amount at the end of two years if P dollars are invested at 4 %? for 3 years at 5 %?

20. What sum of money will amount to $3500 if invested at 5 % simple interest for 5 years?

21. How long will it take $1500 to amount to $2000 if invested at 5 %? $(2000 = 1500 + 1500 \cdot \frac{5}{100} \cdot t.$ Solve the equation for t.)

22. How long will it take $1200 to double itself at 6 %?

23. Letting A represent the number of dollars in the amount, and P, r, and t the usual numbers, show that the amount may be expressed by the formula:

$$A = P + \frac{Prt}{100}.$$

Solve the following problems by substituting in this formula:

24. In how many years will $3500 amount to $4550 at 5 % simple interest?

25. The members of a certain company paid $300 per share for some stock. At the end of 7 years, they received $800 per share for their stock. What rate of simple interest did their money earn for them during that time?

HISTORICAL NOTE. — The symbol % was used first about the year 1685.

IV. PARENTHESES

45. Terms which are parts of a single number expression are often inclosed in **Symbols of Grouping**.

The **Parentheses**, ( ), are symbols of grouping; thus,

$$3a - (2x + y - z)$$

means that $2x + y - z$ is to be subtracted from $3a$.

Other symbols of grouping are the **Brackets** [ ], the **Braces**, { }, and the **Vinculum**, ———.

All are used in the same manner as the parentheses, and are referred to collectively as *parentheses*.

HISTORICAL NOTE. — The parentheses are used most commonly now. They were introduced by Girard, a Dutch mathematician, about 1629. Previously the brackets and the braces had been used by Vieta, about 1593, although Bombelli, an Italian, had made the first start in the direction of their use in 1572. Descartes used the vinculum.

REMOVAL OF PARENTHESES

46. Parentheses preceded by a Plus Sign.

DEVELOPMENT. 1. Consider $a^4 + a^2 + (a^3 - a)$.

This means that $a^3 - a$ is to be added to $a^4 + a^2$.

$$\begin{array}{l} a^4 + a^2 \\ a^3 - a \\ \hline \text{Sum: } a^4 + a^3 + a^2 - a \end{array}$$

$\therefore a^4 + a^2 + (a^3 - a)$
$= a^4 + a^2 + a^3 - a.$

2. Consider $a - b + (c - d)$.

SOLUTION:

$$\begin{array}{l} a - b \\ + c - d \\ \hline \text{Sum: } a - b + c - d \end{array}$$

$\therefore a - b + (c - d)$
$= a - b + c - d.$

55

3. Notice that the signs of the terms which are within the parentheses are not changed when the parentheses are removed. This fact suggests the

Rule. — To remove parentheses preceded by a plus sign:

Rewrite all terms which are within the parentheses without changing their signs.

47. Parentheses preceded by a Minus Sign.

DEVELOPMENT. 1. Consider $a^4 + a^2 - (a^3 - a)$.

SOLUTION: This means that $(a^3 - a)$ is to be subtracted from $a^4 + a^2$.

$$
\begin{array}{ll}
\quad a^4 \quad\quad + a^2 & \therefore\ a^4 + a^2 - (+ a^3 - a) \\
\quad\quad + a^3 \quad - a & = a^4 + a^2 - a^3 + a.
\end{array}
$$
Remainder: $a^4 - a^3 + a^2 + a$

2. Consider $a - b - (+ c - d)$.

SOLUTION:

$$
\begin{array}{ll}
a - b & \therefore\ a - b - (+ c - d) \\
\quad + c - d & = a - b - c + d.
\end{array}
$$
Remainder: $a - b - c + d$

3. Notice that the signs of the terms which are within the parentheses are changed when the parentheses are removed. This fact suggests the

Rule. — To remove parentheses preceded by a minus sign:

Rewrite all terms which are within the parentheses, but change their signs from $+$ to $-$, or from $-$ to $+$.

EXAMPLE 1. Remove the parentheses from
$$2a - 3b - (5a - 4b) + (4a - b).$$

SOLUTION: By the rules, the expression becomes
$$2a - 3b - 5a + 4b + 4a - b.$$

When this is simplified, the result is a.

CHECK: Let $a = 1$, and $b = 2$.
$$2a - 3b - (5a - 4b) + (4a - b) = 2 - 6 - (5 - 8) + (4 - 2)$$
$$= 2 - 6 - (-3) + 2$$
$$= 2 - 6 + 3 + 2 = + 1.$$

Also the result $a = 1$.

PARENTHESES

48. The above rules apply equally to the removal of all symbols of grouping (§ 45).

It should be noticed in each case that the sign of the first term within the symbol of grouping is not the sign prefixed to the symbol of grouping; thus, in $-(a-b)$ the term a is positive within the parentheses.

49. Parentheses sometimes inclose others; in this case, the following rule should be observed by beginners.

RULE. — To remove two or more parentheses, when one incloses another:

1. Combine the terms within the innermost parentheses, if possible; then remove these parentheses according to the rules in §§ 46 and 47.

2. Combine the terms within the resulting innermost parentheses, and remove these parentheses.

3. Continue doing this until all parentheses are removed.

EXAMPLE 2. Simplify $4x - \{3x + (-2x - [x-a])\}$.

The brackets are the innermost symbols of grouping; they are preceded by a minus sign. Remember that the sign of x within the brackets is $+$.

SOLUTION:

1.	$4x - \{3x + (-2x - [x-a])\}$	
2.	$= 4x - \{3x + (-2x - x + a)\}$	Removing the [ ].
3.	$= 4x - \{3x + (-3x + a)\}$	Combining within the ( ).
4.	$= 4x - \{3x - 3x + a\}$	Removing the ( ).
5.	$= 4x - a.$	Combining within the { }.

EXERCISE 26

Simplify the following expressions by removing the symbols of grouping:

1. $3m - (2n + p).$
2. $4x + (z - 2y).$
3. $5a - (2b - c).$
4. $7v + (-3w + x).$
5. $6r - [-3a + b].$
6. $8s + \{-3m - t\}.$

ALGEBRA

7. $9k - [p - 2q]$.
8. $2a + (3b - c)$.
9. $l - \{m - n\}$.
10. $8 - [-2a + b]$.

In the following examples, since neither symbol of grouping incloses the other, remove both at once. Tell what each example means; thus in 11: "subtract the number $(c-d)$ from the number $(2a-b)$."

11. $(2a - b) - (c - d)$.
12. $(a - b) - (c + d)$.
13. $[r + s] + [t - v]$.
14. $\{r - s\} - \{t + v\}$.
15. $(x - y) - (z + w)$.
16. $(x - y) - (z - w)$.
17. $[m + n] + [p - q]$.
18. $\{m + n\} - \{p - q\}$.
19. $(-a + b) + (-c + d)$.
20. $(-a + b) - (-c - d)$.

In the following examples, combine terms after removing the parentheses:

21. $3c - (5c - 6)$.
22. $(2a - b) - (5a - b)$.
23. $2a - (3a - b) + 2b$.
24. $a^2 + a - (a^2 - a)$.
25. $(5x - 6) - (2x - 4)$.
26. $(3b - 11) - (4b + 5)$.
27. $(+x + y) - (-2x + y)$
28. $5x^2 - (-2x^2 + x) + 6$.
29. $(2r - s) - (3r - 2s)$.
30. $(3p - 2q) + (-3p - 2q)$
31. $9m - (4m + 6n) + (3m - n)$.
32. $8r + (5r - [2s + t])$.
33. $3x - (2y + [5x - y])$.
34. $5a - (4a - \{3a - 1\})$.
35. $6b - \{7b - (9b + 4) - 7\}$.
36. $(7t - r) - [8t - (10r + t) - 3r]$.
37. $3x - (5x - [7x + 9a - 4] - 3a)$.
38. $5ab - [(3ab - 10) - (4ab + 7)]$.
39. $7c - (5c + [12c - \{6c + 2\}])$.
40. $m - [(6m - 7n) - n] - [3m + 4n - (2m - 3n)]$

PARENTHESES

INTRODUCTION OF PARENTHESES

50. Sometimes it is necessary to introduce parentheses into an expression.

DEVELOPMENT. 1. What is the rule for removing parentheses preceded by a plus sign?

2. What, then, should be done with the signs of terms which are *placed within* parentheses preceded by a plus sign?

3. Inclose the last two terms of $a + b + c - d$ in parentheses preceded by a plus sign.

4. What is the rule for removing parentheses preceded by a minus sign?

5. What, then, should be done with the signs of terms which are *placed within* parentheses preceded by a minus sign?

6. Inclose the last two terms of $a + b + c - d$ in parentheses preceded by a minus sign.

Rule.—1. **To inclose terms in parentheses preceded by a plus sign, rewrite the terms without changing their signs.**

2. **To inclose terms in parentheses preceded by a minus sign, rewrite the terms, changing the signs from + to —, and from — to +.**

EXAMPLE. Inclose the last three terms of $r + s - t + v$ in parentheses preceded by a minus sign.

SOLUTION: 1. $r + s - t + v = r - (-s + t - v)$. (Rule 2).

CHECK: If the parentheses are removed, the result is the original expression.

EXERCISE 27

Inclose the last three terms of the following expressions in parentheses preceded by a plus sign:

1. $m + n - c + d$.
2. $a + b - r - s$.
3. $x + y + z - w$.
4. $r - s + t + x$.
5. $p - q - a + b$.
6. $a^2 + b^2 - 2bc + c^2$.
7. $a^2 - b^2 + 2bc - c^2$.
8. $a^2 - 4b^2 + 12b - 9$.
9. $x^2 - 2yz + y^2 + z^2$.
10. $n^4 - 5n^3 - 8n^2 + 6n + 7$.

ALGEBRA

11–20. Inclose the last two terms of the foregoing expressions in parentheses preceded by a minus sign.

21–30. Inclose the last three terms in parentheses preceded by a minus sign.

EXERCISE 28

Indicate and simplify, where possible, the following:

1. The sum of a and 5; a and b.

2. The sum of x and $(x+3)$; x and $(x-5)$.

3. The difference between a and 5; a and b.

4. The difference between $(a-2)$ and $3a$; $(a+7)$ and $3a$.

5. The sum of $(3a+5)$ and $(2a-6)$; also their difference.

6. The amount by which 15 is greater than 12; greater than a; greater than $(a+2)$.

7. The amount by which $5x$ is greater than 10; greater than $2x$; greater than $(x-4)$.

8. The amount by which 20 exceeds 15; exceeds t; exceeds $(t-3)$.

9. The amount by which $3p$ exceeds 5; exceeds $(p+1)$; exceeds $(p-3)$.

10. The amount by which $(2a+3)$ exceeds $(a-5)$.

11. The smaller part of 15, if l is the larger part.

12. The smaller part of x, if 7 is the larger part.

13. The larger part of n, if 3 is the smaller part.

14. The smaller part of $2a$, if $(a-3)$ is the larger part.

15. The larger part of $(3c-2)$, if $(c+1)$ is the smaller part.

16. The sum of two numbers is 50; the smaller is p. Represent the larger number.

PARENTHESES

17. The sum of two numbers is 37; the larger is l. Represent the smaller.

18. The difference between two numbers is 5; the smaller is s. Represent the larger.

19. The difference between two numbers is x; the smaller is 3. Represent the larger.

20. The difference between two numbers is 10; the larger is n. Represent the smaller.

21. The integer which is consecutive to the integer a.

HINT: 6 is consecutive to 5; 7 is consecutive to 6.

22. The second integer consecutive to a.

23. The sum of a and the consecutive integer.

24. The sum of n and the two consecutive integers.

25. If a is an odd number, what is the consecutive odd number?

HINT: 5 is consecutive to 3; 11 to 9; 17 to 15.

51. Parentheses are used in equations and problems.

EXAMPLE. The sum of two numbers is 88. The larger number exceeds the smaller by 36. Find the numbers.

SOLUTION: 1. Let l = the larger number.
2. Then $(88 - l)$ = the smaller number.
3. Then $l - (88 - l) = 36$.
4. Removing ( ), $l - 88 + l = 36$. (§ 47)

$$2l - 88 = 36.$$

5. A_{88}:* $\qquad 2l = 124.$
6. D_2: $\qquad l = 62,$ the larger number.

$$88 - 62 = 26, \text{ the smaller number.}$$

CHECK: $\qquad 62 - 26 = 36.$

* See § 42 for the symbol A_{88}.

ALGEBRA

EXERCISE 29

Solve the following equations

1. $2r - (r+6) = 11$.
2. $(3x+4) - (2x+9) = 15$.
3. $12A + (2A-3) = 6A - (-7A - 15)$.
4. $(4t-5) - (2t+5) = (2t-9) - (4t-7)$.
5. $(-10x+12) - (6x-5) = (13-8x) - (15+9x)$.
6. $(3x+5) - (2x-7) = (4x+9) - (2x-11)$.
7. $(6y-8) - (9y+4) = (9-13y) - 11y$.
8. $(13-4m) - (3m+9) = (2m-8) - (6+7m)$.
9. $(8t-11) - (7-5t) = 12 - (13+4t)$.
10. $(17z-1) - (9z-10) = 15 - (13z+6) - 2z$.

11. The sum of two numbers is 30. The greater number exceeds the smaller number by 4. Find the numbers.

12. The sum of the ages of A and B is 115 years. A is 13 years younger than B. What are their ages?

13. Divide the number 123 into two parts such that the greater exceeds the smaller by 67.

14. The sum of the ages of A and B is 102 years. A is 26 years older than B. Find their ages.

15. Divide $93 between A and B so that A may receive $23 less than B.

16. The Library of Congress at Washington consists of three main stories, whose total height is 64 feet. The height of the second story exceeds that of the first by 7 feet, and is 8 feet less than that of the third story. Find the height of each of the three stories.

17. The total length of the Upper Steel Arch Bridge at Niagara Falls is 1240 feet. Its main span, the longest of the kind in the world, exceeds twice the remaining part of the bridge by 40 feet. Find the length of its main span.

PARENTHESES

18. The first appropriation for a library for Congress was made in 1800. The present Library of Congress was completed at a total expense of over $6,000,000. The cost of the gold leaf on the dome of the present building increased by $1200 equals the appropriation made in 1800; and the sum of that first appropriation and the cost of the gold leaf is $8800. Find each of these amounts.

19. Seven major planets besides the earth revolve around the sun. The number of planets which are farther from the sun than the earth exceeds by one twice the number which are nearer to the sun than the earth. Find the number of planets nearer to and the number farther from the sun than the earth.

20. The sum of two consecutive integers is 35. Find them. (See Example 21, Exercise 28.)

21. The sum of three consecutive integers is 108. Find the numbers.

22. The sum of four consecutive integers is 218. Find them.

23. The sum of two consecutive odd integers is 196. Find them.

24. Find the integer which is such that when increased by the first consecutive integer, and their sum decreased by the second consecutive integer, the result is 75.

25. There are four angles which make up the total angular magnitude around a point. (See § 13, Example 15). The second angle is 3 times the first; the second exceeds the third by 10°, and exceeds the fourth by 50°. Find the angles. Illustrate with a figure.

26. An angle exceeds its supplement by 30°. Find the angle. (See Example 11, § 13).

27. The complement of a certain angle exceeds the angle itself by 20°. Find the angle. (See § 13.)

28. The sum of the supplement and complement of a certain angle is 120°. Find the angle.

29. The fertility of farm land is maintained by adding fertilizers which contain certain plant foods, such as nitrogen, potash, and phosphoric acid. In 100 pounds of a good corn fertilizer, the amount of phosphoric acid should exceed the amount of nitrogen by 10 pounds, and the amount of potash should equal in weight the sum of the other two. Find the number of pounds of each plant food in the mixture.

30. Texas is the largest state in the Union, and Rhode Island is the smallest. The area of Texas exceeds 213 times the area of Rhode Island by 72 square miles. The sum of their areas is 267,144 square miles. Find the area of each state.

HISTORICAL NOTE. — In Examples 5 and 8, negative roots are found. The mathematicians of the 16th century were slow to admit that such roots had any meaning. Cardan called them *numerœ fictœ*. Even such men as Vieta and Harriot, who contributed so much to the growth of algebra, admitted only positive solutions. Girard (1590–1632) and Descartes (1673) were especially instrumental in establishing the fact that negative roots should have the same meaning as positive roots.

V. MULTIPLICATION

52. The **Law of Signs for Multiplication** of positive and negative numbers (§ 25), may be written:

Rule. — 1. The product of two numbers having like signs is positive.

2. The product of two numbers having unlike signs is negative.

HISTORICAL NOTE. — Until the time of Michael Stifel (1553), little progress was made toward finding the rule for multiplying powers of the same base, owing to the cumbersome notation that had been used previously to denote the various powers. Some men even made a table corresponding to our multiplication table, giving the products of some of the powers. Stifel introduced a better notation, used the word exponent, and gave the rule which we now use.

53. The Law of Exponents for Multiplication.

DEVELOPMENT. 1. Review the definitions of exponent, base, and power of a number, given in paragraph 15.

2. What does a^3 mean? x^5? r^7? e^8?

3. Write in exponent form:

(a) $b \cdot b \cdot b \cdot b$; (b) $m \cdot m \cdot m$; (c) $y \cdot y \cdot y \cdot y \cdot y$;

(d) $r \cdot r \cdots r$ (if there are 10 factors);

(e) $x \cdot x \cdots x$ (if there are 8 factors).

4. Find the product of a^3 and a^4.

$$a^3 = a \cdot a \cdot a;\ a^4 = a \cdot a \cdot a \cdot a.$$
$$\therefore a^3 \cdot a^4 = (a \cdot a \cdot a) \times (a \cdot a \cdot a \cdot a) = a \cdot a \cdot a \cdot a \cdot a \cdot a \cdot a = a^7.$$

5. Find as in 4, the following products and write down the results as in part (a):

(a) $a^3 \cdot a^4 = a^7$.

(b) $x^2 \cdot x^4 = ?$

(c) $r^3 \cdot r^5 = ?$

(d) $m^4 \cdot m^5 = ?$

ALGEBRA

6. Observing the results in 5, see if you can get the following products mentally; check as in 4:

(a) $m^2 \cdot m^3 = ?$
(b) $m^3 \cdot m^6 = ?$
(c) $x^2 \cdot x^5 = ?$
(d) $y^6 \cdot y^2 = ?$

7. The facts observed lead to the

Rule. — To find the exponent of any number in a product, add the exponents of that number in the multiplicand and multiplier.

EXERCISE 30

Find the indicated products

1. $x^3 \cdot x^9$.
2. $a^4 \cdot a^6$.
3. $m^3 \cdot m^7$.
4. $t^4 \cdot t^7$.
5. $t^9 \cdot t^6$.
6. $t^5 \cdot t^3$.
7. $m^{10} \cdot m^2$.
8. $s^{12} \cdot s^3$.
9. $y^8 \cdot y^9$.
10. $2^8 \cdot 2^2$.
11. $3^2 \cdot 3^4$.
12. $5^2 \cdot 5^3$.

54. The Commutative Law of Multiplication.

DEVELOPMENT. 1. 3×4 and 4×3 each equal 12.

2. Notice, in step 1, that the same factors occur in each product, but that the order is changed. Does changing the order of the factors change the value of the product?

3. Compare $3 \times 4 \times 5$ and $3 \times 5 \times 4$, by finding their values.

4. Write these same factors in some other order, and compare the product with the products obtained in step 3.

5. Arrange the factors 2, 4, and 5 in three different ways and compare the products.

Rule. — The factors of a product may be arranged in any order without changing the value of the product.

EXERCISE 31

Arrange each of the following sets of factors in two ways and find the products.

1. 3, 7.
2. 2, 5, 6.
3. 3, 4, 6.
4. 5, 2, 4.
5. 6, 5, 3.
6. 6, 4, 2.

MULTIPLICATION

MULTIPLICATION OF MONOMIALS

55. DEVELOPMENT. 1. Find the product of $7a$ and $-2b$.

SOLUTION: 1. $\qquad -2b = (-2)b \qquad$ (See § 31)
2. Then $\qquad 7a(-2b) = 7 \cdot a \cdot (-2) \cdot b$
Then, since the order of the factors may be changed, (§ 54)
3. $\qquad 7a(-2b) = 7 \cdot (-2) \cdot a \cdot b$
$\qquad\qquad\qquad = -14\, ab.$ (§ 5)

2. Find the product of $-5x$ and $-6x^2y$.

SOLUTION: 1. $(-5x)(-6x^2y) = (-5) \cdot x \cdot (-6) \cdot x^2 \cdot y$
$\qquad\qquad\qquad = (-5) \cdot (-6) \cdot x \cdot x^2 \cdot y$
$\qquad\qquad\qquad = +30\, x^3y.$

3. Find similarly the product of $3\,mn$ and $2\,p$.

4. Find similarly the product of $+2\,a^3b$ and $+5\,ab$.

5. Give at sight, if possible, the following:

(a) $2\,rs \cdot 5\,t$.
(b) $3\,xy \cdot 2\,z$.
(c) $7\,a \cdot 3\,a^2$.
(d) $4\,m \cdot 5\,mx$.

Rule. — To find the product of two monomials:

1. Find the product of the numerical coefficients, using **the Law of Signs for Multiplication**.

2. Multiply this product by the literal factors, giving to each an exponent equal to its exponent in the multiplicand plus its exponent in the multiplier.

EXAMPLE 1. Multiply $2\,a^5$ by $9\,a^4b^2$.

SOLUTION: $\qquad (2\,a^5)(9\,a^4b^2) = + (2 \times 9) \cdot a^{(5+4)} \cdot b^2$
$\qquad\qquad\qquad = 18\,a^9b^2.$

EXAMPLE 2. Multiply $-5\,x^3yz^5$ by $+6\,xy^2w$.

SOLUTION: $(-5\,x^3yz^5)(+6\,xy^2w) = -(5 \times 6) \cdot x^{(3+1)} \cdot y^{(1+2)} \cdot z^5 \cdot w$
$\qquad\qquad\qquad = -30\,x^4y^3z^5w.$

ALGEBRA

EXERCISE 32

Find the following indicated products:

1. $x^5 \cdot x^9$.
2. $a^2 \cdot a^3 \cdot a^4$.
3. $x^5 \cdot x^3 \cdot x^6$.
4. $y^4 \cdot y^3 \cdot y^5$.
5. $m^8 \cdot m \cdot m^2$.
6. $a^{12} \cdot a^4 \cdot a^3$.
7. $E^9 \cdot E^7 \cdot E$.
8. $a^2b^3 \cdot ab$.
9. $x^4y^2 \cdot xy^3$.
10. $a^3x \cdot ax^3$.
11. $x^2yz \cdot xy^2z$.
12. $r^2s^3t \cdot rst^2$.
13. $ab^2c^3 \cdot ab^2c^3$.
14. $r^2s \cdot rs^2t^3$.
15. $2^5 \cdot 2^3$.
16. $4^5 \cdot 4^3$.
17. $5^6 \cdot 5^4$.
18. $10^3 \cdot 10^2$.
19. $pr^2t \cdot r^3$.
20. $mx^2 \cdot mnx^3$.

Multiply:

21. $7\,a^3$ by $3\,a^2$.
22. $-9\,m^2$ by $8\,m^4$.
23. $-5\,ab$ by $2\,a^2$.
24. $-3\,rs^2$ by $-9\,rs$.
25. $5\,xyz$ by $-11\,xyz$.
26. $-11\,xy^2$ by $9\,x^2y$.
27. $-6\,d^3b$ by $-4\,ab^4$.
28. $-6\,x^2y^3$ by $+12\,xy^2$.
29. $-9\,m^2n^3$ by $7\,m^2n^3$.
30. $-12\,rst$ by $-9\,s^2$.
31. $-6\,a^3b^6$ by $-b^3c^5$.
32. $+9\,ax^2$ by $-9\,ay^2$.
33. $8\,x^2z^7$ by $-8\,y^3z^3$.
34. $-7\,AB^2$ by $+12\,AB^3C$.
35. $12\,a^2bc$ by $6\,bcd^2$.
36. $13\,a^2$ by $-7\,a^3b^2c$.
37. $-14\,m^2n$ by $-6\,mn^2$.
38. $-16\,a^3bc^4$ by $+5\,a^4b^5c$.
39. $-3\,x^3y^3z^3$ by $-17\,x^2y^3z$.
40. $-4\,mn$ by $+17\,m^2n$.

Find the product of:

41. $3\,a^5$, $5\,a^3$, and $6\,a^2$.
42. $-4\,x^3$, $-9\,y^2$, and $2\,z^3$.
43. x^3y^2, $-y^2z$, and xz^3.
44. $-12\,a^7b^2$, $-b^4c^3$, and $-8\,c^3a^2$.
45. a^5, $-3\,a$, $-5\,a^6$, and $-4\,a^3$.

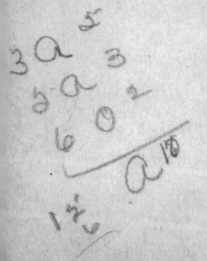

MULTIPLICATION

46. $-7\,m^2n$, $+8\,mr^2$, and $-2\,n^2r$.

47. -3 and $+\dfrac{5\,a^2}{3}$.

48. $+5$ and $-\dfrac{2\,m^3}{5}$.

49. $+4$ and $-\dfrac{3\,n}{2}$.

50. $+12$ and $-\dfrac{5\,r}{3}$.

51. -15 and $-\dfrac{6\,s}{5}$.

52. -10 and $-\dfrac{7\,t}{2}$.

53. -9 and $+\dfrac{4\,p}{3}$.

54. $+14$ and $-\dfrac{3\,w}{7}$.

55. -18 and $+\dfrac{6\,s}{9}$.

56. $+20$ and $-\dfrac{3}{10}x$.

57. $\tfrac{1}{2}ab^2$ and $-\tfrac{2}{5}a^2b$.

58. $-\tfrac{3}{8}mn$ and $-\tfrac{2}{3}m^2$.

59. $+.5\,rs^3$ and $-.3\,r^2s$.

60. $-.12\,t^3$ and $-.7\,t$.

56. Numbers, and relations between them, may be represented by geometrical figures.

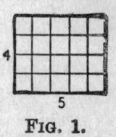

EXAMPLE 1. The product 4×5 may be represented by the rectangle in Fig. 1. Note that the area of the rectangle is 20 square units.

FIG. 1.

EXAMPLE 2. The product $4(3+7)$ may be represented by the Fig. 2.

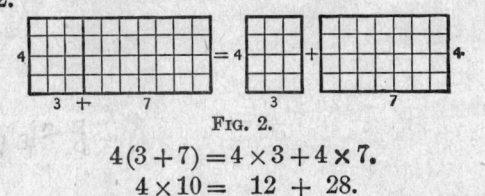

FIG. 2.

$$4(3+7) = 4 \times 3 + 4 \times 7.$$
$$4 \times 10 = 12 + 28.$$

EXAMPLE 3. The product $a(b+c)$ may be represented by the Fig. 3.

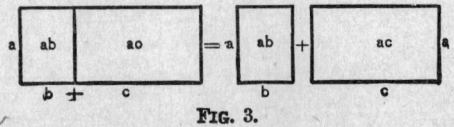

FIG. 3.

$$a(b+c) = ab + ac.$$

EXERCISE 33

1. Draw a figure representing $5(3+4)$, as in Example 2.
2. Draw a figure representing $4(2+3+5)$, as in Example 2.
3. Draw a figure representing $a(b+c+d)$, as in Example 3.

MULTIPLICATION OF POLYNOMIALS BY MONOMIALS

57. DEVELOPMENT. **1.** From the geometrical illustration in § 56, it is clear that:

(a) $5(7+3) = (5 \times 7) + (5 \times 3) = 35 + 15 = 50$.
(b) $6(4+5) = (6 \times 4) + (6 \times 5) = 24 + 30 = 54$.
(c) $a(b+c+d) = ab + ac + ad$.

In every case, each term of the polynomial is multiplied by the monomial.

Rule. — To multiply a polynomial by a monomial:
1. Multiply each term of the polynomial by the monomial.
2. Unite the results with the proper signs.

EXAMPLE. Multiply $3\,a^2 - 2\,ab + b^2$ by $-3\,ab$.
SOLUTION: $(3\,a^2 - 2\,ab + b^2) \times (-3\,ab) = -9\,a^3b + 6\,a^2b^2 - 3\,ab^3$.
CHECK: This result is true for any values of a and b. Let $a = 1$, and $b = 1$.
$3\,a^2 - 2\,ab + b^2 = 3 - 2 + 1 = 2$, $-3\,ab = -3$, and $2 \cdot (-3) = -6$;
also, $-9\,a^3b + 6\,a^2b^2 - 3\,ab^3 = -9 + 6 - 3 = -12 + 6 = -6$.

EXERCISE 34

Multiply:

1. $4\,a - 9$ by $5\,a$.
2. $m^2 - mn + n^2$ by mn.
3. $3\,x^2 + x - 5$ by $-9\,x^2$.
4. $8\,x^3y - 5\,xy^3$ by $-3\,xy^4$.
5. $2\,a^3 - 6\,a^2 - 7$ by $-7\,a^3$.
6. $r^2 - 2\,rs + s^2$ by $-r^3s^3$.
7. $6\,x^5 - 5\,x^6 - 7\,x^4$ by $-7\,x^3$.
8. $-3\,c^2 - d^2 + 5\,cd$ by $4\,c^2d^3$.
9. $-3\,x^2y + x^3 - 3\,xy^2$ by $-x^2y$.
10. $x^5 - x^3 + x$ by $-x^3$.

MULTIPLICATION

11. $5m^2 - 6mn - 4n^2$
    $\underline{3m^2}$

12. $6p^2 - 5pq + 9q^2$
    $\underline{4pq}$

13. $x^2 - 5xy + y^2$
    $\underline{-2xy}$

14. $a^3 - 3a^2b + 3ab^2 - b^3$
    $\underline{-ab}$

Perform the following indicated multiplications:

15. $7x \cdot (x - 5)$.
16. $-6ab \cdot (10a^2 - 7b^2)$.
17. $x^2y \cdot (x^4 - 4x^2y^2 + y^4)$.
18. $-rs \cdot (r^2 - rs + s^2)$.
19. $-3ab \cdot (a^2 - 2ab + b^2)$.
20. $8x^5 \cdot (6x^3 - 5x - 12)$.
21. $-4a^3b^3 \cdot (3a^2 - 2ab - 4b^2)$.
22. $-5m^4 \cdot (8m^4 - m^2 - 3)$.

23. Simplify the expression: $3(2x - 5) - 2(x + 6)$.

This means that $(2x - 5)$ is to be multiplied by 3; that $(x + 6)$ is to be multiplied by 2; and that the second result is to be subtracted from the first.

SOLUTION:
$$3(2x - 5) - 2(x + 6) = (6x - 15) - (2x + 12).$$
$$= 6x - 15 - 2x - 12.$$
$$= 4x - 27.$$

In the following examples, first tell what each means, as in Example 23; then, simplify.

24. $5(6a + 3b) + 4(5a - 2b)$.
25. $2a(3x - y) - 3a(2x + y)$.
26. $x(x - y) - y(x + y)$.
27. $3(2m + 8) - 2(6 - 5m)$.
28. $3c(2m - 4) - 6c(2m + 4)$.
29. $r(r^2 - s) + s(r - s^2)$.

Multiply and then simplify the following:

30. $6\left(\dfrac{x}{2} - \dfrac{x}{3} + \dfrac{1}{6}\right)$.
31. $12\left(\dfrac{m}{3} - \dfrac{2m}{3} + \dfrac{m}{4}\right)$.
32. $15\left(\dfrac{r}{5} - \dfrac{1}{3} + r\right)$.
33. $16\left(\dfrac{s}{4} - \dfrac{3s}{2} + \dfrac{1}{8}\right)$.
34. $\tfrac{1}{2}(2x^3 - 4x + 6)$.
35. $6(\tfrac{1}{2}x^2 - \tfrac{1}{6}xy + \tfrac{1}{3}y^2)$.
36. $10\left(\dfrac{3t}{5} - \dfrac{t}{2} + \dfrac{7}{10}\right)$.
37. $15\left(\dfrac{3x}{5} - \dfrac{2}{3} + \dfrac{x}{3}\right)$.
38. $20\left(\dfrac{x}{4} - \dfrac{2x}{5} + \dfrac{1}{10}\right)$.
39. $24\left(\dfrac{m}{3} - \dfrac{3m}{4} + \dfrac{m}{8}\right)$.
40. $-\tfrac{1}{3}x^2(3x^4 - 24x^2 + 15)$.
41. $\tfrac{1}{2}mn(\tfrac{1}{4}m^2 - \tfrac{1}{6}mn + \tfrac{1}{9}n^2)$.

ALGEBRA

...PLICATION OF A POLYNOMIAL BY A POLYNOMIAL

58. A number may be multiplied by $(2+3)$ by multiplying first by 2 and then by 3, and adding the products. Thus,

$(2+3) \times 6 = (2 \times 6) + (3 \times 6) = 12 + 18 = 30$, for $(5) \times 6 = 30$.

Similarly, $(2+3) \cdot (a+b) = 2(a+b) + 3(a+b)$
$$= 2a + 2b + 3a + 3b = 5a + 5b,$$
for $(5) \cdot (a+b) = 5a + 5b$.

The multiplier in each case consists of the sum of 2 and 3; the multiplicand is multiplied separately by 2 and by 3, and the products are added. This illustrates the

Rule. — To multiply one polynomial by another:
1. Multiply the multiplicand by each term of the multiplier.
2. Add the partial products.

EXAMPLE 1. Multiply $3a - 4b$ by $2a - 5b$.

SOLUTION: In accordance with the rule, multiply $3a - 4b$ by $2a$ and then by $-5b$, and add the partial products. A convenient arrangement is suggested by the arrangement of multiplication problems in arithmetic.

$$
\begin{array}{ll}
43 & \qquad 3a - 4b \\
\underline{12} & \qquad \underline{2a - 5b} \\
86 = 2 \times 43 & \qquad 6a^2 - 8ab \qquad\quad = 2a(3a - 4b) \\
\underline{430} = 10 \times 43 & \qquad \underline{\quad -15ab + 20b^2} = -5b(3a - 4b) \\
516 = \text{sum} & \qquad 6a^2 - 23ab + 20b^2 = \text{sum}
\end{array}
$$

NOTE: In arithmetic, the multiplication proceeds from right to left; in algebra, the multiplication proceeds from left to right.

EXAMPLE 2. Multiply $a^3 - 8x^3 - 2a^2x$ by $2x + a$.

SOLUTION: It is convenient to arrange the multiplicand and multiplier in the same order of powers of some letter (§ 37) and to write the partial products in the same order. Leave spaces for any powers which may not be present in the multiplicand.

Arranging the expressions according to the descending powers of a, we have,

$$
\begin{array}{l}
a^3 - 2a^2x \qquad\qquad\quad - 8x^3 \\
\underline{a \ + 2x} \\
a^4 - 2a^3x \qquad\qquad\quad - 8ax^3 \\
\underline{\quad + 2a^3x - 4a^2x^2 \qquad\qquad - 16x^4} \\
a^4 \qquad\quad - 4a^2x^2 - 8ax^3 - 16x^4
\end{array}
$$

MULTIPLICATION

CHECK: This result should be true for all values of a and x.

Let $a = 1$ and $x = 1$.
Then, $a^3 - 2a^2x - 8x^3 = 1 - 2 - 8 = -9$,
$a + 2x = 1 + 2 = +3$,
and $(-9) \times (+3) = -27$;
also, $a^4 - 4a^2x^2 - 8ax^3 - 16x^4 = 1 - 4 - 8 - 16 = -27.$

EXERCISE 35

Multiply:

1. $x + 3$ by $x + 5$.
2. $r - 7$ by $r - 4$.
3. $2s - 5$ by $s - 3$.
4. $3m + 2$ by $m - 4$.
5. $4t - 9$ by $t + 3$.
6. $3x + 7$ by $2x + 3$.
7. $2m + 5$ by $5m - 1$.
8. $6p - 3$ by $2p + 7$.
9. $5y - 1$ by $6y - 8$.
10. $7z + 10$ by $4z - 5$.
11. $2a + b$ by $a + b$.
12. $3c - 2d$ by $2c + d$.
13. $5r + 6s$ by $3r - 2s$.
14. $5x - 2y$ by $3x - 4y$.
15. $6m - 3p$ by $4m + 5p$.
16. $7y - 9z$ by $6y + 8z$.
17. $11a + 5d$ by $6a - 4d$.
18. $12p + 7q$ by $8p - 7q$.
19. $2x^2 - y^2$ by $x^2 - 3y^2$.
20. $9w^2 - 7v$ by $11w^2 + 3v$.
21. $m^2 - m - 3$ by $m + 3$.
22. $2a^2 + 7a - 9$ by $5a - 1$.
23. $x^2 - 2xy + 3y^2$ by $x - 3y$.
24. $x^2 - xy + y^2$ by $x + y$.
25. $x^2 + 4xy + 16y^2$ by $x - 4y$.
26. $m^2 + mn + n^2$ by $m^2 - mn + n^2$.
27. $a^3 + a - 2 - 2a^2$ by $a^2 + 2a - 3$.
28. $3 + a^3 - 7a - 4a^2$ by $2a + 1$.
29. $9x + 2x^2 - 5$ by $4 + 3x^2 - 7x$.
30. $6n - 8 + 4n^2$ by $-4 + 2n^2 - 3n$.
31. $9r^2 - 5y^2 + 6ry$ by $8ry + 4y^2 + 7r^2$.
32. $3a^2 - 5ab - 8b^2$ by $4a^2 - 9ab - 7b^2$.

33. $a - b + c$ by $a - b - c$.
34. $r + s + t$ by $r - s - t$.
35. $2n^2 + m^2 + 3mn$ by $2n^2 - 3mn + m^2$.
36. $a^3 + 3ab^2 - 3a^2b - b^3$ by $a^2 + b^2 - 2ab$.
37. $m^4 - 3m^3 + 9m^2 - 27m + 81$ by $m + 3$.
38. $4a + 6b + 10c$ by $2a - 3b + 5c$.
39. $x^4 + 4x^2 + 8x + 2x^3 + 16$ by $x - 2$.
40. $a^2 + b^2 + c^2 + ab - bc + ac$ by $a - b - c$.
41. $\frac{1}{3}a - \frac{1}{4}b$ by $\frac{1}{3}a + \frac{1}{4}b$.
42. $\frac{1}{2}m - \frac{1}{3}n$ by $\frac{1}{2}m + \frac{1}{3}n$.
43. $\frac{1}{4}x - \frac{1}{9}y$ by $\frac{1}{4}x + \frac{1}{9}y$.
44. $2a - \frac{1}{3}b$ by $a + \frac{1}{2}b$.
45. $\frac{2}{3}x - \frac{3}{4}y$ by $\frac{3}{2}x - \frac{4}{3}y$.
46. $(3x - 5)^2$.
47. $(2m - 3n)^3$.
48. $(4r + 5)^3$.
49. $(2x - 3)^4$.
50. $(3a - 4b)^3$.

Find the product of the following:

51. $a + 3$, $a - 4$, and $a + 2$.
52. $m + 4$, $2m - 3$, and $m - 5$.
53. $x + y$, $x^2 - xy + y^2$, and $x^3 - y^3$.
54. $m + n$, $m^2 + n^2$, and $m - n$.
55. $x^2 + xy + y^2$, $x^2 - xy + y^2$, and $x^2 - y^2$.

PARENTHESES IN MULTIPLICATION

59. Example. Simplify $(a - 2x)^2 - 2(3a + x)(a - x)$.

SOLUTION: To simplify this expression, first multiply $(a - 2x)$ by itself (§ 15); second, find the product of 2, $3a + x$ and $a - x$; third, subtract the second result from the first.

$$
\begin{array}{ll}
1.\ a - 2x & 2.\ 3a + x \\
a - 2x & a - x \\ \hline
a^2 - 2ax & 3a^2 + ax \\
\ \ -2ax + 4x^2 & \ \ -3ax - x^2 \\ \hline
a^2 - 4ax + 4x^2 & 3a^2 - 2ax - x^2 \\
& 2 \\ \hline
& 6a^2 - 4ax - 2x^2
\end{array}
$$

MULTIPLICATION

3. Then $\quad (a-2x)^2 - 2(3a+x)(a-x)$
4. $\quad = (a^2 - 4ax + 4x^2) - (6a^2 - 4ax - 2x^2)$
5. $\quad = a^2 - 4ax + 4x^2 - 6a^2 + 4ax + 2x^2 \quad (\S 47)$
6. $\quad = -5a^2 + 6x^2.$ *Answer.*

NOTE. Be careful to place the results of steps 1 and 2 in parentheses as in step 4.

EXERCISE 36

Tell, as in the above solution, what must be done to simplify the following; then simplify:

1. $(3a+8)(a-6) + (2a+7)(4a-9)$.
2. $(2m+7)(3m-5) - (2m-5)(3m+7)$.
3. $(a-2x)(a+3x) + (a+2x)(a-3x)$.
4. $(2a-3b)^2 - 4(a-b)(a+5b)$.
5. $2(h+3)(h-2) - (h+5)(h-6)$.
6. $5(x-4)(x+1) - 3(x-3)(x+2)$.
7. $2(3x+2)(4x-3) - (3x-2)(4x+3)$.
8. $3(3a+5)(2a-8) - 2(4a-7)(a+6)$.
9. $4(3x-2)(x+6) - 5(2x-7)(x+2)$.
10. $(a+b)(a^2+b^2) - (a-b)(a^2-b^2)$.

USE OF MULTIPLICATION IN EQUATIONS

60. EXAMPLE 1. Seven times the complement of a certain angle exceeds twice its supplement by 20°. Find the angle.

SOLUTION: 1. Let a = the number of degrees in the angle.
2. Then, $\quad 90 - a$ = the number of degrees in the complement.
3. and, $\quad 180 - a$ = the number of degrees in the supplement.
4. Hence, $\quad 7(90-a) = 2(180-a) + 20$.
5. Multiplying, $\quad 630 - 7a = 360 - 2a + 20$.
6. Combining, $\quad 630 - 7a = 380 - 2a$.
7. S_{630}: $\quad -7a = -250 - 2a$.
8. A_{2a}: $\quad -5a = -250$.
9. M_{-1}: $\quad 5a = 250$.
10. D_5: $\quad a = 50$.

CHECK: The angle is one of 50°. The complement contains 40° and the supplement, 130°. Does $7 \times 40° = 2 \times 130° + 20°$? Yes.

EXAMPLE 2. Solve the equation,
$$(2a+5)(3a-7)-(2a-5)(3a+7)=4.$$

SOLUTION: 1. $\quad (2a+5)(3a-7)-(2a-5)(3a+7)=4.$
2. Multiplying, $\quad (6a^2+a-35)-(6a^2-a-35)=4.$
3. Removing ( ), $\quad 6a^2+a-35-6a^2+a+35=4.$
4. Combining terms, $\quad 2a=4.$
5. D_2: $\quad a=2.$

CHECK: Does $(2 \cdot 2+5)(3 \cdot 2-7)-(2 \cdot 2-5)(3 \cdot 2+7)=4$?
Does $\quad (9) \cdot (-1)-(-1)(+13)=4$?
Does $\quad -9-(-13)=4$?
Does $\quad -9+13=4$? Yes.

NOTE: In Exercises like Example 2, be careful to put the products obtained in step 1, in parentheses as in step 2.

EXERCISE 37

Solve the following equations:

1. $2(m-3)=20.$
2. $4(y-5)+7=15.$
3. $3(2x-4)+2(x-5)=5(x+1).$
4. $6(2-3x)+3=3(4x-5).$
5. $12-5(3a-2)=2(a-6).$
6. $2(v+9)+3(v-4)=16.$
7. $4(t-3)+3(2t+5)=33(4-t).$
8. $10-5(3l-4)=6(3-2l).$
9. $7g-6(2g-5)=6(6-g).$
10. $3n-2(2n-7)=3(n-2).$
11. $3(4m-5)-4(m-6)=3(m+17)-7.$
12. $(x-5)(x+6)-(x+3)(x-4)=0.$
13. $(y-7)(y+2)-(y-9)(y+3)=0.$
14. $(2r+3)(3r-5)-6(r-4)(r-3)+5=0.$
15. $3(2s-4)(s+7)-2(3s-2)(s+5)=-3(s-2).$

MULTIPLICATION

16. The sum of two numbers is 75. The larger exceeds the smaller by 11. Find the numbers.

17. The sum of two numbers is 100. If four times the greater be diminished by 22, the result is 5 times the smaller. Find the two numbers.

18. The distance from New York to Paris exceeds the distance from New York to London by 280 miles. Four times the distance to London exceeds three times the distance to Paris by 2900 miles. Find the two distances.

19. One number exceeds another number by 7. If 6 times the smaller is diminished by 5 times the larger, the remainder is 5. Find the numbers.

20. Separate 60 into two parts such that 4 times the smaller shall exceed 2 times the larger by 30.

21. The sum of two numbers is 80. If twice the greater be decreased by 12, the result exceeds 4 times the smaller by 4. Find the numbers.

22. The Library of Congress stands upon a rectangular base whose perimeter is 1620 feet. The length exceeds the width by 130 feet. Find the dimensions of the building.

23. There are two consecutive numbers such that the sum of twice the smaller and three times the larger is 78. What are the numbers?

24. There are two consecutive integers whose product exceeds the square of the larger by 20. What are they?

25. The total population of Chicago, Philadelphia and Greater New York (1910 Census), was 8,501,174. The population of Chicago exceeded the population of Philadelphia by 636,275; the population of New York exceeded twice the population of Chicago by 396,317. Find the population of each of the cities.

ALGEBRA

EXERCISE 38

Algebraic Expression

1. A is now 15 years of age. Express his age:

(a) 5 years ago; (b) m years ago; (c) y years ago;
(d) 8 years from now; (e) m years from now.

2. B is b years of age. Express his age:

(a) 4 years from now; (b) m years from now;
(c) 6 years ago; (d) x years ago; (e) t years ago.

3. A is now x years of age. B's present age exceeds the age of A by 5 years.

(a) Express B's present age; (b) the sum of their ages.

(c) Express the age of each 10 years ago.

(d) Express the age of each 10 years from now.

4. A is now a years of age; B is twice as old.

(a) Express B's present age.

(b) Express the age of each 3 years ago.

(c) Express the age of each 7 years from now.

(d) Express the fact that B's age 5 years ago was 3 times A's age at that time.

5. Express the value of:

(a) $(15 - x)$ pounds of tea at 40 ¢ per pound;

(b) x pounds of tea at 60 ¢ per pound;

(c) the entire amount of tea.

6. Express the value in cents of:

(a) x nickels; (b) $2x$ dimes; (c) $3x$ dollars;
(d) $4x$ quarters; (e) all of the coins.

7. Express the value in cents of:

(a) d dimes; (b) $(15 - d)$ quarters;
(c) $(15 + 3d)$ half dollars; (d) all of the coins.

MULTIPLICATION

8. Express in inches:

(a) m feet;   (b) $3m$ yards.

(c) the combined length of m feet and $3m$ yards.

9. Express in pints:

(a) $3x$ pints plus $2x$ quarts plus $5x$ gallons.

(b) $2c$ pints plus $(3c-2)$ quarts plus $(5-3c)$ gallons.

EXERCISE 39

1. The sum of the ages of A and B is 50 years; in 5 years A will be 5 times as old as B. Find their ages.

SOLUTION: 1. Let $a =$ the number of years in A's age *now*.

2. Then $(50-a) =$ the number of years in B's age *now*.

3. Then $a+5 =$ the number of years in A's age in 5 yr.

4. and $(50-a+5)$ or $55-a$

$\qquad =$ the number of years in B's age in 5 yr.

5. $\qquad \therefore (a+5) = 5(55-a)$.

Complete the solution.

NOTE. Represent with care the present ages of both persons; also their ages at the other time mentioned; then form the equation.

2. A father is now 9 times as old as his son. In 9 years he will be only 3 times as old as his son. What are their present ages?

3. The difference between the present ages of a father and son is 25 years. In 10 years the father will be twice as old as his son. What are their present ages?

4. A is 5 times as old as B. In 9 years he will be only 3 times as old as B. What are their ages?

5. B is twice as old as A. 35 years ago he was 7 times as old as A. What are their present ages?

6. A is 68 years of age, and B is 11. In how many years will A be 4 times as old as B?

HINT. Let N equal the number of years. Find the age of each in N years, and then form the equation.

ALGEBRA

7. A is 25 years of age and B is 65. How many years ago was B 6 times as old as A?

8. A grocer has two grades of tea, a 60¢ grade and a 90¢ grade. He wishes to make a mixture which he can sell for 80¢ per pound. How many pounds of each must he use in a mixture of 120 pounds?

SOLUTION: 1.   Let n = the number of pounds of 60¢ tea used.

2.   ∴ $(120 - n)$ = the number of pounds of 90¢ tea used.

3.   ∴ $60 n$ = the value of the 60¢ tea in cents.

4.   and $90(120 - n)$ = the value of the 90¢ tea in cents.

5.   ∴ $60 n + 90(120 - n)$ = the value of the mixture in cents

6.   But 120×80 = the value of the mixture in cents.

7.   ∴ $60 n + 90(120 - n) = 9600$.

8. From the equation $n = 40$, $120 - n = 80$.

CHECK: 40 pounds of tea at 60¢ are valued at $24.

        80 pounds of tea at 90¢ are valued at $72.

        Total value of the mixture is $96.

        Also, 120 pounds at 80¢ are valued at $96.

9. A grocer has tea worth 70¢ per pound and other tea worth 40¢ per pound. How many pounds of each must he take to form a mixture of 50 pounds which he may sell at 49¢ per pound?

10. A grocer has coffee which he sells at 36¢ per pound, and other coffee which he sells at 20¢ per pound. How many pounds of each must he take to make a mixture of 100 pounds which he may sell at 25¢ per pound?

11. A seedsman wishes to make a mixture of grass seed consisting of clover seed and blue grass seed. He sells his clover seed at 40¢ per pound, and his blue grass seed at 22¢ per pound. How many pounds of each must he take to make a mixture of 200 pounds which he may sell for 25¢ per pound?

12. A sum of money amounting to $2.80 consists of dimes and quarters. The number of dimes exceeds the number of quarters by 7. Find the number of each kind of coin.

MULTIPLICATION

SOLUTION: 1. Let q = the number of quarters.
2. Then $q + 7$ = the number of dimes.
3. $\therefore 25q$ = the number of cents in the quarters,
and $10(q+7)$ = the number of cents in the dimes.
4. $\therefore 25q + 10(q+7) = 280$.

Complete the solution and check it.

13. A man has two kinds of money, dimes and fifty-cent pieces. If he is offered $4.00 for 20 coins, how many of each kind must he give?

14. A sum of money amounting to $2.20 consists of five-cent pieces and quarters. There are in all 16 coins. How many are there of each kind?

15. A sum of money amounting to $24.90 consists of $2 bills, fifty-cent pieces and dimes. There are 5 more fifty-cent pieces than $2 bills, and 3 times as many dimes as $2 bills. How many are there of each denomination?

61. Equations having Fractional Coefficients.

EXAMPLE 1. If the sum of a certain number and one half of itself be diminished by three fifths of the number, the remainder is 9. Find the number.

SOLUTION: 1. Let x = the number.

Then $x + \dfrac{x}{2} - \dfrac{3x}{5} = 9$.

2. The denominators must be eliminated.

M_{10}: $\quad 10\left(x + \dfrac{x}{2} - \dfrac{3x}{5}\right) = 10 \cdot 9$. (§ 10)

3. $\quad 10x + \overset{5}{\cancel{10}} \cdot \dfrac{x}{\cancel{2}} - \overset{2}{\cancel{10}} \cdot \dfrac{3x}{\cancel{5}} = 90$. (§ 57)

4. $\quad 10x + 5x - 6x = 90$.
5. Combining, $\quad 9x = 90$.
6. D_9: $\quad x = 10$. (§ 9)

CHECK: Does $10 + \dfrac{\overset{5}{\cancel{10}}}{\cancel{2}} - \dfrac{3 \cdot \overset{2}{\cancel{10}}}{\cancel{5}} = 9$?

$10 + 5 - 6 = 9$? Yes.

NOTE. In order to eliminate the denominators, multiply the equation by the Lowest Common Multiple of the denominators.

ALGEBRA

Example 2. Solve the equation $\dfrac{7m}{6} - \dfrac{5}{3} = \dfrac{3m}{5} - \dfrac{1}{4}$.

Solution: 1. The L.C.M. of 6, 3, 5, and 4 is 60.

2. M_{60}: $\qquad 60\left(\dfrac{7m}{6} - \dfrac{5}{3}\right) = 60\left(\dfrac{3m}{5} - \dfrac{1}{4}\right).$ (§ 10)

3. $\qquad\qquad 70m - 100 = 36m - 15.$

4. A_{100}: S_{36m}: $\qquad 70m - 36m = 100 - 15.$ (§ 41)

5. $\qquad\qquad \therefore 34m = 85;\ m = \tfrac{85}{34} = \tfrac{5}{2} = 2.5.$

Check: This solution may be checked by substitution or by going over the solution again. If the latter method is used, great care must be taken, as it is easy to overlook an error.

EXERCISE 40

Solve the following equations:

1. $\dfrac{x}{2} - \dfrac{x}{3} = \dfrac{5}{6}.$

2. $\dfrac{m}{3} - \dfrac{m}{5} = \dfrac{8}{15}.$

3. $r + \dfrac{r}{3} = \dfrac{8}{3}.$

4. $\dfrac{2s}{3} = \dfrac{s}{4} + 5.$

5. $\dfrac{5a}{3} = \dfrac{3a}{4} + \dfrac{11}{6}.$

6. $\dfrac{m}{2} + 1 = \dfrac{3m}{5}.$

7. $\dfrac{2t}{7} = \dfrac{t}{3} + 1.$

8. $\dfrac{6w}{5} = 1 + \dfrac{5w}{4}.$

9. $\dfrac{5x}{14} = \dfrac{4x}{7} - \dfrac{3}{2}.$

10. $\dfrac{y}{3} + \dfrac{4y}{8} = \dfrac{5}{2}.$

11. $\dfrac{r}{2} + \dfrac{2r}{3} - \dfrac{5r}{6} = 6.$

12. $m - \dfrac{3m}{5} = 9 - \dfrac{m}{2}.$

13. $\dfrac{c}{2} - \dfrac{5}{3} = \dfrac{3c}{4} - \dfrac{2c}{3}.$

14. $4d - \dfrac{6d}{5} = \dfrac{d}{2} + \dfrac{23}{20}.$

15. $\dfrac{4t}{9} - \dfrac{5t}{6} = \dfrac{2}{3} - \dfrac{3t}{2}.$

16. $a + \dfrac{a}{2} = 11 - \dfrac{a}{3}.$

17. $\dfrac{2z}{3} - \dfrac{9}{8} = \dfrac{5z}{6} - \dfrac{5}{4}.$

18. $\dfrac{3y}{2} - \dfrac{y}{3} = \dfrac{5y}{4} - \dfrac{1}{8}.$

19. $\dfrac{4t}{9} - 1 = \dfrac{7t}{9} - \dfrac{16}{3}.$

20. $\dfrac{7m}{2} - \dfrac{4m}{3} = \dfrac{11}{6} - \dfrac{2m}{5}.$

MULTIPLICATION

EXERCISE 41

1. One fifth of a certain number exceeds one eighth of the same number by 3. Find the number.

2. The sum of three numbers is 65. The second is one half of the first, and the third is two thirds of the first. Find the numbers.

3. What number increased by one half of itself equals the sum of two thirds of itself and 25?

4. What number exceeds the sum of its third, sixth, and fourteenth parts by 18?

5. What number is such that if four sevenths of it be subtracted from itself, the result equals the excess of three fourths of the number over 18?

6. What number is such that if two thirds of it be increased by 100, the result equals four fifths of it?

7. Seven eighths of a certain number is as much less than 21 as three tenths of it exceeds $2\frac{1}{2}$. What is the number?

8. The difference between the third and fifteenth parts of a certain number is 28. Find the number.

9. In a triangle commonly used by draughtsmen, the second angle is two thirds of the first, and the third angle is one half of the second. Find the angles of the triangle. (§ 13)

10. In another triangle used by draughtsmen, there are two equal angles, each of which is one half of the third angle. Find the angles of this triangle.

11. There are three consecutive numbers such that the sum of the second and third exceeds three halves of the first by 9. Find the three numbers.

12. A man has $4.35 in dollars, dimes, and cents. He has one fourth as many dollars as dimes, and five times as many cents as dollars. How many coins of each kind does he have?

13. The Treasury at Washington is one of the most imposing of the national buildings. Its perimeter is 1400 feet. Its

width exceeds one half of its length by 25 feet. Find its dimensions.

14. The greatest depth of Lake Superior is one half that of Lake Michigan; the greatest depth of Lake Huron exceeds one sixth that of Lake Michigan by 700 feet. The depth of Lake Huron exceeds that of Lake Superior by 100 feet. Find the depth of each.

15. Probably the largest room in the world under one roof is the passenger concourse of the Union Station in Washington, D.C. Its perimeter is 1780 feet. One fifth of its length exceeds its width by 22 feet. Find its dimensions.

16. Ten times the population of the United States in 1820, in millions, exceeded the population in 1910 by 3.8 millions; the population in 1910 exceeded 7 times the population in 1820 by 25 millions. Find the population in both years.

17. Plants feed upon certain plant foods present in the soil, such as potash, nitrogen, and phosphoric acid. A fair crop of potatoes will remove from an acre of ground about 99 pounds of these three foods. The amount of potash removed is 5 times, and the amount of nitrogen $2\frac{1}{4}$ times that of phosphoric acid. Find the number of pounds of each removed.

18. The length of the foundation of the Capitol in Washington exceeds twice the width by $51\frac{1}{3}$ feet. The perimeter of the foundation is $2202\frac{2}{3}$ feet. Find the dimensions of the foundations of the Capitol.

19. The average wholesale value of oak lumber in 1899 was $13.78 per thousand feet. This exceeded one half of the wholesale value in 1909 by $3.53. What was the wholesale value per thousand in 1909?

20. The distance from San Francisco to London *via* New York is 6990 miles. The part of the journey by rail is 50 miles less than $\frac{15}{17}$ of the part by water. Find the part of the journey on land and the part on water.

VI. DIVISION

62. Division is the process of finding one of two numbers when their product and the other number are given.

To divide 15 by 3 means to find the number by which 3 must be multiplied to give the product 15.

The **Dividend** is the product of the numbers; it is the number divided.

The **Divisor** is the other given number; it is the number by which the dividend is divided.

The **Quotient** is the required number.

63. It is clear that $a \div a = 1$; for $a \times 1 = a$.

64. It is agreed that the product of zero and any number is zero. This makes division by zero impossible.

Thus, if we try to find the quotient of $6 \div 0$, and let q equal the quotient, we should have the relation

$$6 = 0 \cdot q.$$

But $0 \cdot q = 0$ and not 6, so there cannot be any ordinary number to use as q. Hence, there is no number to represent the quotient of $6 \div 0$

65. Division is **indicated** by writing a fraction whose numerator is the dividend and whose denominator is the divisor.

Thus, the quotient of $15 \div 5$ is written $\tfrac{15}{5}$.

The quotient of $7\,abc \div 3\,xy$ is written $\dfrac{7\,abc}{3\,xy}$.

NOTE. The line, —, was used to indicate division long before the symbol, $\div$.

66. Division of a Product by a Number.

EXAMPLE. Divide 6×8 by 2.

SOLUTION: 1. $\qquad 6 \times 8 \div 2 = \dfrac{6 \times 8}{2}.$

2. If 6 is divided by 2, $\dfrac{6 \times 8}{2} = \dfrac{\overset{3}{\cancel{6}} \times 8}{\cancel{2}} = 24.$

3. If 8 is divided by 2, $\dfrac{6 \times 8}{2} = \dfrac{6 \times \overset{4}{\cancel{8}}}{\cancel{2}} = 24.$

4. If both 6 and 8 are divided by 2,

$$\dfrac{6 \times 8}{2} = \dfrac{\overset{3}{\cancel{6}} \times \overset{4}{\cancel{8}}}{\cancel{2}} = 12.$$

5. Since we know that $\dfrac{6 \times 8}{2} = 48 \div 2$ or 24, it is clear that the results obtained in steps 2 and 3 are correct, but that the result in step 4 is incorrect. Hence,

Rule. — To divide the product of two or more numbers by a number, divide any one of the factors by the number, but divide only one of them by it.

EXERCISE 42

Find each of the following indicated divisions in two ways:

1. $\dfrac{9 \times 12}{3}.$ 2. $\dfrac{18 \times 24}{6}.$ 3. $\dfrac{28 \times 56}{7}.$

67. The Law of Signs for Division.

Since $(+2) \times (+3) = +6$, then $(+6) \div (+2) = +3.$
Since $(-2) \times (+3) = -6$, then $(-6) \div (-2) = +3.$
Since $(+2) \times (-3) = -6$, then $(-6) \div (+2) = -3.$
Since $(-2) \times (-3) = +6$, then $(+6) \div (-2) = -3.$

If the signs of the dividend, the divisor, and the quotient in each of the previous statements are examined, the following rules become clear:

Rule. — **1.** The quotient of two numbers having like signs is positive.

2. The quotient of two numbers having unlike signs is negative.

DIVISION

EXERCISE 43

1. Divide each of the following numbers by $+3$:
$+12$; $+15$; $+27$; -18; -36; -42; -57.

2. Divide each of the following numbers by $+2$:
-18; $+48$; $+72$; -24; -96; $+54$; -108.

3. Divide each of the numbers in Example 2 by:

    (a) -3; (b) $+6$; (c) -2; (d) -12.

4. Divide each of the numbers in Example 1 by -3.

5. Divide each of the numbers in Example 1 by -2.

68. The Law of Exponents for Division.

DEVELOPMENT. **1.** Review the definitions of *exponent*, *base*, and *power* of a number in § 15.

2. Divide a^5 by a^3.

SOLUTION:
$$\frac{a^5}{a^3} = \frac{a \cdot a \cdot a \cdot a \cdot a}{a \cdot a \cdot a} = 1 \cdot a \cdot a = a^2.$$

Therefore $a^5 \div a^3 = a^2$. CHECK: $a^3 \cdot a^2 = a^5$.

Each a in the denominator is divided into one of the a's in the numerator. The quotient in each case is 1, since $a \div a = 1$.

3. Find as in step 2 the following quotients and write the results as in part a:

(a) $a^5 \div a^3 = a^2$.
(b) $y^6 \div y^4 = ?$
(c) $m^7 \div m^4 = ?$
(d) $t^{10} \div t^6 = ?$

4. Examine carefully the exponents in the dividend, the divisor, and the quotient. In the following problems, try to give the results immediately without going through the solution as in step 2. Test by multiplication.

(a) $p^8 \div p^5 = ?$
(b) $a^9 \div a^7 = ?$
(c) $b^{10} \div b^6 = ?$
(d) $c^8 \div c^3 = ?$

5. Divide a^4b^6 by a^3b^2.

SOLUTION: $a^4b^6 \div a^3b^2 = \dfrac{a^4b^6}{a^3b^2} = \dfrac{\overset{1}{\cancel{a}} \cdot \overset{1}{\cancel{a}} \cdot \overset{1}{\cancel{a}} \cdot a \cdot \overset{1}{\cancel{b}} \cdot \overset{1}{\cancel{b}} \cdot b \cdot b \cdot b \cdot b}{\underset{1}{\cancel{a}} \cdot \underset{1}{\cancel{a}} \cdot \underset{1}{\cancel{a}} \cdot \underset{1}{\cancel{b}} \cdot \underset{1}{\cancel{b}}} = ab^4.$

Rule. — The exponent of any number in the quotient is equal to its exponent in the dividend minus its exponent in the divisor.

HISTORICAL NOTE. — This rule was known to Stifel (see note § 53).

DIVISION OF MONOMIALS BY MONOMIALS

69. EXAMPLE 1. Divide $-14\,a^3b^2$ by $+7\,a^2$.

SOLUTION: Use the Law of Signs, § 67, and the Law of Exponents, § 68.

$$\dfrac{-14\,a^3b^2}{+7\,a^2} = -2\,a^{(3-2)}b^2 = -2\,ab^2.$$

CHECK: $(+7\,a^2)(-2\,ab^2) = -14\,a^3b^2.$

EXAMPLE 2. Divide $54\,a^7b^2c^3$ by $-9\,a^4b^2c^2$.

SOLUTION: $\dfrac{54\,a^7b^2c^3}{-9\,a^4b^2c^2} = -6\,a^{(7-4)}b^{(2-2)}c^{(3-2)} = -6\,a^3b^0c = -6\,a^3c.$

CHECK: $(-6\,a^3c) \times (-9\,a^4b^2c^2) = +54\,a^7b^2c^3.$

Notice that by the law of exponents, $b^2 \div b^2 = b^{2-2} = b^0$.
No meaning has been given to the zero power of a number.
Since $b^2 \div b^2$ must equal 1, we agree that $b^0 = 1$.

The zero power of any number is 1. Thus:

$$a^0 = 1;\ \ 5^0 = 1;\ \ c^0 = 1.$$

Rule. — To divide a monomial by a monomial:

1. Make the quotient positive, if the dividend and divisor have like signs; make it negative, if they have unlike signs.

2. Find the quotient of the absolute values of the numerical coefficients.

3. Multiply the quotient of step 2 by the product of the literal factors, giving each its exponent in the dividend minus its exponent in the divisor.

4. Omit any literal factor which has the same exponent in the dividend and divisor.

DIVISION

EXAMPLE. Divide $-33\,a^6bx^2y^4$ by $+3\,a^5x^2y$.

SOLUTION. $(-33\,a^6bx^2y^4) \div (+3\,a^5x^2y) = -11\,aby^3$. **Ans.**

CHECK: These solutions may be checked by substitution, for they must be correct for all values of the literal numbers (except 0 sometimes). A better way is to use the rule that the divisor times the quotient equals the dividend.

Here, does $(+3\,a^6x^2y) \times (-11\,aby^3) = -33\,a^6bx^2y^4$? Yes.

EXERCISE 44

Divide:

1. x^5 by x^3.
2. r^7 by r^4.
3. p^9 by p^3.
4. m^4 by m^2.
5. a^2b^3 by ab.
6. r^3s^2 by r^2s.
7. x^5y^4 by x^2y^3.
8. $a^{10}b^2$ by a^4b.
9. $12\,a^4$ by $2\,a^3$.
10. $15\,x^5$ by $3\,x^2$.
11. $20\,r^3s^2$ by $4\,r^2s^2$.
12. $18\,c^3d^5$ by $9\,cd^3$.
13. $-14\,mn$ by $-2\,m$.
14. $+16\,a^2b$ by $-4\,ab$.
15. $-10\,xy^2$ by $+5\,xy$.
16. $-21\,p^3$ by $-7\,p^2$.
17. $-18\,x^3y$ by $2\,xy$.
18. $2\,m^5n^3$ by m^3n^2.
19. $-36\,a^6b^4c^2$ by $+6\,a^4b^3c^2$.
20. $-96\,x^7y^{11}$ by $-16\,x^3y^6$.
21. $-24\,a^4b^2c$ by $-8\,a^4b^2$.
22. $28\,x^5yz^3$ by $-7\,x^3y$.
23. $-33\,a^6x^2y^4$ by $-3\,a^4y^2$.
24. $65\,x^6y^5z^3$ by $-13\,xy^5$.
25. $28\,a^7b^6c^8$ by $-14\,a^2bc^7$.
26. $-72\,x^7y^8$ by $-6\,x^7y^8$.
27. $-40\,a^2b^4c^5$ by $-8\,bc$.
28. $-55\,x^5y^3z^6$ by $-11\,y^2z^6$.
29. $-70\,a^7b^3c^2$ by $14\,ab^3c$.
30. $-96\,m^3n^4$ by $-12\,mn^4$.
31. $64\,ab^2c$ by $-4\,ab^2c$.
32. $-63\,r^4s^6$ by $7\,r^2s^3$.
33. $3\,mn$ by $-6\,m$.
34. $-5\,r^3s$ by $15\,r^2$.
35. $4\,x^2y$ by $-\frac{1}{2}xy$.
36. $12\,ab^2c$ by $-24\,ab^2$.
37. 10^5 by 10^3.
38. 2^8 by 2^5.
39. $3^5 \cdot 4^2$ by $3^4 \cdot 4^2$.
40. $7^3 \cdot 8^2 \cdot 5$ by $7^2 \cdot 5$.

DIVISION OF POLYNOMIALS BY MONOMIALS

70. DEVELOPMENT. 1. Since $2 \times 9 = 18$, then $\frac{18}{2} = 9$.

2. Since $2(x+3) = 2x+6$, then $\frac{2x+6}{2} = x+3$.

3. Since $3(a-5) = 3a-15$, what does $\frac{3a-15}{3}$ equal?

4. What does each of the following equal? Test the result by multiplying the divisor and quotient.

(a) $\frac{2x+2}{2}$; (b) $\frac{6r+4}{2}$; (c) $\frac{6m-9}{3}$.

5. Since $a(b+c) = ab + ac$,

then $\frac{ab+ac}{a} = b+c$.

Rule. — To divide a polynomial by a monomial:

1. Divide each term of the dividend by the divisor.
2. Unite the results with their proper signs.

EXAMPLE 1. Divide $12x^3 - 6x^2 + 3x$ by $-3x$.

SOLUTION: $\frac{12x^3 - 6x^2 + 3x}{-3x} = -4x^2 + 2x - 1$.

CHECK: $(-4x^2 + 2x - 1) \cdot (-3x) = 12x^3 - 6x^2 + 3x$.

EXAMPLE 2. Divide $-9a^3 + 3a^2 - 12a^4$ by $-3a^2$.

SOLUTION: $(-12a^4 - 9a^3 + 3a^2) \div (-3a^2) = 4a^2 + 3a - 1$.

CHECK: Multiply the quotient by the divisor; the result should equal the dividend.

EXERCISE 45

Divide:

1. $3a - 6b$ by 3.
2. $16r - 8s$ by 8.
3. $12x^2 - 16y^3$ by 4.
4. $20a^2 - 15a$ by $5a$.
5. $x^3 - x^2 + x$ by x.
6. $-3x^4 + 6x^2$ by $-3x^2$.
7. $+21r^3 - 14r^2s$ by $-7r^2$.
8. $18m^3n - 27mn^3$ by $9mn$.
9. $-44a^2b + 55a^3b$ by $11a^2b$.
10. $36c^3d^3 - 48c^2d^4$ by $12c^2d^3$.

DIVISION

11. $16\ x^9 + 28\ x^6 - 24\ x^3$ by $4\ x^2$.
12. $104\ m^2n^3 - 52\ m^3n^2$ by $-13.mn$.
13. $6\ a^3b^7c^3 - 15\ a^6b^3c^5 + 3\ a^4b^8c$ by $-3\ a^3b^2c$.
14. $-63\ x^5y^6z^2 - 84\ x^3y^4z^7$ by $+7\ x^3yz^2$.
15. $20\ m^8n^5 - 35\ m^4n^3 - 30\ m^4n^9$ by $-5\ m^4n^3$.
16. $-36\ a^{11} + 108\ a^9 - 60\ a^7$ by $-12\ a^5$.
17. $32\ a^3b^2c - 24\ ab^3c^2 + 48\ ab^2c^3$ by $-8\ abc$.
18. $-63\ ax^{10} - 18\ x^7 + 45\ x^6 - 99\ x^4$ by $-9\ x^4$.
19. $-12\ x^4y + 6\ x^3y^2 - 16\ x^2y^3 + 20\ xy^4$ by $-2\ xy$.
20. $60\ a^{14} - 30\ a^{12} + 15\ a^{10} - 45\ a^8$ by $-15\ a^7$.
21. $(a^4b - a^3b^2 + a^2b^3) \div (a^2b)$.
22. $(8\ x^4 - 12\ x^3y) \div (-4\ x^3)$.
23. $(-21\ c^3d^2 - 42\ cd^3) \div (-7\ cd^2)$.
24. $(-6\ m^3 + 9\ m^2 - 12\ m) \div (-3)$.
25. $(-x^4 + x^2 - 1) \div (-1)$.

DIVISION OF POLYNOMIALS BY POLYNOMIALS

71. Division of a polynomial by a polynomial is like long division in arithmetic.

Divide 864 by 24.

1. $86 \div 24 = 3+$.
2. $24 \times 3 = 72$; subtract
3. $14 \div 2 = 6+$.
4. $24 \times 6 = 144$; subtract

$$\begin{array}{r} 36 \\ 24\overline{)864} \\ \underline{72} \\ 144 \\ \underline{144} \end{array}$$

Divide $10\ x^3 - 21\ x^2 - 11\ x + 12$ by $2\ x^2 - 3\ x - 4$.

1. $10\ x^3 \div 2\ x^2 = 5\ x$.
2. $(2\ x^2 - 3\ x - 4) \times (5\ x)$; subtract
3. $(-6\ x^2) \div (2\ x^2) = -3$.
4. $(2\ x^2 - 3\ x - 4) \times (-3)$; subtract

$$\begin{array}{r} 5\ x - 3 \\ 2\ x^2 - 3\ x - 4\ \overline{)10\ x^3 - 21\ x^2 - 11\ x + 12} \\ \underline{10\ x^3 - 15\ x^2 - 20\ x} \\ -6\ x^2 + 9\ x + 12 \\ \underline{-6\ x^2 + 9\ x + 12} \end{array}$$

The following explanation of the process may be given.

We are to find an expression which, when multiplied by the divisor, $2x^2 - 3x - 4$, will produce the dividend.

The term containing the highest power of x in the product is the product of the terms containing the highest powers of x in the multiplicand and multiplier.

Therefore, $10x^3$ is the product of $2x^2$ and the term containing the highest power of x in the quotient. Dividing $10x^3$ by $2x^2$ gives $5x$, which is the term containing the highest power of x in the quotient.

When the dividend is formed, the divisor is multiplied by each term of the quotient, and the results are added. Now reversing the process, multiply the divisor by $5x$ and subtract the result, $10x^3 - 15x^2 - 20x$, from the dividend.

The remainder, $-6x^2 + 9x + 12$, must be the product of the divisor and the rest of the quotient. Consider it a new dividend.

Its term containing the highest power of x, $-6x^2$, is the product of $2x^2$ and the term containing the next lower power of x in the quotient. Dividing $-6x^2$ by $2x^2$ gives the next term, -3. Multiply the divisor by -3 and subtract the result from the previous remainder. There is now no remainder.

The quotient is therefore $5x - 3$.

Rule. — To divide a polynomial by a polynomial:

1. Arrange the dividend and the divisor in either ascending or descending powers of some common letter.

2. Divide the first term of the dividend by the first term of the divisor, and write the result as the first term of the quotient.

3. Multiply the whole divisor by the first term of the quotient; write the product under the dividend and subtract it from the dividend.

4. Consider the remainder a new dividend, and repeat steps 1, 2, and 3.

NOTE 1. The terms of the quotient are placed above the terms of the dividend from which they are obtained.

NOTE 2. The like terms are carefully arranged in a vertical column.

NOTE 3. Spaces should be left for any powers of the common letter which are not present in the dividend.

NOTE 4. As in arithmetic, there may be a final remainder.

EXAMPLE 1. Divide $9ab^2 + a^3 - 9b^3 - 5a^2b$ by $3b^2 + a^2 - 2ab$

SOLUTION: 1. Arrange according to descending powers of a.

DIVISION

2. $a^3 \div a^2 = a$.
3. $(a^2 - 2ab + 3b^2) \times a$; subtract
4. $-3a^2b \div a^2 = -3b$.
5. $(a^2 - 2ab + 3b^2) \times (-3b)$; subtract

$$a^2 - 2ab + 3b^2 \overline{\smash{\big)}\, a^3 - 5a^2b + 9ab^2 - 9b^3} \quad \begin{array}{c} a - 3b \\ \hline \end{array}$$

$$\underline{a^3 - 2a^2b + 3ab^2}$$
$$-3a^2b + 6ab^2 - 9b^3$$
$$\underline{-3a^2b + 6ab^2 - 9b^3}$$

Check: Let $a = 1$ and $b = 1$.

Divisor: $\qquad a^2 - 2ab + 3b^2 = 1 - 2 + 3 = 2$.

Dividend: $a^3 - 5a^2b + 9ab^2 - 9b^3 = 1 - 5 + 9 - 9 = -4$.

Dividend $\div$ divisor: $\quad (-4) \div (2) = -2$.

Quotient: $\qquad a - 3b = 1 - 3 = -2$.

EXAMPLE 2. Divide $x^2y^2 + x^4 - y^4$ by $-xy + y^2 + x^2$.

SOLUTION:

$$x^2 - xy + y^2 \overline{\smash{\big)}\, x^4 \qquad + x^2y^2 \qquad - y^4} \quad \begin{array}{c} x^2 + xy + y^2 \\ \hline \end{array}$$

$$\underline{x^4 - x^3y + x^2y^2}$$
$$+ x^3y \qquad\qquad - y^4$$
$$\underline{+ x^3y - x^2y^2 + xy^3}$$
$$x^2y^2 - xy^3 - y^4$$
$$\underline{x^2y^2 - xy^3 + y^4}$$
$$-2y^4$$

NOTE. The quotient is $x^2 + xy + y^2$; the remainder is $-2y^4$. As in arithmetic, the complete quotient may be written:

Complete quotient: $x^2 + xy + y^2 + \dfrac{-2y^4}{x^2 - xy + y^2}$.

CHECK: Let $x = 1$, and $y = 1$. Then, dividend $= 1$, and divisor $= 1$

$$Quotient = 1 + 1 + 1 + \frac{-2}{1 - 1 + 1} = 3 + \frac{-2}{1} = 3 - 2 = 1.$$

Since $1 \times 1 = 1$, the quotient is correct.

Another check would be to multiply the divisor by the quotient and add the remainder; the sum should equal the dividend.

EXERCISE 46

Divide:

1. $x^2 + 5x + 6$ by $x + 2$.
2. $x^2 + 7x + 12$ by $x + 4$.
3. $y^2 + 7y + 10$ by $y + 5$.
4. $m^2 + 8m + 12$ by $m + 2$.
5. $A^2 + 11A + 24$ by $A + 3$.
6. $r^2 - 12r + 32$ by $r - 8$.

7. $s^2 - 13s + 42$ by $s - 7$.
8. $t^2 + 63 - 16t$ by $t - 9$.
9. $c^2 + 72 - 17c$ by $c - 8$.
10. $d^2 - 12d + 36$ by $d - 6$
11. $x^2 + x - 6$ by $x - 2$.
12. $t^2 - t - 30$ by $t + 5$.
13. $a^2 - 3a - 28$ by $a - 7$.
14. $m^2 + 2m - 15$ by $m + 5$.
15. $n^4 - 7n^2 - 30$ by $n^2 + 3$.
16. $x^2 - 17ax + 60a^2$ by $x - 5a$.
17. $a^2 + 5ab - 66b^2$ by $a + 11b$.
18. $x^2 - 2xz - 35z^2$ by $x - 7z$.
19. $x^4 + 5x^2y - 24y^2$ by $x^2 - 3y$.
20. $x^2y^2 - 15xy + 36$ by $xy - 3$.
21. $15x^2 - 11x - 14$ by $3x + 2$.
22. $6a^2 + 35 - 29a$ by $2a - 5$.
23. $12a^2 - 28a + 15$ by $6a - 5$.
24. $30x^2 + 8 - 53x$ by $6x - 1$.
25. $32x^2 - 15y^2 + 28xy$ by $4x + 5y$.
26. $25m^2 + 40mn + 16n^2$ by $5m + 4n$.
27. $x^3 - 6x^2 - 19x + 84$ by $x - 7$.
28. $6a^3 - 18a - 11a^2 + 20$ by $2a - 5$.
29. $4x^3 - 12y^3 + 17xy^2 - 12x^2y$ by $2x - 3y$.
30. $12a^3 + 6ab^2 + 5b^3 - 23a^2b$ by $4a - 5b$.
31. $x^4 + 4xy^3 + 3y^4$ by $x^2 - 2xy + 3y^2$.
32. $2n^2 - 4 + 5n^3 - 19n$ by $-8n + 5n^2 - 3$.
33. $12 + 13x^2 - 19x - 12x^3$ by $-3x^2 - 4 + x$.
34. $2a^4 + 8a - a^3 + 15$ by $2a^2 - 3a + 5$.
35. $-9m^2 - 16 + m^4 - 24m$ by $3m + m^2 + 4$.
36. $x^4 + y^4 + x^2y^2$ by $x^2 + y^2 - xy$.

DIVISION

37. $x^3 + 8$ by $x + 2$.
38. $x^4 - 16$ by $x - 2$.
39. $x^4 - y^4$ by $x + y$.
40. $x^4 - y^4$ by $x - y$.
41. $x^5 + y^5$ by $x + y$.
42. $x^5 + y^5$ by $x - y$.
43. $x^5 + 32$ by $x + 2$.
44. $1 - 16 a^4$ by $1 + 2 a$.
45. $n^4 - 16$ by $2 n^2 + 8 + 4 n + n^3$.
46. $13 x^3 + 71 x - 70 x^2 - 20 + 6 x^4$ by $4 + 3 x^2 - 7 x$.
47. $n^8 + 4 m^2 n^4 + 16 m^4$ by $2 mn^2 + 4 m^2 + n^4$.
48. $63 x^4 + 114 x^3 + 49 x^2 - 16 x + 20$ by $9 x^2 - 5 + 6 x$.
49. $x^5 + 50 - 70 x + 37 x^2$ by $10 - 2 x + x^2$.
50. $10 ab^3 - a^2 b^2 - 25 b^4 + 16 a^4$ by $5 b^2 + 4 a^2 - ab$.
51. $x^2 + \frac{3}{2} x - 1$ by $x + 2$.
52. $x^2 - \frac{10}{3} x + 1$ by $x - \frac{1}{3}$.
53. $6 x^2 - \frac{5}{6} x - \frac{1}{6}$ by $2 x - \frac{1}{2}$.
54. $\frac{1}{6} a^2 + \frac{13}{6} a + 6$ by $\frac{1}{3} a + 3$.

HISTORICAL NOTE. — Stifel (1486-1567) seems to have been one of the first to divide a polynomial by a polynomial. Sir Isaac Newton (1642-1727), in a book published in 1707, pointed out the advantage of arranging the dividend and divisor according to ascending or descending powers of the same letter.

VII. SIMPLE EQUATIONS

72. An **Equation** expresses the equality of two numbers. Equations are of two kinds.

73. An **Identity** or **Identical Equation** is an equation whose members are equal for all values of the literal numbers involved; as, $3x(a-b) = 3ax - 3bx$.

If $a = 3$, $b = 1$, $x = 2$, $3x(a-b) = 3 \cdot 2(3-1) = 6 \cdot 2 = 12$;
also, $3ax - 3bx = 3 \cdot 3 \cdot 2 - 3 \cdot 1 \cdot 2 = 18 - 6 = 12$.

Any other set of values of a, b, and x will produce equal numerical results in the two members of the equation.

An identity is like a declarative sentence; it makes a statement of actual equality.

74. An equation is said to be *satisfied* by a set of values of the letters involved in it when, after substituting these values for the letters, the equation becomes an identity.

Thus, $xa - xb = 2a - 2b$ is satisfied by $x = 2$, for
$2a - 2b = 2a - 2b$ is an identity.
$x - y = 5$ is satisfied by $x = 8$, $y = 3$, for
$8 - 3 = 5$ is an identity.

75. A **Conditional Equation** is an equation involving one or more literal numbers, which is not satisfied by all values of the literal numbers.

Thus, (a) $x + 2 = 5$ is not satisfied by any value of x except $x = 3$.

(b) $x^2 - 5x = -6$ is satisfied by $x = 2$ and by $x = 3$, but by no other values of x.

A conditional equation is like an interrogative sentence; it implies a question.

SIMPLE EQUATIONS

Thus, $3x - 5 = 4$, asks "for what value of x is $3x - 5 = 4$?"
The answer is, "x must be 3," for $3 \times 3 - 5 = 9 - 5 = 4$.

The word "equation" usually refers to a conditional equation.

76. If an equation contains only one unknown number, any value of the unknown number which satisfies the equation is called a **Root** of the equation.

To solve an equation is to find its root or roots.

Thus, 3 is the root of the equation $x + 2 = 5$.

77. If an equation has only one unknown number, if the unknown does not appear in the denominator of any fraction, and if the unknown appears only with the exponent 1, then the equation is called **an Equation of the First Degree**, or a **Simple Equation**.

Thus, $3x - 5 = 4$ is a simple equation.

HISTORICAL NOTE. — The idea of the *degree* of an equation was introduced by Descartes.

PROPERTIES OF EQUATIONS

78. Previously, in solving equations, four rules have been employed:

1. The same number may be added to both members of an equation without destroying the equality. (§ 41.)

2. The same number may be subtracted from both members of an equation without destroying the equality. (§ 41.)

3. Both members of an equation may be multiplied by the same number without destroying the equality. (§ 10.)

4. Both members of an equation may be divided by the same number without destroying the equality. (§ 9.)

All simple equations are solved by the application of one or more of these rules. However, observation of the results of solving equations by means of these rules leads to certain more mechanical methods of solution which may be used.

79. Transposition.
Solve the equation $10x - 5 = 3x + 30$.

Solution: 1. $10x - 5 = 3x + 30$.
2. A_5: $10x = 3x + 30 + 5$.
3. S_{3x}: $10x - 3x = 30 + 5$.
4. $7x = 35$.
5. $x = 5$.

In equation 3, the term $-3x$ in the left member corresponds to the term $+3x$ in the right member of equation 1; and the term $+5$ in the right member of equation 3 corresponds to the term -5 in the left member of equation 1. These are two examples of *transposition*. The result is the same *as if* a term were taken from one member of the equation and placed in the other, with its sign changed.

Rule. — A term may be transposed from one member of an equation to the other, provided its sign is changed.

HISTORICAL NOTE. — Our word *algebra*, curiously, is associated with this process, *transposition*. About the first quarter of the ninth century an Arabian mathematician, Mohammed ben Musa, wrote an algebra, for the title of which he used, Ilm al-jabr wa'l muqabalah. Al-jabr meant the process of transposing terms. This title was used in various forms in Europe until about the fifteenth century, when the last part was dropped and *algebra* came into use.

The Greeks had no special name for their algebra. The Hindu writers called it *reckoning with unknowns*.

80. Cancelling Terms in an Equation.

EXAMPLE. Solve the equation $x + a = b + a$.

Solution: $x + a = b + a$.
S_a: $x = b$.

Thus, the term a, which appeared in both members of the given equation, does not appear at all in the next equation; the result is the same *as if* the term a were *simply* dropped from both members.

Rule. — If the same term, preceded by the same sign, occurs in both members of an equation, it may be cancelled.

SIMPLE EQUATIONS

81. Changing Signs in an Equation.

EXAMPLE. Solve the equation $a - x = b - c$.

SOLUTION: 1. $a - x = b - c$.
2. M_{-1}: $-a + x = -b + c$.
     or $x - a = c - b$.

Thus, the signs of all terms of the equation in step 2 are exactly opposite to the signs of these terms in the equation of step 1. The result is the same *as if* the signs of all the terms of the equation were *simply* changed.

Rule. — The signs of all of the terms of an equation may be changed, without destroying the equality.

NOTE. The rules given in §§ 79, 80, and 81 are valuable, but the student should endeavor to remember that they arise out of the more fundamental rules given in § 78.

EXAMPLE. Solve the equation
$$7 - 5x - 9x = 15 - 9x - 3x.$$

SOLUTION: 1. $7 - 5x - 9x = 15 - 9x - 3x$.
2. Cancelling the term $-9x$: $7 - 5x = 15 - 3x$.   (§ 80)
3. Transposing $+7$ and $-3x$:
$$-5x + 3x = 15 - 7.$$ (§ 79)
$$-2x = 8.$$
4. Changing the signs of the terms: (§ 81)
$$2x = -8.$$
5. D_2: $x = -4$.

Check as usual.

EXERCISE 47

Find the roots of the following equations; check the solution:

1. $5a + 5 = 61 - 3a$.
2. $9m - 7 = 3m - 37$.
3. $13 - 6x = 13x - 6$.
4. $7t + 10 = 16t - 17$.
5. $15 - 6n = 5n + 48$.
6. $13 + 4p = 11p - 22$.
7. $5r - 12 = 16 - 9r$.
8. $21 - 15z = -8z - 7$.
9. $30 + 17c = 27c + 22$.
10. $19 - 16y = 27 - 28y$.

11. $2(5m+1)+16=4+3(m-7)$.
12. $8t-5(4t+3)=-3-4(2t-7)$.
13. $5c-6(3-4c)=c-7(4+c)$.
14. $2(4x+7)-6(2x+3)=8(3x-4)-7(2x-3)$.
15. $10r-(3r+2)=9r-(5r-4)$.
16. $19-5c(4c+1)=40-10c(2c-1)$.
17. $3-(x-3)=5-2x$.
18. $4(m-7)=5(m+10)-6(m+8)$.
19. $2(r-1)=4(r-5)-3(r-2)$.
20. $5=3(x-2)-10(x-6)$.

82. No general rule can be given for the solution of problems. The following suggestions will prove helpful:

1. Every problem gives a relation between some unknown numbers.

2. There are as many distinct statements as there are unknown numbers.

3. Represent one of the unknown numbers by a letter; then, using all but one of the statements, represent the other unknowns in terms of that same letter.

4. Using the remaining statement, form an equation.

EXERCISE 48

1. Divide 44 into two parts such that one divided by the other shall give 2 as the quotient and 5 as the remainder.

HINT: The dividend = divisor × quotient + remainder.

2. If 11 be added to a certain number, and the sum be multiplied by 5, the product equals -6 times the number. Find the number.

3. Divide 19 into two parts such that 7 times the less shall exceed 6 times the greater by 3.

4. Divide 38 into two parts such that twice the greater shall be less by 22 than 5 times the less.

SIMPLE EQUATIONS

5. The age of a father is 5 times that of his son; his age 5 years from now will exceed 3 times his son's age by 4 years. Find their present ages.

6. There are three consecutive odd integers such that when three times the first is increased by the second, the sum exceeds 3 times the third by 5. Find the numbers.

7. Divide $22 among A, B, and C so that A may receive $2.25 more than B and $1.75 less than C.

8. Divide 49 into two parts such that one divided by the other may give 2 as quotient and 7 as remainder.

9. Twice the width of the Pennsylvania Station in New York exceeds its length by 80 feet. Four times the length exceeds the perimeter by 700 feet. Find the dimensions.

10. Find the three sides of a triangle if the perimeter is 45 inches, if the second side is twice the third side, and if the first side exceeds the third by 5 inches.

11. Divide 134 into two parts such that one divided by the other may give 3 as quotient and 26 as remainder.

12. The elevation of Mt. Whitney, in California, the highest point recorded in the United States, is 14,501 feet, measured from sea level. The lowest point of dry land in the United States is in Death Valley, California. If 52 times the elevation of Death Valley be diminished by 45 and the result be increased by the elevation of Mt. Whitney, the sum is zero. Find and interpret the elevation of Death Valley.

13. A now has one third as much money as B; after B gives him $24, he will have 3 times as much money as B has left. How much has each?

14. A cab driver finds at the end of the day that he has $11.55. He has 3 less nickels than quarters, twice as many half-dollars as quarters, and as many dimes as he has nickels and quarters together. How many of each kind of coin has he?

15. A gardener decides to buy $25 worth of gladiolus bulbs. He wants some of the pink variety which sell at $2 a hundred; two thirds as many of the yellow variety, at $3.50 per hundred, as of the pink variety; and four times as many of the scarlet variety, at $1.50 per hundred, as of the yellow variety. How many of each shall he order?

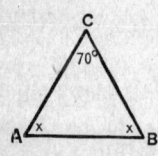

16. In an isosceles triangle, two sides are equal and, also, the angles opposite these sides are equal. Find the three angles of an isosceles triangle if the angle between the equal sides is 70°.

17. Find the sides of an isosceles triangle if its perimeter is 720 inches and its base is 150 inches.

18. The highest temperature recorded in the United States up to 1907 was 119°, recorded in Arizona. The lowest temperature was recorded at one time in Montana. If twice the lowest temperature be decreased by 9 and the result be added to the highest temperature, the result is zero. Find and interpret the lowest temperature.

19. The area of Nebraska exceeds the area of Virginia by 34,893 square miles; the area of California exceeds three times the area of Virginia by 30,416 square miles; and the area of California exceeds twice the area of Nebraska by 3257 square miles. Find the area of each of the states.

20. In 1910, the total number of boys and girls in the public secondary schools was 915,061. The number of boys exceeded three fourths of the number of girls by 11,123. Find the number of boys and of girls.

21. The total annual income from two investments is $250. One sum is invested at 4 % and the other sum, which exceeds the first by $500, is invested at 5 %. Find each of the sums invested.

SOLUTION: 1.   Let s = the smaller sum in dollars.
2.   ∴ $.04 s$ = the interest on this sum.

SIMPLE EQUATIONS

3.   ∴ $(s + 500)$ = the larger sum in dollars.
4.   ∴ $.05(s + 500)$ = the interest on this sum.
5.   ∴ $.04 s + .05 (s + 500) = 250.$
6.   ∴ $.04 s + .05 s + 25 = 250.$
7.   ∴ $.09 s = 225.$
8.   ∴ $s = 2500.$
9.   ∴ $s + 500 = 3000.$

CHECK: 5% of $3000 = $150; 4% of $2500 = $100;
and $150 + $100 = $250.

22. One sum of money is invested at 5%; a second sum is invested at 6%. If 3 times the first sum exceeds the second sum by $100, and if the total income is $155, find the sums invested.

23. A man has $5000 invested at 4%. How much money must he invest at 6% to make the total income equivalent to 5% on the total amount invested?

24. A man has $3000 invested at 3.5%, and $4500 at 4%. How much must he invest at 6% to make the total income equivalent to 5% on the total sum invested?

25. A man owns a number of shares of U. S. Steel Preferred Stock ($1000 par value) which pay 7% annually, and 5 times as many bonds of the Chicago Edison Company, ($1000 par value) which pay 5%. If his total income is $960, how much has he invested in each form?

83. Distance, Rate, and Time Problems. — If a train goes a distance of 240 miles in 6 hours, it travels at an average rate of 40 miles per hour.

The *time* (t) is expressed as a number of units of time; as hours, minutes, days.

The *rate* (r) is expressed as a number of units of distance covered in the unit of time; as, a number of miles per hour, or a number of feet per second, etc.

The *distance* (**d**) is expressed as a number of units of distance covered in the total time.

From the example and the definitions, it is clear that:

the distance equals the rate multiplied by the time.

$$d = rt. \tag{1}$$

From equation (1), $\dfrac{d}{t} = r$ or $r = \dfrac{d}{t}$; that is

the rate equals the distance divided by the time.

From the equation (1), $\dfrac{d}{r} = t$ or $t = \dfrac{d}{r}$; that is,

the time equals the distance divided by the rate;

thus the time occupied in going 200 miles at 40 miles per hour is 5 hours.

EXERCISE 49

1. Express the distance covered by a train in 15 hours at the rate of:

(a) 5 miles per hour; (c) $(x+7)$ miles per hour;
(b) R miles per hour; (d) $(2y-3)$ miles per hour.

2. Express the distance covered by a train in H hours at the rate of:

(a) m miles per hour; (b) $(x+9)$ miles per hour.

3. Express the time required by an automobile to go a distance of 300 miles at the rate of:

(a) 30 miles per hour; (c) $(x+5)$ miles per day;
(b) n miles per hour; (d) $(m-4)$ miles per day.

4. Express the time for a trip of N miles at the rate of:
(a) 10 miles per hour; (b) x miles per hour.

5. At what rate does a man travel who goes 250 miles:

(a) in 10 days; (c) in $(x-5)$ hours;
(b) in n days; (d) in $(r+7)$ days.

SIMPLE EQUATIONS

6. At what rate does a man travel who goes D miles:
(*a*) in 15 hours;   (*b*) in t days;   (*c*) in $(x-4)$ minutes.

7. The rate of one train is r miles per hour. Express the rate of a train which travels 5 miles more per hour.

8. Express the distance traveled by each of the trains in Example 7 in 15 hours.

9. Suppose that the distance gone by the second train exceeds that gone by the first train by 75 miles. Form an equation expressing this fact.

10. A man on foot and a man on a bicycle both travel for 5 hours, the rate of the latter exceeding that of the former by 7 miles per hour. Let r represent the rate of the former.

(*a*) Express the rate of the second man.

(*b*) Express the distance each travels.

(*c*) Form an equation expressing the fact that the sum of the distances is 60 miles.

Equations

In the following problems, express the time, rate, and distance traveled by each party, and then form the equation from the given relations. It is usually wise to illustrate the problems geometrically.

11. Two men travel toward each other from points which are 150 miles apart at rates of 5 and 15 miles an hour respectively. In how many hours will they meet?

SOLUTION: 1. Let $h=$ the number of hours until they meet.

2.

Then for	the time is	the rate is	the distance
one man	h hours	5 m. an hr.	$5h$ miles
the other man	h hours	15 m. an hr.	$15h$ miles

3. Since the sum of the distances is 150 miles, $5h + 15h = 150$.

12. Suppose that the more rapid traveler starts two hours after the other in Problem 11. When will they meet?

13. Suppose that two men, who travel at the rate of 6 miles and 10 miles per hour respectively, start from the same place in opposite directions. In how many hours will they be 200 miles apart?

14. Suppose that A, traveling 10 miles per hour, leaves a place 3 hours before B; suppose that B travels 15 miles per hour. In how many hours will B overtake A?

HINT: A is at C when B starts; B overtakes A at D.

15. Suppose A, traveling 15 miles per hour, starts 4 hours before B. At what rate must B travel to overtake A in 10 hours?

16. Two hours after A left, B starts after him in an automobile at the rate of 27 miles an hour and overtakes him in $2\frac{1}{2}$ hours. At what rate was A traveling?

17. A and B travel toward each other from points separated by 250 miles, A at a rate which exceeds B's rate by 8 miles an hour. If they meet in 5 hours, at what rate did each travel?

18. Some boys who are boating on a river know that they can go with the current 6 miles per hour and can return against the current at the rate of 3 miles per hour. How far may they go if they have only 3 hours for the trip?

19. A man has 11 hours at his disposal. How far may he go in a buggy at the rate of 10 miles an hour if he plans to return at an average rate of 7 miles per hour?

20. An automobile is traveling at the rate of 25 miles an hour. In how many hours will a second automobile overtake the first if the second starts 2 hours later than the first, and travels at the rate of 35 miles an hour?

SIMPLE EQUATIONS

21. An express train whose rate is 36 miles an hour starts 54 minutes after a slow train and overtakes it in 1 hour and 48 minutes. What is the rate of the slow train?

22. An automobile party is traveling at the rate of 20 miles per hour. At what rate must a second automobile travel in order to overtake the first if it starts 2 hours after the first and wishes to overtake it in 3 hours?

23. Chicago, and Madison, Wisconsin are about 140 miles apart. Suppose that a train starts from each city toward the other, one at the rate of 35 miles per hour and the other at the rate of 40 miles per hour. How soon will they meet?

84. Problems about Thermometers. There are two kinds of thermometers in common use, the **Fahrenheit** and the **Centigrade**. The Fahrenheit is the one with which most of us are familiar. The Centigrade is used by scientists throughout the world.

It is necessary at times to change a temperature reading on one scale to the corresponding reading on the other scale.

The temperature at which water boils and that at which it freezes are called the "boiling" and the "freezing" points. On the Fahrenheit scale these points are marked 212° and 32°; on the Centigrade scale, 100° and 0° respectively. The number of Fahrenheit degrees between these two points is 180, and the number of Centigrade is 100. Hence, 100 Centigrade degrees correspond to 180 Fahrenheit degrees, or 1 Centigrade degree to $\frac{9}{5}$ Fahrenheit degree.

NOTE. This does not mean that a temperature of 1° C. is the same as $\frac{9}{5}$° F. 1° C. is one degree above 0; the corresponding Fahrenheit reading is $\frac{9}{5}$° above 32 (the freezing point), or $33\frac{4}{5}$°. Thus, a temperature of 1° C. = a temperature of $33\frac{4}{5}$° F.

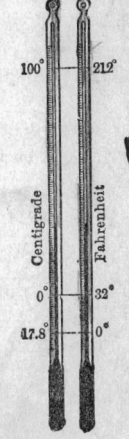

EXERCISE 50

1. How many Fahrenheit degrees are equal to the following number of Centigrade degrees?

(a) 15; (b) 25; (c) 50; (d) 100.

2. Remembering that Centigrade degrees above freezing are counted from zero, and Fahrenheit from 32, what Fahrenheit temperature corresponds to the following Centigrade temperature?

$$(a) \; +15° \text{ C.}$$

SOLUTION: **1.** 15 Centigrade degrees = 27 Fahrenheit degrees.
2. 15° C. above freezing = 27° F. above 32 = 59° F.
∴ 15° C. corresponds to 59° F.

(b) +30° C.; (c) +55° C.; (d) −10° C.

3. Derive a formula for changing Centigrade temperature readings into Fahrenheit readings.

SOLUTION: **1.** Let $C° =$ the Centigrade reading.
Let $F° =$ the Fahrenheit reading.
2. C Centigrade degrees $= (\tfrac{9}{5} C)$ Fahrenheit degrees.
3. $C°$ counted from 0, the Centigrade freezing point, $= (\tfrac{9}{5} C)°$ counted from 32, the Fahrenheit freezing point.

$$\therefore F = 32 + \tfrac{9}{5} C.$$

CHECK: Let $C = 0$. ∴ $F = 32 + \tfrac{9}{5} \cdot 0 = 32$.
Let $C = 100$. ∴ $F = 32 + \tfrac{9}{5} \cdot 100 = 32 + 180 = 212$.

Since the freezing and boiling temperatures correspond, the solution is correct.

4. The formula can be used to change Fahrenheit into Centigrade readings.

Change −13° F. to Centigrade.

SOLUTION: **1.** $-13 = 32 + \tfrac{9}{5} C.$ (Substituting in the formula.)
2. ∴ $-65 = 160 + 9 C.$
3. ∴ $-225 = 9 C$, or $C = -25°$;
i.e. 25° below zero Centigrade.

SIMPLE EQUATIONS

5. In Physics and Chemistry, the temperature $-273°$ C. is important. To what Fahrenheit temperature does this correspond? (Substitute in the formula.)

6. The following substances melt at the temperatures indicated. To what Fahrenheit temperatures do these correspond?

| Paraffin | $+ 55°$ C. | Iron | $+1200°$ C. |
| Tin | $+232°$ C. | Mercury | $-39°$ C. |

7. Attempts have been made to get record-breaking low temperatures. The following table gives low temperatures produced, the name of the experimenter, and the date of the experiment. To what Fahrenheit temperatures do these correspond?

Date	Temperature	Experimenter
1714	$-17°$ C.	Fahrenheit
1823	$-102°$ C.	Faraday
1898	$-262°$ C.	Dewar
1908	$-269°$ C.	Onnes

8. The temperatures at three places in the United States on a certain day were:

(a) $+50°$ F.; (b) $+12°$ F.; (c) $-8°$ F.

What would these temperatures be on a Centigrade scale?

9. The following liquids boil at the temperatures indicated:

Alcohol $172.4°$ F.   Turpentine $320°$ F.

Give the boiling temperatures on the Centigrade scale.

10. Air can be liquefied by reducing its temperature until it reaches $-182°$ C. To what Fahrenheit temperature does this correspond?

VIII. SPECIAL PRODUCTS AND FACTORING

85. In arithmetic, it is found necessary to memorize the multiplication table as an aid in multiplication, division, and factoring. In algebra, also, certain forms of number expressions occur frequently, which must be multiplied, divided, or factored by inspection.

86. To Factor an algebraic expression is to find two or more expressions which will produce the given expression when they are multiplied together.

Review the definitions of factor (§ 28) and common factor (§ 11).

87. A number which has no factors except itself and unity is called a **Prime Number**; as, 3, a, and $x+y$.

A monomial is expressed in items of its *prime factors* thus:

$$12\, a^3 b^2 c = 2 \cdot 2 \cdot 3 \cdot a \cdot a \cdot a \cdot b \cdot b \cdot c.$$

88. Squaring a Monomial.

DEVELOPMENT. 1. What does x^2 mean? $(xy)^2$? $(2\,r^3s)^2$?

2. Find each of the following squares by multiplication:

(a) $(2\,xy)^2$; (b) $(3\,a^2b^2)^2$; (c) $(-2\,r^3s^4)^2$.

3. Compare the exponent of each letter of the square with the exponent of that letter in the given monomial.

Rule. — To square a monomial:

Square its numerical coefficient, and multiply the result by each of the literal factors of the monomial, giving each letter twice its original exponent.

SPECIAL PRODUCTS AND FACTORING

89. Cubing a Monomial.

DEVELOPMENT. 1. Find each of the following cubes by multiplication:

(a) $(2\,x^2y)^3$;   (b) $(3\,r^2s^3)^3$;   (c) $(-2\,x^2y^2)^3$.

2. Compare the exponent of each letter of the cube with the exponent of that letter in the given monomial.

Rule. — To cube a monomial:

Cube its numerical coefficient, making the result negative if the given monomial is negative, and multiply the result by the literal factors of the monomial, giving each letter three times its original exponent.

EXAMPLE 1. Find $(-5\,x^2y^3)^2$.
SOLUTION: $(-5\,x^2y^3)^2 = +25\,x^4y^6$.

EXAMPLE 2. Find $(-5\,x^2y^3)^3$.
SOLUTION: $(-5\,x^2y^3)^3 = -125\,x^6y^9$.

EXERCISE 51

1. What sign does the square of any number have?
2. What sign does the cube of a negative number have?
3. Learn thoroughly the squares of the numbers from 1 to 20.
4. Learn thoroughly the cubes of the numbers from 1 to 6.

Give the values of the following indicated powers:

5. $(a^2b)^2$.
6. $(-a^3b^2)^2$.
7. $(2\,x^3y^2)^2$.
8. $(+abc)^3$.
9. $(+2\,a^2b)^3$.
10. $(+3\,x^3y^2z)^3$.
11. $(-5\,m^5)^2$.
12. $(-2\,x^2y)^3$.
13. $(-3\,x^4y^2)^3$.
14. $(-6\,x^2y^3)^2$.
15. $(-7\,x^3y^5)^2$.
16. $(+8\,a^3b^4)^2$.
17. $(-5\,m^2n^4)^3$.
18. $(-9\,r^2st^3)^2$.
19. $(+4\,c^5d^2)^3$.
20. $(11\,ab^2c^3)^2$.
21. $(-12\,m^3n^2)^2$.
22. $(+5\,m^4n^3)^3$.
23. $(-15\,v^4z^3)^2$.
24. $(-10\,c^4d^6)^3$.
25. $(-18)^2$.
26. $(-16\,t^3)^2$.
27. $(+6\,mn)^3$.
28. $(\tfrac{1}{2}\,a)^2$.
29. $(\tfrac{1}{3}\,mn)^3$.
30. $(-\tfrac{1}{2}\,nx^2)^3$.
31. $(+\tfrac{3}{5}\,a^2b)^2$.
32. $(-\tfrac{2}{3}\,cd^2)^3$.
33. $(-\tfrac{4}{5}\,xy)^3$.
34. $(-\tfrac{5}{6}\,r^2s)^2$.

90. The Square Root of a Monomial. If an expression can be resolved into two equal factors, it is said to be a **Perfect Square**, and one of the factors is said to be its **Square Root**.

Thus, $4\,a^2b^6$ is equal to $2\,ab^3 \times 2\,ab^3$; hence it is a perfect square and $2\,ab^3$ is its square root.

NOTE. $4\,a^2b^6$ is also equal to $(-2\,ab^3) \times (-2\,ab^3)$, so that $-2\,ab^3$ is also a square root. In this chapter, only the positive square root will be considered.

The following questions lead to the rule for extracting the square root of a perfect square monomial.

DEVELOPMENT. 1. What sign does the square of any monomial have?

2. When squaring a monomial, what do you do with the exponents of the literal factors? with the coefficient?

3. In finding the square root, then, what should you do with the exponents of the literal factors? with the coefficient?

4. Find the square root of each of the following monomials, and test the result by multiplication:

(a) x^4;   (b) $4\,x^2y^2$;   (c) $16\,r^2s^4$;   (d) $25\,x^2y^2z^6$.

Rule. — 1. A perfect square monomial is positive, has a perfect square numerical coefficient, and only even numbers as exponents.

2. To find its square root: find the square root of its numerical coefficient, and multiply the result by the literal factors of the monomial, giving each letter one half of its original exponent.

The symbol for extracting the square root is the **Radical Sign**, $\sqrt{}$; the vinculum is usually combined with it, $\sqrt{}$.

EXAMPLE. Find the square root of $25\,m^4n^6$.
SOLUTION: $\sqrt{25\,m^4n^6} = 5\,m^2n^3$.

91. The Cube Root of a Monomial. If an expression can be resolved into three equal factors, it is said to be a **Perfect Cube**, and one of the factors is said to be its **Cube Root**.

Thus, since $27\,a^6b^3$ is equal to $3\,a^2b \cdot 3\,a^2b \cdot 3\,a^2b$, it is a perfect cube, and $3\,a^2b$ is its cube root.

SPECIAL PRODUCTS AND FACTORING

The following questions lead to the rule for extracting the cube root of a perfect cube monomial.

DEVELOPMENT. 1. What sign does the cube of a positive number have? of a negative number?

2. When cubing a monomial, what do you do with the exponents of the literal factors? with the coefficient?

3. In finding the cube root, then, what should you do with the exponents of the literal factors of the monomial? with the coefficient?

4. Find the cube root of each of the following monomials and test the result by multiplication:

(a) a^3;   (b) x^6;   (c) y^9;   (d) m^3n^3;
(e) $8a^3$;   (f) $27m^3$;   (g) $-c^6$;   (h) $-64x^3y^3$.

Rule. — 1. A perfect cube monomial has a perfect cube numerical coefficient, whose sign may be + or −, and its literal factors have exponents which are exactly divisible by 3.

2. To find its cube root: find the cube root of the numerical coefficient, making it positive or negative, according as the sign of the monomial is + or −; and multiply the result by the literal factors of the monomial, giving each letter one third of its original exponent.

The symbol for extracting the cube root is the radical sign with the **Index** 3, as follows: $\sqrt[3]{}$.

EXAMPLE. Find the cube root of $-125\,a^6b^9$.
SOLUTION. $\sqrt[3]{-125\,a^6b^9} = -5\,a^2b^3$.

EXERCISE 52

Find the indicated roots:

1. $\sqrt{4\,m^2}$.
2. $\sqrt{9\,m^6}$.
3. $\sqrt{25\,a^2b^2}$.
4. $\sqrt[3]{a^6b^9}$.
5. $\sqrt[3]{8\,a^3b^6}$.
6. $\sqrt[3]{27\,m^3n^3}$.
7. $\sqrt{36\,a^2b^6}$.
8. $\sqrt[3]{-8\,a^3b^3}$.
9. $\sqrt[3]{-125\,m^6n^{12}}$.
10. $\sqrt{169\,m^6n^8}$.
11. $\sqrt[3]{-64\,x^3y^9}$.
12. $\sqrt{225\,x^{10}y^2}$.
13. $\sqrt{256\,r^2t^4}$.
14. $\sqrt[3]{+216\,c^3d^6e^3}$.
15. $\sqrt[3]{-27\,r^3t^{15}}$.

16. $\sqrt[3]{+125\,R^3}$.
17. $\sqrt{\tfrac{1}{4}\,a^2}$.
18. $\sqrt{\tfrac{1}{9}\,m^2n^2}$.
19. $\sqrt[3]{-216\,v^3t^3}$.
20. $\sqrt{\tfrac{25}{9}\,c^4d^2}$.
21. $\sqrt{\dfrac{1}{49\,x^2}}$.
22. $\sqrt{\dfrac{4\,a^2}{25\,c^2}}$.
23. $\sqrt[3]{\tfrac{1}{27}}$.
24. $\sqrt{\tfrac{1}{4}\,a^2b^2}$.
25. $\sqrt{\tfrac{9}{25}\,m^2n^4}$.
26. $\sqrt{\dfrac{m^2}{16}}$.
27. $\sqrt[3]{\tfrac{1}{8}\,a^3}$.
28. $\sqrt[3]{\tfrac{1}{27}\,m^3n^3}$.
29. $\sqrt[3]{\tfrac{64}{125}\,x^6}$.
30. $\sqrt{\dfrac{25\,a^4b^2}{49\,c^2}}$.
31. $\sqrt{\dfrac{256\,m^4}{169\,n^8}}$.

92. It is not always possible to factor a polynomial. Those polynomials which can be factored are the products of certain special forms of number expressions.

CASE I

Type Form: $a(b+c) = ab + ac$.

93. Multiplication. The rule for multiplying a polynomial by a monomial is given in § 57.

EXERCISE 53

Find:

1. $2\,x^2(x^2 - 3\,xy + y^2)$.
2. $-3\,xy(x^3 + xy - y^3)$.
3. $+3\,mn(m^3 - m^2n + n^3)$.
4. $+5\,a(3\,x^2 - 2\,xy + y^2)$.
5. $ab(3\,a^2 - 2\,ab + b^2)$.
6. $-3\,a(2\,a - b + c)$.

94. Factoring a Polynomial whose Terms have a <u>Common Monomial Factor</u>.

EXAMPLE 1. Factor $ax + 3\,a - ba$.

SOLUTION: 1. Each term has the factor a. Divide the expression by a.

2. Then $ax + 3\,a - ba = a(x + 3 - b)$.

CHECK: $a \cdot (x + 3 - b) = ax + 3\,a - ab$.

EXAMPLE 2. Factor $14\,xy^4 - 35\,x^3y^2$

SOLUTION: 1. Each term contains the factor $7\,xy^2$.

2. Dividing the expression by $7\,xy^2$, the quotient is $2\,y^2 - 5\,x^2$.

SPECIAL PRODUCTS AND FACTORING

3. Whence $14 xy^4 - 35 x^3y^2 = 7 xy^2(2 y^2 - 5 x^2)$.
CHECK: $7 xy^2(2 y^2 - 5 x^2) = 14 xy^4 - 35 x^3y^2$.

Rule. — To factor a polynomial whose terms have a common monomial factor:

1. Find the greatest common factor of its terms.
2. Divide the polynomial by it.
3. The factors are the common factor found in step 1, and the quotient obtained in step 2.

EXERCISE 54

Factor the following polynomials:

1. $3 x + 3 y$.
2. $4 m - 4 a$.
3. $2 r - 6 s$.
4. $5 xt - 10 xs$.
5. $3 ax^2 - 2 ay^2$.
6. $2 rm^3 - 16 rn^3$.
7. $x^3 + 4 x$.
8. $3 m^2 - 6 m$.
9. $x^4 - x^3$.
10. $30 r^2 - 5 r^3$.
11. $2 m^2 + 4 mn + 2 n^2$.
12. $x^2y + xy^2 + y^3$.
13. $4 a^2 - 8 ab + 4 b^2$.
14. $3 x^2 - 3 xy + 3 y^2$.
15. $r^2x^2 - 2 r^2xy + r^2y^2$.
16. $12 a^4 - 20 a^3 + 4 a^2$.
17. $3 x^2 - 15 x + 18$.
18. $ar^6 - 5 ar^3 + 6 a$.
19. $49 m^4t^5 - 16 n^2t^5$.
20. $15 b^2 - 6 b^5$.
21. $4 a^2b^3 - 20 ab^3x + 25 b^3x^2$.
22. $-2 a^2b + 16 ab - 32 b$.
23. $3 n^2y^3 - 21 ny^3 + 18 y^3$.
24. $5 ax^2y - 5 axy - 30 ay$.
25. $4 abx^2 + 16 abxy - 20 aby^2$.
26. $9 m^2t - 6 mt - 63 t$.
27. $48 x^4y^2 - 144 x^3y^3 + 108 x^2y^4$.
28. $x^5 - x^4 + x^3 - x^2$.
29. $3 am^2 - 6 amn + 3 an^2 - 3 ap^2$.
30. $5 ax^3 - 15 ax^2y + 15 axy^2 - 5 ay^3$.

ALGEBRA

31. Recall that the area of a triangle is $\frac{1}{2}$ of the product of its base and altitude. Thus, the area of $\triangle ABC = \frac{1}{2} a \cdot b$. (§ 17)

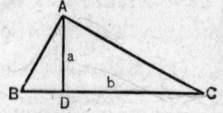

Indicate the area of a triangle of base m and altitude p.

32. Suppose that the polygon $ABCDEF$ can be divided into six triangles, such that their altitudes are all equal. Call the altitudes each a, and the bases b, c, d, e, f, and g.

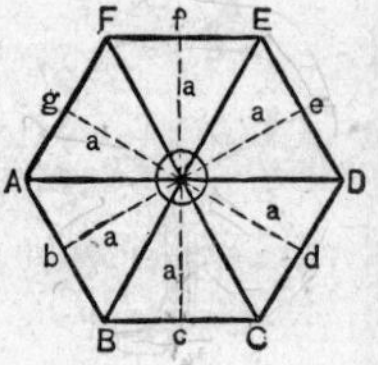

(a) What is the area of $\triangle OBC$? $\triangle ODC$? $\triangle ODE$? etc.?

(b) Indicate the sum of these areas.

(c) Simplify that sum by removing the monomial factor.

(d) Simplify the result by substituting p for
$$(b + c + d + e + f + g).$$
The final result should be: area $= \frac{1}{2} ap$.

33. Suppose that the altitude of $\triangle RXT$ is a, and the altitude of $\triangle RST$ is c. The base of each is b.

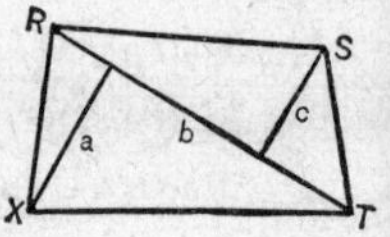

(a) Represent the area of each.

(b) Indicate the sum of these areas.

(c) Simplify the result by removing the monomial factor.

34. The area of a circle whose radius is r is πr^2.

(a) What is the area of the circle of radius R?

(b) How can you find the area of the ring between the large and small circles? Indicate this area.

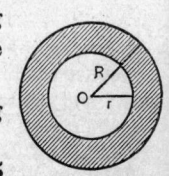

(c) Simplify the result of step b by removing the monomial factor.

(d) Find the value of the result when R is 5 and r is 4.

SPECIAL PRODUCTS AND FACTORING

35. Suppose that, in the adjoining figure, the rectangles have equal bases of length m, and altitudes of length a, b, c, etc.

(a) Represent the area of each.
(b) Indicate the sum of these areas.
(c) Simplify the resulting expression by removing the monomial factor.

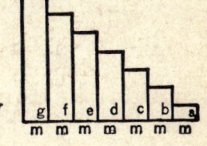

CASE II

Type Form: $(a+b)^2 = a^2 + 2ab + b^2$.

95. The Square of a Binomial.

DEVELOPMENT. **1.** What does $(a+5)^2$ mean?

2. Find the value of the following by actual multiplication, as in § 58, and write the results as in part (a):

(a) $(a+6)^2 = a^2 + 12a + 36$.
(b) $(b+4)^2 = ?$
(c) $(m+5)^2 = ?$
(d) $(x+8)^2 = ?$

3. Observe carefully the results in step 2. Then try to find the following squares mentally, first, and check by multiplication:

(a) $(x+2)^2 = ?$
(b) $(y+3)^2 = ?$
(c) $(z+7)^2 = ?$
(d) $(k+10)^2 = ?$

4. Write the sum of x and y. Indicate the square of that sum. Find the value of the square either mentally or by multiplication.

5. Prove by multiplication the following fact:
$$(a+b)^2 = a^2 + 2ab + b^2.$$

Rule. — To square the sum of two numbers:

Square the first number; add twice the product of the two numbers; add the square of the second number.

EXAMPLE. Square $(3a + 2bc)$.

SOLUTION: $(3a + 2bc)^2 = (3a)^2 + 2(3a)(2bc) + (2bc)^2$
$= 9a^2 + 12abc + 4b^2c^2$.

118 ALGEBRA

The solution may be checked by substitution, but it is necessary to acquire such skill in doing these problems that checking in that manner will be unnecessary.

Rule. — To square the difference of two numbers:

Square the first number; subtract twice the product of the two numbers; add the square of the second number.

EXAMPLE. Square $(4\,a^2 - 5\,b^3)$.

SOLUTION: $(4\,a^2 - 5\,b^3)^2 = (4\,a^2)^2 - 2(4\,a^2)(5\,b^3) + (5\,b^3)^2$
$= 16\,a^4 - 40\,a^2b^3 + 25\,b^6.$

NOTE. In actual practice, pupils should do all of this work mentally, passing from the given problem to the result as follows:

$$(3\,m - 5\,n)^2 = 9\,m^2 - 30\,mn + 25\,n^2.$$

This is called "finding the result by *inspection*."

The following figure illustrates the square of $(a+b)$.

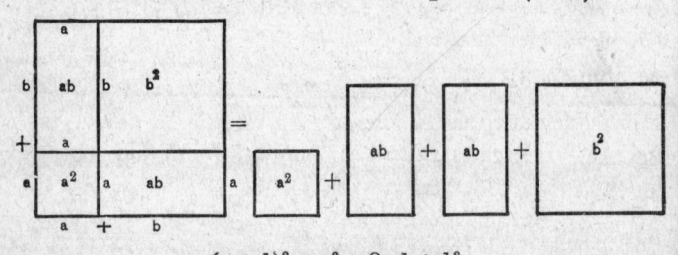

$$(a+b)^2 = a^2 + 2\,ab + b^2.$$

EXERCISE 55

Square the following binomials by inspection:

1. $a + 5.$
2. $b + 6.$
3. $c - 7.$
4. $d - 3.$
5. $m^2 + 4.$
6. $n^2 - 8.$
7. $p^2 + 9.$
8. $w^3 - 10.$
9. $r^2 + 12.$
10. $mn - 11.$
11. $2\,a + b.$
12. $3\,a - c.$
13. $a + 2\,b.$
14. $r - 3\,s.$
15. $m + 4\,n.$
16. $2\,p - 3\,q.$
17. $x^2 - 3\,y.$
18. $2\,x + 5.$
19. $5\,m - 6.$
20. $3\,a^2 - 2\,b^2.$
21. $2\,xy + 9.$

SPECIAL PRODUCTS AND FACTORING

22. $3 a^3 - 6 b$.
23. $10 r + 4 t^2$.
24. $11 s - 5 t$.
25. $9 a^2 + 5 r^4$.
26. $7 - 2 a^2$.
27. $8 c + 3 m^2 n^3$.
28. $2 xy - 9 z^2$.
29. $7 ab - 5 cd$.
30. $9 a^4 + 6 b^2$.

NOTE. For additional drill problems, if desired, square a binomial like $3 x + b$, making b successively 1, 2, 3, etc. up to 10. Then change 3 to 4 or any other number. Short daily drills of this sort afford good mental arithmetic.

Expand the following:

31. $(m - \frac{3}{5})^2$.
32. $(y - \frac{1}{5})^2$.
33. $(z + \frac{2}{3})^2$.
34. $(x + \frac{1}{3})^2$.
35. $(n + \frac{1}{2})^2$.
36. $(p - \frac{3}{4})^2$.
37. $(r + \frac{1}{6})^2$.
38. $(s + \frac{2}{7} t)^2$.
39. $(x - \frac{3}{8} y)^2$.

40. Square 29 mentally.

SOLUTION: $29^2 = (30 - 1)^2 = 900 - 60 + 1 = 901 - 60 = 841$.
This should be done mentally.

41. Square 32. (HINT: $32 = 30 + 2$).

Square mentally the following numbers:

42. 21.
43. 22.
44. 23.
45. 31.
46. 42.
47. 33.
48. 19.
49. 18.
50. 49.
51. 28.
52. 39.
53. 38.
54. 52.
55. 43.
56. 57.

57. *Problem.* Find a rule for squaring any number ending in 5.

SOLUTION: 1. $35 = 3 \times 10 + 5$; $45 = 4 \times 10 + 5$; $55 = 5 \times 10 + 5$.

2. Similarly, any number ending in 5 may be represented by
$$10 n + 5.$$

Thus, for 95, n is 9, since $9 \times 10 + 5 = 95$.

3.
$$(10 n + 5)^2 = 100 n^2 + 100 n + 25$$
$$= 100 n(n + 1) + 25,$$

or, $n \cdot (n + 1)$ hundreds $+ 25$.

Thus the square of 95, in which $n = 9$, is

$9 \cdot (9 + 1)$ hundreds $+ 25$, or 9025.

Rule. — To square a number ending in 5, drop the 5, multiply the balance of the number by the consecutive integer, and affix 25 to the result.

EXAMPLE. $85^2 = 7225$.

I.e. $8 \times 9 = 72$; affixing 25, the result is 7225.

58. Find by this rule the squares of some numbers ending in 5, such as 35, 45, 105, 115, etc.

96. Factoring Perfect Square Trinomials. In algebra, it is necessary to be able to recognize a perfect square trinomial.

DEVELOPMENT. 1. Square the following binomials, and write the result as in part (a):

(a) $(a + b)^2 = a^2 + 2ab + b^2$. (c) $(3x + 4y)^2 = ?$
(b) $(2a + 3b)^2 = ?$ (d) $(4m - 5n)^2 = ?$

2. How many terms are there always in the square?

3. What sign does the first term of the square have? the third term?

4. Notice that the first and third terms are perfect squares and that the second term is twice the product of the square roots of these two terms.

5. Are the following perfect squares? Give the reason for your opinion. Give the square roots of the perfect squares:

(a) $c^2 + 2cd + d^2$. (c) $r^2 - 6r + 9$.
(b) $m^2 + 2mn + n^2$. (d) $x^2 - 10x - 25$.

Rule. — 1. A trinomial is a perfect square when two of its terms are perfect squares and positive, and when the remaining term is twice the product of the square roots of the perfect square terms.

2. To find the square root of a perfect square trinomial: extract the square roots of the two perfect square terms, and connect them by the sign of the remaining term.

EXAMPLE 1. Is $4x^2 + 9y^4 - 12xy^2$ a perfect square?

SOLUTION: $4x^2$ is a perfect square; its square root is $2x$.
$9y^4$ is a perfect square; its square root is $3y^2$.

$$12xy^2 = 2(2x)(3y^2).$$

SPECIAL PRODUCTS AND FACTORING

Hence $4x^2 + 9y^4 - 12xy^2$ is a perfect square, and its square root is $2x - 3y^2$.

EXAMPLE 2. Is $9a^2 + 7ab + 4b^2$ a perfect square?

SOLUTION: $9a^2$ and $4b^2$ are perfect squares. Their square roots are $3a$ and $2b$, respectively.

$2(3a)(2b) = 12ab$. Since the third term is $7ab$, and not $12ab$, $9a^2 + 7ab + 4b^2$ is not a perfect square.

To be a perfect square, the term $7ab$ would need to be changed to $+$ or $-12ab$.

Then $\sqrt{9a^2 \pm 12ab + 4b^2} = 3a \pm 2b$.

EXERCISE 56

Supply the missing term so as to make perfect square trinomials of the following expressions, and then give the square roots:

1. $x^2 + (?) + m^2$.
2. $a^2 - (?) + t^2$.
3. $m^2 - (?) + n^2$.
4. $r^6 - (?) + t^2$.
5. $x^4 - (?) + 9y^2$.
6. $9x^2 + (?) + 4y^2$.
7. $16r^4 - (?) + 25t^2$.
8. $100m^2 + (?) + 4n^6$.
9. $25c^2 - (?) + 9d^2$.
10. $81c^8 - (?) + 25d^2$.
11. $m^2 + 4m + (?)$.
12. $x^2 - 6x + (?)$.
13. $y^2 - 12y + (?)$.
14. $z^4 - 10z^2 + (?)$.
15. $9a^2 + 6a + (?)$.
16. $144A^2 - (?) + 25$.
17. $9b^2 - (?) + 36c^2$.
18. $25x^4 + (?) + 36y^2$.
19. $49r^2 - (?) + 25s^2$.
20. $9x^2 - (?) + 64$.

In the following, determine whether the trinomials are perfect squares; find the factors *when possible*.

21. $4m^2 - 20mn^2 + 25n^4$.

SOLUTION: 1. This is a perfect square, according to the rule. (§ 96, Rule 1.)

2. Hence, $4m^2 - 20mn^2 + 25n^4 = (2m - 5n^2)^2$
$= (2m - 5n^2)(2m - 5n^2)$.

ALGEBRA

22. $m^2 - 10\,mn + 25\,n^2$.

23. $x^4 + 12\,x^2y + 36\,y^2$.

24. $m^2x^2 + 18\,mx + 81$.

25. $64\,a^2 + 15\,ab + b^2$.

26. $100\,x^4 - 60\,x^2y + 9\,y^2$.

27. $49\,x^2y^2 - 70\,xyz + 25\,z^2$.

28. $4\,a^2 - 22\,ax + 25\,x^2$.

29. $81\,x^2 + 16\,y^2 - 72\,xy$.

30. $4\,a^2 - 28\,ax + 49\,x^2$.

31. $25\,x^2 + 16\,y^2 - 40\,xy$.

32. $9\,m^2n^2 + 25\,r^4 - 30\,mnr^2$.

33. $4\,t^4 + 36\,x^2 - 12\,xt^2$.

34. $169\,m^6 - 26\,m^3n + n^2$.

35. $64\,a^2b^2 + 16\,abcd + c^2d^2$.

36. $100\,x^8 - 80\,x^4 + 16$.

37. $49\,m^4 + 112\,m^2 + 64$.

38. $9\,a^2 + 42\,ab + 49\,b^2$.

39. $121\,a^2b^2 + 130\,abc + 36\,c^2$.

40. $64\,a^2 + 176\,ab + 121\,b^2$.

41. $x^2 + x + \frac{1}{4}$.

42. $y^2 + \frac{2}{3}y + \frac{1}{9}$.

43. $z^2 + \frac{4}{25}w^2 - \frac{4}{5}zw$.

44. $\frac{1}{9}m^2 + 25\,n^2 - \frac{10}{3}mn$.

45. $\frac{4}{25}x^2 + \frac{12}{5}xy + 9\,y^2$.

97. Complete Factoring. When a number is to be factored, all of its prime factors should be found. The factors found first may sometimes be factored again.

Thus, $48 = 8 \cdot 6 = 4 \cdot 2 \cdot 2 \cdot 3 = 2 \cdot 2 \cdot 2 \cdot 2 \cdot 3$.

In algebra, this sort of factoring is frequently necessary.

EXAMPLE 1. Find the prime factors of
$$5\,am^2 - 50\,amn + 125\,an^2.$$

SOLUTION:
$$5\,am^2 - 50\,amn + 125\,an^2$$
$$= 5\,a(m^2 - 10\,mn + 25\,n^2) \qquad (\S\,94)$$
$$= 5\,a(m - 5\,n)(m - 5\,n). \qquad (\S\,96)$$

Do not fail to rewrite all factors, like the $5\,a$, which are not factored again.

Rule. — To find the prime factors of an expression:

1. First remove any monomial factor which may be present.

2. Then factor the resulting expression, when possible, rewriting all expressions which cannot be factored.

SPECIAL PRODUCTS AND FACTORING

EXERCISE 57

Find all of the prime factors:

1. $3\,mx^2 + 24\,mx + 48\,m$.
2. $18\,t - 12\,at + 2\,a^2t$.
3. $7\,m^2n^3 + 70\,mn^4 + 175n^5$.
4. $5\,x^2y^2z + 70\,xyz + 245\,z$.
5. $11\,mx^2y^2 + 22\,mxy + 44\,m$.
6. $20\,a^6 - 20\,a^3bc^2 + 5\,b^2c^4$.
7. $30\,a^2b - 120\,ab + 120\,b$.
8. $3\,ax^2 - 3\,axy + 3\,ay^2$.
9. $75\,cx^2 + 48\,cy^2 - 120\,cxy$.
10. $5\,r^2s - 10\,rst + 20\,st^2$.

CASE III

Type Form: $(a+b)(a-b) = a^2 - b^2$.

98. The Product of the Sum and the Difference of Two Numbers.

DEVELOPMENT. 1. Find by multiplication the following products, and write the results as in part (*a*):

(*a*) $(x+3)(x-3) = x^2 - 9$.
(*b*) $(m+7)(m-7) = ?$
(*c*) $(k+10)(k-10) = ?$
(*d*) $(r+9)(r-9) = ?$

2. Observe the results in step 1; try to find the following products mentally. Check the results by multiplication.

(*a*) $(a+6)(a-6) = ?$
(*b*) $(c+8)(c-8) = ?$
(*c*) $(d+4)(d-4) = ?$
(*d*) $(y+5)(y-5) = ?$

3. Write the sum of x and y; write their difference. Find the product of the results.

4. Prove by multiplication the following fact:
$$(a+b)(a-b) = a^2 - b^2.$$

Rule. — To find the product of the sum and the difference of two numbers:

1. Square each of the numbers.
2. Subtract the second square from the first.

EXAMPLE 1. Find $(5\,a^2 + m)(5\,a^2 - m)$.
SOLUTION: $(5\,a^2 + m)(5\,a^2 - m) = (5\,a^2)^2 - (m)^2 = 25\,a^4 - m^2$.

EXAMPLE 2. Find mentally the product of 24 and 16.
SOLUTION: $24 \times 16 = (20+4)(20-4) = 400 - 16 = 384$.

EXERCISE 58

Find by inspection the products:

1. $(a+2)(a-2)$.
2. $(r-3)(r+3)$.
3. $(s^2+4)(s^2-4)$.
4. $(x^2+5y)(x^2-5y)$.
5. $(3m+4n)(3m-4n)$.
6. $(m^4-1)(m^4+1)$.
7. $(z-3a)(z+3a)$.
8. $(8k^2-9t)(8k^2+9t)$.
9. $(3ab-7c)(3ab+7c)$.
10. $(4r-5s^2)(4r+5s^2)$.
11. $(10xy-11)(10xy+11)$.
12. $(13m^2-12)(13m^2+12)$.
13. $(a^5-b^5)(a^5+b^5)$.
14. $(x^3-y^3)(x^3+y^3)$.
15. $(x^6-8y^6)(x^6+8y^6)$.
16. $(7xy^2z-10)(7xy^2z+10)$.
17. $(\frac{2}{3}x-\frac{1}{5})(\frac{2}{3}x+\frac{1}{5})$.
18. $(\frac{3}{4}m+\frac{1}{7})(\frac{3}{4}m-\frac{1}{7})$.
19. $(\frac{2}{9}r^2-\frac{3}{11})(\frac{2}{9}r^2+\frac{3}{11})$.
20. $(\frac{7}{8}n^2-\frac{5}{4})(\frac{7}{8}n^2+\frac{5}{4})$.

21. $(9+5)(9-5)$.
22. $(25+2)(25-2)$.
23. $22 \cdot 18$.
24. $23 \cdot 17$.
25. $32 \cdot 28$.
26. $53 \cdot 47$.
27. $62 \cdot 58$.
28. $98 \cdot 102$.
29. $55 \cdot 65$.
30. $33 \cdot 37$.
31. $41 \cdot 49$.
32. $22 \cdot 23$.

33. Find the cost of 18 dozen of eggs at 22¢ per dozen.
34. Find the cost of 16 yards of gingham at 24¢ per yard.
35. Find the cost of 45 yards of scrim at 55¢ per yard.

99. Factoring the Difference of Two Perfect Squares.

DEVELOPMENT. 1. What is the product of $(a+2)$ and $(a-2)$? What, then, are the factors of a^2-4?

2. Find the factors of:

    (a) a^2-9;
    (b) m^2-16;
    (c) k^2-l^2;
    (d) $9r^2-4s^2$.

3. Write the square of r; of t; the difference of these squares. Factor the result.

4. Similarly, the factors a^2-b^2 are:

$$(a^2-b^2)=(a+b)(a-b).$$

SPECIAL PRODUCTS AND FACTORING

Rule. — To factor the difference of two squares:

1. Find the square root of the two perfect square terms.
2. One factor is the sum of the results; the other factor is the difference of the results.

EXAMPLE 1. Find the factors of $25\ r^4 - 16\ t^6$.

SOLUTION: $25\ r^4 - 16\ t^6 = (5\ r^2)^2 - (4\ t^3)^2$
$= (5\ r^2 + 4\ t^3)(5\ r^2 - 4\ t^3)$.

EXAMPLE 2. Find mentally the value of $13^2 - 7^2$.

SOLUTION: $13^2 - 7^2 = (13 + 7)(13 - 7)$
$= 20 \times 6 = 120$.

This example shows how the above rule can be used to simplify arithmetical work.

EXERCISE 59

Factor the following *when possible:*

1. $a^4 - b^2$.
2. $c^2 - 9$.
3. $16 - d^2$.
4. $x^2 - 1$.
5. $1 - y^4$.
6. $x^2 - 4\ y^2$.
7. $9 - m^2$.
8. $r^4 s^2 - t^2$.
9. $16\ x^2 - 25\ y^2$.
10. $81\ r^2 - 16\ z^4$.
11. $25\ a^6 - 81\ z^8$.
12. $36 - 49\ y^4$.
13. $1 - 36\ a^2 b^2$.
14. $x^2 - \frac{1}{4}$.
15. $100\ z^4 x^2 - 49$.
16. $y^6 - \frac{1}{9}\ m^2$.
17. $\frac{4}{9}\ a^2 - \frac{1}{36}\ c^2$.
18. $64\ m^4 - 81\ n^6$.
19. $169\ a^2 - 196$.
20. $25\ a^3 - 1$.
21. $144\ x^3 - 121\ y^2$.
22. $\frac{4}{25}\ b^2 - \frac{1}{49}$.
23. $100\ a^2 b^2 c^2 - 1$.
24. $c^4 - \frac{4}{9}\ d^2$.
25. $81\ x^{10} - 196\ y^6 z^2$.
26. $256\ n^4 - m^2$.
27. $225 - 64\ t^2$.
28. $85\ x^2 - y^2$.
29. $\frac{1}{a^2} - \frac{c^2}{d^2}$.
30. $\frac{25}{r^2} - \frac{s^2}{36}$.

Find mentally the following:

31. $16^2 - 9^2$.
32. $23^2 - 7^2$.
33. $24^2 - 6^2$.
34. $33^2 - 17^2$.
35. $24^2 - 16^2$.
36. $35^2 - 15^2$.
37. $27^2 - 13^2$.
38. $26^2 - 4^2$.
39. $95^2 - 5^2$.
40. $75^2 - 25^2$.

ALGEBRA

Find the prime factors of the following:

41. $5x^2 - 5y^2$. (See § 94.)
42. $m^2t - 25t$.
43. $3ar^2 - 12as^4$.
44. $4c^2d - 9d^3$.
45. $32y - 2x^4y$.

46. $36xw^2 - xv^2$.
47. $\pi R^2 - \pi s^2$.
48. $\tfrac{1}{4}\pi d^2 - \tfrac{1}{4}\pi m^2$.
49. $m^4 - n^4$.
50. $x^8 - y^8$.

Find the following quotients:

51. $(x^2 - y^2) \div (x - y)$.
52. $(a^2 - m^2) \div (a + m)$.
53. $(r^2 - 9) \div (r - 3)$.
54. $(l^2 - 25) \div (l + 5)$.
55. $(4s^2 - t^2) \div (2s - t)$.
56. $(9x^2 - 16y^2) \div (3x + 4y)$.
57. $(25m^2 - 16n^2) \div (5m + 4n)$.
58. $(169 - 100a^2) \div (13 - 10a)$.

Tell what binomial will divide each of the following; give the quotient:

59. $9x^2 - 4y^4$.
60. $m^2 - 16n^2$.
61. $25a^6 - 36b^4$.
62. $144r^6 - 121$.
63. $256c^4 - 400$.
64. $100r^2 - 36t^4$.

EXERCISE 60

Review

Expand the following:

1. $(x^2 - y^2)^2$.
2. $2a(x + y)(x - y)$.
3. $3m(x^3 - y^3)(x^3 + y^3)$.
4. $2pg(r^2 - s^2)(r^2 + s^2)$.
5. $3c(2a - b)^2$.
6. $5ab(a^2 - b^2)^2$.

Factor completely the following:

7. $r^4 - 2r^2s^2 + s^4$.
8. $mc^4 - 2mc^2 + m$.
9. $5tx^4 - 5ty^4$.
10. $3ax^4 - 6ax^2y^2 + 3ay^4$.
11. $5mx^2 - 10mxy + 5my^2$.
12. $2r^3m^4 - 4r^3m^2n^2 + 2r^3n^4$.

SPECIAL PRODUCTS AND FACTORING

CASE IV

Type Form: $(x+a)(x+b) = x^2 + (a+b)x + ab.$

100. The Product of Two Binomials having a Common Term.

DEVELOPMENT. 1. Find by actual multiplication the following products, and write the results as in part (a):

(a) $(x+2)(x+3) = x^2 + 5x + 6.$
(b) $(x+5)(x+3) = ?$
(c) $(a+5)(a+6) = ?$
(d) $(m-7)(m-2) = ?$
(e) $(s-5)(s-8) = ?$

2. Observe carefully the results in 1. Try to find the following products mentally; check the results by multiplication:

(a) $(b+4)(b+2).$
(b) $(c+4)(c+3).$
(c) $(x-3)(x-7).$
(d) $(y-4)(y-5).$

Rule. — To obtain the product of two binomials having a common term:

1. Square the common term.
2. Multiply the common term by the algebraic sum of the second terms of the binomials.
3. Find the product of the second terms.
4. Add the results.

EXAMPLE 1. Find the product of $x-8$ and $x+5.$

SOLUTION: $(x-8)(x+5) = x^2 + (-8+5)x + (-8)(+5)$
$= x^2 - 3x - 40.$

EXAMPLE 2. Find $(ab+2)(ab-11).$

SOLUTION: $(ab+2)(ab-11) = a^2b^2 - 9ab - 22.$

NOTE. Here, one glances at $+2$ and -11, notes that their sum is -9 and that their product is -22, and writes the result as above.

EXAMPLE 3. Find mentally the product of 23 and 24.

SOLUTION: 1. $23 \times 24 = (20+3)(20+4) = 400 + 7 \cdot 20 + 12$
$= 400 + 140 + 12 = 552.$

EXERCISE 61

Find the following products:

1. $(x+2)(x+3)$.
2. $(x+2)(x+4)$.
3. $(a+3)(a+5)$.
4. $(a+4)(a+6)$.
5. $(m+5)(m+9)$.
6. $(b-3)(b-7)$.
7. $(b-4)(b-8)$.
8. $(c-5)(c-7)$.
9. $(r-6)(r-8)$.
10. $(r-9)(r-10)$.
11. $(r+2)(r-8)$.
12. $(m+3)(m-10)$.
13. $(n+5)(n-11)$.
14. $(s+6)(s-12)$.
15. $(t+4)(t-11)$.
16. $(x-2)(x+10)$.
17. $(y+11)(y-3)$.
18. $(z+10)(z-5)$.
19. $(w-4)(w+9)$.
20. $(a-1)(a+8)$.
21. $(s^2-6)(s^2+10)$.
22. $(t^3-12)(t^3+9)$.
23. $(xy-10)(xy+15)$.
24. $(r-5s)(r+3s)$.
25. $(x-2y)(x+8y)$.
26. $(rs-8t)(rs-3t)$.
27. $(a+3b)(a+13b)$.
28. $(c-4d)(c-12d)$.
29. $(x^2-8y)(x^2-10y)$.
30. $(x^3+5y^3)(x^3-2y^3)$.
31. $(p^2+11q)(p^2+15q)$.
32. $(r^3-12)(r^3+20)$.
33. $(s^3-15)(s^3+8)$.
34. $(t^3-16w)(t^3-4w)$.
35. $(x^3-18y)(x^3+5y)$.
36. $(a+17t^2)(a-3t^2)$.
37. $(x-9a)(x+15a)$.
38. $(x+11b)(x-8b)$.
39. $(y^2-13z)(y^2-7z)$.
40. $(t+15r)(t-10r)$.
41. $(a^2-14b)(a^2-10b)$.
42. $(c-22x)(c+20x)$.
43. $(x+19y)(x-5y)$.
44. $(a-33b)(a+6b)$.
45. $(c^2+25d)(c^2-10d)$.
46. $(x-35)(x+20)$.
47. $(m-\frac{1}{5})(m-5)$.
48. $(z+\frac{1}{2})(z+1)$.
49. $(y+\frac{1}{3})(y+3)$.
50. $(x+\frac{1}{2})(x+\frac{1}{4})$.

51. Find mentally the product of 62×68.

SOLUTION: $62 \times 68 = (60+2)(60+8) = 3600 + 600 + 16 = ?$

SPECIAL PRODUCTS AND FACTORING 129

Find mentally the following arithmetical products:

52. 22×28.
53. 33×37.
54. 34×36.
55. 24×26.
56. 32×38.
57. 44×46.
58. 52×54.
59. 23×25.
60. 33×34.

Perform mentally the multiplications in the following problems:

61. Find the area of a rectangle whose base is 26 inches and altitude is 24 inches.

62. Find the cost of 12 yards of lawn at 18 ¢ per yard.

63. Find the cost of 22 yards of scrim at 25 ¢ per yard.

64. Find the cost of 53 bushels of corn at 55 ¢ per bushel.

65. Find the cost of an 11-pound roast at 18 ¢ per pound.

101. Factoring Trinomials of the Form $x^2 + px + q$

A trinomial of the form $x^2 + px + q$ can be factored if it is the product of two binomials having a common term (§ 100).

DEVELOPMENT. 1. $(x+5)(x-3) = x^2 + 2x - 15$.

In obtaining this product, the algebraic sum of $+5$ and -3 is taken for the coefficient of x, and the product of $+5$ and -3 is taken for the third term.

To factor $x^2 + 2x - 15$, it is necessary to find two numbers whose product is -15, and whose algebraic sum is $+2$.

2. Factor $x^2 + 7x + 12$.

Two numbers whose product is $+12$, are $+3$ and $+4$, and their sum is $+7$. Try as the factors $(x+3)$ and $(x+4)$.

CHECK: Does $(x+3)(x+4) = x^2 + 7x + 12$? Yes.

Rule. — To factor a trinomial of the form $x^2 + px + q$:

1. Find two numbers whose algebraic product is *q* and whose algebraic sum is *p*.

2. One factor is *x +* one number; the other factor is *x +* the other number.

ALGEBRA

EXAMPLE 1. Factor $x^2 - 26x - 192$.

SOLUTION: It is necessary to find two numbers whose sum is -26 and whose product is -192; the number of greater absolute value must be negative. If necessary write all possible pairs of factors of -192, one of which is $+$ and the other $-$. We have:

$(+1) \times (-192)$; sum $= -191$. $(+4) \times (-48)$; sum $= -44$.
$(+2) \times (-96)$; sum $= -94$. $(+6) \times (-32)$; sum $= -26$.
$(+3) \times (-64)$; sum $= -61$.

$\therefore +6$ and -32 are the numbers required.
$\therefore x^2 - 26x - 192 = (x+6)(x-32)$.

EXERCISE 62

Factor:

1. $a^2 + 14x + 45$.

SOLUTION: 1. Find two numbers whose product is 45 and whose sum is $+14$.

2. Factors of 45 are, 1 and 45; 3 and 15; 5 and 9.

3. $5 + 9 = 14$, hence the factors are $(x+5)(x+9)$.

CHECK: $(x+5)(x+9) = x^2 + 14x + 45$.

NOTE. This solution should all be done mentally; decide upon a pair of factors of 45 and immediately determine their sum.

2. $x^2 + 5x + 6$.
3. $x^2 + 8x + 15$.
4. $r^2 + 10r + 21$.
5. $a^2 + 11a + 28$.
6. $m^2 + 9m + 20$.
7. $t^2 + 9t + 18$.

8. $p^2 - 12p + 32$.

SOLUTION: 1. Since 32 is positive, the second terms of the factors must have the same sign; since the sum of the second terms is -12, the second terms are negative.

2. $(-8) \times (-4) = +32$; and $(-8) + (-4) = -12$.

Therefore the factors are $(p-8)(p-4)$.

CHECK: $(p-8)(p-4) = p^2 - 12p + 32$.

9. $x^2 - 7x + 12$.
10. $y^2 - 9y + 14$.
11. $z^2 - 11z + 24$.
12. $w^2 - 10w + 24$.
13. $a^2 - 11a + 30$.
14. $c^2 - 12c + 35$.

SPECIAL PRODUCTS AND FACTORING

15. $x^2 + 6x - 16$.

SOLUTION: Since -16 is negative, the second terms of the factors must have unlike signs; since the sum of the second terms is $+6$, the term of greater absolute value must be positive.

2. Factors of -16 of this sort are: $(+16, -1)$ and $(+8, -2)$.
3. $(+8) + (-2) = +6$, therefore the factors are $(x+8)$ and $(x-2)$.
CHECK: $(x+8)(x-2) = x^2 + 6x - 16$. (By § 100.)

16. $x^2 + 3x - 40$.
17. $x^2 + 2x - 24$.
18. $y^2 + 4y - 21$.
19. $z^2 + 4z - 32$.
20. $w^2 + 4w - 60$.
21. $a^2 + 3a - 54$.

22. $m^2 - 4m - 21$.

SOLUTION: 1. The factors of -21 must have unlike signs; the one of greater absolute value is negative, since the sum is -4.

2. Such factors of -21 are: -21 and $+1$; -7 and $+3$.
3. $(-7) + (+3) = -4$; therefore the factors are $(m-7)$ and $(m+3)$.
CHECK: $(m-7)(m+3) = m^2 - 4m - 21$. (See § 100.)

23. $x^2 - 2x - 35$.
24. $n^2 - 7n - 18$.
25. $a^2 - 8a - 33$.
26. $r^2 - 4r - 45$.
27. $m^4 - 11m^2 + 30$.
28. $a^2 - 15a + 54$.
29. $r^2 + r - 2$.
30. $x^4 + 6x^2 + 8$.
31. $c^2 + 15cd + 36d^2$.
32. $x^2 - 12xy + 32y^2$.
33. $z^2 + 2z - 63$.
34. $c^2d^2 - cd - 6$.
35. $y^2 + 10yz + 9z^2$.
36. $x^2 - 13xw + 22w^2$.
37. $m^2 - 7m - 44$.
38. $r^4 + 2r^2s - 48s^2$.
39. $s^2 - 6st - 55t^2$.
40. $w^6 - 18w^3 + 72$.
41. $y^2 + 4y - 96$.
42. $a^2 - 70 - 3a$. (Rearrange it.)
43. $b^2 - 24 - 10b$.
44. $c^2 + 20c + 84$.
45. $z^2 - 36 + 5z$.
46. $a^4 + 25a^2 - 150$.
47. $-19m^2 + m^4 + 84$.
48. $x^4 + 50 - 27x^2$.

ALGEBRA

49. $t^2 - st - 20 s^2$.
50. $a^2 + 7 ab - 60 b^2$.
51. $x^2 - 20 ax + 99 a^2$.
52. $r^3 + rs - 72 s^2$.
53. $x^2 + 50 y^4 - 15 xy^2$.
54. $a^2 + 16 a + 15$.
55. $a^2b^2 - 16 abc + 28 c^2$.
56. $x^2 - 21 xyz + 108 y^2z^2$.
57. $a^2 - 21 ab^2 + 110 b^4$.
58. $c^2d^2 - 10 cd - 96$.
59. $a^2c^2 - 26 ac + 160$.
60. $r^3 - 7 rs - 120 s^2$.

Find all of the prime factors:

61. $3 ab^2 - 15 ab + 18 a$.

SOLUTION: $3 ab^2 - 15 ab + 18 a = 3 a(b^2 - 5 b + 6)$
$= 3 a(b-2)(b-3)$.

62. $5 t^2 + 35 t + 60$.
63. $mr^2 + 2 mr - 15 m$.
64. $3 cx^2 + 6 cx - 9 c$.
65. $7 y^2z + 21 yz - 126 z$.
66. $abn^2 - 7 abn + 6 ab$.
67. $11 x^2 - 11 x - 66$.
68. $8 x^2 + 48 x - 56$.
69. $m^3n^2 + 2 m^3n - 63 m^3$.

CASE V

Type Form: $(ax + b)(cx + d)$.

102. The Product of Two Binomials of the Form $(ax + b)$.

DEVELOPMENT. 1. Find by actual multiplication the following products, and write the results as in part (a):

(a) $(2 x + 3)(3 x + 1) = 6 x^2 + 11 x + 3$.
(b) $(3 m + 2)(2 m + 3) = ?$ (c) $(2 y + 4)(3 y - 2) = ?$

2. Examine carefully the results in 1, then try to get the first and third terms of the following products *mentally*; possibly you can get the second term also. Check by actual multiplication.

(a) $(2 r + 4)(3 r + 1)$.
(b) $(2 r + 5)(r + 2)$.
(c) $(3 s + 5)(2 s + 1)$.
(d) $(4 x + 2 y)(2 x + 3 y)$.

SPECIAL PRODUCTS AND FACTORING

3. Below is given the product of $(5x-4y)$ and $(2x+3y)$.

$$
\begin{array}{r}
5x - 4y \\
2x + 3y \\
\hline
10x^2 - 8xy \\
+ 15xy - 12y^2 \\
\hline
10x^2 + 7xy - 12y^2
\end{array}
$$

$\therefore (5x-4y)(2x+3y) = 10x^2 + (-8+15)xy - 12y^2.$

Rule.—1. The first term of the product is the product of the first terms of the binomials. ($5x \cdot 2x = 10x^2$.)

2. The third term of the product is the product of the second terms of the binomials. $(-4y) \cdot (+3y) = -12y^2.$

3. The second term of the product is the algebraic sum of the "cross products." (Notice the position of these cross products on the left of the equation: $-4y \cdot 2x$ and $5x \cdot 3y$).

EXAMPLE 1. Find the product $(5r-6s)(2r+3s)$.

SOLUTION: In all of these examples, the only difficulty is that of finding the "middle term."

1. $5r \cdot 3s = 15rs$, $-6s \cdot 2r = -12rs$, and $(15rs)+(-12rs) = +3rs$.
2. $\therefore (5r-6s)(2r+3s) = 10r^2 + 3rs - 18s^2$.

EXAMPLE 2. Find the product $(9x+4y)(3x-6y)$.

SOLUTION: $9 \cdot -6 = -54$, $4 \cdot 3 = 12$, and $(-54)+(12) = -42$.

$\therefore (9x+4y)(3x-6y) = 27x^2 - 42xy - 24y^2$.

In this example, the coefficient of the middle term was found first and then xy was affixed. In practice all of this should be done mentally as in the following example.

EXAMPLE 3. Find the product $(7m-4n)(8m+5n)$.

SOLUTION: $(7m-4n)(8m+5n) = 56m^2 + 3mn - 20n^2$.

[Middle term: $7 \cdot 5 = 35$, $-4 \cdot 8 = -32$, $35 + (-32) = 3$.]

Pupils should try to acquire such skill that they can find the correct products mentally. This is the manner in which experts do it

EXERCISE 63

1. $(2x+2)(x+3)$.
2. $(2x+3)(x+2)$.
3. $(2x+1)(x+3)$.
4. $(3x+1)(2x+3)$.
5. $(2x+3)(3x+2)$.
6. $(3a-2)(2a-1)$.
7. $(3a-4)(a-2)$.
8. $(3a-4)(a-3)$.
9. $(3a-5)(2a-3)$.
10. $(4a-5)(2a-5)$.
11. $(3r+5)(2r-1)$.
12. $(4r+7)(2r-3)$.
13. $(5r+4)(4r-2)$.
14. $(7r+6)(3r-2)$.
15. $(8r+9)(4r-3)$.
16. $(6s-5)(3s+2)$.
17. $(10s-7)(4s+1)$.
18. $(11s-12)(5s+4)$.
19. $(9s-12)(4s+5)$.
20. $(15s-20)(3s+2)$.
21. $(6ab+2)(3ab-5)$.
22. $(7mn-4)(6mn-3)$.
23. $(8r^2-3)(9r^2+4)$.
24. $(13x^3+7)(5x^3-3)$.
25. $(6p^2-7)(4p^2+3)$.
26. $(11m^2-4)(5m^2+6)$.
27. $(9c^3-2)(6c^3+1)$.
28. $(10n^3+3)(15n^3-4)$.
29. $(14x^2-5)(2x^2+1)$.
30. $(16t^3-9)(3t^3+2)$.
31. $(14rs-9)(5rs+3)$.
32. $(2a-3b)(4a+5b)$.
33. $(6m+5s)(7m-4s)$.
34. $(8t-3x)(9t-x)$.
35. $(x-5y)(x+5y)$.
36. $(2x-3y)(2x+3y)$.
37. $(2m-5n)(2m-5n)$.
38. $(3t+4n)(3t+4n)$.
39. $(9ab-4c)(3ab+5c)$.
40. $(6xy-7z)(5xy+6z)$.
41. $(7r^2+8s)(8r^2-9s)$.
42. $(10x^3-11y^3)(11x^3+12y^3)$.
43. $(9mn^2+4)(6mn^2-3)$.
44. $(2+9x)(3+2x)$.
45. $(5-7t^2)(6+9t^2)$.
46. $(8+3z^3)(10-4z^3)$.
47. $(7-6xy)(5+6xy)$.
48. $(9-11xy^2)(4-xy^2)$.
49. $(10a^2b-6c)(9a^2b-2c)$.
50. $(12x^2+7y)(5x^2-4y)$.
51. $(9t^2-5x^2)(7t^2+5x^2)$.
52. $(8m^2-9n)(4m^2+5n)$.

SPECIAL PRODUCTS AND FACTORING 135

53. $(7x^2 + 3y^2)(5x^2 - 2y^2)$.
54. $(11c^2 - 5d)(4c^2 - 5d)$.
55. $(15p^2 + 2q)(9p^2 - 2q)$.
56. $(20a - 7b)(8a + 3b)$.
57. $(15m - 2n)(6m + 5n)$.
58. $(6m + \frac{1}{2})(4m + \frac{1}{3})$.
59. $(8x - \frac{2}{3}y)(9x - \frac{1}{2}y)$.
60. $(12a + \frac{2}{3}b)(10a - \frac{2}{3}b)$.

103. Factoring Trinomials of the Form $mx^2 + nx + p$. The product of two binomials like $(2x + 3)$ and $(3x + 5)$ is a binomial of the *form* $mx^2 + nx + p$.

This means that there is a term containing the second power of x, one containing the first power (as a rule), and one free from x.

The following discussion shows how to factor trinomials of the form $mx^2 + nx + p$, when they are factorable.

DEVELOPMENT 1. Find the products:

(a) $(2x + 6)(3x + 2)$. (b) $(3x - 5)(4x + 7)$.

2. How do you obtain the "middle term" of the product?

3. Factor $12x^2 + 23x + 5$.

SOLUTION: 1. The first terms of the binomials might be $2x$ and $6x$, for their product is $12x^2$. Place them in parentheses thus: $(2x\quad)(6x\quad)$.

2. The second terms of the binomials are both positive since 5 and $23x$ are positive. Place the factors $+5$ and $+1$ in the parentheses and note the middle term which results.

(a) $(2x + 5)(6x + 1)$; middle term, $+32x$. Incorrect.
(b) $(2x + 1)(6x + 5)$; middle term, $+16x$. Incorrect.

3. Step 2 shows that the factors $2x$ and $6x$ for $12x^2$ are incorrect. Try $3x$ and $4x$ for $12x^2$, thus: $(3x\quad)(4x\quad)$.

(a) $(3x + 1)(4x + 5)$; middle term, $+19x$. Incorrect.
(b) $(3x + 5)(4x + 1)$; middle term, $+23x$. Correct.

CHECK: $(3x + 5)(4x + 1) = 12x^2 + 23x + 5$.

NOTE. This may seem a long process at first, but practice soon develops such skill that most of the trial of factors can be done mentally.

ALGEBRA

EXERCISE 64

Factor:

1. $3x^2 + 5x + 2$.
2. $3a^2 + 7a + 2$.
3. $5m^2 + 7m + 2$.
4. $7y^2 + 9y + 2$.
5. $6x^2 + 7x + 2$.
6. $12t^2 + 13t + 3$.
7. $7a^2 + 10a + 3$.
8. $6t^2 + 13t + 6$.
9. $12w^2 - 17w + 6$.

SOLUTION: 1. Since 6 is positive, its factors must have like signs; and, since -17 is negative, the cross products must both be negative. Therefore the factors of 6 must both be negative.

2. To get $12w^2$, use $(2w\ \ )(6w\ \ )$.

To get $+6$, try -2 and -3.

(a) $(2w - 3)(6w - 2)$; middle term, $-22w$. Incorrect.

(b) $(2w - 2)(6w - 3)$; middle term, $-18w$. Incorrect.

3. To get $12w^2$, use $(3w\ \ )(4w\ \ )$.

To get $+6$, try -2 and -3.

(a) $(3w - 2)(4w - 3)$; middle term, $-17w$. Correct.

CHECK: Does $(3w - 2)(4w - 3) = 12w^2 - 17w + 6$? Yes.

NOTE. In step 2, the factors 3 and 2 were used in both ways, as in (a) and (b); usually this is a wise plan, although in this case an explanation could be given to show that it was unnecessary.

10. $2w^2 - 11w + 5$.
11. $2w^2 - 7w + 3$.
12. $3b^2 - 19b + 6$.
13. $6m^2 - 7m + 2$.
14. $2w^2 - 9w + 4$.
15. $6m^2 - 11m + 3$.
16. $8a^2 - 22a + 15$.
17. $5c^2 - 23c + 12$.

18. Factor $15x^2 + 14x - 8$.

SOLUTION: 1. The factors of -8 must have unlike signs. Arrange the signs so that the cross product of greater absolute value is positive.

2. For $15x^2$, try $(3x\ \ )(5x\ \ )$. For 8, try 2 and 4.

(a) $(3x - 2)(5x + 4)$; middle term, $+2x$. Incorrect.

The sign of 4 is made $+$, because $4 \cdot 3$ is greater than $2 \cdot 5$.

(b) $(3x + 4)(5x - 2)$; middle term, $+14x$. Correct.

The sign of 4 is made $+$, because $4 \cdot 5$ is greater than $3 \cdot 2$.

CHECK: Does $(3x + 4)(5x - 2) = 15x^2 + 14x - 8$? Yes.

SPECIAL PRODUCTS AND FACTORING

19. Factor $24m^2 - m - 10$.

SOLUTION: 1. The factors of -10 must have unlike signs. The cross product of greater absolute value must be negative.

2. For $24m^2$, try $(6m\ )(4m\ )$. For 10, try 5 and 2.
   (a) $(6m + 2)(4m - 5)$; middle term, $-22m$. Incorrect.
   (b) $(6m - 5)(4m + 2)$; middle term, $-8m$. Incorrect.
3. For $24m^2$, try $(3m\ )(8m\ )$.
   (a) $(3m - 5)(8m + 2)$; middle term, $-34m$. Incorrect.
   (b) $(3m - 2)(8m + 5)$; middle term, $-m$. Correct.

CHECK: Does $(3m - 2)(8m + 5) = 24m^2 - m - 10$? Yes.

NOTE. In this last step, for example, after placing 2 and 5 in the parentheses, we see that 2×8 is greater than 3×5; therefore make 2 negative and 5 positive.

20. $2x^2 - 3x - 5$.

21. $3m^2 + 4m - 7$.

22. $5t^2 - 2t - 7$.

23. $7r^2 + 4r - 11$.

24. $6s^2 - 7s - 5$.

25. $12s^2 + 5s - 3$.

26. $2x^2 + x - 15$.

27. $9r^2 - 6r - 8$.

28. $15c^2 - 4c - 3$.

29. $21A^2 + 2A - 8$.

30. $5y^2 + 16y + 3$.

31. $18x^2 - 3x - 10$.

32. $4x^2 - 24x + 35$.

33. $10x^2 - 13x - 30$.

34. $3z^2 + 22z + 7$.

35. $18m^2 + 17m - 15$.

36. $6x^2 + 31x + 35$.

37. $14m^2n^2 - 31mn - 10$.

38. $4r^2s^2 + 4rs - 15$.

39. $12x^2 + 17x + 6$.

40. $24m^2 - 18m - 15$.

41. $12t^2 + 13tx - 35x^2$.

42. $2w^2 - 3wr - 20r^2$.

43. $15y^2 + 19yz + 6z^2$.

44. $10n^2 + 9nt - 9t^2$.

45. $9b^2 + 3bc - 56c^2$.

46. $15a^2 - 26ab - 21b^2$.

47. $7x^2 - 26xy - 8y^2$.

48. $15a^2 + 29ab + 12b^2$.

49. $21x^2 - 29xy - 10y^2$.

50. $6r^2 - 25rs + 25s^2$.

51. $4c^2 - 8cd - 21d^2$.

52. $9d^4 - 6d^2 - 35$.

53. $8p^6 + 18p^3 - 35$.

ALGEBRA

54. $10 m^4 + 19 m^2n - 15 n^2$.
55. $14 v^2 + 29 v - 15$.
56. $15 k^2x - 16 kx - 15 x$.
   (Remove the monomial first.)
57. $35 at^2 + at - 12 a$.
58. $24 x^2r^3 - 7 xyr^3 - 6 y^2r^3$.
59. $55 m^2x^5 + 2 mnx^5 - 21 n^2x^5$
60. $24 c^2d^3 + 2 cd^3 - 15 d^3$.

EXERCISE 65

Perform the various steps of the following indicated multiplications mentally:

1. $3 a(2 a + 5)(a - 4)$.

SOLUTION: $3 a(2a + 5)(a - 4) = 3 a(2 a^2 - 3 a - 20)$
$= 6 a^3 - 9 a^2 - 60 a$.

2. $2 m(3 m - 1)(2 m + 6)$.
3. $4 ab(5 x - 2)(5 x + 2)$.
4. $7(3 c + 5 d)(3 c - 4 d)$.
5. $5(2 r - 5 s)^2$.
6. $-3(6 a - 5)(2 a + 3)$.
7. $-2(7 r - 4 s)(2 r + 3 s)$

Solve the following equations, performing mentally all of the steps of the solution:

8. $2(3 x - 2)(x + 4) - (6 x + 5)(x - 3) = 65$.

SOLUTION: 1. $2(3 x - 2)(x + 4) - (6 x + 5)(x - 3) = 65$.
2. $\quad 2(3 x^2 + 10 x - 8) - (6 x^2 - 13 x - 15) = 65$.

3. Complete this example by removing parentheses, combining terms, etc.

9. $(5 x - 4)(3 x + 4) - 3(5 x + 6)(x - 7) = 10(9 x + 15)$.
10. $(4 r - 5)(3 r + 7) - 2(r + 1)(6 r - 7) = 3(2 r + 3)$.

Find *all* of the prime factors in the following; remember to remove the monomial factor first:

11. $24 m^2a + 18 mna - 15 n^2a$.
12. $18 bc^2 - 2 bx^2$.
13. $12 x^4y - 8 x^3y^2 - 4 x^2y^3$.
14. $15 c^3d - 10 c^2d - 25 cd$.
15. $18 k^2r^2 - 60 klr^2 + 50 l^2r^2$.
16. $48 cd^2 + 120 cde + 75 ce^2$.

SPECIAL PRODUCTS AND FACTORING

17. $39\ m^2nx^2 + 20\ m^2nxy - 4\ m^2ny^2.$

18. $3\ x^4 - 17\ x^3 - 56\ x^2.$

19. $4\ x^4y^2 + 2\ x^3y^3 - 7\ x^2y^2.$

20. $45\ r^4s - 80\ r^2s^5.$

CASE VI

Type Form: $a^3 - b^3 = (a - b)(a^2 + ab + b^2).$

104. Factoring the Difference of Two Cubes.

DEVELOPMENT. 1. Divide $x^3 - 27$ by $x - 3$; by $x + 3$.

2. Divide $x^3 - y^3$ by $x - y$; by $x + y$.

3. Write the cube of a; the cube of b; the difference of these cubes.

4. Examine the results in 1 and 2; by what do you think you can divide $a^3 - b^3$ and get an exact quotient?

5. Prove by division the following fact:
$$(a^3 - b^3) \div (a - b) = a^2 + ab + b^2.$$
Hence, memorize $\quad a^3 - b^3 = (a - b)(a^2 + ab + b^2).$

Rule. — 1. The difference of the cubes of two numbers may be divided exactly by the difference of the numbers.

2. The quotient is the square of the first number, plus the product of the two numbers, plus the square of the second number.

EXAMPLE 1. Find a divisor of $8\ x^3 - 27$; find the quotient.

SOLUTION: 1. $8\ x^3 - 27 = (2\ x)^3 - 3^3.$

2. ∴ It is the difference of the cubes of $2\ x$ and 3, and can be divided exactly by $(2\ x - 3)$.

3. ∴ The quotient is $(2\ x)^2 + (2\ x)(3) + (3)^2$, or
$$4\ x^2 + 6\ x + 9.$$
Check by substitution or by multiplication.

EXAMPLE 2. Factor $8\ x^6 - 64\ y^3.$

SOLUTION: 1. $8\ x^6 - 64\ y^3 = (2\ x^2)^3 - (4\ y)^3$

2. $\qquad = (2\ x^2 - 4\ y)\{(2\ x^2)^2 + (2\ x^2)(4\ y) + (4\ y)^2\}$

3. $\qquad = (2\ x^2 - 4\ y)\{4\ x^4 + 8\ x^2y + 16\ y^2\}.$

NOTE. The middle term is *not* twice the product of the first and second numbers; try not to confuse this type with the one in § 96.

EXERCISE 66

Factor:

1. $a^3 + 8$.
2. $b^3 + 64$.
3. $c^3 + 125$.
4. $c^3 + 8 d^3$.
5. $m^6 + 64 n^3$
6. $r^6 + 8$.
7. $s^9 + 125$.
8. $x^{12} + 64 y^3$.
9. $8 b^3 + a^3$.
10. $64 m^3 + 1$.
11. $8 x^6 + 125 y^3$.
12. $3 x^3 - 24 y^3$.
    (Remove monomial first.)
13. $40 a^3 - 5 b^3$.
14. $24 x^6 - 81 y^9$.
15. $4 a - 500 ax^6$.
16. $320 m^3 - 5 n^6$.
17. $x^3 - \frac{1}{8}$.
18. $y^3 - \frac{8}{27}$.
19. $z^3 - \frac{t^3}{125}$.

What is the quotient of:

20. $(x^3 - a^3) \div (x - a)$?
21. $(r^3 - x^6) \div (r - x^2)$?
22. $(27 x^3 y^3 - 1) \div (3 xy - 1)$?
23. $(64 a^6 - b^6) \div (4 a^2 - b^2)$?
24. $(8 - x^9) \div (2 - x^3)$?
25. $(m^{12} - 27) \div (m^4 - 3)$?
26. $(27 w^6 - 64 v^3) \div (3 w^2 - 4 v)$?
27. $(1 - 125 m^6) \div (1 - 5 m^2)$?

CASE VII

Type Form: $(a^3 + b^3) = (a + b)(a^2 - ab + b^2)$.

105. Factoring the Sum of Two Cubes.

DEVELOPMENT. 1. Divide $(x^3 + 27)$ by $(x + 3)$; by $x - 3$.

2. Write the cube of m; of n; the sum of these results. Write the sum of m and n.

3. Divide the sum of the cubes of m and n, by the sum of m and n; also by their difference.

4. Prove by division the following fact:
$$(a^3 + b^3) \div (a + b) = a^2 - ab + b^2.$$
Hence $\quad (a^3 + b^3) = (a + b)(a^2 - ab + b^2)$.

SPECIAL PRODUCTS AND FACTORING

Rule 1. — The sum of the cubes of two numbers may be divided exactly by the sum of the two numbers.

2. The quotient is the square of the first number, minus the product of the two numbers, plus the square of the second number.

EXAMPLE 1. Find an exact divisor of $x^6 + 8$; find the quotient.

SOLUTION: $x^6 + 8 = (x^2)^3 + (2)^3$.

Since it is the sum of the cubes of two numbers, it may be divided exactly by the sum of the two numbers $(x^2 + 2)$. (Rule 1.)

The quotient is $(x^2)^2 - (x^2) \cdot (2) + (2)^2$ or $x^4 - 2x + 4$. (Rule 2.)

NOTE. The middle term is *not twice* the product of the two numbers.

EXAMPLE 2. Find the prime factors of $3\,mx^3 + 81\,my^6$.

SOLUTION: $3\,mx^3 + 81\,my^6 = 3\,m(x^3 + 27\,y^6)$.
$$= 3\,m[(x)^3 + (3\,y^2)^3]$$
$$= 3\,m[x + 3\,y^2][x^2 - (3\,y^2) \cdot x + (3\,y^2)^2]$$
$$= 3\,m(x + 3\,y^2)(x^2 - 3\,xy^2 + 9\,y^4).$$

EXERCISE 67

Change the sign in each example of Exercise 66 from minus to plus. This will give 27 examples.

106. Summary. In this chapter, seven special forms of algebraic expressions have been considered. These type forms are collected here for reference:

I. $a(x + y + z + \ldots) = ax + ay + az + \ldots$
II. $(a \pm b)^2 = a^2 \pm 2\,ab + b^2$.
III. $(a + b)(a - b) = a^2 - b^2$.
IV. $(x + a)(x + b) = x^2 + (a + b)x + ab$.
V. $(ax + b)(cx + d) = acx^2 + (ad + bc)x + bd$.
VI. $(a - b)(a^2 + ab + b^2) = a^3 - b^3$.
VII. $(a + b)(a^2 - ab + b^2) = a^3 + b^3$.

Familiarity with these forms makes it possible:

(a) to perform many multiplications in algebra and arithmetic mentally;

(b) to perform many divisions mentally;

(c) to factor many algebraic expressions.

These are the more important forms. Others are discussed in a later chapter. (XVI.)

Rule. — To perform an indicated multiplication of two or more factors by means of the type forms:

1. First find the product of all binomial and polynomial factors.
2. Then multiply by the monomial factor.

EXAMPLE. Find the product $3x(2x+y)(2x-y)(4x^2+y^2)$.

SOLUTION: $3x(2x+y)(2x-y)(4x+y^2)$
$= 3x \cdot (4x^2-y^2)(4x^2+y^2)$
$= 3x \cdot (16x^4-y^4)$
$= 48x^5 - 3xy^4$.

Rule. — To find the prime factors of a given expression:

1. First remove any monomial factor of the expression.
2. Factor the resulting polynomial factor or factors by the proper methods, until all of the prime factors have been found.

EXAMPLE. Factor $3ax^6 - 21ax^3 - 24a$.

SOLUTION: $3ax^6 - 21ax^3 - 24a$
$= 3a(x^6 - 7x^3 - 8)$
$= 3a(x^3 - 8)(x^3 + 1)$
$= 3a(x-2)(x^2+2x+4)(x+1)(x^2-x+1)$.

EXERCISE 68

MISCELLANEOUS EXAMPLES

Expand the following expressions:

1. $(3x+2y)(4x-3y)$.
2. $(\frac{3}{11}x - 6y)(\frac{3}{11}x + 6y)$.
3. $(a^4 + a^2 + 1)(a^2 - 1)$.
4. $(2a - b^2)^2$.
5. $(7a^2 + b^2)(3a^2 - 8b^2)$.
6. $(a+b)(a-b)(a^2+b^2)$.
7. $(9x - 2y)(x+y)$.
8. $3x(a-b)(a+b)$.
9. $(5a - 4b^2)(5a - 6b^2)$.
10. $3m(m^4 - 4m^2n^2 + 2n^4)$.

SPECIAL PRODUCTS AND FACTORING

11. $7n(n^3+1)(n^3-1)$.
12. $3a(a+1)(a-1)$.
13. $(a^2-12y)(a^2+9y)$.
14. $(x+y)(x^2-xy+y^2)(x^3-y^3)$.
15. $(x-\frac{3}{4}y)^2$.
16. $(m-\frac{1}{2})(m-\frac{1}{4})$.
17. $2x(3x+1)(x-4)$.
18. $(B^2-4AC)(B^2-6AC)$.
19. $a(a^3+3)(a^3-3)$.
20. $5(a-b)(2a+3b)$.
21. $3y(2-y)(5+3y)$.
22. $7(3m+1)(m-6)$.
23. $(x^3+y^2)(x^3-y^2)$.
24. $(xy-4)(xy+16)$.
25. $2(x-4y)^2$.
26. $(x+1)(x-1)(x^2-3)$.
27. $(x+\frac{1}{2})(x^2-\frac{1}{2}x+\frac{1}{4})$.
28. $(\frac{2}{5}x^2-\frac{3}{4})(\frac{2}{5}x^2+\frac{3}{4})$.
29. $(2n-\frac{1}{2})^2$.
30. $(x-\frac{3}{4})(x+\frac{5}{8})$.

Find the prime factors of the following:

31. $5x^2-40x+80$.
32. ax^6+6ax^3+9a.
33. $x^2y^2-5abxy+6a^2b^2$.
34. $3x^2-60xy-288y^2$.
35. $c^2+44c-45$.
36. c^3-64d^3.
37. $3x^3+24y^3$.
38. $m^4+23m^2n+132n^2$.
39. a^4-18a^2+77.
40. $x^6-3x^3y-108y^2$.
41. $4x^2-28xy+49y^2$.
42. $169m^2r-n^2t^2r$.
43. $a^2+17a-38$.
44. $3c^2+132c-135$.
45. x^8-y^8.
46. $2d^2-26d-136$.
47. $125x^6-8y^3$.
48. $8a^2-5a-3$.
49. $169a^2+78ab+9b^2$.
50. $30m^2-47m-5$.
51. $24x^3m+81y^3m$.
52. a^6+14a^3+49.
53. $x^3y-216y^4$.
54. $3k^2+33k+72$.
55. $9x^2-4xy-13y^2$.
56. $3x^6-3y^6$.
57. a^4-256.
58. $3a^3-108a$.
59. $c^2d^2+9cd-52$.
60. $5x^{12}-5y^{12}$.
61. $25r^2+60rs+36s^2$.
62. $x^2+\frac{2}{9}x+\frac{1}{81}$.

144   ALGEBRA

63. $196 y^2 - \frac{25}{169} a^4$.
64. $-25 x + x^2 + 100$.
65. $300 m^4 - 243 x^2$.
66. $y^2 + 12 y - 108$.
67. $x^2 z^2 - 20 xz - 69$.
68. $18 - 19 c + c^2$.
69. $b - 16 + 15 b^2$.
70. $-50 a + a^2 + 49$.

107. The skill acquired in this chapter in performing some multiplications mentally is of use in solving certain equations.

EXAMPLE. Solve the equation:
$$6(4-x)^2 - 5(2x+7)(x-2) = 22 - (2x+3)^2.$$

SOLUTION: Perform the operations mentally.

1. $\quad 6(4-x)^2 - 5(2x+7)(x-2) = 22 - (2x+3)^2$.
2. $\therefore 6(16 - 8x + x^2) - 5(2x^2 + 3x - 14) = 22 - (4x^2 + 12x + 9)$.
3. $\therefore 96 - 48x + 6x^2 - 10x^2 - 15x + 70 = 22 - 4x^2 - 12x - 9$.
4. $\qquad \therefore 166 - 63x - 4x^2 = 13 - 12x - 4x^2$.
5. $\qquad \therefore -63x + 12x = 13 - 166$.
6. $\qquad \therefore -51x = -153$.
7. $\qquad \therefore x = 3$.

CHECK: Does $6(4-3)^2 - 5(6+7)(3-2) = 22 - (6+3)^2$?
(with numbers 1, 13, 1, 81 written above)
Does $\qquad 6 - 65 = 22 - 81$?
Does $\qquad -59 = -59$? Yes.

EXERCISE 69

Solve the following examples performing all **of the work** mentally:

1. $(5x+7)(3x-8) = (5x+4)(3x-5)$.
2. $(4m-7)^2 = (2m-5)(8m+3) - 2$.
3. $(5-3r)(3+4r) - (7+3r)(1-4r) = -28$.
4. $(1-3p)^2 - (p+5)^2 = 4(p+1)(2p-3)$.
5. $2t(t+7) - (t-5)^2 = (t+3)(t-11)$.
6. $(3x+5)(2x-3) - 6(x-2)(x+13) = 11$.
7. $(7a-2)(3a+5) - (4a+3)^2 = 5a(a+2) + 1$.

SPECIAL PRODUCTS AND FACTORING

8. $(5n-6)(5n+6) - 5(2n-3)^2 = 5(n+12)(n-1)$.

9. $3(4a-5)^2 - (6a-1)^2 = 7 + (2a-9)(6a-11)$.

10. $(2x-7)^2 - (5x-2)^2 + 3x(7x+5) = -4$.

11. Find two numbers whose difference is 6, and the difference of whose squares is 120.

12. Find two numbers whose sum is 13, and the difference of whose squares is 65.

13. Divide the number 20 into 2 parts such that the square of one exceeds the square of the other by 40.

14. Find four consecutive numbers such that the product of the first and third shall be less than the product of the second and fourth by 9.

15. Find two consecutive numbers such that the difference of their squares, plus 5 times the greater number, exceeds 4 times the less number by 27.

16. Find two consecutive numbers such that the sum of their squares exceeds twice the square of the smaller by 251.

17. One man travels a certain distance in as many hours as he travels miles per hour; another man travels the same distance in two hours less time by going three miles per hour faster. What was the rate and time of the first man?

EXERCISE 70

Problems about Area

1. Express the area of each of the following figures, assuming for each an altitude of 20 inches and a base of 30 inches:

(a) A rectangle (§ 17).   (b) A triangle (§ 17).

(c) A parallelogram (§ 17).

2. Express the same areas if the altitude is $2x$ and the base $(x-5)$.

3. Express the same areas if the base is y and the altitude exceeds the base by 4.

4. The side of a square is s inches.

(a) Express the area of the square.

(b) Express the dimensions of a rectangle if its base is 4 inches more and if its altitude is 3 inches less than the side of the square.

(c) Express the area of the rectangle.

(d) Form an equation expressing the fact that the area of the rectangle exceeds the area of the square by 50 square inches.

5. The base of a rectangle exceeds twice its altitude by 5 inches; the base of a triangle exceeds the base of the rectangle by 4 inches, and its altitude exceeds the altitude of the rectangle by 3 inches. Let a represent the altitude of the rectangle.

(a) Express the dimensions and area of the rectangle.

(b) Express the dimensions and area of the triangle.

(c) Form an equation expressing the fact that the area of the rectangle exceeds the area of the triangle by 25 square inches.

Equations

6. The base of a certain rectangle exceeds its altitude by 8 inches. If the base and altitude are both decreased by 2 inches, the old area exceeds the new by 36 square inches. Find the dimensions of the rectangle.

7. The base of a rectangle is 9 feet more and the altitude is 8 feet less than the side of a square. The area of the rectangle exceeds the area of the square by 15 square feet. Find the dimensions of the rectangle.

8. A man planned a house whose length exceeded its width by 10 feet. He found that it would be too expensive to build the house as planned, so he decided to decrease both

SPECIAL PRODUCTS AND FACTORING

dimensions 5 feet. He found that this made a difference of 425 square feet in the area covered by the house. What were the original and the new dimensions?

9. The main shaft of Washington's Monument is square at the bottom and top. The side of the lower square exceeds the side of the upper square by 21 feet. The area of the lower square exceeds the area of the upper square by 1869 square feet. Find the dimensions of the two squares.

10. A man planned to set out an apple orchard with two more trees to each row than he had rows, but found that that plan left one tree over. He found that if he decreased the number of rows by 3, and increased the number of trees per row by 5, he used all of his trees. How many trees had he?

QUADRATIC EQUATIONS SOLVED BY FACTORING

108. Not all equations are simple or first degree equations. (§ 77.)

EXAMPLE. Find the number whose square exceeds the number itself by 6.

SOLUTION: 1. Let $n =$ the number.

2. Then $n^2 =$ the square of the number,

3. and $\therefore n^2 = n + 6$.

4. $\therefore n^2 - n - 6 = 0$.

5. Factoring: $(n-3)(n+2) = 0$.

6. If $(n-3) = 0$, then $0 \cdot (n+2)$ would also equal zero.
$n - 3 = 0$, if $n = 3$.

7. If $(n+2) = 0$, then $(n-3) \cdot 0$ would also equal zero.
$n + 2 = 0$, if $n = -2$.

8. These values of n, $+3$ and -2, should satisfy equation 4.

CHECK: If $n = 3$, does $(3)^2 - 3 - 6 = 9 - 3 - 6 = 0$? Yes.
If $n = -2$, does $(-2)^2 - (-2) - 6 = 4 + 2 - 6 = 0$? Yes.

9. Moreover, both of these numbers satisfy the conditions of the problem:

3^2 is 9; 9 exceeds 3 by 6.
$(-2)^2$ is 4; 4 exceeds -2 by 6.

109. An equation like $n^2 - n - 6 = 0$ is called **a Quadratic Equation** or an **Equation of the Second Degree**.

Other examples are : $4x^2 - 9 = 0$,

and $$3y^2 - \frac{2y}{5} = \frac{5}{3}y + 9.$$

Notice that the equation has only one unknown; that this unknown does not appear in the denominator of any fraction; that it does appear with exponent 2; that it may or may not appear with exponent 1.

Every quadratic equation has two roots, just as the equation in § 108.

110. Solution of Equations by Factoring depends upon the following numerical fact.

If *one* of *the factors* of a *product is zero,* the *value of the product is also zero.*

Thus, $3 \times 0 = 0$; $(-5) \times 0 = 0$; $2 \times 0 \times (-3) = 0 \times (-3) = 0$.

EXAMPLE 1. Solve the equation $4x^2 - 9 = 0$.

SOLUTION: 1. Factor: $(2x - 3)(2x + 3) = 0$.

2. If $2x - 3 = 0$, then $(2x - 3)(2x + 3) = 0$.

   $2x - 3 = 0$, if $2x = 3$ or $x = +\frac{3}{2}$.

3. If $2x + 3 = 0$, then $(2x - 3)(2x + 3) = 0$.

   $2x + 3 = 0$, if $2x = -3$, or $x = -\frac{3}{2}$.

4. The roots of the equation are $+\frac{3}{2}$ and $-\frac{3}{2}$.

5. CHECK: Does $4(\frac{3}{2})^2 - 9 = 0$?

   Does $\overset{1}{\cancel{4}} \cdot \frac{9}{\cancel{4}} - 9 = 0$? *i.e.* $9 - 9 = 0$? Yes.

   Does $4(-\frac{3}{2})^2 - 9 = 0$?

   Does $\overset{1}{\cancel{4}} \cdot \frac{9}{\cancel{4}} - 9 = 0$? *i.e.* $9 - 9 = 0$? Yes.

Rule. — To solve an equation by factoring:

1. Transpose all terms to the left member.

2. Factor the left member completely.

3. Set each factor equal to zero, and solve the resulting equations

4. The roots obtained in step 3, are the roots of the given equation Check by substitution in the given equation.

SPECIAL PRODUCTS AND FACTORING

EXAMPLE 2. Solve the equation $\dfrac{m^2}{3} - \dfrac{m}{2} = \dfrac{35}{6}$.

SOLUTION: 1. M_6:* $\qquad 2m^2 - 3m = 35.$
2. S_{35}: $\qquad\qquad 2m^2 - 3m - 35 = 0.$
3. Factor: $\qquad (2m+7)(m-5) = 0.$
4. $\qquad\qquad\qquad 2m+7 = 0$ if $m = -\tfrac{7}{2}.$
$\qquad\qquad\qquad\quad m - 5 = 0$ if $m = +5.$
5. The roots of the equation are $+5$ and $-\tfrac{7}{2}$.
Check by substitution.

EXERCISE 71

Solve by factoring the following quadratic equations.

1. $x^2 - 12x + 32 = 0.$
2. $y^2 - 6y = 55.$
3. $n^2 = 63 - 2n.$
4. $m^2 - 18m = -72.$
5. $x^2 - 21x + 110 = 0.$
6. $c^2 = 2 - c.$
7. $d^2 - 7d + 6 = 0.$
8. $v^2 - 21 = 4v.$
9. $9m^2 - 4 = 0.$
10. $36x^2 - 25 = 0.$
11. $x^2 - 5x = 0.$
12. $3c^2 - 2c = 0.$
13. $8a^2 - 5a - 3 = 0.$
14. $4p^2 + 8p = 21.$
15. $24r^2 + 2r = 35.$
16. $4x^2 = 8x - 3.$
17. $3w^2 = -\tfrac{7}{2}w - 1.$
18. $\tfrac{3}{10}t^2 + \tfrac{13}{10}t = 1.$
19. $z^2 - \tfrac{10}{3}z + 1 = 0.$
20. $x^2 + \tfrac{5}{2}x + 1 = 0.$

111. A Literal Equation is one in which some or all of the known quantities are represented by letters; as,

$$2x + a = bx^2 - 10.$$

EXAMPLE 1. Find two numbers whose difference is a, and whose product is 6 times the square of a.

SOLUTION: 1. Let $\qquad x =$ the larger number.
2. Then $\qquad x - a =$ the smaller number.

* For the symbol M_6 see § 42.

ALGEBRA

3. $\therefore x(x-a) = 6a^2.$
4. $\therefore x^2 - ax - 6a^2 = 0.$
5. $\therefore (x-3a)(x+2a) = 0.$
6. $\therefore x = 3a$ or $x = -2a$, the larger number.

CHECK: If $x = 3a$, then $3a - a = 2a$, the smaller number; and $3a \cdot 2a$ does equal $6a^2$.

If $x = -2a$, then $-2a - a = -3a$, the smaller number; and $-2a \cdot -3a$ does equal $+6a^2$.

Each solution is correct, no matter what a may be.

Thus, if a is 5, $3a$ is 15, $2a$ is 10, and 15×10 is 150; also $6 \cdot a^2 = 150$.

EXAMPLE 2. Solve the equation $\dfrac{x^2}{2} - \dfrac{3cx}{2} = 5c^2.$

SOLUTION: 1. $\dfrac{x^2}{2} - \dfrac{3cx}{2} = 5c^2.$

2. M_2: $x^2 - 3cx - 10c^2 = 0.$
3. Factoring: $(x-5c)(x+2c) = 0.$
4. If $x - 5c = 0$, then $x = 5c.$
5. If $x + 2c = 0$, then $x = -2c.$

Check by substitution.

EXERCISE 72

Solve the following equations for x:

1. $x^2 + 2ax - 35a^2 = 0.$
2. $16x^2 - 9b^2 = 0.$
3. $x^2 + 23mx + 130m^2 = 0.$
4. $25x^2 = 9c^2.$
5. $2x^2 + 7ax + 3a^2 = 0.$
6. $7x^2 - 10bx + 3b^2 = 0.$
7. $6x^2 + 7cx = 5c^2.$
8. $13x^2 = tx + 14t^2.$
9. $9x^2 = 4xv + 13v^2.$
10. $7x^2 + 41xk = 6k^2.$
11. $\dfrac{x^2}{2} - ax - \dfrac{3a^2}{2} = 0.$
12. $\dfrac{x^2}{4} = 5p^2 - 2px.$
13. $\dfrac{x^2}{6} + 6c^2 = \dfrac{5cx}{2}.$
14. $\dfrac{x^2}{12} - \dfrac{4xn}{3} + 4n^2 = 0.$

15. $x^2 - \dfrac{15\,bx}{2} = 4\,b^2.$

16. $6\,x^2 - \dfrac{47\,mx}{5} = m^2.$

17. $\dfrac{8\,x^2}{15} = \dfrac{ax}{3} + \dfrac{a^2}{5}.$

18. $\dfrac{x^2}{10} - \dfrac{7\,xt}{15} = \dfrac{t^2}{6}.$

19. $\dfrac{x^2}{2} - \dfrac{5\,rx}{6} = \dfrac{11\,r^2}{3}.$

20. $\dfrac{6\,x^2}{5} - \dfrac{4\,xs}{5} - \dfrac{3\,s^2}{2} = 0.$

112. When solving a problem whose solution leads to a quadratic equation, two sets of results are obtained. In some cases, both sets satisfy the conditions of the problem; in other cases, only one set satisfies the given conditions.

EXAMPLE 1. Find three consecutive odd numbers such that when the product of the first and third is increased by twice the square of the second, the sum equals 23.

SOLUTION: 1. Let $x =$ the smallest number.

2. $\therefore x + 2$ and $x + 4$ are the other two numbers.

(For example, if 3 is the smallest, $3 + 2$ or 5 and $3 + 4$ or 7 are the other two.)

3. $\quad \therefore x(x+4) + 2(x+2)^2 = 23.$

$\therefore x^2 + 4x + 2(x^2 + 4x + 4) = 23.$

$\therefore 3x^2 + 12x + 8 = 23.$

$\therefore 3x^2 + 12x - 15 = 0,$ or $x^2 + 4x - 5 = 0.$

$\therefore (x+5)(x-1) = 0.$

$x = -5$ or $x = +1.$

4. When $x = -5$, $x + 2 = -3$, and $x + 4 = -1$.

When $x = +1$, $x + 2 = 3$, and $x + 4 = 5$.

The solutions are -5, -3, and -1; and 1, 3, and 5.

CHECK: $(-5) \cdot (-1) + 2(-3)^2 = 5 + 18 = 23.\quad 1 \cdot 5 + 2 \cdot 3^2 = 5 + 18 = 23.$

In this case, both solutions are satisfactory.

EXAMPLE 2. Determine the base and altitude of a triangle when the area is 110 square inches and the base exceeds the altitude by 9 inches.

SOLUTION: 1. Let $a = $ the number of inches in the altitude.

2. $\therefore a + 9 = $ the number of inches in the base.

3. $\therefore \dfrac{a(a+9)}{2} = $ the area.

$$\therefore \dfrac{a(a+9)}{2} = 110.$$

$$\therefore a^2 + 9a - 220 = 0.$$

$$\therefore (a+20)(a-11) = 0.$$

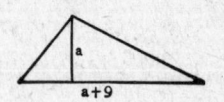

$$\therefore a = 11, \text{ or } -20.$$

4. When $a = 11$, the base is $+20$ and the area is $(11 \times 20) \div 2$ or 110. This satisfies the conditions of the problem.

When $a = -20$, the result can have meaning only if we have triangles with negative altitude. In such cases we agree to take only the positive solution.

EXERCISE 73

1. Twice the square of a certain number equals the excess of 15 over the number. Find the number.

2. Find three consecutive numbers whose sum is equal to the product of the first two.

3. Divide 18 into two parts so that the sum of the squares of the parts shall be 170.

4. Find two numbers whose sum is 7 and the sum of whose cubes is 133.

5. Determine the base and altitude of a triangle such that the area shall be 15 square feet and the altitude shall be 7 feet less than the base.

6. Central Park in New York covers an area of about 800 acres. Its length exceeds its width by 2 miles. Find the dimensions of the park. (A square mile contains 640 acres.)

7. A merchant sold goods for $18.75 and lost as many per cent as the goods cost dollars. What was the cost?

SPECIAL PRODUCTS AND FACTORING 153

8. The length of a certain rectangular farm is three times its width. If its length should be increased by 20 rods, and its width by 8 rods, its area would be trebled. Of how many square rods does the farm consist?

9. The standard size city lot in parts of Chicago is five times as long as it is wide. The lots in parts of Indianapolis are 10 feet wider and 5 feet longer than those in Chicago. Three times the area of a Chicago lot exceeds twice the area of an Indianapolis lot by 275 square feet. Find the dimensions of the lots in both cities.

10. An architect who has made plans for a house with a base 30 × 42 feet finds that he must reduce the size. By what equal amount must he reduce the two dimensions of the house in order to make the area of the new base 925 square feet?

IX. HIGHEST COMMON FACTOR AND LOWEST COMMON MULTIPLE

113. A monomial is said to be **Rational** and **Integral** when it is either an arithmetical number, or a single literal number with unity for its exponent, or the product of two or more such numbers.

Thus, 3, a, $2\,a^3bc^2$ are rational and integral.

114. The **Degree** of a rational and integral monomial is the sum of the exponents of its literal factors.

Thus, a^4bc^3 is of the *eighth* degree.

115. A polynomial is said to be rational and integral when each term is rational and integral; as, $2\,a^2b - 3\,c + d^2$.

The degree of a rational and integral polynomial is the degree of its term of highest degree.

Thus, $2\,a^2b - 3\,c + d^2$ is of the *third* degree.

116. Recall the definition of prime factor of an expression (§ 87), and common factor (§ 11) of two or more expressions.

Thus the prime factors of :
(a) $6\,m^2(x^2 - 1)$ are 2, 3, m, m, $(x - 1)$, and $(x + 1)$.
(b) $9\,m^3(x^3 - 1)$ are 3, 3, m, m, m, $(x - 1)$, and $(x^2 + x + 1)$.
Common factors of (a) and (b) are 3, m, m, and $(x - 1)$.

EXERCISE 74

Select the common factors in the following sets of expressions:

1. $5 \cdot mn^2(x + 1)$.
   $3 \cdot 5 \cdot m^2n(x - 1)$.

2. $2 \cdot 3 \cdot x^3 \cdot y^2(x + 4)(x - 3)$.
   $2 \cdot 2 \cdot 3 \cdot x^4 \cdot y^2(x + 4)$.

HIGHEST COMMON FACTOR

3. $7 \cdot 5 \cdot r^3 \cdot s^2 (x+3)(x-2)(x-1).$
$3 \cdot 7 \cdot 5 \cdot r^2 \cdot s (x-3)(x-2)(x-1).$

4. $6 \cdot 7 \cdot m^5 n^4 (x-a)(x^2+a^2).$
$6 \cdot 7 \cdot 7 \cdot m^7 n^5 (x+a)(x^2+a^2).$

5. $3 \cdot 5 \cdot 7 \cdot 2 \cdot 11.$
$2 \cdot 2 \cdot 3 \cdot 5 \cdot 13.$

6. $3 \cdot 7 \cdot 5 \cdot 2 \cdot 2 \cdot 2.$
$2 \cdot 2 \cdot 7 \cdot 11.$

117. The **Highest Common Factor (H.C.F.)** of two or more rational and integral expressions is the expression of highest degree (§ 114), with greatest numerical coefficient, which will divide each of them without a remainder.

EXAMPLE. Find the H. C. F. of

$$5 m^3 n^2 (x-1)(x+2) \text{ and } 15 m^4 n (x+1)(x+2).$$

SOLUTION: 1. The greatest integer which will divide both expressions is 5.

2. The highest power of m which will divide both is m^3.
The highest power of n which will divide both is n.
The highest power of $(x+2)$ which will divide both is $(x+2)$.
Neither $(x-1)$ nor $(x+1)$ will divide both expressions.

3. ∴ The H. C. F. is $5 m^3 n (x+2)$.

CHECK: $5 m^3 n^2 (x-1)(x+2) \div 5 m^3 n (x+2) = n(x-1).$
$15 m^4 n (x+1)(x+2) \div 5 m^3 n (x+2) = 3 m(x+1).$

Rule. — To find the H. C. F. of two or more expressions:

1. Find all of the prime factors of each expression.

2. Select the factors common to all of the given expressions, and give each the lowest exponent it has in any of the expressions.

3. Form the product of the common factors selected in step 2.

EXAMPLE. Find the H.C.F. of $68(m+n)^2(m-n)^4$ and $85(m+n)^3(m-n)$.

SOLUTION: 1. $68(m+n)^2(m-n)^4 = 2 \cdot 2 \cdot 17 \cdot (m+n)^2 (m-n)^4.$
$85(m+n)^3(m-n) = 5 \cdot 17 \cdot (m+n)^3 (m-n).$

2. ∴ The H. C. F. $= 17(m+n)^2(m-n).$

ALGEBRA

EXERCISE 75

Find the highest common factor of:

1. 16 and 56.
2. 64 a and 96 b.
3. 72 x^2 and 27 xy.
4. 5 a^4b^2 and 2 a^3b^2.
5. 20 x^2y and 15 xy^2.
6. 14 x^3y, 21 xy^4, and 35 x^2y^2.
7. 15 m^5n^3, 45 m^4n^4, and 25 mn^2.
8. 12 x^2, 18 x^3y^2, and 24 x^5y.
9. 16 m^4n^2, 56 m^2n^4, and 88 m^3n^2.
10. 18 r^3s, 27 r^2s^3, and 45 rs^2.
11. $(a+b)(a-b)$ and $2\,a(a+b)$.
12. $3\,x(x+y)(x-y)$ and $2(x+y)(x-y)(x^2+y^2)$.
13. $(x+1)^2(x-3)$ and $(x+1)^2(x+2)$.
14. $(r+s)^3(r-s)^2$ and $(r+s)^2(r-s)^3$.
15. $3(x-2\,y)(x+2\,y)$ and $6(x-2\,y)^2$.
16. $2\,a^3x + 4\,a^2x^2 + 2\,ax^3$ and $3\,a^4x + 3\,ax^4$.

SOLUTION: 1. $2\,a^3x + 4a^2x^2 + 2\,ax^3 = 2\,ax(a^2 + 2ax + x^2)$
$\qquad\qquad\qquad\qquad\qquad = 2\,ax(a+x)(a+x).$
$\qquad 3\,a^4x + 3\,ax^4 = 3\,ax(a^3 + x^3)$
$\qquad\qquad\qquad\qquad = 3\,ax(a+x)(a^2 - ax + x^2).$

2. The H.C.F. $= a \cdot x \cdot (a+x) = ax(a+x).$

17. $a^2 - b^2$ and $a^2 - 2\,ab + b^2$.
18. $x^2 + 2\,x - 24$, $x^2 - 14\,x + 40$, and $x^2 - 8\,x + 16$.
19. $2\,r^2 - 7\,r + 6$ and $6\,r^2 - 11\,r + 3$.
20. $x^3 - 27$ and $x^2 - 11\,x + 24$.
21. $m^5 - 8\,m^2$ and $m^2 + 2\,m + 4$.
22. $6\,a^3b^2 - 15\,a^2b^3$ and $12\,a^4b + 21\,a^3b^2$.
23. $3\,a^3 + 192$ and $a^2 - 7\,a - 44$.
24. $3\,x^2 - 16\,xy + 5\,y^2$ and $x^2 + 10\,xy - 75\,y^2$.
25. $27\,a^3 + 8\,b^3$, $9\,a^2 - 4\,b^2$, and $9\,a^2 + 12\,ab + 4\,b^2$.

LOWEST COMMON MULTIPLE

118. A **Multiple** of a number is any number which contains the given number as an exact divisor. Thus:

(a) Some multiples of 3 are 6, 9, 12, and 30.

(b) Some multiples of $(x + y)$ are $2(x + y)$ and $(x + y)(x - y)$.

119. One number may be a multiple of two or more different numbers. Thus:

(a) 24 is a multiple of 2, 3, 4, 6, 8, and of 12.

(b) $5\, a^2bc$ is a multiple of 5, a^2, b, c, and of a.

(c) $36\, m(x + y)(x - y)$ is a multiple of 3, m, $(x + y)$, and of $(x - y)$.

A **Common Multiple** of two or more numbers is a multiple of each of them; it can be divided exactly by each of them.

120. In arithmetic, it is necessary at times to find the smallest number which is a common multiple of two or more numbers. Thus, 30, 45, and 60 are all common multiples of 3 and 5; but the lowest common multiple of 3 and 5 is 15.

Similar necessity arises in algebra.

121. The **Lowest Common Multiple** of two or more rational and integral expressions is the expression of lowest degree (§ 114), with least numerical coefficient, which can be exactly divided by each of them.

EXAMPLE. Find the L. C. M. of $5\, a^5b^3$ and $7\, a^2b^4$.

SOLUTION: 1. The least number which will contain both 5 and 7 is 35.

2. The lowest power of a which will contain both a^5 and a^2 is a^5.

3. The lowest power of b which will contain both b^3 and b^4 is b^4.

4. The L. C. M. is $35\, a^5b^4$.

CHECK: Does $35\, a^5b^4$ contain each of the given numbers?

$$35\, a^5b^4 \div 5\, a^5b^3 = 7\, b; \quad 35\, a^5b^4 \div 7\, a^2b^4 = 5\, a^3.$$

Rule. — To find the L. C. M. of two or more expressions:

1. Find the prime factors of each of the expressions.

158 ALGEBRA

2. Select all of the different prime factors and give to each the highest exponent with which it occurs in any of the expressions.

3. Form the product of all of the factors selected in step 2.

EXAMPLE. Find the L. C. M. of $25\,a^2b(a+b)^3(a-b)$ and $15\,a^3b^4(a+b)^2(a-b)^3$.

SOLUTION: 1. $25\,a^2b(a+b)^3(a-b) = 5^2\,a^2b(a+b)^3(a-b)$.
$15\,a^3b^4(a+b)^2(a-b)^3 = 3 \cdot 5\,a^3b^4(a+b)^2(a-b)^3$.

2.   3 occurs with 1 as its highest exponent.
     5 occurs with 2 as its highest exponent.
     a occurs with 3 as its highest exponent.
     b occurs with 4 as its highest exponent.
$(a+b)$ occurs with 3 as its highest exponent.
$(a-b)$ occurs with 3 as its highest exponent.

3. The L. C. M. $= 3 \cdot 5^2\,a^3b^4(a+b)^3(a-b)^3$.

CHECK: Does the L. C. M. contain each of the expressions ?

$75\,a^3b^4(a+b)^3(a-b)^3 \div 25\,a^2b(a+b)^3(a-b) = 3\,ab^3(a-b)^2$.
$75\,a^3b^4(a+b)^3(a-b)^3 \div 15\,a^3b^4(a+b)^2(a-b)^3 = 5(a+b)$.

EXERCISE 76

Find the L. C. M. of the following and obtain the quotient when the L. C. M. is divided by each of the numbers:

1. 5 and 7.
2. 12 and 20.
3. 24 and 30.
4. 12 and 54.
5. 15, 21, and 33.
6. 20, 27, and 90.
7. $3\,ab$ and $7\,a^2b$.
8. $12\,x^2y^3$ and $48\,xy^4$.
9. $12\,m^3$ and $15\,mn^2$.
10. $24\,a^3b^4$ and $16\,a^2b^5$.
11. $14\,r^4s^2$ and $35\,rs^3$.
12. $15\,x^3y$, $30\,xy^2$, and $60\,x^2y^3$.
13. $5\,rm^2$, $15\,rm^3$, and $21\,r^2m$.
14. $24\,p^4$, $32\,p^3r$, and $12\,p^5$.
15. $32\,wv$, $16\,w^3v^2$, and $64\,w^4$.
16. $44\,xy$, $33\,yz$, and $12\,xz$.
17. $(a+b)(a-b)$ and $(a+b)^2$.
18. $2\,a(m+a)$ and $6\,a^2(m+a)(m-a)$.
19. $(x+3)(x-2)$ and $(x-2)(x-3)$.

LOWEST COMMON MULTIPLE

20. $3(r+s)(r-s)$ and $2(r+s)(r-t)$.
21. $(a-4)(a-3)$ and $(a-4)(a-5)$.
22. $(1-x)^3$, $(1-x)(1+x)$, and $(1-x)^2$.
23. $(2-3x)^2$, $3(2-3x)(2+3x)$, and $(2+3x)^2$.
24. $(2-x)(3-x)$, $(3-x)(4-x)$, and $(4-x)(2-x)$.
25. $4x^2 - 4m^2$, $6x + 6m$, and $3x^3 - 3m^3$.

SOLUTION: 1. $\quad 4x^2 - 4m^2 = 4(x^2 - m^2) = 4(x-m)(x+m)$.
$\qquad 6x + 6m = 6(x+m)$.
$\qquad 3x^3 - 3m^3 = 3(x^3 - m^3) = 3(x-m)(x^2 + mx + m^2)$.

2. The L. C. M. $= 12(x-m)(x+m)(x^2 + mx + m^2)$.
3. L. C. M. $\div 4(x-m)(x+m) = 3(x^2 + mx + m^2)$.
$\quad$ L. C. M. $\div 6(x+m) = 2(x-m)(x^2 + mx + m^2)$.
$\quad$ L. C. M. $\div 3(x-m)(x^2 + mx + m^2) = 4(x+m)$.

26. $r^2 - 16$ and $r^2 + 11r + 28$.
27. $a^2 + 2ax + x^2$ and $a^3 + x^3$.
28. $8x^3y - y$ and $22x^2z - 9xz - z$.
29. $b^2 - 12b + 35$, $b^2 + 2b - 63$, and $b^2 - 3b - 108$.
30. $4x^2 - 25$ and $4x^2 - 20x + 25$.
31. $3m^2 - 6m - 72$, $4m^2 + 8m - 192$, and $2m^2 - 24m + 72$.
32. $9n^2 - 27n + 8$ and $3n^2 - 2n - 16$.
33. $1 + 27x^3$ and $1 - 5x - 24x^2$.
34. $x^2 + x - 42$ and $x^2 - x - 30$.
35. $a^3 - a$ and $a^3 - 9a^2 - 10a$.

X. FRACTIONS

122. The quotient of a divided by b is written $\dfrac{a}{b}$. The expression $\dfrac{a}{b}$ is called a **Fraction**; the dividend, a, is called the **Numerator**, and the divisor, b, is called the **Denominator**. The numerator and denominator are called the **Terms** of the fraction. $\dfrac{a}{b}$ is read "a divided by b." The denominator, b, must never be zero (§ 64).

REDUCTION OF FRACTIONS TO LOWEST TERMS

123. A fraction is said to be in its **Lowest Terms** when its numerator and denominator have no common factor except unity. Thus:

(a) $\dfrac{2}{3}$, $\dfrac{a}{b}$, $\dfrac{x+y}{x-y}$ are in their lowest terms.

(b) $\dfrac{3}{12}$, $\dfrac{2\,a^2}{ab}$, $\dfrac{(x+y)^2}{(x^2-y^2)}$ are not in their lowest terms.

124. To reduce a fraction to lowest terms, a principle, easily illustrated by arithmetical fractions, is used.

If, in the fraction $\tfrac{24}{8}$, both terms be divided by 4, a new fraction $\tfrac{6}{2}$ is obtained. But, since $\tfrac{24}{8} = 3$, and $\tfrac{6}{2} = 3$, therefore $\tfrac{24}{8} = \tfrac{6}{2}$. The *value* of the fraction is not changed; its *form* is changed.

Rule. — If the numerator and denominator of a fraction are both divided by the same number, the value of the fraction is not changed.

EXAMPLE 1. Reduce to lowest terms $\dfrac{24\,a^3b^2c}{40\,a^2b^2c}$.

SOLUTION: 1. $\quad \dfrac{24\,a^3b^2c}{40\,a^2b^2c} = \dfrac{2^3 \cdot 3 \cdot a^3 \cdot b^2 \cdot c}{2^3 \cdot 5 \cdot a^2 \cdot b^2 \cdot c}$.

2. Divide both numerator and denominator successively by their common factors, 2^3, a^2, b^2, and c.

FRACTIONS

Then,
$$\frac{24\,a^3b^2c}{40\,a^2b^2c} = \frac{\overset{1}{2^3}\cdot 3\cdot \overset{a}{a^3}\cdot \overset{1}{b^2}\cdot \overset{1}{c}}{\underset{1}{2^6}\cdot 5\cdot \underset{1}{a^2}\cdot \underset{1}{b^2}\cdot \underset{1}{c}} = \frac{3\,a}{5}.$$

NOTE 1. Dividing by all of the common factors is equivalent to dividing both numerator and denominator by their highest common factor.

NOTE 2. The process of removing a common factor from numerator and denominator of a fraction is called cancellation. It depends upon the rule in § 124.

NOTE 3. It is wise to write the quotients 1, a, etc., as they are obtained.

EXAMPLE 2. Reduce to lowest terms $\dfrac{27\,a^3 + 64\,b^3}{9\,a^2 + 24\,ab + 16\,b^2}$.

SOLUTION: $\dfrac{27\,a^3 + 64\,b^3}{9\,a^2 + 24\,ab + 16\,b^2} = \dfrac{\overset{1}{(3a+4b)}(9\,a^2 - 12\,ab + 16\,b^2)}{\underset{1}{(3a+4b)}(3\,a + 4\,b)}$

$= \dfrac{9\,a^2 - 12\,ab + 16\,b^2}{(3\,a + 4\,b)}.$

Here, the numerator and denominator are both divided by $(3\,a + 4\,b)$.

CHECK: These examples may be checked by substitution. It is important to remember that the original fraction and the simplified result are equal for all values of the literal numbers except such as make the denominator zero. (§ 122.)

Rule. — To reduce a fraction to lowest terms:

1. Express numerator and denominator in terms of their prime factors.

2. Divide both numerator and denominator by all of their common factors, *i.e.* by their H. C. F.

125. Errors in Reducing Fractions. One common error occurs in reducing fractions such as

$$\frac{3\,mn^2(x+y)}{3\,mn^2(x+y)} = \frac{\cancel{3\,mn^2(x+y)}}{\cancel{3\,mn^2(x+y)}}.$$

Pupils sometimes think that the result is 0, because all factors have been cancelled. If, as suggested, the quotients are indicated, this danger will be avoided; thus,

$$\frac{3\,mn^2(x+y)}{3\,mn^2(x+y)} = \frac{\overset{1\;1\,1}{\cancel{3\,mn^2}}\overset{1}{\cancel{(x+y)}}}{\underset{1\;1\,1}{\cancel{3\,mn^2}}\underset{1}{\cancel{(x+y)}}} = \frac{1}{1} = 1.\ \textit{Ans.}$$

Another, and more common, error is illustrated in the *following faulty solution:*

$$\frac{2a+b}{ab} = \frac{\overset{1}{2a}+\overset{1}{b}}{\underset{1}{a}\underset{1}{b}} = \frac{2+1}{1} = 3.$$

Test it for $a = 2$, $b = 2$; $\frac{2a+b}{ab} = \frac{4+2}{4} = \frac{6}{4} = \frac{3}{2}$.

The error is in dividing one part of the numerator by a and another part of it by b. Neither a nor b is a factor of the numerator. They cannot be canceled in this problem. The fraction is already in its lowest terms.

EXERCISE 77

Reduce the following fractions to their lowest terms:

1. $\dfrac{12}{15}$.

2. $\dfrac{24}{36}$.

3. $\dfrac{5\,x^3y^4}{3\,xy^5}$.

4. $\dfrac{12\,m^5n^3}{42\,m^3n^5}$.

5. $\dfrac{45\,r^4st^2}{63\,r^3s^2t^2}$.

6. $\dfrac{65\,x^3y^4z}{40\,xy^4z}$.

7. $\dfrac{3\,ab^2c\,(x+y)}{2\,abc\,(x+y)}$.

8. $\dfrac{12\,(a-3)(a+3)}{4\,(a+3)}$.

9. $\dfrac{18\,(2\,r-s)^2(r+s)}{9\,(2\,r-s)(r+s)^2}$.

10. $\dfrac{a^2+7\,a+10}{a^2+4\,a-5}$.

11. $\dfrac{m^2+m-56}{m^2-m-42}$.

12. $\dfrac{x^2-9\,x+18}{3\,x^2+3\,x-36}$.

13. $\dfrac{a^2-11\,ab+28\,b^2}{a^2-14\,ab+49\,b^2}$.

14. $\dfrac{2\,x^2-2\,y^2}{5\,x^3-5\,y^3}$.

15. $\dfrac{3\,am^2-3\,an^2}{3\,m^2+6\,mn+3\,n^2}$.

16. $\dfrac{a^3+b^3}{a^2c-2\,abc-3\,b^2c}$.

17. $\dfrac{8\,x^3-125}{2\,ax^2+ax-15\,a}$.

18. $\dfrac{mx^2-mx-12\,m}{3\,x^2+13\,x+12}$.

19. $\dfrac{16\,r^4+4\,r^2+1}{64\,r^6-1}$.

20. $\dfrac{a^3-8\,a^2+12\,a}{5\,a^2-60\,a+180}$.

FRACTIONS 163

21. $\dfrac{x^2-y^2}{ax^2-2axy+ay^2}.$

22. $\dfrac{a^3-64}{a^2m-16m}.$

23. $\dfrac{a^3y-8y}{(a^2-4)(a-1)}.$

24. $\dfrac{4m^2+16mn+15n^2}{6m^2-mn-15n^2}.$

25. $\dfrac{15x^4y+10x^3y^2}{6x^3y^4+4x^2y^5}.$

26. $\dfrac{3x^4-3y^4}{x^4+2x^2y^2+y^4}.$

126. Signs in Fractions. A fraction is an indicated quotient. Its sign is governed by the law of signs for division (§ 67). Thus:

1. $\dfrac{+12}{+4}=+3.$

2. $\dfrac{+12}{-4}=-3.$

3. $\dfrac{-12}{+4}=-3.$

4. $\dfrac{-12}{-4}=+3.$

From 1 and 2, it is clear that
$$\dfrac{+12}{+4}=-\dfrac{+12}{-4},$$
From 1 and 3, it is clear that
$$\dfrac{+12}{+4}=-\dfrac{-12}{+4},$$
} since $+3=-(-3).$

Rule. — If the sign of one term of a fraction is changed, the sign of the whole fraction must be changed.

From 1 and 4, it is clear that
$$\dfrac{+12}{+4}=\dfrac{-12}{-4}, \text{ since both equal } +3.$$

Rule. — If the signs of both terms of a fraction are changed, the sign of the fraction must not be changed.

Changing the signs of an expression is accomplished by multiplying it by -1.

Example 1. Reduce to lowest terms:
$$\dfrac{x^2-9}{12+2x-2x^2}.$$

Solution: Multiply the denominator of the given fraction by -1, thus changing its signs; also, change the sign of the fraction.

$$\frac{x^2-9}{12+2x-2x^2} = -\frac{x^2-9}{2x^2-2x-12} = -\frac{\overset{1}{\cancel{(x-3)}}(x+3)}{2\underset{1}{\cancel{(x-3)}}(x+2)} = -\frac{x+3}{2(x+2)}.$$

Check. Let $x = 1$. Then $\dfrac{x^2-9}{12+2x-2x^2} = \dfrac{1-9}{12+2-2} = \dfrac{-8}{12} = -\dfrac{2}{3}$;

also, $-\dfrac{x+3}{2(x+2)} = -\dfrac{1+3}{2(1+2)} = -\dfrac{4}{6} = -\dfrac{2}{3}$.

The value of x selected *must not make any* denominator zero (§ 64).

EXAMPLE 2. Reduce to lowest terms:

$$-\frac{(9-m^2)}{m^2-7m+12}.$$

Solution: Multiply the numerator by -1, thus changing its signs; also change the sign of the fraction.

1. $-\dfrac{9-m^2}{m^2-7m+12} = +\dfrac{m^2-9}{m^2-7m+12}$

2. $= \dfrac{\overset{1}{\cancel{(m-3)}}(m+3)}{(m-4)\underset{1}{\cancel{(m-3)}}} = \dfrac{(m+3)}{(m-4)}$.

EXERCISE 78

Reduce to lowest terms:

1. $\dfrac{4y^2-x^2}{2x^2-7xy+6y^2}.$

2. $\dfrac{3x-3y}{y^2+xy-2x^2}.$

3. $\dfrac{a^2-16}{24-2a-a^2}.$

4. $\dfrac{3m^2-3n^2}{n^2+4mn-5m^2}.$

5. $\dfrac{x^2+x-6}{15+2x-x^2}.$

6. $-\dfrac{27-t^3}{t^2-9}.$

7. $-\dfrac{x^2-16}{64-x^3}.$

8. $\dfrac{ar^2-as^2}{2as^2+4ars-6ar^2}.$

9. $\dfrac{3c^3-6c^2d+3cd^2}{5d^2-5c^2}.$

10. $\dfrac{18mx^2-8my^2}{24ny^3-81nx^3}.$

FRACTIONS 165

TO REDUCE A FRACTION TO AN INTEGRAL OR MIXED EXPRESSION

127. An **Integral Expression** is an expression which has no fractional *literal* part; as, $a^2 - 2ab + b^2$, or $\frac{2}{3} ab^2$.

An integral expression may be considered a fraction whose denominator is 1; thus, $a + b$ is the same as $\dfrac{a+b}{1}$.

128. A **Mixed Expression** is an expression which has both integral and fractional literal parts; as, $a + \dfrac{b}{c}$ or $x + \dfrac{y+z}{y-z}$.

Rule. — A fraction may be changed to an integral or mixed expression by performing the indicated division.

EXAMPLE 1. Reduce $\dfrac{6x^2 + 15x - 2}{3x}$ to a mixed expression.

SOLUTION: Using the method of short division (§ 70),

$$\frac{6x^2 + 15x - 2}{3x} = \frac{6x^2}{3x} + \frac{15x}{3x} + \frac{-2}{3x} = 2x + 5 - \frac{2}{3x}. \text{ Ans.}$$

EXAMPLE 2. Reduce $\dfrac{12x^3 - 8x^2 + 4x - 5}{4x^2 + 3}$ to a mixed expression.

SOLUTION: Using the method of long division (§ 71),

$$\begin{array}{r}
3x - 2 \\
4x^2 + 3 \overline{\smash{)}\ 12x^3 - 8x^2 + 4x - 5} \\
\underline{12x^3 + 9x } \\
-8x^2 - 5x - 5 \\
\underline{-8x^2 - 6} \\
-5x + 1
\end{array}$$

$$\therefore \frac{12x^3 - 8x^2 + 4x - 5}{4x^2 + 3} = 3x - 2 + \frac{-5x+1}{4x^2+3}.$$

$$= 3x - 2 - \frac{5x-1}{4x^2+3}.$$

The first term of the numerator of the fraction in the result is negative. Change the signs in the numerator by multiplying the numerator by -1, and also change the sign of the fraction. See § 126.

ALGEBRA

EXERCISE 79

Reduce the following to mixed expressions:

1. $\frac{315}{25}$.
2. $\frac{97}{14}$.
3. $\frac{263}{19}$.
4. $\frac{4350}{216}$.

5. $\dfrac{12\,a^2 - 16\,a + 7}{4\,a}$.

6. $\dfrac{15\,m^3 - 6\,m^2 + 3\,m - 8}{3\,m}$.

7. $\dfrac{15\,p^2 + 12\,p - 4}{3\,p}$.

8. $\dfrac{30\,x^6 + 5\,x^4 - 15\,x^2 - 7}{5\,x^2}$.

9. $\dfrac{9\,y^2 + 5}{3\,y - 1}$.

10. $\dfrac{8\,p^2 + 3}{2\,p + 3}$.

11. $\dfrac{x^3 + 2\,y^3}{x - y}$.

12. $\dfrac{a^3 + 8\,b^3}{a - 2\,b}$.

13. $\dfrac{x^4 + y^4}{x - y}$.

14. $\dfrac{x^3 + x^2 y + 6\,y^3}{x - 2\,y}$.

15. $\dfrac{12\,a^2 + 5\,a + 5}{4\,a - 1}$.

16. $\dfrac{3\,a^3 + 8\,a^2 - 7}{a^2 - 2\,a - 3}$.

TO REDUCE FRACTIONS TO THEIR LOWEST COMMON DENOMINATOR

129. In arithmetic, fractions having a common denominator may be added or subtracted without difficulty. Thus:

(a) $\frac{7}{15} + \frac{4}{15} = \frac{11}{15}$. (b) $\frac{9}{16} - \frac{3}{16} = \frac{6}{16}$.

Fractions which do not have the same denominator must be changed to equal fractions having a common denominator.

(a) $\frac{9}{16} + \frac{3}{8} = \frac{9}{16} + \frac{6}{16} = \frac{15}{16}$, for $\frac{3}{8} = \frac{6}{16}$.

In algebra, also, fractions which do not have a common denominator must be changed to a common denominator before they can be added or subtracted.

130. To change fractions to a common denominator, a principle, easily illustrated arithmetically, is used.

If both terms of the fraction $\frac{6}{2}$ are multiplied by 4, the result is $\frac{24}{8}$. $\frac{6}{2} = \frac{24}{8}$ since both equal 3.

The value of the fraction is not changed; its *form only* is changed.

FRACTIONS

Rule. — If the numerator and denominator of a fraction are both multiplied by the same number, the value of the fraction is not changed.

131. Two fractions which have the same *value* but different *form* are called **Equivalent Fractions.**

Thus, $\frac{a}{b}$ and $\frac{ma}{mb}$ are equivalent fractions; they differ in form, but have the same value, since the second is obtained by multiplying both terms of the first by m.

132. The **Lowest Common Denominator (L. C. D.)** of two or more fractions is the lowest common multiple of their denominators.

EXAMPLE 1. Reduce to their lowest common denominator

$$\frac{3\,mx}{2\,ab^2} \text{ and } \frac{5\,ny}{3\,a^3b}.$$

SOLUTION: 1. The L. C. M. of $2\,ab^2$ and $3\,a^3b$ is $6\,a^3b^2$. (§ 121)

2. To change the denominator $2\,ab^2$ into $6\,a^3b^2$, we must multiply $2\,ab^2$ by $3\,a^2$, that is by $6\,a^3b^2 \div 2\,ab^2$. In order not to change the value of the fraction, the numerator $3\,mx$ must also be multiplied by $3\,a^2$.

Then, $$\frac{3\,mx}{2\,ab^2} = \frac{3\,a^2 \cdot 3\,mx^2}{3\,a^2 \cdot 2\,ab^2} = \frac{9\,a^2mx}{6\,a^3b^2}.$$ (§ 130)

3. For the second fraction, $6\,a^3b^2 \div 3\,a^3b = 2\,b$. Multiply both numerator and denominator by $2\,b$.

Then, $$\frac{5\,ny}{3\,a^3b} = \frac{2\,b \cdot 5\,ny}{2\,b \cdot 3\,a^3b} = \frac{10\,bny}{6\,a^3b^2}.$$ (§ 130)

Rule. — To reduce fractions to their lowest common denominator:
1. Find the prime factors of the denominators.
2. Find the L. C. M. of the given denominators; this is the L. C. D.
3. For each fraction, divide the L. C. D. by the given denominator; multiply both numerator and denominator by the quotient.

EXAMPLE 2. Reduce to their lowest common denominator:

$$\frac{4\,a}{a^2 - 4} \text{ and } \frac{3\,a}{a^2 - 5\,a + 6}.$$

ALGEBRA

Solution: **1.** $$\frac{4a}{a^2-4} = \frac{4a}{(a-2)(a+2)}$$

2. $$\frac{3a}{a^2-5a+6} = \frac{3a}{(a-2)(a-3)}$$

3. The L. C. D. is $(a+2)(a-2)(a-3)$.

4. L. C. D. $\div (a-2)(a+2) = a-3$.

$$\therefore \frac{4a}{(a-2)(a+2)} = \frac{4a(a-3)}{(a-2)(a+2)(a-3)}.$$

5. L. C. D. $\div (a-2)(a-3) = (a+2)$.

$$\therefore \frac{3a}{(a-2)(a-3)} = \frac{3a(a+2)}{(a-2)(a+2)(a-3)}$$

Check: The final fractions in steps 4 and 5 may be changed into the original fractions by cancellation.

EXERCISE 80

Reduce the following to equivalent fractions having their lowest common denominator:

1. $\frac{2}{3}$; $\frac{3}{4}$; $\frac{5}{6}$.

2. $\frac{3}{5}$; $\frac{7}{15}$; $\frac{9}{20}$.

3. $\frac{3a}{4}$; $\frac{5b}{6}$.

4. $\frac{4x}{3}$; $\frac{2y}{5}$; $\frac{3z}{2}$.

5. $\frac{5mn}{6}$; $\frac{7mp}{4}$; $\frac{3np}{5}$.

6. $\frac{2}{a}$; $\frac{3}{b}$; $\frac{5}{c}$.

7. $\frac{2x}{a}$; $\frac{3y}{a^2}$; $\frac{5z}{a^3}$.

8. $\frac{ab}{xy}$; $\frac{c}{xz}$; $\frac{d}{yz}$.

9. $\frac{1}{2m^3n}$; $\frac{2}{3mn^3}$; $\frac{6}{5m^2n^2}$.

10. $\frac{r^2s}{2m^2n}$; $\frac{r^3}{3mn^2}$; $\frac{s^3}{5m^4n^3}$.

11. $\frac{2a-5c}{9ab}$; $\frac{4a+3b}{12ac}$.

12. $\frac{3x-4z}{4xz^3}$; $\frac{6x-5z}{3x^2z}$.

13. $\frac{2ab}{a^2-b^2}$; $\frac{b}{a+b}$.

14. $\frac{4a^2}{4a^2-9}$; $\frac{2}{6a^2-9a}$.

15. $\frac{2x}{x+2y}$; $\frac{3y}{x-2y}$.

16. $\frac{3x}{5x-10}$; $\frac{5}{2x-4}$.

FRACTIONS

17. $\dfrac{x}{x^2-6x+8}$; $\dfrac{x^2}{x^2-16}$.

18. $\dfrac{3n}{n^3-8}$; $\dfrac{5}{n^2-4n+4}$.

19. $\dfrac{a+b}{a^2-2ab}$; $\dfrac{a-b}{ab+b^2}$.

20. $\dfrac{3}{a+1}$; $\dfrac{6}{a-1}$; $\dfrac{9}{a^2-1}$.

21. $\dfrac{a+5}{a^2-a-6}$; $\dfrac{a+3}{a^2+7a+10}$.

22. $\dfrac{a+3b}{a^2-7ab+12b^2}$; $\dfrac{a-3b}{a^2-ab-12b^2}$.

23. $\dfrac{a-b}{x^2-2xy+y^2}$; $\dfrac{x+y}{(a+b)(x-y)}$.

24. $\dfrac{x+y}{x^3-27y^3}$; $\dfrac{xy}{x^2-9y^2}$.

25. $\dfrac{a+2}{a^2+2a-3}$; $\dfrac{a-3}{a^2-3a+2}$; $\dfrac{a+1}{a^2+a-6}$.

ADDITION AND SUBTRACTION OF FRACTIONS

133. EXAMPLE 1. Perform the indicated addition:

$$\frac{4a+3}{4a^2b}+\frac{1-6b^2}{6ab^3}.$$

SOLUTION: 1. The fractions cannot be added because they do not have a common denominator. By the methods of § 132, change the two fractions to equivalent fractions having their lowest common denominator.

2. The L. C. D. $= 12\,a^2b^3$. Multiply the terms of the first fraction by $12\,a^2b^3 \div 4\,a^2b$, or $3\,b^2$; and the terms of the second fraction by $12\,a^2b^3 \div 6\,ab^3$, or $2\,a$. Then,

3. $\dfrac{4a+3}{4a^2b}+\dfrac{1-6b^2}{6ab^3} = \dfrac{3\,b^2 \times (4\,a+3)}{3\,b^2 \times 4\,a^2b} + \dfrac{2\,a \times (1-6\,b^2)}{2\,a \times (6\,ab^3)}$

$\qquad = \dfrac{(12\,ab^2+9\,b^2)}{12\,a^2b^3} + \dfrac{(2\,a-12\,ab^2)}{12\,a^2b^3}$

$\qquad = \dfrac{(12\,ab^2+9\,b^2)+(2\,a-12\,ab^2)}{12\,a^2b^3}$

$\qquad = \dfrac{12\,ab^2+9\,b^2+2\,a-12\,ab^2}{12\,a^2b^3}$

$\qquad = \dfrac{9\,b^2+2\,a}{12\,a^2b^3}.$

CHECK: Let $a = 1$; $b = 1$.

$$\frac{4a+3}{4a^2b} = \frac{7}{4}, \quad \frac{1-6b^2}{6ab^3} = \frac{-5}{6}, \text{ and } \frac{7}{4} + \frac{(-5)}{6} = \frac{11}{12};$$

also,
$$\frac{9b^2+2a}{12a^2b^3} = \frac{9+2}{12} = \frac{11}{12}.$$

Rule. — To add or subtract fractions:

1. Reduce them, if necessary, to equivalent fractions having their lowest common denominator.

2. For the numerator of the result, combine the numerators of the resulting fractions, in parentheses, preceding each by the sign of its fraction.

3. For the denominator of the result, write the L. C. D.

4. Simplify the numerator by removing parentheses and combining like terms.

5. Reduce the result to lowest terms.

EXAMPLE 2. Simplify $\dfrac{5x-4y}{6} - \dfrac{7x-2y}{14}$.

SOLUTION: 1. $\quad \dfrac{5x-4y}{6} - \dfrac{7x-2y}{14} = \dfrac{7(5x-4y)}{42} - \dfrac{3(7x-2y)}{42}$

2. $\qquad\qquad\qquad\qquad = \dfrac{7(5x-4y) - 3(7x-2y)}{42}$

3. $\qquad\qquad\qquad\qquad = \dfrac{35x - 28y - 21x + 6y}{42}$

4. $\qquad\qquad\qquad\qquad = \dfrac{14x - 22y}{42}$

5. $\qquad\qquad\qquad\qquad = \dfrac{2(7x-11y)}{42} = \dfrac{7x-11y}{21}.$

CHECK. Let $x = 1$; $y = 1$.

$$\frac{5x-4y}{6} = \frac{5-4}{6} = \frac{1}{6}, \quad \frac{7x-2y}{14} = \frac{5}{14}, \text{ and } \frac{1}{6} - \frac{5}{14} = \frac{-8}{42} = \frac{-4}{21};$$

also, $\quad \dfrac{7x-11y}{21} = \dfrac{7-11}{21} = \dfrac{-4}{21}.$ The solution is correct.

NOTE. In the first step of the solution, the numerator and denominator of the first fraction are multiplied by 7, and of the second fraction, by 3.

FRACTIONS

EXERCISE 81

Perform the indicated additions and subtractions:

1. $\dfrac{2}{9} - \dfrac{5}{27} + \dfrac{1}{3}.$

2. $\dfrac{4}{15} + \dfrac{6}{5} - \dfrac{3}{20}.$

3. $\dfrac{5}{16} + \dfrac{3}{8} - \dfrac{1}{4}.$

4. $\dfrac{3}{14} + \dfrac{2}{21} - \dfrac{5}{84}.$

5. $\dfrac{5a}{4} + \dfrac{3a}{2}.$

6. $\dfrac{6m}{7} - \dfrac{3m}{14}.$

7. $\dfrac{15x}{8} - \dfrac{7x}{4} + \dfrac{3x}{2}.$

8. $\dfrac{a}{3} - \dfrac{b}{6} + \dfrac{c}{15}.$

9. $\dfrac{10r}{9} - \dfrac{2s}{3} + \dfrac{7t}{27}.$

10. $\dfrac{ab}{5} + \dfrac{bc}{10} - \dfrac{ac}{15}.$

11. $\dfrac{6a-5}{8} + \dfrac{3a+7}{12}.$

12. $\dfrac{2a-8}{7} + \dfrac{3a+5}{14}$

13. $\dfrac{3m+4}{12} - \dfrac{2m+5}{9}.$

14. $\dfrac{4a-9}{9} - \dfrac{3a-8}{12}$

15. $\dfrac{5a+1}{6} + \dfrac{2b+3}{8} - \dfrac{7c-4}{12}.$

16. $\dfrac{3a+4}{3} - \dfrac{4a-3}{4} + \dfrac{5a+2}{6}.$

17. $\dfrac{2a-3b}{9} - \dfrac{3a+b}{18} + \dfrac{4a-5b}{27}.$

18. $\dfrac{6m+1}{3} - \dfrac{5m-2}{6} + \dfrac{8m-3}{9} - \dfrac{7m+4}{12}.$

19. $\dfrac{4r-3s}{5} + \dfrac{6r+5s}{10} - \dfrac{5r+2s}{15} - \dfrac{3r-10s}{20}.$

20. $\dfrac{3t-2x}{4} - \dfrac{7t-8x}{6} + \dfrac{9t+4x}{8} - \dfrac{10t+7x}{9}.$

ALGEBRA

21. $\dfrac{3}{a} - \dfrac{5}{2a}.$

22. $\dfrac{2}{3x} + \dfrac{3}{4y}.$

23. $\dfrac{2}{a^2} - \dfrac{1}{ab} + \dfrac{3}{b^2}.$

24. $\dfrac{1}{r} + \dfrac{2}{s} - \dfrac{3}{t}.$

25. $\dfrac{a}{y} + \dfrac{b}{x} - \dfrac{c}{z}.$

26. $\dfrac{a}{2m^2} - \dfrac{b}{mn} - \dfrac{c}{5n^2}.$

27. $\dfrac{5a+1}{6a} + \dfrac{3a-2}{2a}.$

28. $\dfrac{10x+3y}{2x^2y} - \dfrac{3x+5y}{xy^2}.$

29. $\dfrac{x-y}{xy} + \dfrac{y-2z}{2yz} + \dfrac{z-3x}{3zx}.$

30. $\dfrac{2a-b}{ab} + \dfrac{2b-c}{bc} + \dfrac{2c-a}{ca}.$

31. $\dfrac{1}{x^2+x} - \dfrac{1}{x^2-x}.$

SOLUTION: 1. $\dfrac{1}{x^2+x} - \dfrac{1}{x^2-x} = \dfrac{1}{x(x+1)} - \dfrac{1}{x(x-1)}$

2. $\qquad = \dfrac{(x-1)}{x(x+1)(x-1)} - \dfrac{(x+1)}{x(x+1)(x-1)}$

3. $\qquad = \dfrac{(x-1)-(x+1)}{x(x+1)(x-1)}$

4. $\qquad = \dfrac{x-1-x-1}{x(x+1)(x-1)}$

5. $\qquad = \dfrac{-2}{x(x^2-1)} = \dfrac{+2}{x(1-x^2)}.$

Notice that in line 2, the L.C.D. is $x(x+1)(x-1)$; that the numerator and denominator of the first fraction are multiplied by $(x-1)$, and of the second fraction by $(x+1)$; that parentheses are used in lines 2 and 3; that in line 5, the signs of both numerator and denominator are changed. Check by substitution.

32. Simplify $\dfrac{a+b}{4a^2-9b^2} - \dfrac{a-b}{(2a+3b)^2}.$

SOLUTION: 1. $\dfrac{a+b}{4a^2-9b^2} - \dfrac{a-b}{(2a+3b)^2}$

2. $\qquad = \dfrac{a+b}{(2a-3b)(2a+3b)} - \dfrac{a-b}{(2a+3b)(2a+3b)}$

3. $\qquad = \dfrac{(a+b)(2a+3b)}{(2a-3b)(2a+3b)(2a+3b)} - \dfrac{(a-b)(2a-3b)}{(2a-3b)(2a+3b)(2a+3b)}$

FRACTIONS

4. $= \dfrac{(2a^2 + 5ab + 3b^2) - (2a^2 - 5ab + 3b^2)}{(2a - 3b)(2a + 3b)(2a + 3b)}$

5. $= \dfrac{2a^2 + 5ab + 3b^2 - 2a^2 + 5ab - 3b^2}{(2a - 3b)(2a + 3b)(2a + 3b)}$

6. $= \dfrac{10ab}{(2a - 3b)(2a + 3b)(2a + 3b)}.$

CHECK: Let $a = 1$, $b = 1$.

$\dfrac{a+b}{4a^2 - 9b^2} = \dfrac{2}{-5} = -\dfrac{2}{5},\quad \dfrac{a-b}{(2a+3b)^2} = \dfrac{0}{25} = 0,$ and $-\dfrac{2}{5} - 0 = -\dfrac{2}{5}$;

also, $\dfrac{10ab}{(2a-3b)(2a+3b)^2} = \dfrac{10}{(2-3)(5)^2} = \dfrac{10}{-25} = -\dfrac{10}{25} = -\dfrac{2}{5}.$

Notice that the indicated products in step 3 in the numerator are found and inclosed in parentheses in step 4. All of this solution should be done mentally.

33. $\dfrac{m}{m-1} - \dfrac{1}{m+1}.$

34. $\dfrac{r}{r+3} + \dfrac{r}{r-3}.$

35. $\dfrac{3}{5m-2} - \dfrac{2}{2m+3}.$

36. $\dfrac{3b}{3a-4} - \dfrac{5b}{5a+6}.$

37. $\dfrac{3y}{3y-x} - \dfrac{2x}{2x-3y}.$

38. $\dfrac{x}{2x+2y} + \dfrac{y}{3x-3y}.$

39. $\dfrac{1}{3a-7} - \dfrac{2}{6a+15}.$

40. $\dfrac{3}{4p-6} - \dfrac{4}{15p-12}.$

41. $\dfrac{2-x}{2+x} - \dfrac{2+x}{2-x}.$

42. $\dfrac{4p^2+1}{4p^2-1} - \dfrac{2p-1}{2p+1}.$

43. $\dfrac{1}{2a+b} - \dfrac{(2a-b)^2}{8a^3+b^3}.$

44. $\dfrac{x+3}{x-3} - \dfrac{x^3+27}{x^3-27}.$

45. $\dfrac{x+2}{x-2} - \dfrac{x-2}{x+2} - \dfrac{16}{x^2-4}.$

46. $\dfrac{1}{a+b} + \dfrac{1}{a-b} - \dfrac{2a}{a^2-b^2}.$

47. $\dfrac{1}{a-x} - \dfrac{3x}{a^2-x^2} + \dfrac{ax}{a^3-x^3}.$

48. $\dfrac{m+n}{m-n} - \dfrac{m-n}{m+n} - \dfrac{4mn}{m^2-n^2}.$

49. $\dfrac{2}{x^2-5x+6} - \dfrac{5}{x^2+2x-15}.$

ALGEBRA

50. $\dfrac{a+1}{a^2-a-6} - \dfrac{a-4}{a^2-4a+3} + \dfrac{a+3}{a^2+a-2}.$

51. $\dfrac{3a+2}{6a^2-a-1} + \dfrac{a+3}{3a^2+7a+2} - \dfrac{a-2}{2a^2+3a-2}.$

52. $\dfrac{r}{r^2-6ar+9a^2} - \dfrac{a}{r^2+4ar-21a^2}.$

53. $\dfrac{x+2}{x^2+4x+3} - \dfrac{2(x-1)}{x^2+x-6} + \dfrac{x-3}{x^2-x-2}.$

54. $\dfrac{1}{a+1} - \dfrac{a}{a^2-a+1} + \dfrac{a^2-4}{a^3+1}.$

55. Simplify $\dfrac{3}{a-b} + \dfrac{2b+a}{b^2-a^2}.$

SOLUTION: 1. Notice that $b^2 - a^2$ is not in the same order as $a - b$. Change the signs of the denominator and also the sign of the fraction (§ 126).

2. $\dfrac{3}{a-b} + \dfrac{2b+a}{b^2-a^2} = \dfrac{3}{a-b} - \dfrac{a+2b}{a^2-b^2}.$

3. $\qquad = \dfrac{3}{a-b} - \dfrac{a+2b}{(a-b)(a+b)}$

4. $\qquad = \dfrac{3(a+b) - (a+2b)}{(a-b)(a+b)}$

5. $\qquad = \dfrac{3a+3b-a-2b}{(a-b)(a+b)}$

6. $\qquad = \dfrac{2a+b}{a^2-b^2}.$

Check by substitution.

56. $\dfrac{3a}{a^2-9} + \dfrac{5}{3-a}.$

57. $\dfrac{1}{y^2-xy} - \dfrac{1}{x^2-xy}.$

58. $\dfrac{x+4}{3x-6} - \dfrac{2x-5}{8-4x}.$

59. $\dfrac{a}{4m-m^2} + \dfrac{a}{m^2-16}.$

60. $\dfrac{3}{a+1} + \dfrac{3}{1-a} - \dfrac{6}{a^2-1}.$

61. $\dfrac{r}{r+2} - \dfrac{r}{2-r} - \dfrac{r^2}{r^2-4}.$

FRACTIONS

62. $\dfrac{a}{a+b} - \dfrac{b}{a-b} - \dfrac{2b^2}{b^2-a^2}.$

63. $\dfrac{2x}{6-x-x^2} + \dfrac{3x}{x^2+3x-10}.$

64. $13 + \dfrac{6}{5} - \dfrac{1}{3}.$

65. $a - 4 + \dfrac{2+11a}{3a}.$

66. $\dfrac{x-y}{x+y} + 1.$

67. $1 - \dfrac{5a-b}{5a+b}.$

68. $3a + 1 - \dfrac{3-7a}{2a-3}.$

69. $a - b - \dfrac{a^3-b^3}{a^2+ab+b^2}.$

70. $3m + 4 - \dfrac{9m^2+16}{3m-4}.$

71. $r^2 - rs + s^2 - \dfrac{2s^3}{r+s}.$

MULTIPLICATION OF FRACTIONS

134. In arithmetic, the product of two fractions is the product of their numerators divided by the product of their denominators. Thus, $\frac{3}{5} \times \frac{2}{11} = \frac{6}{55}.$

In algebra, the same rule is followed.

EXAMPLE 1. Multiply $\dfrac{5a}{2x}$ by $\dfrac{4x^2}{15a^2}.$

SOLUTION: 1. $\dfrac{5a}{2x} \cdot \dfrac{4x^2}{15a^2} = \dfrac{20\,ax^2}{30\,a^2x}.$

2. Reduce to lowest terms:

$$\dfrac{20\,ax^2}{30\,a^2x} = \dfrac{\overset{2\ \ x}{\cancel{20\,ax^2}}}{\underset{3\ a}{\cancel{30\,a^2x}}} = \dfrac{2x}{3a}.$$

It is customary to cancel the common factors in step 1 as in the following example.

EXAMPLE 2. Simplify $\dfrac{a^2+2a-3}{a^2-16} \cdot \dfrac{a^2-4a}{a^2-1}.$

SOLUTION: 1. $\dfrac{a^2+2a-3}{a^2-16} \cdot \dfrac{a^2-4a}{a^2-1}$

$= \dfrac{(a+3)\cancel{(a-1)}}{\cancel{(a-4)}(a+4)} \cdot \dfrac{a\cancel{(a-4)}}{(a+1)\cancel{(a-1)}}$

$= \dfrac{a(a+3)}{(a+4)(a+1)} = \dfrac{a^2+3a}{a^2+5a+4}.$

176　ALGEBRA

CHECK: Let $a = 2$.

$$\left. \begin{array}{l} \dfrac{a^2 + 2a - 3}{a^2 - 16} = \dfrac{4 + 4 - 3}{4 - 16} = \dfrac{5}{-12} = \dfrac{-5}{12}, \\ \dfrac{a^2 - 4a}{a^2 - 1} = \dfrac{4 - 8}{4 - 1} = \dfrac{-4}{3}, \end{array} \right\}$$ and $\dfrac{-5}{12} \cdot \dfrac{-4}{3} = \dfrac{+20}{36}$
$$= \dfrac{5}{9};$$

also, $\qquad \dfrac{a^2 + 3a}{a^2 + 5a + 4} = \dfrac{4 + 6}{4 + 10 + 4} = \dfrac{10}{18} = \dfrac{5}{9}.$

Notice that the factors $(a - 1)$ of the first numerator and of the second denominator are each divided by $(a - 1)$, or, are cancelled; similarly the factors $(a - 4)$ of the first denominator and the second numerator.

Rule. — To find the product of two or more fractions:

1. Find all of the prime factors of the numerators and denominators.

2. Divide out (cancel) factors common to a numerator and a denominator.

3. Multiply the remaining factors of the numerators for the numerator of the product, and of the denominators for the denominator of the product.

EXERCISE 82

Find the following indicated products:

1. $\dfrac{3}{14} \cdot \dfrac{21}{20} \cdot \dfrac{10}{9}.$

2. $\dfrac{5}{18} \cdot \dfrac{6}{10} \cdot \dfrac{12}{7}.$

3. $\dfrac{6\,a^2 b}{15\,x^3 y} \cdot \dfrac{5\,xy^2}{2\,ab}.$

4. $\dfrac{3\,am^2}{20\,b^2} \cdot \dfrac{25\,b^3}{3\,a^2 m^2}.$

5. $\dfrac{5\,a}{4\,b} \cdot \dfrac{6\,b}{10\,c} \cdot \dfrac{8\,c}{12\,a}.$

6. $\dfrac{5\,a^2 b}{2\,ac^2} \cdot \dfrac{b^2 c}{3\,ba^2} \cdot \dfrac{6\,c^2 a}{5\,b^2 c}.$

7. $\dfrac{4\,a^6}{9\,b^3} \cdot \dfrac{15\,b^4}{7\,c^4} \cdot \dfrac{21\,c^5}{10\,a^5}.$

8. $\dfrac{27\,m^3 y^2}{20\,m^4 x} \cdot \dfrac{30\,n}{14\,x^2 y^3} \cdot \dfrac{7\,x^4 y^2}{18\,n^3}.$

9. $\dfrac{x^2 - a^2}{x^2 + 2\,ax + a^2} \cdot \dfrac{2x + 2a}{3\,x}.$

10. $\dfrac{4\,m^2 - 1}{m^3 - 16\,m} \cdot \dfrac{m^2 + 4\,m}{2\,m + 1}.$

11. $\dfrac{a^2 + 2a - 35}{6\,a^3} \cdot \dfrac{2\,a(a - 3)}{(a + 7)(a - 3)}.$

FRACTIONS

12. $\dfrac{p^2 + 4p - 45}{4pr - 20r} \cdot \dfrac{3pr - 3r^2}{p^2 - 81}$.

13. $\dfrac{a^2 + 3a - 18}{a^4 - 8a^3 + 12a^2} \cdot \dfrac{2a^3 - 4a^2}{a^2 - 36}$.

14. $\dfrac{x^4 - x^2}{x^3 + 8} \cdot \dfrac{x^2 - 2x + 4}{x^3 + 2x^2 + x}$.

15. $\dfrac{xy^2 - y^3}{x^3 + x^2 y} \cdot \dfrac{x^2 - xy - 2y^2}{x^2 - 2xy + y^2}$.

16. $\dfrac{2a^2 + 5a + 2}{2a^2 + a - 6} \cdot \dfrac{2a^2 - 3a}{6a^3 + 3a^2}$.

17. $\dfrac{6r^2 - rs - 2s^2}{12r^2 + 5rs - 2s^2} \cdot \dfrac{8r^2 - 6rs + s^2}{4r^2 - s^2}$.

18. $\dfrac{5m + 10}{8m - 4} \cdot \dfrac{3m - 9}{10m + 5} \cdot \dfrac{8m^2 - 2}{3m^2 - 12}$.

19. $\dfrac{x^4 - y^4}{2x^2 + 2y^2} \cdot \dfrac{x^2 + xy - 2y^2}{x^2 + 3xy + 2y^2} \cdot \dfrac{5x + 5y}{x^2 - 2xy + y^2}$.

20. $\dfrac{8x^3 - 27}{4x^2 - 9} \cdot \dfrac{4x^2 + 12x + 9}{8x^2 + 12x + 18} \cdot \dfrac{4x - 6}{6x^2 + 5x - 6}$.

21. $\dfrac{m^4 - 1}{16m^4 - 9n^2} \cdot \dfrac{4m^2 - 3n}{2m^2 + 2} \cdot \dfrac{4m^2 + 3n}{m - 1}$.

22. $\dfrac{2a^2 - a}{4a^2 - 1} \cdot \dfrac{4a^2 + 4a + 1}{5a} \cdot \dfrac{10a^2 - 10a}{4a^2 - 2a - 2}$.

23. $\dfrac{1 - x^2}{2x - 4} \cdot \dfrac{x^2 - 4}{x^2 - x - 2} \cdot \dfrac{3x - 6}{x^2 + x - 2}$.

24. $\dfrac{a^3 - x^3}{a^2 + 2ax + x^2} \cdot \dfrac{5x}{3x - 3a} \cdot \dfrac{6a + 6x}{5a^2 + 5ax + 5x^2}$.

25. $\dfrac{m^3 + n^3}{m^3 - n^3} \cdot \dfrac{n - m}{n + m} \cdot \dfrac{[(m + n)^2 - mn]}{[(m - n)^2 + mn]}$.

DIVISION OF FRACTIONS

135. In arithmetic, to divide a fraction by another fraction, we multiply the dividend by the inverted divisor. Thus:

(a) $\quad \dfrac{9}{10} \div \dfrac{3}{5} = \dfrac{\cancel{9}^{3}}{\cancel{10}_{2}} \times \dfrac{\cancel{5}}{\cancel{3}} = \dfrac{3}{2}.$

(b) $\quad 3\tfrac{2}{3} \div 2\tfrac{1}{5} = \dfrac{11}{3} \div \dfrac{11}{5} = \dfrac{\cancel{11}}{3} \times \dfrac{5}{\cancel{11}} = \dfrac{5}{3}.$

In algebra, it is advisable to factor the expressions first, and then use the same process as in arithmetic.

EXAMPLE. Divide $\dfrac{x^2 - x}{x^3 + 1}$ by $\dfrac{x^2 - 2x + 1}{x^3 - x^2 + x}$.

SOLUTION: 1. $\dfrac{x^2 - x}{x^3 + 1} \div \dfrac{x^2 - 2x + 1}{x^3 - x^2 + x}$

2. $= \dfrac{x(x-1)}{(x+1)(x^2 - x + 1)} \div \dfrac{(x-1)(x-1)}{x(x^2 - x + 1)}$

3. $= \dfrac{x\cancel{(x-1)}^{1}}{(x+1)\cancel{(x^2 - x + 1)}_{1}} \cdot \dfrac{x\cancel{(x^2 - x + 1)}^{1}}{\cancel{(x-1)}_{1}(x-1)}$

4. $= \dfrac{x^2}{(x+1)(x-1)} = \dfrac{x^2}{x^2 - 1}.$

CHECK: Let $x = 2$.

$$\dfrac{x^2 - x}{x^3 + 1} = \dfrac{2}{9}, \quad \dfrac{x^2 - 2x + 1}{x^3 - x^2 + x} = \dfrac{1}{6}, \text{ and } \dfrac{2}{9} \div \dfrac{1}{6} = \dfrac{4}{3};$$

also, $\qquad\qquad\qquad\qquad \dfrac{x^2}{x^2 - 1} = \dfrac{4}{3}.$

Rule. — To divide one fraction by another:

1. Factor the numerators and denominators of the fractions.
2. Invert the divisor fraction.
3. Multiply the dividend fraction by the inverted divisor.

FRACTIONS

EXERCISE 83

Perform the following indicated divisions:

1. $\dfrac{5}{18} \div \dfrac{10}{9}.$

2. $\dfrac{7a}{15b} \div \dfrac{5a}{6b}.$

3. $\dfrac{21c^2}{32d} \div \dfrac{3c}{8d^2}.$

4. $\dfrac{15x^2y}{16xy^2} \div \dfrac{3x^2}{4y^2}.$

5. $\dfrac{32m^3}{15n^2} \div \dfrac{8}{35n^3}.$

6. $\dfrac{24a^4b^2}{5x^4y^3} \div 6a^2b^2.$

7. $\dfrac{3a}{a^2-6x+8} \div \dfrac{2a}{a^2-x-12}.$

8. $\dfrac{4r^2-25v^2}{16r^2-9v^2} \div \dfrac{2rv-5v^2}{4r^2+3rv}.$

9. $\dfrac{e^3-e}{3e^3+3} \div \dfrac{(e-1)^2}{6e^3-6e^2+6e}.$

10. $\dfrac{c^4-d^4}{(c-d)^2} \div \dfrac{(c^2+d^2)}{(c+d)}.$

11. $\dfrac{r^3-s^3}{r^2+rs+s^2} \div \dfrac{(r-s)^2}{4r+4s}.$

12. $\dfrac{(t+2s)^2}{(t-s)} \div \dfrac{ts+2s^2}{t^2-ts}.$

13. $\dfrac{a^2m+10am+21m}{a^3-4a^2+3a} \div \dfrac{a^2m^3-9m^3}{a^3-a^2}.$

14. $\dfrac{w^3-8}{w^2+7w+10} \div \dfrac{w^2+2w+4}{w^2+2w}.$

15. $\dfrac{a^2-5ab-14b^2}{a^2+5ab-24b^2} \div \dfrac{a^2-3ab-28b^2}{a^2-8ab+15b^2}.$

16. $\dfrac{m^3-y^3}{m^2y^2-y^4} \div \dfrac{m^3+m^2y+my^2}{my^2+y^3}.$

Perform the indicated multiplications and divisions:

17. $\dfrac{x^2+7xy+10y^2}{x^2+6xy+5y^2} \cdot \dfrac{x+y}{x^2+4xy+4y^2} \div \dfrac{1}{x+2y}.$

18. $\dfrac{a^2-b^2}{a^2-3ab+2b^2} \cdot \dfrac{ab-2b^2}{b^2+ab} \div \dfrac{(a-b)^2}{a(a-b)}.$

19. $\dfrac{(2r-3s)^2}{r^2+4rs+4s^2} \cdot \dfrac{4r^2-4s^2}{4r^2-9s^2} \div \dfrac{3rs-3s^2}{5r^2+10rs}.$

20. $\dfrac{am^4-an^4}{bm^3-bn^3} \div \dfrac{m^2+n^2}{m^2-n^2} \cdot \dfrac{bm^2+bmn+bn^2}{am^2+2amn+an^2}.$

ALGEBRA

136. Sometimes there are mixed expressions in an algebra problem. These mixed expressions should always be reduced to fractional form as in arithmetic.

EXAMPLE 1. Simplify $12\tfrac{3}{8} \div 3\tfrac{1}{4}$.

SOLUTION: $12\tfrac{3}{8} \div 3\tfrac{1}{4} = \dfrac{99}{8} \div \dfrac{13}{4} = \dfrac{\overset{1}{\cancel{99}}}{\underset{2}{\cancel{8}}} \times \dfrac{\overset{1}{\cancel{4}}}{13} = \dfrac{99}{26}$.

EXAMPLE 2. Simplify $\left(5 - \dfrac{a^2 - 19\,x^2}{a^2 - 4\,x^2}\right) \div \left(3 - \dfrac{a - 5\,x}{a - 2\,x}\right)$.

SOLUTION: In the first parentheses, the fraction is to be subtracted from 5, and in the second, the fraction is to be subtracted from 3. (Use rule, § 133.)

1. $\left(5 - \dfrac{a^2 - 19\,x^2}{a^2 - 4\,x^2}\right) \div \left(3 - \dfrac{a - 5\,x}{a - 2\,x}\right)$

2. $= \left(\dfrac{5(a^2 - 4\,x^2) - (a^2 - 19\,x^2)}{a^2 - 4\,x^2}\right) \div \left(\dfrac{3(a - 2\,x) - (a - 5\,x)}{a - 2\,x}\right)$

3. $= \left(\dfrac{5\,a^2 - 20\,x^2 - a^2 + 19\,x^2}{a^2 - 4\,x^2}\right) \div \left(\dfrac{3\,a - 6\,x - a + 5\,x}{a - 2\,x}\right)$

4. $= \left(\dfrac{4\,a^2 - x^2}{a^2 - 4\,x^2}\right) \div \left(\dfrac{2\,a - x}{a - 2\,x}\right)$

5. $= \dfrac{(2\,a - x)(2\,a + x)}{(a - 2\,x)(a + 2\,x)} \times \dfrac{(a - 2\,x)}{(2\,a - x)} = \dfrac{2\,a + x}{a + 2\,x}$.

CHECK: Let $a = 1$; $x = 1$.

$\left. \begin{aligned} 5 - \dfrac{a^2 - 19\,x^2}{a^2 - 4\,x^2} &= 5 - \dfrac{1 - 19}{1 - 4} = 5 - \dfrac{-18}{-3} = 5 - 6 = -1, \\ 3 - \dfrac{a - 5\,x}{a - 2\,x} &= 3 - \dfrac{1 - 5}{1 - 2} = 3 - \dfrac{-4}{-1} = 3 - 4 = -1, \end{aligned} \right\}$ and $(-1) \div (-1) = 1$;

also, $\dfrac{2\,a + x}{a + 2\,x} = \dfrac{2 + 1}{1 + 2} = \dfrac{3}{3} = 1$.

NOTE. In such examples, first perform carefully the indicated additions and subtractions *within the parentheses* and, afterwards, the multiplications and divisions.

FRACTIONS

EXERCISE 84

Perform the indicated operations:

1. $(3 + \tfrac{2}{3}) \cdot (3 + \tfrac{3}{11})$.

2. $(5 - \tfrac{1}{4}) \cdot (2 - \tfrac{2}{19})$.

3. $\left(1 - \dfrac{x}{y}\right) \cdot \left(\dfrac{y}{y^2 - x^2}\right)$.

4. $\left(a + \dfrac{b^2}{a}\right) \cdot \left(1 - \dfrac{b^2}{a^2 + b^2}\right)$.

5. $\left(\dfrac{2}{a} - \dfrac{3}{b}\right) \div \left(\dfrac{2}{a} + \dfrac{3}{b}\right)$.

6. $\left(\dfrac{a}{b} - \dfrac{c}{d}\right) \div \left(\dfrac{a}{b} + \dfrac{c}{d}\right)$.

7. $\left(2 - \dfrac{a}{b}\right)\left(\dfrac{3\,b^2}{8\,b^3 - a^3}\right)$.

8. $\left(\dfrac{a^2}{5\,b} - \dfrac{a}{2}\right) \div \left(\dfrac{2\,a^2}{3\,b} + \dfrac{a}{2}\right)$.

9. $\left(b - \dfrac{a^2}{b}\right) \div (b - a)$.

10. $\left(\dfrac{a}{4\,b} - \dfrac{b}{a}\right) \cdot \left(\dfrac{8\,a^2 b^2}{a + 2\,b}\right)$.

11. $\left(2 - \dfrac{y}{x+y}\right) \div \left(2 - \dfrac{x}{x+y}\right)$.

12. $\left(4 - \dfrac{1}{x+1}\right) \div \left(16 + \dfrac{7}{x^2 - 1}\right)$.

13. $\left(1 - \dfrac{2\,ab}{a^2 + ab + b^2}\right) \cdot \left(1 - \dfrac{2\,b^3}{a^3 + b^3}\right)$

14. $\left(a + 1 - \dfrac{30}{a}\right) \div \left(a - 4 - \dfrac{5}{a}\right)$

15. $\left(r + s + \dfrac{s^2}{r}\right) \cdot \left(2 + \dfrac{2\,s^3}{r^3 - s^3}\right)$.

16. $\left(6 + \dfrac{5\,x + 2}{x^2 - 1}\right) \div \left(2 + \dfrac{1}{x - 1}\right)$.

17. $\left(\dfrac{2\,m^2 + 7\,m - 15}{2\,m^2 - 3\,m - 14}\right) \cdot \left(\dfrac{2\,m^2 - 19\,m + 42}{8\,m - 12}\right) \div \left(\dfrac{m^2 - m - 30}{3\,m + 6}\right)$.

18. $\left(\dfrac{1}{v^2} - \dfrac{2}{vx} + \dfrac{1}{x^2}\right)\left(1 + \dfrac{2\,v}{x - v}\right) \div \left(\dfrac{x}{v} - \dfrac{v}{x}\right)$.

19. $\left(1 + \dfrac{5\,a + 4}{a^2 - 3\,a - 4}\right) \cdot \left(1 + \dfrac{a - 16}{a^2 - a}\right) \div \left(\dfrac{a^2 + 6\,a + 8}{a^2 + a}\right)$.

20. $\left(\dfrac{x^3 + 27}{x^2 + x - 12}\right) \div \left\{\dfrac{x^2 - 3\,x + 9}{x^2 + 2\,x - 8} \cdot \dfrac{x^2 + x - 6}{3\,x - 9}\right\}$.

COMPLEX FRACTIONS

137. A **Complex Fraction** is a fraction having one or more fractions in either or both of its terms; as,

$$(a)\ \frac{a}{b-\dfrac{c}{d}}; \qquad (b)\ \frac{\left(\dfrac{a}{a-b}-\dfrac{a}{a+b}\right)}{\left(\dfrac{b}{a-b}+\dfrac{a}{a+b}\right)}.$$

138. A complex fraction is simply a case of division of fractions. The problems are very similar to those in the last paragraph. The numerator and denominator should be simplified separately and then the division performed.

EXAMPLE 1. Simplify $\dfrac{a}{b-\dfrac{c}{d}}$.

SOLUTION: This means divide a by the result obtained by subtracting $\dfrac{c}{d}$ from b.

$$\frac{a}{b-\dfrac{c}{d}} = \frac{a}{\left(\dfrac{bd-c}{d}\right)} = a \cdot \left(\frac{d}{bd-c}\right) = \frac{ad}{bd-c}.$$

CHECK: Let $a=1,\ b=2,\ c=1,\ d=1$.

$$\frac{a}{b-\dfrac{c}{d}} = \frac{1}{2-\dfrac{1}{1}} = \frac{1}{2-1} = \frac{1}{1} = 1;$$

also, $\qquad \dfrac{ad}{bd-c} = \dfrac{1}{2-1} = 1.$

EXAMPLE 2. Simplify $\dfrac{\left(\dfrac{a}{a-b}-\dfrac{a}{a+b}\right)}{\left(\dfrac{b}{a-b}+\dfrac{a}{a+b}\right)}$.

This means: find the difference of the fractions in the numerator, and the sum of the fractions in the denominator; divide the first result by the second. The work may be arranged as follows:

FRACTIONS

SOLUTION: 1. $\dfrac{\dfrac{a}{a-b} - \dfrac{a}{a+b}}{\dfrac{b}{a-b} + \dfrac{a}{a+b}}$

2. $= \dfrac{a(a+b) - a(a-b)}{(a-b)(a+b)} \div \dfrac{b(a+b) + a(a-b)}{(a-b)(a+b)}$

3. $= \dfrac{a^2 + ab - a^2 + ab}{(a-b)(a+b)} \div \dfrac{ab + b^2 + a^2 - ab}{(a-b)(a+b)}$

4. $= \dfrac{2ab}{(a-b)(a+b)} \div \dfrac{a^2 + b^2}{(a-b)(a+b)}$

5. $= \dfrac{2ab}{\cancel{(a-b)(a+b)}} \times \dfrac{\cancel{(a-b)(a+b)}}{a^2 + b^2} = \dfrac{2ab}{a^2 + b^2}.$

CHECK: Let $a = 2$; $b = 1$.

$$\dfrac{\dfrac{a}{a-b} - \dfrac{a}{a+b}}{\dfrac{b}{a-b} + \dfrac{a}{a+b}} = \dfrac{\dfrac{2}{1} - \dfrac{2}{3}}{\dfrac{1}{1} + \dfrac{2}{3}} = \dfrac{\dfrac{4}{3}}{\dfrac{5}{3}} = \dfrac{4}{3} \times \dfrac{3}{5} = \dfrac{4}{5};$$

also, $\dfrac{2ab}{a^2 + b^2} = \dfrac{4}{4+1} = \dfrac{4}{5}.$

EXERCISE 85

1. $\dfrac{\frac{2}{3} - \frac{3}{4}}{\frac{2}{3} + \frac{3}{4}}.$

2. $\dfrac{1 + \frac{1}{6}}{3 - \frac{1}{12}}.$

3. $\dfrac{2 - \frac{1}{8}}{1 - \frac{1}{2}}.$

4. $\dfrac{4}{6 - \frac{3}{5}}.$

5. $\dfrac{3 - \frac{1}{2}}{1 - \frac{1}{3}}.$

6. $\dfrac{\dfrac{3ab}{x}}{\dfrac{6a^2b}{x^2}}.$

7. $\dfrac{\dfrac{x+y}{2}}{\dfrac{x^2 - y^2}{6}}.$

8. $\dfrac{3}{1 + \frac{2}{x}}.$

9. $\dfrac{\dfrac{2}{m}}{2 - \dfrac{1}{m}}.$

10. $\dfrac{1 + \dfrac{1}{2a}}{a - \dfrac{1}{4a}}.$

11. $\dfrac{p - \dfrac{1}{p^2}}{1 - \dfrac{1}{p}}.$

12. $\dfrac{\dfrac{1}{x^3} - x}{\dfrac{1}{x^2} - 1}.$

13. $\dfrac{\dfrac{a}{b}-\dfrac{c}{d}}{\dfrac{a}{b}+\dfrac{c}{d}}.$

14. $\dfrac{\dfrac{2x}{3y}-2+\dfrac{3y}{2x}}{\dfrac{2}{y}-\dfrac{3}{x}}.$

15. $\dfrac{x+1-\dfrac{20}{x}}{x-2-\dfrac{8}{x}}.$

16. $\dfrac{x^2-13+\dfrac{36}{x^2}}{x+1-\dfrac{6}{x}}.$

17. $\dfrac{a-\dfrac{2b^2}{a-b}}{a+\dfrac{b^2}{a+2b}}.$

18. $\dfrac{\dfrac{x^2}{y^2}-\dfrac{8y}{x}}{\dfrac{x}{y}+2+\dfrac{4y}{x}}.$

19. $\dfrac{\dfrac{m}{n}+\dfrac{m+n}{m-n}}{\dfrac{n}{m}+\dfrac{m+n}{m-n}}.$

20. $\dfrac{a^2-a+1-\dfrac{2}{a+1}}{a+\dfrac{1}{a+1}}.$

21. $\dfrac{\dfrac{a}{a+b}}{1+\dfrac{b}{a-b}}.$

22. $\dfrac{1-\dfrac{8(x^2+y^2)}{9x^2-y^2}}{1-\dfrac{2(x+2y)}{3x+y}}.$

23. $\dfrac{6+\dfrac{17x+22}{x^2-3x-4}}{2+\dfrac{9}{x-4}}.$

24. $\dfrac{a-\dfrac{a-x}{1+ax}}{1+\dfrac{a^2-ax}{1+ax}}.$

25. $\dfrac{\dfrac{2a-b}{a+3b}+\dfrac{2a+b}{a-3b}}{\dfrac{2a-b}{a-3b}-\dfrac{2a+b}{a+3b}}.$

XI. SIMPLE EQUATIONS — (*Continued*)

FRACTIONAL EQUATIONS

139. If the unknown number, or numbers, of an equation *do not appear* in the denominator of a fraction, the equation is called an **Integral Equation**; as, $3x - 5 = 2x + 7$.

140. If the unknown number, or numbers, of an equation *do appear* in the denominator of a fraction, the equation is called a **Fractional Equation**; as, $\dfrac{3}{x} - 5 = \dfrac{2}{x} + 7$.

141. A fractional equation may be changed into an integral equation by **Clearing of Fractions**.

EXAMPLE. Solve the equation $\dfrac{3x-1}{4} - \dfrac{4x-5}{5} = 4 + \dfrac{7x+5}{10}$.

SOLUTION: 1. The lowest common multiple of 4, 5, and 10 is 20. Multiply both members of the equation by 20.

2. $\quad \overset{5}{\cancel{20}} \cdot \dfrac{(3x-1)}{4} - \overset{4}{\cancel{20}} \cdot \dfrac{(4x-5)}{5} = 20 \cdot 4 + \overset{2}{\cancel{20}} \cdot \dfrac{(7x+5)}{\cancel{10}}$.

3. $\quad \therefore 5(3x-1) - 4(4x-5) = 80 + 2(7x+5)$.

4. $\quad \therefore 15x - 5 - 16x + 20 = 80 + 14x + 10$.

5. $\quad \therefore 15 - x = 90 + 14x$.

6. $\quad \therefore -15x = 75$.

7. $D_{-15}:\quad x = -5$.

CHECK: Does $\dfrac{3(-5)-1}{4} - \dfrac{4(-5)-5}{5} = 4 + \dfrac{7(-5)+5}{10}$?

Does $\dfrac{-16}{4} - \dfrac{-25}{5} = 4 + \dfrac{-30}{10}$? Does $-4 + 5 = 4 - 3$? Yes.

EXERCISE 86

Solve the following equations:

1. $\dfrac{x+5}{2} - \dfrac{x+1}{4} = 3.$

2. $\dfrac{y-7}{5} + 2 = \dfrac{y+8}{10}.$

3. $\dfrac{11+m}{6} - \dfrac{10-m}{3} = 1.$

4. $\dfrac{1}{3}(a+5) - 4 = \dfrac{a-10}{4}.$

5. $\dfrac{1}{3}(r+2) - \dfrac{1}{5}(r-2) = 2.$

6. $\dfrac{c-2}{4} - \dfrac{c-4}{6} = \dfrac{2}{3}.$

7. $\dfrac{w+12}{9} = \dfrac{w-9}{2}.$

8. $\dfrac{m+11}{6} - \dfrac{10-m}{3} = -1.$

9. $\dfrac{t-1}{3} + 3 = \dfrac{t+14}{9}.$

10. $\dfrac{s+18}{4} - \dfrac{3}{7}(s-3) = 4.$

11. $\dfrac{1}{10}(7w+1) - \dfrac{1}{4}(w-9) = 1.$

12. $\dfrac{3(x-1)}{10} - \dfrac{5x+7}{3} = \dfrac{17}{6}.$

13. $\dfrac{4b+1}{2} - \dfrac{1}{3}(2b+3) = \dfrac{5b-1}{4}.$

14. $\dfrac{n+5}{2} - \dfrac{1}{3}(4n+9) = \dfrac{1}{9}(5n+8).$

15. $\dfrac{6t-1}{4} - \dfrac{1}{10}(8t+3) = \dfrac{1}{5}(4t-3).$

16. $\dfrac{7x-8}{14} - \dfrac{7x+6}{4x} = \dfrac{x-5}{2} - \dfrac{4x+9}{7x}.$

SOLUTION: 1. Multiply both members by $28x$, the L. C. M. of the denominators.

2. $\cancel{28x} \cdot \dfrac{(7x-8)}{\cancel{14}}^{2x} - \cancel{28x} \cdot \dfrac{(7x+6)}{\cancel{4x}}^{7} = \cancel{28x} \cdot \dfrac{(x-5)}{\cancel{2}}^{14x} - \cancel{28x} \cdot \dfrac{(4x+9)}{\cancel{7x}}^{4}$

3. $\therefore 2x(7x-8) - 7(7x+6) = 14x(x-5) - 4(4x+9).$

4. $\therefore 14x^2 - 16x - 49x - 42 = 14x^2 - 70x - 16x - 36.$

5. $\therefore -65x - 42 = -86x - 36.$

6. $\therefore +21x = +6.$

7. $\therefore x = \tfrac{6}{21} = \tfrac{2}{7}.$

Check the solution either by substitution or by going over the steps carefully.

SIMPLE EQUATIONS

It is essential that roots of fractional equations be checked. For reasons that are given in a later course in algebra, whenever the *apparent root* makes the denominator of any fraction zero, *that number is not a root at all.*

17. $\dfrac{6}{a} - \dfrac{1}{a} = \dfrac{5}{3}.$

18. $\dfrac{5}{4m} - \dfrac{2}{3m} = \dfrac{7}{48}.$

19. $\dfrac{3}{4x} + \dfrac{7}{x} = 15\tfrac{1}{2}.$

20. $\dfrac{x-2}{5x} = \dfrac{4}{x} - 2.$

21. $\dfrac{12}{x} - \dfrac{2x+8}{5x} + 3 = 0.$

22. $\dfrac{5t+4}{2t} - \dfrac{11t-2}{6t} = 3.$

23. $\dfrac{3m-5}{4} - \dfrac{9m-7}{12} = \dfrac{2}{3m}.$

24. $\dfrac{30}{7} - \dfrac{10x+9}{21x} + \dfrac{7}{3x} = 0.$

25. $\dfrac{5x-4}{5} - \dfrac{10x+9}{10} = \dfrac{51}{6x}.$

26. $\dfrac{r-3}{2r} = \dfrac{1}{3} - \dfrac{3r-7}{2r}.$

27. Solve the equation $\dfrac{2}{x-2} - \dfrac{5}{x+2} - \dfrac{2}{x^2-4} = 0.$

SOLUTION: 1. The L. C. M. of $(x-2)$, $(x+2)$, and (x^2-4) is (x^2-4). Multiplying both members of the equation by x^2-4,

2. $(x^2-4) \cdot \dfrac{2}{(x-2)} - (x^2-4) \cdot \dfrac{5}{(x+2)} - (x^2-4) \cdot \dfrac{2}{(x^2-4)} = (x^2-4) \cdot 0.$

3. $\therefore 2(x+2) - 5(x-2) - 2 = 0.$

4. $\therefore 2x + 4 - 5x + 10 - 2 = 0.$

5. $\therefore -3x + 12 = 0.$

6. $\therefore -3x = -12,$ or, $x = 4.$

28. $\dfrac{12}{x-2} = 3.$

29. $\dfrac{10}{m-3} = \dfrac{9}{m-5}.$

30. $\dfrac{x+5}{x-3} + \dfrac{4}{x-3} = 5.$

31. $\dfrac{5x+1}{2x-3} + 3 = \dfrac{x}{2x-3}.$

32. $\dfrac{4-x}{1-x} = \dfrac{12}{3-x} + 1.$

33. $\dfrac{2x}{3x-4} = \dfrac{4x+5}{6x-1} - \dfrac{3}{3x-4}.$

34. $\dfrac{15x^2 - 5x - 8}{3x^2 + 6x + 4} = 5.$

35. $\dfrac{6x+5}{2x^2-2x} + \dfrac{2}{x^2-1} = \dfrac{3x}{x^2-1}.$

ALGEBRA

36. $\dfrac{3m}{2m+3} - \dfrac{2m}{2m-3} = \dfrac{2m^2-15}{4m^2-9}$.

37. $\dfrac{9}{3t-5} - \dfrac{2}{t-2} = \dfrac{1}{t-3}$.

38. $\dfrac{3}{r-2} - \dfrac{4}{2r-1} = \dfrac{1}{r+4}$.

39. $\dfrac{2(y-7)}{y^2+3y-28} + \dfrac{y-2}{y-4} - \dfrac{y+3}{y+7} = 0$.

40. $\dfrac{a+2}{a-4} - \dfrac{2a-3}{a+3} = \dfrac{26-a^2}{a^2-a-12}$.

41. $\dfrac{3m}{2m-6} - \dfrac{4}{5m-15} = \dfrac{1}{2}$.

42. $\dfrac{3a}{2a-5} - \dfrac{7}{3a+1} = \dfrac{3}{2}$.

43. $\dfrac{2z+1}{2z-16} - \dfrac{2z-1}{2z+12} = \dfrac{9z+17}{z^2-2z-48}$.

44. $\dfrac{2t+7}{6t-4} - \dfrac{3t-5}{9t+6} = \dfrac{17t+7}{9t^2-4}$.

45. $\dfrac{3x-2}{x+3} = \dfrac{36-4x}{x^2-9} - \dfrac{2+3x}{3-x}$.

46. Solve the equation $\dfrac{6x+1}{15} - \dfrac{2x-4}{7x-16} = \dfrac{2x-1}{5}$.

SOLUTION: 1. Clear of fractions only partially at first by multiplying by the L. C. M. of 15 and 5.

M_{15}: $\qquad 6x + 1 - \dfrac{15(2x-4)}{7x-16} = 6x - 3$.

2. Transposing and uniting terms, $4 = \dfrac{30x-60}{7x-16}$.

3. $M_{(7x-16)}$. $\qquad 28x - 64 = 30x - 60$.

4. Completing the solution, $x = -2$.

Check it by substitution.

47. $\dfrac{2a-1}{2} - \dfrac{a+2}{2a+5} = \dfrac{6a-5}{6}.$

48. $\dfrac{y}{3} + \dfrac{2y^2}{3y-4} = \dfrac{y-2}{9}.$

49. $\dfrac{2x+7}{14} - \dfrac{5x-4}{3x+1} = \dfrac{x+6}{7}.$

50. $\dfrac{5t+1}{5} - \dfrac{4t+7}{5t+8} - \dfrac{3t-2}{3} = 0.$

EXERCISE 87

1. Divide 56 into two parts such that five eighths of the greater shall exceed seven twelfths of the less by 6.

2. If the base of a certain rectangle be increased by 2 feet, the altitude is equal to one third of the result. The perimeter of the rectangle is 36 feet. Find the base, altitude, and area of the rectangle.

3. A has $52 and B has $38. After giving B a certain sum, A has left only three sevenths as much money as B then has. What sum was given to B?

4. Divide 45 into two parts such that the sum of four ninths of the greater and two thirds of the smaller shall equal 24.

5. The denominator of a certain fraction exceeds the numerator by 27; if 9 be subtracted from both terms of the fraction, the value of the fraction becomes $\frac{1}{4}$. Find the fraction.

6. A's age is three eighths of B's, and 8 years ago it was two sevenths of B's age. Find their ages at present.

7. Washington was admitted to the Union 18 years before Oklahoma, and may therefore be said to be 18 years older than Oklahoma as a state. One fourth of Washington's age in 1911 exceeded Oklahoma's age by $1\frac{1}{2}$ years. Find the year when each was admitted.

8. If a certain number be diminished by 23, one fourth of the result is as much less than 37 as the number is greater than 56. Find the number.

9. If the number of states admitted to the Union since its formation by the 13 original states is diminished by 9, the quotient obtained by dividing that number by 2 equals the original number of states. Find the present number of states (1912).

10. The numerator of a certain fraction is 6 less than the denominator; if the denominator is increased by 1 and the resulting fraction be multiplied by 3, the product equals $\frac{5}{4}$. Find the fraction.

11. Find the angle such that 3 times its complement increased by two thirds of its supplement equals 137°.

12. I buy some bulbs from a seed store for $3, paying 75¢ per dozen for one variety, and 50¢ per dozen for another variety. The number of the first variety purchased exceeds the number of the second variety by 18. Find the number of each variety purchased.

13. If a railroad train consists of a certain type of passenger engine, one parlor car, and five sleeping cars, its value is $129,200. The value of each sleeping car exceeds the value of the engine by $300; the value of the parlor car is five sixths of the remainder when the cost of the engine is diminished by $100. Find the value of the engine, the parlor car, and of a sleeping car.

14. A man has $3000 invested, part at 5% and part at 6%. His total income per year is $157. How much has he invested at each rate?

15. In 1912, the "age" of Maine was $4\frac{2}{11}$ times that of Wyoming; in 1920, it will be $3\frac{1}{3}$ times it. Find when each state was admitted to the Union.

SIMPLE EQUATIONS

16. The denominator of a certain fraction is 7 less than the numerator; if 5 be added to the numerator, the value of the fraction becomes $\frac{9}{5}$. Find the fraction.

17. The income at 5% on one sum of money exceeds by $35.50 the income at 4% on a sum which is $350 less than the first. Find the two sums invested.

18. The denominator of a certain fraction exceeds the numerator by 5; if the denominator be decreased by 20, then the resulting fraction, increased by 1, is equal to twice the original fraction. Find the fraction.

19. The supplement of a certain angle divided by its complement gives as quotient $2\frac{1}{2}$. Find the angle.

20. If twice a certain number be diminished by 5 and the result be divided by the number, the quotient exceeds 1 by a fraction whose numerator is 7 more than the number and whose denominator is 3 less than the number. Find the number.

142. Work Problems. If a man can do a piece of work in 8 days, then in one day he can do *one eighth* of it, and in three days he can do *three eighths* of it.

If a man can do a piece of work in x days, then in one day he can do $\frac{1}{x}$ part of it, and in 5 days he can do $5 \times \frac{1}{x}$ or $\frac{5}{x}$ part of it.

EXERCISE 88

1. If a man can plow a field in 15 days, what part can he plow in one day? in 4 days? in x days?

2. If a machine can do a piece of work in x days, how much can it do in one day? in 7 days?

3. A can do a piece of work in 5 days, and B the same work in 8 days.

(*a*) How much can A do in one day? in x days?
(*b*) How much can B do in one day? in x days?

(c) How much can they do together in one day? in x days?

(d) How much can A do in 2 days?

(e) How much can B do in 3 days?

(f) How much can they do together if A works 2 days and B 3 days?

Equations

4. A can do a piece of work in 10 hours and B can do it in 5 hours; how long will it take them to do it together?

SOLUTION: 1. Let x = the number of hours it will take them to do it together.

2. A does $\frac{1}{10}$ in 1 hour; $\therefore$ he will do $\frac{x}{10}$ in x hours.

B does $\frac{1}{5}$ in 1 hour; $\therefore$ he will do $\frac{x}{5}$ in x hours.

$\therefore$ they will do $\left(\frac{x}{10}+\frac{x}{5}\right)$ in x hours.

3. They complete the task in x hours. Represent the whole task by $\frac{10}{10}$ of itself or by 1.

4. $\qquad \therefore \frac{x}{10}+\frac{x}{5}=1.$

5. M_{10}: $\qquad x+2x=10.$

6. $\qquad 3x=10, x=3\frac{1}{3}$ hours, or 3 hours and 20 minutes

5. A painter can paint a house alone in 5 days, and an apprentice can do it alone in 15 days. In how many days can they do it if they work together?

6. A man can plow a certain field in 6 days; his son can plow it in 9 days. How long will it take them to plow the field if they work together?

7. In a newspaper office there is one machine which can print the morning issue of the paper in 2 hours, and another which can do it in 3 hours. In how many hours can they turn out the edition, if they are run together?

8. A can do a piece of work in 15 hours, and B can do it in 18 hours. If A works for 7 hours, how many hours must B work to complete the task?

SIMPLE EQUATIONS

9. A can do a piece of work in 15 hours, while B can do it in 25 hours. After A has worked a certain time, B completes the work. If B works 9 hours longer than A, how long did A work?

10. A can do a piece of work in 18 days. If he and B can do three fifths of it in 6 days, how long will it take B alone to do the work?

143. Problems about the Lever. A teeter board is one form of *lever*. The point which supports the lever is called the *fulcrum*; the parts of the lever to the right and left of the fulcrum are called the *lever arms*.

If the weights L and R just balance, it is well known that, if R moves farther to the right, while L is stationary, then the right side goes down; and if R moves toward the fulcrum, then the right side goes up. Thus, the influence of R upon the lever depends both upon the weight of R and its distance from the fulcrum.

The influence of a weight upon a lever is called its *leverage*. It can be shown that the *leverage of a weight is measured by the product of the weight and its distance from the fulcrum*.

Thus, if R weighs 50 pounds and is 4 feet from the fulcrum, its leverage is 200; and, if L weighs 80 pounds and is $2\frac{1}{2}$ feet from the fulcrum, its leverage is $80 \times 2\frac{1}{2}$ or 200 also. The two will balance.

This truth may be tested in the following manner.

1. Remove a side and an end from a crayon box. Balance a stiff ruler on the edge of the box (the fulcrum).

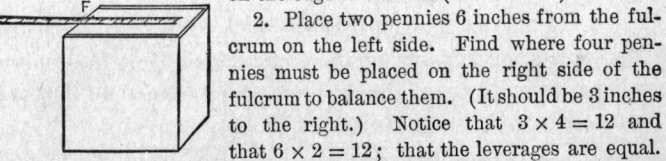

2. Place two pennies 6 inches from the fulcrum on the left side. Find where four pennies must be placed on the right side of the fulcrum to balance them. (It should be 3 inches to the right.) Notice that $3 \times 4 = 12$ and that $6 \times 2 = 12$; that the leverages are equal.

3. Find where 3 pennies must be placed, on the right, to balance the 2 pennies on the left. Find the leverage of the 3 pennies and compare it with the leverages in step 2.

4. Keeping the two pennies 6 inches to the left, place two others 2 inches to the right, and 2 four inches to the right. The ruler should be in perfect balance again.

The leverage of the first two pennies on the right is 2×2 or 4; of the second two, is 2×4 or 8; $4 + 8 = 12$.

EXAMPLE. Suppose that the weights and distances in the figure are:

A. 40 pounds; distance 5 feet.
B. 45 pounds; distance 4 feet.
C. 55 pounds; distance 6 feet.
D. 60 pounds; distance 6 feet.
E. 50 pounds; distance x feet.

Where must E be placed so that the lever will balance?

SOLUTION: 1. The leverages are:

A. $5 \times 40 = 200$.   *C.* $6 \times 55 = 330$.   *E.* $50 \times x = 50\,x$.
B. $4 \times 45 = 180$.   *D.* $6 \times 60 = 360$.

2. $\therefore 200 + 180 + 330 = 360 + 50\,x$.
$\therefore 350 = 50\,x$
$\therefore 7 = x$.

Rule. — To make a simple lever balance:

The sum of the leverages of all weights (forces) on one side of the fulcrum must equal the sum of the leverages of all weights (forces) on the other side of the fulcrum.

EXERCISE 89

1. A boy weighing 70 pounds sits 6 feet from the fulcrum and balances a boy who is sitting $3\frac{1}{2}$ feet from the fulcrum on the other side. Find the weight of the second boy.

2. A, weighing 96 pounds, sits $5\frac{1}{2}$ feet to the left of the fulcrum. If B weighs 66 pounds, where must he sit on the right in order to balance A?

SIMPLE EQUATIONS

3. A, who weighs 92 pounds, and B, who weighs 115 pounds, wish to sit at the ends of a teeter board which is 9 feet long. How far from A must the fulcrum be placed so that they will balance?

4. A boy wishes to carry two heavy packages over his shoulder by balancing them at the ends of a stiff rod which is 4 feet long. If one package weighs 20 pounds and the other 30 pounds, how far from the end upon which the 20 pound package is carried must the rod rest upon his shoulder?

5. Three children, weighing 62, 75, and 89 pounds respectively, arrange themselves upon a teeter board, the first sitting 4 feet from the fulcrum, and the second 5 feet from the fulcrum on the same side. Where must the third sit in order to balance the other two?

6. Three boys, A weighing 73 pounds, B weighing 95 pounds, and C weighing 65 pounds, sit on a teeter. A is 5 feet from the fulcrum on the left side, B is on the other side 4 feet away, C is on the left side 4 feet away. Can two other boys weighing 80 pounds and 115 pounds respectively arrange themselves one on each side and at equal distances from the fulcrum so as to balance the teeter? Where must the boy weighing 80 pounds sit?

144. Additional Distance, Rate, and Time Problems.

EXERCISE 90

1. What is meant by "the rate"? "the time"? "the distance"? (§ 83.)

2. Give a simple arithmetical problem involving time, rate, and distance.

3. What is the rule for finding the

(*a*) distance when the rate and time are known?

(*b*) rate when the time and distance are known?

(*c*) time when the rate and distance are known?

4. The rate of one train exceeds that of another by 5 miles per hour. Let r represent the rate of the slow train.

(a) Express the rate of the faster train.

(b) Express the time required by each train in going 100 miles.

5. The rate of one train is $\frac{3}{5}$ that of another. Let x represent the rate of the faster train.

(a) Express the time each requires for a trip of 50 miles.

(b) Form an equation to express the fact that the time of the slow train exceeds that of the faster train by 1 hour.

6. The time required by one train in going a certain distance is $\frac{3}{2}$ that of another train. Express the time of the slow train by t.

(a) Express the rate at which each train travels in going a distance of 100 miles in the time mentioned.

(b) Form an equation to express the fact that the rate of the faster train exceeds the rate of the slow train by 20 miles per hour.

Equations

7. The rate of an express train is three times that of a slow train. It covers 180 miles in 8 hours less time than the slow train. Find the rate of each train.

8. A messenger starts out to deliver a package to a point 24 miles distant, at the rate of 8 miles per hour. At what rate must a second messenger travel to arrive at the same time as the first messenger, if he starts 1 hour after him?

9. The rate of a passenger train exceeds twice the rate of a freight train by 5 miles per hour. It can go 350 miles while the freight train goes 150 miles. Find the rate of each train.

10. A man just missed a train. He knew that it would stop at a station 15 miles distant from the central station and decided to try to catch it by going to the second station in an automobile. If the train runs at the rate of 20 miles per hour, at what rate must he travel in the automobile in order to arrive at the station 10 minutes ahead of the train, if it takes him 5 minutes to get the automobile and if it is 20 miles to the station by road?

River Problems

On a river, the direction in which the water is flowing is called *downstream*, and the opposite direction is called *upstream*. When going downstream, a boat is carried along by the *current* of the river and whatever force is exerted within the boat; when coming upstream, its progress is retarded by the current of the river. This is something like the effect of the wind upon a person who is walking, when going with the wind, he is carried along by it, and when going against the wind, he is retarded by it.

11. The rate of the current of a river is 3 miles per hour: (*a*) at what rate will some boys go downstream if their own rowing is at the rate of 5 miles per hour in still water? (*b*) upstream?

12. How long will it take the boys in Example 11: (*a*) to go 24 miles downstream? (*b*) 24 miles upstream? (*c*) for the trip down and back?

13. (*a*) How long will it take the same boys to go d miles downstream? (*b*) d miles upstream? (*c*) Form an equation to express the fact that the time down and back is 5 hours. (*d*) Find d from the equation in step (*c*).

14. Some boys who can row 4 miles an hour in still water made a trip on a river whose current is 2 miles an hour. If it took them 8 hours for the trip, how far did they go?

15. A party take a trip in a motor boat which runs at the rate of 15 miles an hour. They take 3 hours for the trip. What distance did they go, if the rate of the current is 3 miles an hour?

EXERCISE 91

Supplementary Problems

1. Three times the difference between one fourth and one tenth of a certain number exceeds five by one fifth of the number. Find the number.

2. A's age 11 years from now divided by his age 11 years ago is the fraction $\frac{16}{5}$. Find his present age.

3. The width of a room is three fifths of its length; if 12 feet be added to the width and taken from the length, the room will be a square. Find its dimensions.

4. Five lines radiate from a point making angles such that the second is one half of the first, the third is twice the first, the fourth is the sum of the second and third, and the fifth is three times the third. Find the angles. (See § 13.)

5. Find the three angles of a triangle if the second angle is one half of the remainder obtained by diminishing the first angle by 1°, and if the third angle is $\frac{4}{3}$ of the remainder obtained by diminishing the first angle by 7°. (See § 13.)

6. Two men, A and B, 57 miles apart, travel towards each other, B starting 20 minutes after A. A travels at the rate of 6 miles an hour and B at the rate of 5 miles an hour. How far will each have traveled when they meet?

7. Washington's Monument, the highest piece of masonry in the world, consists of a main shaft surmounted by a pyramid. The height of the main shaft exceeds that of the pyramid by 445 feet; if the height of the pyramid be decreased by 5 feet and the result be divided by the height of the main shaft, the quotient is the fraction $\frac{1}{10}$. Find the height of the two parts of the monument.

8. The rate of an express train is five thirds of that of a slow train. It travels 36 miles in 32 minutes less time than the slow train. Find the rate of each train.

SIMPLE EQUATIONS

9. If the third of three consecutive even numbers is divided by each of the first two in turn, the difference of the fractions obtained is equal to the quotient of 7 divided by three times the first number. Find the numbers.

10. A workman does one third of a piece of work in 5 days; he and a second workman complete the task together in 4 days. How manys days would it take the second man to do the work alone?

11. Some boys row on a river whose current is known to be $2\frac{1}{2}$ miles per hour. They find that it takes them as long to go upstream 2 miles as downstream 7 miles. What is their rate of rowing?

12. A's age exceeds twice B's age by 7 years. The sum of three fifths of B's age 2 years ago and of four sevenths of A's age 4 years from now is 26 years. Find their present ages.

13. The income on one sum of money at $4\frac{1}{2}\%$ and the income on a sum $600 greater at $3\frac{1}{2}\%$ together amount to $421 per year. Find the total amount invested.

HINT: $4\frac{1}{2}\% = \frac{9}{2}\% = \frac{9}{200}$.

14. The rate of an express train is three halves that of a slow train. It covers 270 miles in 3 hours less time than the slow train. Find the rate of the train.

15. A water reservoir can be filled by an old pump in 12 hours. After a new one is installed, it is found that the reservoir can be filled by the two pumps together in 4 hours. How long would it take the new pump alone to fill the reservoir?

16. A man invests a sum of money in $4\frac{1}{2}\%$ stock and a sum $180 greater than the first in $3\frac{1}{2}\%$ stock. If the incomes from the two investments are equal, find the sums invested.

17. Some boys are rowing on a river whose current is 5 miles per hour in one stretch and 3 miles in another. They find when going downstream that they can go 4 miles where the current is rapid in the same time that they can go 3 miles where the current is slower. Find the rate at which they row in still water?

The following three equations arise in the solution of three problems in applied mathematics. Solve them.

18. $80\,T - \tfrac{1}{2}gT^2 = 80(T-2) - \tfrac{1}{2}g(T-2)^2$, where $g = 32$. Determine T.

19. $\dfrac{5 \times 7.7}{x} = 13.6 + \dfrac{5-x}{x}$. Get the result to two decimals.

20. $\dfrac{9\,v}{10} + \dfrac{.0013\,x\,v}{10} = xv$. Determine x.

SOLUTION OF LITERAL EQUATIONS

145. A **Literal Equation** is one in which some or all of the known numbers are represented by letters.

EXAMPLE 1. $2x + a = 7a - x$.

The problem is to determine a number x, such that the equation is satisfied for all values of a.

SOLUTION: 1. $\qquad 2x + a = 7a - x$.
2. Transposing, $\qquad 3x = 6a$.
3. D_3: $\qquad x = 2a$.
CHECK: Does $\qquad 2(2a) + a = 7a - 2a$?
Does $\qquad 4a + a = 7a - 2a$? Yes.

This solution means that the number x is always double the number a.

EXAMPLE 2. Determine the number x in the equation
$$(b - cx)^2 - (a - cx)^2 = b(b-a).$$

SOLUTION: 1. $\qquad (b-cx)^2 - (a-cx)^2 = b(b-a)$.
2. Expanding, $(b^2 - 2bcx + c^2x^2) - (a^2 - 2acx + c^2x^2) = b^2 - ab$.
3. $\qquad \therefore b^2 - 2bcx + c^2x^2 - a^2 + 2acx - c^2x^2 = b^2 - ab$.
4. Transposing and uniting terms, $\quad 2acx - 2bcx = a^2 - ab$.
5. Factoring, $\qquad 2cx(a-b) = a(a-b)$.
6. $D_{2c(a-b)}$: $\qquad \dfrac{2cx(a-b)}{2c(a-b)} = \dfrac{a(a-b)}{2c(a-b)}$.
7. $\qquad \therefore x = \dfrac{a}{2c}$.

SIMPLE EQUATIONS

CHECK: Does $\left(b - \dfrac{ac}{2c}\right)^2 - \left(a - \dfrac{ac}{2c}\right)^2 = b(b-a)$?

Does $b^2 - ab + \dfrac{a^2}{4} - a^2 + a^2 - \dfrac{a^2}{4} = b^2 - ab$? Yes.

NOTE. After simplifying the equation until it takes the form of the equation in step 5, divide both members of the resulting equation by the coefficient of x.

EXERCISE 92

Solve the following equations for x:

1. $3x - 5a = 2(a + x)$.
2. $5(x - 3b) = 3x - 11b$.
3. $a(3bx - 2a) = b(2a - 3bx)$.
4. $5rx - 6s = 3(rx - s)$.
5. $ax - ac = bx - bc$.
6. $ax - a^2 = -b(b + x)$.
7. $r(x - r) = s(s + 2r - x)$.
8. $c(x - c^2) = d(d^2 - x)$.
9. $x - 1 - \dfrac{x-2}{m} = \dfrac{1}{m^2}$.
10. $\dfrac{m^2}{nx} - \dfrac{1}{m} = \dfrac{1}{n} - \dfrac{n^2}{mx}$.
11. $\dfrac{a-x}{5bx} = \dfrac{10b-a}{15ax} - \dfrac{1}{3a}$.
12. $\dfrac{x^2 - b}{ax} - \dfrac{b-x}{a} = \dfrac{2x}{a} - \dfrac{b}{x}$.
13. $2n\left(\dfrac{n}{2} + \dfrac{mx}{n}\right) = 4\left(m^2 + \dfrac{n^2}{4}\right)$.
14. $\dfrac{x-a}{x} + \dfrac{2x}{x-a} = 3$.
15. $\dfrac{3x-4}{3x+4} = \dfrac{5m-2n}{5m+2n}$.
16. $\dfrac{2x+3a}{2x-3b} = \dfrac{3x+4b}{3x-4a}$.
17. $\dfrac{x+n}{x-m} - \dfrac{x-n}{x+m} = \dfrac{2(m+n)^2}{x^2 - m^2}$.
18. $\dfrac{2nx-3}{nx-1} = 5 - \dfrac{9nx+2}{3nx-1}$.
19. $\dfrac{a}{x-a} - \dfrac{b}{x-b} = \dfrac{a^2 - b^2}{b(x-b)}$.
20. $\dfrac{ax-b}{bx} + \dfrac{bx+a}{ax} = 2 + \dfrac{a-b}{abx}$.
21. $\dfrac{10x - 3a}{3a} = \dfrac{9x - 5a^3}{3a^3} - \dfrac{3(x + 2a^3)}{a^3}$.
22. $\dfrac{x}{2} - \dfrac{a - 2bcx}{4bc} = \dfrac{5x}{6c} - \dfrac{8ac - 8bx - 9a}{12bc}$.

23. $\dfrac{x-b}{x-2a} - \dfrac{x+b}{x+2a} = \dfrac{4a^2}{x^2-4a^2}.$

24. $\dfrac{3x(a-b)}{x^2-b^2} - \dfrac{a-2b}{x+b} = \dfrac{a-b}{x-b}.$

25. $\dfrac{2x}{3x-a} - \dfrac{3a}{x+2a} = \dfrac{2x^2+ax}{3x^2+5ax-2a^2}.$

146. Applied Algebra. Some of the equation problems given up to this point illustrate one use of algebra; an unknown number may sometimes be found by means of an equation if numerical relations involving the number are known. In order to solve the equations that arise, skill in the fundamental operations (§ 16), factoring, and fractions, is necessary.

In § 17 and § 94, another application of algebra is illustrated; a *formula* is often used to express in convenient form a rule of computation. In *deriving formulæ* and in using them, all of the algebra so far studied, and much more, frequently, is necessary.

147. Deriving and Using Formulæ. Three examples of the methods of deriving formulæ will be given, besides those in § 17.

EXAMPLE 1. Derive a formula for the total area of the walls of a room in terms of the height, length, and width.

SOLUTION : 1. Let h = the height of the room in feet.
Let w = the width of the room in feet.
Let l = the length of the room in feet.
Let S = the total area of the walls in square feet.

2. Then, hw = the area of one end wall in square feet.
hw = the area of the other end wall.
hl = the area of one side wall.
hl = the area of the other side wall.

3. $\therefore S = hw + hw + hl + hl = 2hw + 2hl.$
$\therefore S = 2h(w + l).$

Thus, if the height is 9 feet, the width 14 feet, and the length 18 feet, the total area of the walls is

$$S = 2 \times 9 \times (14 + 18) = 18(32) = 576 \text{ square feet.}$$

SIMPLE EQUATIONS

Example 2. Derive formulæ for two numbers whose sum is a and such that the larger exceeds the smaller by b.

Solution: Let $\qquad s =$ the smaller number.
Then, $\qquad s + b =$ the larger number.

2. $\qquad \therefore s + (s + b) = a$, or $2s + b = a$.

$$\therefore 2s = a - b, \text{ or } s = \frac{a-b}{2}.$$

$$\therefore s + b = \frac{a-b}{2} + b = \frac{a+b}{2}.$$

The smaller number is $\dfrac{a-b}{2}$ and the larger number is $\dfrac{a+b}{2}$.

Thus, if a is 25 and b is 7, the smaller number is $\dfrac{25-7}{2}$ or $\dfrac{18}{2}$, or 9, and the larger is $\dfrac{25+7}{2}$, or 16.

$$9 + 16 = 25 \text{ and } 16 = 9 + 7.$$

Example 3. Derive a formula for the *rate* in terms of the *amount*, the *principal*, and the *time*.

Solution: 1. The formula for the amount (§ 44) is

$$A = P + \frac{Prt}{100}.$$

2. M_{100}: $\qquad 100 A = 100 P + Prt$.
3. S_{100P}: $\qquad 100 A - 100 P = Prt = (Pt)r$.
4. D_{Pt}: $\qquad \dfrac{100 A - 100 P}{Pt} = r$, or $r = \dfrac{100(A-P)}{Pt}$.

This formula enables us to find r when A, P, and t are known. Thus, if a man receives $3500 at the end of 6 years from an investment of $2400, what rate of simple interest has his money earned?

Here, $\qquad A = \$3500, P = \$2400, \text{ and } t = 6$.

$$\therefore r = \frac{\cancel{100}(3500 - 2400)}{\underset{24}{\cancel{2400}} \times 6} = \frac{1100}{144} = 7.6^+;$$

that is, the rate is 7.6 %.

In the following list of examples, a number of formulæ, taken from physics, chemistry, geometry, and engineering, are given. It is impossible to show in this text how these formulæ are derived, as that calls for special knowledge of these various subjects.

ALGEBRA

EXERCISE 93

(a) Express each of the first 6 formulæ in words.
(b) Solve each of them for the letters indicated.

1. $A = ab$.   (a) Solve for a; (b) for b. (§ 17)

2. $A = \dfrac{ab}{2}$.   (a) Solve for a; (b) for b. (§ 17)

3. $C = 2\pi r$.   Solve for r. (§ 17)

4. $V = lwh$.   (a) Solve for w; (b) for h. (§ 17)

5. $V = \tfrac{1}{3} bh$.   (a) Solve for b; (b) for h. (§ 17)

6. $F = \tfrac{9}{5} C + 32$.   Solve for C. (§ 84)

7. $A = \dfrac{a(b+c)}{2}$ is a formula from geometry.

   (a) Find A when $a = 15$; $b = 24$; and $c = 20$.
   (b) Find c when $A = 550$; $b = 30$; and $a = 22$.
   (c) Solve the formula for a; (d) for b.

8. $A = P + \dfrac{Prt}{100}$.

   (a) Solve for P.   (b) for t.

9. $T = \dfrac{1}{a} + t$ is a formula from physics.

   (a) Solve it for t.   (b) for a.

10. $mg - T = mf$ is a formula from physics.
    (a) Solve it for T; (b) for f; (c) for m.

11. $u = \left(\dfrac{m}{M+m}\right)v$ is a formula from physics.

    (a) Solve it for m; (b) for M.

12. $C = \dfrac{Kab}{b-a}$ is a formula from physics.

    (a) Solve it for a; (b) for b.

SIMPLE EQUATIONS

13. $s = \dfrac{c-b}{b-a}$ is a formula from physics.

(a) Solve it for b; (b) for a.

14. $h = k(1 + \frac{1}{273} t)$ is a formula from physics.
(a) Solve it for t; (b) for k.

15. $l = \dfrac{L-M}{Mt}$ is a formula from physics.

(a) Solve it for L; (b) for M.

16. $w = \dfrac{5a}{1 + \dfrac{l^2}{600\, d^2}}$ is a formula from engineering.

(a) Find w, correct to two decimals, when $a = 18$, $l = 12$, and $d = 10$.

(b) Solve the formula for a.

17. $p = \dfrac{ad^2}{t} + d$ is a formula from engineering.

(a) Find p when $a = .56$, $d = \frac{1}{4}$, $t = \frac{3}{8}$.
(b) Solve the formula for t.

18. $C = \dfrac{E}{R + \dfrac{r}{n}}$ is a formula from physics.

(a) Simplify it in the right member.
(b) Solve it for n; (c) for r.

19. $F = \dfrac{mv^2}{gr}$ is a formula from physics.

(a) Find F when $m = 150$, $v = 25$, $g = 32$, and $r = 5$.
(b) Solve it for r; (c) for m.

20. $\dfrac{1}{f} = \dfrac{1}{p} + \dfrac{1}{q}$ is a formula from physics.

(a) Find p when $f = 30$ and $q = 40$.
(b) Solve it for p; (c) for q.

XII. GRAPHICAL REPRESENTATION

148. Certain mathematical relations may be represented by means of geometrical figures. Paper ruled as in the figures below is used; such paper is called **Coördinate Paper**.

Figure 1 is an illustration of this manner of comparing numbers. The lines represent the lengths of some of the rivers of America. The side of one square represents 200 miles; from this fact, the lengths of the rivers may be determined.

Such representations of number relations are called **Graphical Representations**, or simply **Graphs**.

EXERCISE 94

1. Determine the lengths of the rivers in Fig. 1.

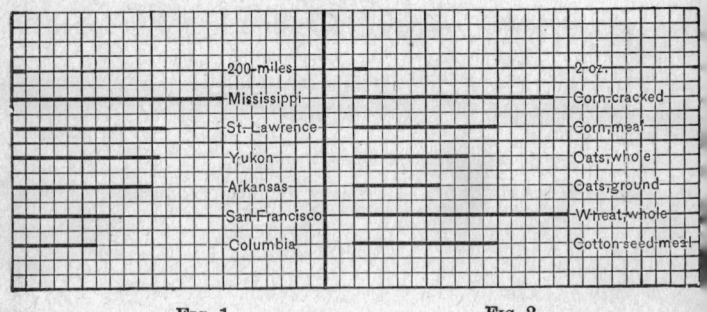

FIG. 1   FIG. 2

2. In Fig. 2, the weight per quart of certain grains is represented. Find the weight of each kind of grain.

3. Find the length of each line in Fig. 3, and arrange your results in the form of a table; when:

206

GRAPHICAL REPRESENTATION

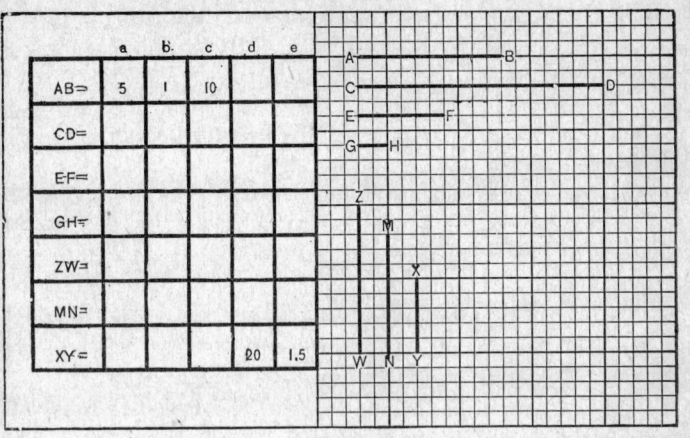

Fig. 3

Represent by means of lines the following sets of statistics:

4. A family used the following amounts of gas during the months of the year:

January	3600 cu. ft.	July	2300 cu. ft.
February	3200 cu. ft.	August	2200 cu. ft.
March	2900 cu. ft.	September	3100 cu. ft.
April	3100 cu. ft.	October	3200 cu. ft.
May	2900 cu. ft.	November	2800 cu. ft.
June	2900 cu. ft.	December	2200 cu. ft.

HINT. Let the side of one square represent 100 cu. ft., or 200 cu. ft.; then represent the various given numbers by lines of appropriate length.

5. The same family used the following amounts of electricity during the months of the year.

January	27 k.w.	July	10 k.w.
February	27 k.w.	August	8 k.w.
March	24 k.w.	September	18 k.w.
April	19 k.w.	October	42 k.w.
May	15 k.w.	November	49 k.w.
June	9 k.w.	December	45 k.w.

A k.w. is a "kilowatt-hour," the unit used for measuring the quantity of electricity consumed.

6. The following statistics give in cents the cost per pound of certain common articles of food in 1910.

Wheat	2.5	Egg	20
Rye	3	Bacon	22.5
Navy Beans	6	Milk	4
Potatoes	1.3	Apples	5
Rice	10	Oatmeal	10
Beefsteak	17	Buckwheat	2.5

7. The average hourly velocity of wind in miles at the following points in the United States is:

Boise, Idaho	4	Portland, Me.	5
Atlanta, Ga.	9	Vicksburg, Miss.	6
Buffalo, N. Y.	11	Philadelphia, Pa.	10
Duluth, Minn.	7	Chicago, Ill.	9
Omaha, Neb.	8	Boston, Mass.	11

8. The average annual precipitation (rain and melted snow), in inches, at the following cities is:

San Diego, Cal.	10	Mobile, Ala.	62
Denver, Colo.	14	Flagstaff, Ariz.	23
Springfield, Ill.	37	Salt Lake City, Utah	16
Dubuque, Ia.	34	Wilmington, N.C.	51
Baltimore, Md.	43	Portland, Me.	42.5

149. In drawing the graph of a set of statistics, the paper is usually prepared as in Fig. 4. Two lines are drawn at right angles. The numbers to be represented are examined in order to decide what number shall be represented by the side of one square. The number represented by one side of a square is called the **Unit**.

Instead of drawing full lines to represent the various numbers, it is customary to place points where the lines of proper length would end. Finally these points are connected by a smooth line. One line, that at 11 A.M., is drawn in full in this graph.

GRAPHICAL REPRESENTATION

EXAMPLE 1. Draw a graph representing the temperature readings at the hours indicated.

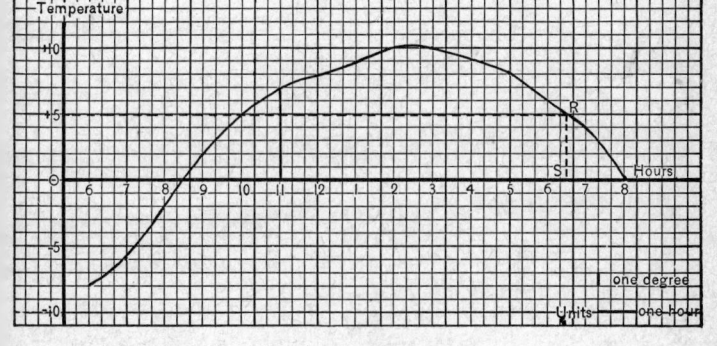

6 A.M.	−8°	11 A.M.	+7°	4 P.M.	+9°
7 A.M.	−6°	12 M.	+8°	5 P.M.	+8°
8 A.M.	−2°	1 P.M.	+9°	6 P.M.	+6°
9 A.M.	+2°	2 P.M.	+10°	7 P.M.	+4°
10 A.M.	+5°	3 P.M.	+10°	8 P.M.	0

FIG. 4

Notice that the units of time and of temperature are indicated; that the line upon which the hours are indicated is placed near the center of the paper to allow for the *negative* temperatures; that the vertical line is placed at the left edge to allow space for all of the hours of the day; that the line connecting the points is made a smooth curve. Review § 24.

150. The graph in Fig. 4 may be used to illustrate another advantage of graphical representation.

A graph may assist in finding new information.

What was the approximate temperature at 6.30 P.M.?

SOLUTION: 1. On the graph, the point *S* would indicate the time 6.30

2. The point *R*, above it on the graph, indicates the temperature.

3. *R* is opposite + 5° on the vertical line.

4. The approximate temperature then at 6.30 P.M. was 5°.

ALGEBRA

EXERCISE 95

1. Draw a graph representing the following temperature readings:

6 A.M.	$+12°$	1 P.M.	$+16°$
7 A.M.	$+14°$	2 P.M.	$+12°$
8 A.M.	$+18°$	3 P.M.	$+6°$
9 A.M.	$+20°$	4 P.M.	$0°$
10 A.M.	$+22°$	5 P.M.	$-4°$
11 A.M.	$+22°$	6 P.M.	$-6°$
12 M.	$+19°$	7 P.M.	$-7°$

2. From the graph in 1, find the approximate temperature at 7.30, 8.30, 11.30, 2.30, 5.30.

3. Get the temperature readings in your own school district to-morrow, and draw the graph.

4. In order to protect his orchard from a frost, a man tried to warm the air in the orchard by burning oil heaters. Below are given the temperature readings within the heated area and outside of it. Plot the two sets of readings on the same sheet, making one line for the readings within the heated area, and one for the other readings.

Time	Temperature Inside	Outside	Time	Temperature Inside	Outside
8.00	35°	35°	10.30	36°	32°
8.15	38°	35°	11.00	35°	31°
8.30	39°	33°	11.30	36.5°	30°
8.45	40°	32°	12.00	36.5°	28°
9.00	40°	34°	12.30	34.5°	27°
9.30	40°	34°	1.00	34.5°	27°
10.00	40°	34°			

5. Savings banks and trust companies pay compound interest on money left with them; that is, interest upon interest.

The following table shows the amount of money which must be saved annually at 4 % compound interest to amount to $1000 in a definite number of years. (To simplify the problem even dollars are taken.)

10 years	$80	25 years	$23
15 years	$48	30 years	$17
20 years	$32	35 years	$13

6. Assume that a train leaves station A at 1 P.M. and that it arrives at F and J, the distances of which from A are given, at the times indicated. Draw the graph representing the time when the train reaches points between these three stations, making the graph a **broken** line, (/‾‾‾) From the graph, determine when the train reaches the other points, thus making a time-table for the train between A and H.

A. 0 miles. 1 P.M.
B. 6 miles.
C. 15 miles.
D. 24 miles.
E. 42 miles.
F. 60 miles. 3 P.M.
G. 80 miles.
H. 104 miles.
I. 120 miles.
J. 140 miles. 5 P.M.

HINT. If possible, lay off the distances on the horizontal line, making the unit 2 or 6 miles, and the time on the vertical line, making the unit 6 or 12 minutes.)

7. Complete the following table showing the number of dollars simple interest at 6% on $100 for the number of years indicated and draw the graph.

1 year; interest $6.
2 years; interest $12.
3 years; interest ?
4 years; interest ?
5 years; interest ?
6 years; interest ?
7 years; interest ?
8 years; interest ?

8. From the graph, determine the interest for 5 years and 6 months.

151. Certain terms used in mathematics in connection with graphical representation will now be given. Referring to Fig. 5 below: the lines XX' and YY', drawn at right angles, are called **Axes**: XX', the **Horizontal Axis**, and YY', the **Vertical Axis**; the point O is called the **Origin**. From P, perpendiculars

are drawn to the axes; the line *PR* is called the **Ordinate** of *P*,
and the line *PS* is called the **Abscissa** of *P*; together they are
called the **Coördinates** of *P*. The axes are called **Coördinate
Axes**. On the axes, the scale used is indicated. The distances

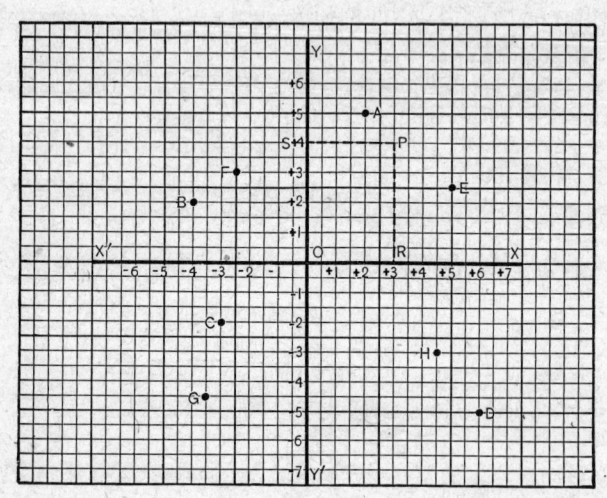

FIG. 5

on *OX* are positive, on *OX'* are negative; on *OY* are positive,
and on *OY'* are negative. The abscissa of *P* is 3 and the
ordinate is 4: the point *P* is called **The Point** (3, 4). Notice
that the *abscissa* is written *first*, and the *ordinate, second*.

EXERCISE 96

1. What is the abscissa of the point *A*? *B*? *C*? *D*?
2. What is the ordinate of the point *A*? *B*? *C*? *D*?
3. What are the coördinates of *E*? *F*? *G*? *H*?
4. Prepare a piece of graph paper similar to that used for Fig. 5. Locate the points: (3, 6); (4, 2); (5, −3); (−2, 5); (−4, −6).

GRAPHICAL REPRESENTATION

5. Locate the points $A : (1, 1)$; $B : (2, 6)$; $C : (11, 6)$; $D : (10, 1)$.

Draw the lines AB, BC, CD, and AD. What figure is formed? Draw the diagonals of the figure, and find the coördinates of the point where they meet.

6. Locate the points $A : (3, -5)$; $B : (4, -2)$; $C : (7, -2)$; $D : (8, -5)$; $E : (7, -8)$; $F : (4, -8)$. Draw the lines joining the points in order. What figure is formed?

152. The numbers which are represented graphically in mathematics are usually connected by an equation.

EXAMPLE. Draw the graph of the equation

$$\frac{x}{2} + \frac{y}{4} = 1.$$

SOLUTION: **1.** Solve the equation for y.

M_4: $\qquad 2x + y = 4.$
S_{2x}: $\qquad y = 4 - 2x.$

2. Select any value of x and find the corresponding value of y. Thus, if $x = 1$, $y = 4 - 2 = 2$. Similarly:

when $x =$	-5	-3	-1	0	$+2$	$+4$	$+6$	$+7$
then $y =$	$+14$	$+10$	$+6$	$+4$	0	-4	-8	-10

3. Use the pairs of numbers so obtained as coördinates of points; thus, locate the points $(-5, +14)$; $(-3, +10)$; $(-1, +6)$; etc.

4. Draw the line connecting the points. (Graph on page 214.)

Notice that the graph seems to be a straight line. The coördinates of the point A on the graph are $+3.5$ and -3. Do these satisfy the equation?

$$\frac{x}{2} + \frac{y}{4} = 1.$$

Does $\dfrac{3.5}{2} + \dfrac{-3}{4} = 1$?

Does $1.75 + (-.75) = 1$? Yes.

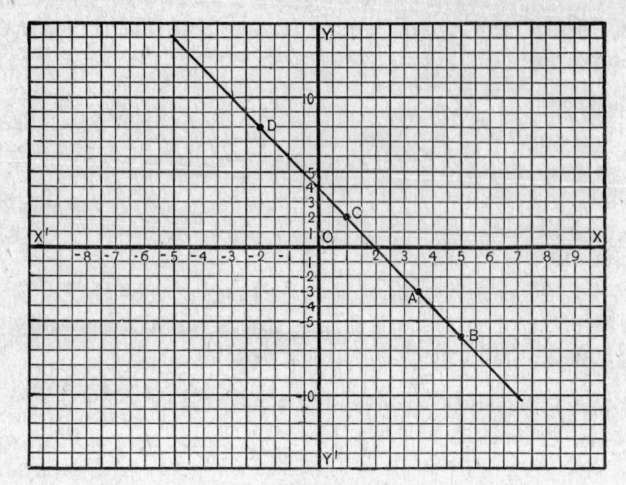

Fig. 6

EXERCISE 97

1. Determine the coördinates of B, C, and D. Determine whether they satisfy the equation of the graph?

2. Select any point not on the graph, find its coördinates, and determine whether they satisfy the equation of the graph.

3. Similarly, draw the graph of $y = x + 3$. For x select the values $-1, -2, -3, -4, +1, +2, +3, +4, 0$. What does the graph appear to be?

4. Select three new points which are on the resulting graph, find their coördinates, and determine whether they satisfy the equation given in Example 3.

5. Draw the graph of $\dfrac{y}{2} - \dfrac{x}{6} = 1$.

Select at least four negative and four positive values of x, and from them determine the corresponding values of y. What sort of graph do you obtain?

6. Select any three points on the graph and determine whether their coördinates satisfy the equation.

153. The equations in the preceding paragraph have each had *two unknown numbers*. The following facts are to be remembered from the examples of § 152:

1. The graph of an equation of the first degree (§ 77) having two unknowns is a straight line. For this reason, first degree equations are also called *linear equations*.

2. The coördinates of every point on the line satisfy the equation.

3. The coördinates of every point not on the line do not satisfy the equation.

154. A Solution of an equation having two or more unknowns is a set of values of the unknowns which satisfy the equation.

Be careful not to confuse the word "solution" in the sense of this paragraph with the same word when it is used to mark the process of solving an example as is done in the text.

EXAMPLE. Consider the equation $x + y = 5$.

(1, 4) is a solution because $1 + 4 = 5$.
(-8, $+13$) is a solution because $-8 + 13 = 5$.

155. Number of Solutions. There are an indefinitely large number of points upon a straight line. This is expressed by saying that there are an *infinite number* of points on a straight line. Since the coördinates of each point satisfy the equation of the line, then: *there are an infinite number of solutions of a linear equation with two unknowns.*

This fact is evident also because for every value of one of the unknowns, a value of the other may be found.

EXAMPLE. Consider the equation $2x + 3y = 15$.

When $x = 1$, $2 \cdot 1 + 3y = 15$ or $3y = 13$, $y = 4\frac{1}{3}$;
then $\quad\quad\quad x = 1$, $y = 4\frac{1}{3}$ is one solution.

Similarly when,

$\quad\quad x = 2;\quad y = 1\frac{1}{3}.\quad\quad x = -3;\ y = +7.$
$\quad\quad x = 3;\quad y = 3.\quad\quad\quad x = -5;\ y = +8\frac{1}{3}.$

Thus as *x* changes in value, in such an equation, *y* also changes in value, acquiring a new value. *x* and *y* are said to *vary*, and are called **Variables**. Hereafter these equations will be called *equations having two variables*.

An equation of the first degree having two variables has an infinite number of solutions.

Such equations are called **Indeterminate Equations**.

156. The graph of an indeterminate linear equation with two variables is always a straight line by § 153. A straight line may be drawn with a ruler as soon as two of its points are known. This leads to the

Rule. — To draw the graph of a linear equation having two variables:

1. Select one value for one variable and determine the corresponding value of the other variable; this gives one solution.

2. Determine a second solution as in step 1.

3. Plot the two points whose coördinates are the pairs of numbers and connect them with a straight line.

4. Check the result by finding a third solution, and plotting the corresponding point. The third point should fall upon the graph obtained in step 3.

EXAMPLE. Draw the graph of $4x - 3y = 6$.

SOLUTION: 1. Let $x = 0$; then $y = -2$.

$(4 \cdot 0 - 3y = 6; \; -3y = 6; \; y = -2.)$

2. Let $x = 3$; then $y = 2$.

$(4 \cdot 3 - 3y = 6; \; -3y = 6 - 12; \; -3y = -6; \; y = 2.)$

3. Plot the points and draw the line. See Fig. 7.

CHECK: Let $x = 6$; then $y = 6$. Is this point on the line?

NOTE. To get the best results, it is necessary to use coördinate paper for the following exercises. Fair results may be obtained by using paper ruled by the pupil.

GRAPHICAL REPRESENTATION

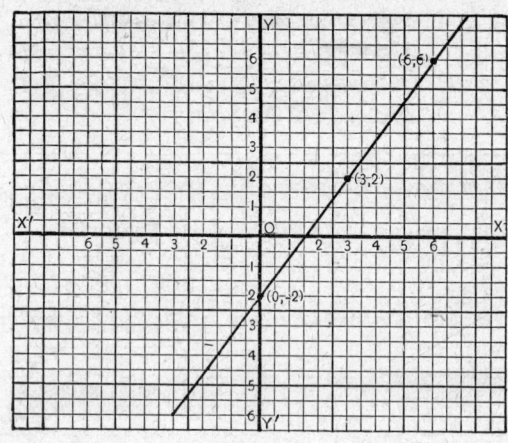

Fig. 7

EXERCISE 98

Draw the graphs of the following equations, each on a separate sheet of graph paper:

1. $x + y = 5$.
2. $2x - y = 6$.
3. $2x + 3y = 6$.
4. $3x - 2y = 12$.
5. $5x + 4y = 20$.
6. $3x - 5y = 15$.
7. $7x + 4y = 2$.
8. $5x - 3y = -6$.
9. $x - 6y = -10$.
10. $3x = 5 - 7y$.

157. Independent Equations and Simultaneous Equations.

EXAMPLE. Draw upon the same sheet the graph of

$$2x - y = 4. \qquad (1)$$
$$2x + 3y = 12. \qquad (2)$$

SOLUTION: 1. For equation 1: $2x - y = 4$.
If $x = 0$, $y = -4$; if $y = 0$, $x = +2$.
Solutions: $(0, -4)$ and $(+2, 0)$.

2. For equation 2: $2x + 3y = 12$.
If $x = 0$, $y = 4$; if $y = 0$, $x = 6$.

Solutions: $(0, +4)$ and $(+6, 0)$.

3. See Fig. 8 for the graphs.

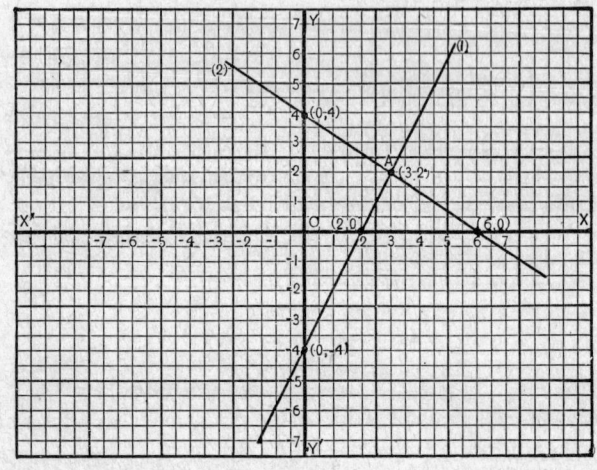

FIG. 8

QUESTIONS: **1.** What is true about the coördinates of all points on line 1? (§ 153.)

2. What is true about the coördinates of all points on line 2?

3. What then is true of the coördinates of point A?

4. Are there any other points whose coördinates will satisfy both equations?

Two equations, each having two variables, are called **Independent Equations** when each has solutions which do not satisfy the other. Thus, the equations above are independent. Their graphs are two different straight lines.

Two linear equations which are independent and which have one common solution are called **Simultaneous Linear Equations**. Their graphs cross at one point. The above equations are simultaneous since they have the common solution (3, 2).

GRAPHICAL REPRESENTATION

Rule. — To determine graphically the common solution of two simultaneous linear equations having two variables:

1. Draw upon one sheet the graphs of both equations.

2. Find the coördinates of the point common to the two lines. This is the common solution.

3. Test the common solution by substituting it in both equations.

HISTORICAL NOTE. One of the notable advances in mathematics is intimately associated with the subject of this chapter. The idea of representing some geometrical figures by algebraic expressions occurred to mathematicians early. In the 14th century, Oresme, a French mathematician, discussed certain mathematical ideas by means of coördinates. He, however, used only positive coördinates, thus confining himself to what is called the first quadrant.

To the French mathematician, Descartes (1596–1650), is due the extension of the use of coördinates. He considered negative as well as positive coördinates and also discussed two or more lines, or curves, drawn with respect to the same system of coördinate axes. His improvement brought with it a better understanding of negative numbers and of negative roots of equations, and laid the foundation for Analytic Geometry, one of the subjects of great interest to mathematicians.

EXERCISE 99

Determine graphically which of the following pairs of equations are simultaneous, and which are *dependent;* if simultaneous, find their common solution:

1. $\begin{cases} a + b = 5. \\ a - b = 9. \end{cases}$

2. $\begin{cases} 2x + y = 7. \\ 2x - y = 5. \end{cases}$

3. $\begin{cases} x + 2y = 12. \\ 3x - y = 1. \end{cases}$

4. $\begin{cases} 3x - 2y = -12. \\ 4x + 2y = -2. \end{cases}$

5. $\begin{cases} 2x + y = 4. \\ 6x + 3y = 12. \end{cases}$

6. $\begin{cases} 5x + 2y = 10. \\ x - y = 9. \end{cases}$

7. $\begin{cases} 3a - 2b = 6. \\ 6a - 4b = 12. \end{cases}$

8. $\begin{cases} 5x - 6y = 8. \\ 9x - 4y = -6. \end{cases}$

9. Draw on one sheet the graphs of the following equations and thus determine whether they have a common solution:

(a) $5x - 2y = 7$; (b) $3x + 2y = 17$; (c) $x - 3y = -9$.

10. Determine whether the following equations have a common solution:

(a) $2x - y = 8$; (b) $2x - y = 4$; (c) $2x + 3y = 20$.

158. Inconsistent Equations. Two equations may be independent (§ 157), and yet not be simultaneous; that is, they may not have a common solution. The graphs of two simultaneous linear equations are two intersecting straight lines.

Two independent linear equations which do not have a common solution are called **Inconsistent Equations**. Their graphs are parallel lines.

EXERCISE 100

Determine graphically which sets of equations are inconsistent; if simultaneous, determine the common solution.

1. $\begin{cases} x - 3y = 6. \\ 2x - 6y = -18. \end{cases}$

2. $\begin{cases} 5a - 2b = 10. \\ 15a - 6b = -24. \end{cases}$

3. $\begin{cases} 2x - 3y = 18 \\ x + 3y = 0. \end{cases}$

4. $\begin{cases} 4m - 3n = 12. \\ 16m - 12n = 24. \end{cases}$

5. $\begin{cases} 2x - 5y = -16. \\ 3x + 7y = 5. \end{cases}$

6. $\begin{cases} 2x + 3y = 6. \\ 4x + 6y = 8. \end{cases}$

159. Sometimes it is difficult to find the common solution accurately by this graphical method. As an example, find the common solution of the pair of equations:

(1) $5x - 9y = 11$; (2) $3x + 7y = 9$.

In the next chapter, other methods of solving simultaneous linear equations are given.

XIII. SIMULTANEOUS LINEAR EQUATIONS

DEFINITIONS

160. If a rational and integral monomial (§ 113) involves two or more letters, its degree *with respect to them* is denoted by the sum of their exponents.

Thus, $2\,a^2bxy^3$ is of the *fourth* degree with respect to x and y.

161. If each term of an equation containing one or more unknown numbers is rational and integral, the **Degree of the Equation** is the degree of its term of highest degree.

Thus, if x and y represent unknown numbers,

$ax - by = c$ is an equation of the *first* degree;
$x^2 + 4x = -2$ is an equation of the *second* degree;
$2x^2 - 3xy^2 = 5$ is an equation of the *third* degree.

162. An equation of the first degree is also called **a Linear Equation**.

163. A **Solution** of an equation with two unknowns is a set of values of the unknowns which together satisfy the equation.

Thus $x = 12$ and $y = 2$ is a solution of $x + 2y = 16$.

A linear equation with two unknowns has an *infinite* number of solutions. A solution is obtained by assigning any value to one unknown and finding the corresponding value of the other unknown. Thus:

(a) Some of the solutions of the equation $x + 2y = 16$ are:

$x = +1$	$+2$	-4	$+10$	$+20$
$y = +7.5$	$+7$	$+10$	$+3$	-2

(b) Some of the solutions of the equation $x - 2y = 4$ are:

$x = +1$	$+2$	-4	$+10$	$+20$
$y = -1.5$	-1	-4	$+3$	$+8$

222 ALGEBRA

An equation with two unknowns is called an **Indeterminate Equation,** and the unknowns are called **Variables.**

164. Two linear equations, each containing two variables, are said to be **Independent Equations** if each has solutions which are not solutions of the other.

The two equations in § 163 are independent. Why?

The equations $x + y = 5$ and $2x + 2y = 10$ are not independent; for the second equation can be reduced to the form of the first by dividing each term by 2; hence every solution of one equation is also a solution of the other. They are called *dependent* equations.

165. Two independent linear equations having *one common solution* are called **Simultaneous Equations.**

The two equations in § 163 are simultaneous. Why?

166. Two independent linear equations which do not have any common solution are called **Inconsistent Equations.**

The equations $x + 2y = 16$ and $2x + 4y = 21$ are inconsistent.

167. To **Solve** a *set* of simultaneous equations is to find their common solution.

EXAMPLE 1. Solve the equations $\begin{cases} 5x - 3y = 19. & (1) \\ 7x + 4y = 2. & (2) \end{cases}$

SOLUTION: 1. M_4* (1): $\qquad 20x - 12y = 76.$ (3)

2. M_3 (2): $\qquad 21x + 12y = 6.$ (4)

3. Add (3) and (4): $\qquad 41x = 82.$ (5)

4. D_{41} (5): $\qquad x = 2.$ (6)

5. Substitute this value of x in (1): $10 - 3y = 19.$ (7)

$\qquad\qquad\qquad\qquad\qquad\qquad -3y = 9.$ (8)

$\qquad\qquad\qquad\qquad\qquad\qquad y = -3.$ (9)

6. The common solution is $\qquad x = 2, y = -3.$

CHECK: Substitute in (1): $\qquad 10 + 9 = 19.$

Substitute in (2): $\qquad 14 - 12 = 2.$

---

* See § 42 for the symbol M_4. Read this "multiply both members of equation (1) by 4."

SIMULTANEOUS LINEAR EQUATIONS

NOTICE: 1. That, in equations (1) and (2), the coefficients of y are not the same.

2. That, by multiplications, the coefficients of y are made the same in absolute value in equations (3) and (4).

3. That, by addition, $12\,y$ disappears in equation (5), and that $20\,x$ and $21\,x$ are combined, giving $41\,x$. This is allowable because we assume that x and y represent the same numbers respectively in all of the equations, namely, the particular numbers which together form the common solution of equations (1) and (2). y is said to be **Eliminated.**

Elimination means to cause to disappear; thus y was made to disappear by adding the two equations (3) and (4).

4. That the remaining number, x, is then easily found.

The solution is an example of **Elimination by Addition.**

EXAMPLE 2. Solve the equations $\begin{cases} 15\,a + 8\,b = 1. & (1) \\ 10\,a - 7\,b = -24. & (2) \end{cases}$

SOLUTION: 1. M_2 (1): $\qquad\qquad 30\,a + 16\,b = 2.$ (3)

2. M_3 (2): $\qquad\qquad 30\,a - 21\,b = -72.$ (4)

3. Subtract (4) from (3): $\qquad\qquad 37\,b = 74.$ (5)

4. D_{37} (5): $\qquad\qquad b = 2.$ (6)

5. Substitute the value of b in (1): $\quad 15\,a + 16 = 1.$ (7)

$\qquad\qquad\qquad\qquad\qquad\therefore 15\,a = -15.$ (8)

$\qquad\qquad\qquad\qquad\qquad\therefore a = -1.$ (9)

The solution is: $\qquad\qquad a = -1;\ b = +2.$

Substitute the values of a and b in equations (1) and (2).

The solution is an example of **Elimination by Subtraction.**

Rule. — To solve two simultaneous linear equations having two variables by the addition or subtraction method of elimination:

1. Multiply, if necessary, both the first and second equations by such numbers as will make the coefficients of one of the variables of equal absolute value.

2. If the coefficients have the same sign, subtract one equation from the other; if they have opposite signs, add the equations.

3. Solve the equation resulting from step 2 for the other variable.

4. Substitute the value of the variable found in step 3 in any equation containing both variables, and solve for the remaining variable.

5. Check the solution by substituting it in both of the original equations.

ALGEBRA

HISTORICAL NOTE. Little progress was made in solving linear equations having more than one unknown until the latter part of the 15th century, although mathematicians before that time had considered such problems. After Stifel and Stevin had introduced somewhat simple notations for several unknowns and their powers, definite methods for solving equations of the first degree with two unknowns were developed. Johannes Buteo, a French monk, (1492–1572), solved equations with three unknowns in a text on algebra which appeared in 1559.

EXERCISE 101

Solve by the method of addition or subtraction:

1. $\begin{cases} 3x + y = 11. \\ 5x - y = 13. \end{cases}$

2. $\begin{cases} 4a + 3b = -1. \\ 5a + b = 7. \end{cases}$

3. $\begin{cases} r - 6s = -10. \\ 2r - 7s = -15. \end{cases}$

4. $\begin{cases} 5m + 4n = 22. \\ 3m + n = 9. \end{cases}$

5. $\begin{cases} 7c - 2d = 31. \\ 4c - 3d = 27. \end{cases}$

6. $\begin{cases} 5a + 3b = -9. \\ 3a - 4b = -17. \end{cases}$

7. $\begin{cases} 6x + 2y = -3. \\ 5x - 3y = -6. \end{cases}$

8. $\begin{cases} 3s + 7t = 4. \\ 7s + 8t = 26. \end{cases}$

9. $\begin{cases} 11p - 5q = 4. \\ 8p - 6q = 10. \end{cases}$

10. $\begin{cases} 5r - 9y = 1. \\ 8r - 10y = -5. \end{cases}$

11. $\begin{cases} 8c + 9t = 3. \\ 8c - 9t = 77. \end{cases}$

12. $\begin{cases} 6x - 11y = -4. \\ 15x + 4y = 53. \end{cases}$

13. $\begin{cases} 3x + 7y = 2. \\ 7x + 8y = -2. \end{cases}$

14. $\begin{cases} 4v + 15g = 7. \\ 14v + 6g = 9. \end{cases}$

15. $\begin{cases} 28x - 36y = 1. \\ 14x + 15y = 6. \end{cases}$

16. $\begin{cases} 7x + 9y = 8. \\ 9x - 8y = 69. \end{cases}$

17. $\begin{cases} 2x - \frac{5}{2}y = 13. \\ \dfrac{x}{3} + \dfrac{y}{5} = \dfrac{14}{15}. \end{cases}$

18. $\begin{cases} \dfrac{7}{6}r + 2 = \dfrac{s}{2}. \\ \dfrac{s}{4} - \dfrac{r}{3} = 1\frac{3}{4}. \end{cases}$

19. $\begin{cases} \frac{3}{8}m + n = \frac{1}{4}. \\ \dfrac{m}{2} - \dfrac{5n}{7} = 1\frac{5}{14}. \end{cases}$

20. $\begin{cases} \dfrac{a}{4} + \dfrac{b}{5} = 1. \\ \dfrac{2a}{9} + 2 = \dfrac{b}{9}. \end{cases}$

SIMULTANEOUS LINEAR EQUATIONS

168. Elimination by Substitution is a second common method of solving simultaneous equations.

EXAMPLE. Solve the equations $\begin{cases} 7x - 9y = 15. & (1) \\ 8y - 5x = -17. & (2) \end{cases}$

SOLUTION: 1. Solve (1) for x in terms of y:

$$7x = 15 + 9y;\ x = \left(\frac{15 + 9y}{7}\right). \qquad (3)$$

2. Substitute this value of x in (2):

$$8y - 5\left(\frac{15 + 9y}{7}\right) = -17. \qquad (4)$$

3. M$_7$ (4): $\qquad 56y - 5(15 + 9y) = -119.$ $\qquad$ (5)

4. Expanding: $\qquad 56y - 75 - 45y = -119.$ $\qquad$ (6)

5. Combining: $\qquad 11y - 75 = -119.$ $\qquad$ (7)

6. A$_{75}$: $\qquad 11y = -44.$

7. D$_{11}$: $\qquad y = -4.$

8. Substituting the value of y in (3):

$$x = \frac{15 + 9(-4)}{7} = \frac{15 - 36}{7} = \frac{-21}{7} = -3.$$

9. The solution is: $x = -3,\ y = -4$. Check it by substitution in equations (1) and (2).

NOTE. In step 3, when multiplying $5\left(\dfrac{15 + 9y}{7}\right)$ by 7, one obtains $7 \cdot \dfrac{5(15 + 9y)}{7}$. The 7's cancel, giving the result $5(15 + 9y)$.

Rule. — To solve two simultaneous linear equations having two variables by the substitution method of elimination:

1. Solve one equation for one variable in terms of the other variable.

2. Substitute for this variable in the other equation the value found for it in step 1.

3. Solve the equation resulting in step 2 for the second variable.

4. Substitute the value of the second variable, obtained in step 3, in any equation containing both variables and solve for the first variable.

5. Check the solution by substituting it in the original equations.

226 ALGEBRA

HISTORICAL NOTE. The earliest use of the Substitution Method of Elimination in print, of which we have any record, is in Newton's Arithmetica Universalis, in 1707.

EXERCISE 102

Solve by the substitution method:

1. $\begin{cases} 3m + 2n = 17. \\ 4m + n = 16. \end{cases}$

2. $\begin{cases} r - 6s = 2. \\ 3s - 8r = 29. \end{cases}$

3. $\begin{cases} 5x + 8y = +2. \\ 10x - 12y = +32. \end{cases}$

4. $\begin{cases} 2x + 5y = 13. \\ 7x - 4y = -19. \end{cases}$

5. $\begin{cases} 8x + 5y = 18. \\ 16x - 3y = 10. \end{cases}$

6. $\begin{cases} 8p + 5q = 5. \\ 3p - 2q = 29. \end{cases}$

7. $\begin{cases} 5m - 12n = -31. \\ 3m + 22n = -4. \end{cases}$

8. $\begin{cases} 2x - 3y = -14. \\ 3x + 7y = 48. \end{cases}$

9. $\begin{cases} 5x + 9y = 8. \\ 6y - 9x = -7. \end{cases}$

10. $\begin{cases} 7r - 6t = 63. \\ 9r + 2t = 13. \end{cases}$

11. $\begin{cases} 8p + 5q = -6. \\ 12p + 10q = -5. \end{cases}$

12. $\begin{cases} 6w - 9x = 19. \\ 15w + 7x = -41. \end{cases}$

13. $\begin{cases} 15A - 12B = -54. \\ 10A + 9B = -2. \end{cases}$

14. $\begin{cases} 7M + 8N = 19. \\ 9M - 6N = 57. \end{cases}$

15. $\begin{cases} 8p - 3q = -1. \\ 4p + 6q = +7. \end{cases}$

16. $\begin{cases} 6x - 10y = 5. \\ 15y - 14x = -15. \end{cases}$

17. $\begin{cases} 9c + 8d = -6. \\ 12c + 10d = -7. \end{cases}$

18. $\begin{cases} 3e + 7f = -23. \\ 5e + 4f = -23. \end{cases}$

19. $\begin{cases} 7g + 8k = -10. \\ 11g + 6k = -19. \end{cases}$

20. $\begin{cases} 5r - 8s = 60. \\ 6r + 7s = -11. \end{cases}$

169. As a rule, the equations containing two variables do not occur in as simple form as those given in §§ 167, 168.

EXAMPLE. Solve the equations

$$\begin{cases} \dfrac{7}{x+3} - \dfrac{3}{y+4} = 0. \quad (1) \\ x(y-2) - y(x-5) = -13. \quad (2) \end{cases}$$

SIMULTANEOUS LINEAR EQUATIONS

Solution: 1. Simplify equation (1):

$$\frac{7}{x+3} - \frac{3}{y+4} = 0.$$

$$\therefore 7(y+4) - 3(x+3) = 0.$$

$$3x - 7y = 19. \tag{3}$$

2. Simplify equation (2):

$$x(y-2) - y(x-5) = -13.$$

$$2x - 5y = +13. \tag{4}$$

3. The equations (1) and (2) thus become in (3) and (4):

$$3x - 7y = 19. \tag{3}$$

$$2x - 5y = 13. \tag{4}$$

Solve these equations by either of the two methods of elimination; the solution will be found to be $x = 4$, $y = -1$.

CHECK: Substitute the values of x and y in equations (1) and (2).

Equations (3) and (4) are called the **Standard Form** of equations (1) and (2).

Rule. — To solve complicated simultaneous linear equations having two variables:

1. Reduce the equations to the standard form by clearing of fractions and simplifying.
2. Solve the resulting equations by either of the two methods.
3. Check by substituting in the original equations.

EXERCISE 103

Reduce to the standard form and solve:

1. $\begin{cases} \dfrac{2x}{3} + \dfrac{3y}{4} = \dfrac{-7}{2}. \\ \dfrac{x}{4} - \dfrac{2y}{5} = \dfrac{11}{2}. \end{cases}$

2. $\begin{cases} 8p + 7q = 12. \\ \dfrac{p+2q}{4} + \dfrac{2p+q}{3} = 1. \end{cases}$

3. $\begin{cases} 10m - \dfrac{y-5}{7} = 11. \\ 8y - \dfrac{m+3}{4} = -17. \end{cases}$

4. $\begin{cases} \dfrac{r}{3} - \dfrac{s}{2} = 1. \\ \dfrac{3+2r}{5} - \dfrac{1+5s}{11} = +2. \end{cases}$

ALGEBRA

5. $\begin{cases} \dfrac{2w}{3}+\dfrac{3t}{4}=\dfrac{1}{6}. \\ 5t-8w=\dfrac{22}{3}. \end{cases}$

6. $\begin{cases} \dfrac{r+t}{2}-\dfrac{r-t}{3}=8. \\ \dfrac{r+t}{3}+\dfrac{r-t}{4}=11. \end{cases}$

7. $\begin{cases} \dfrac{c+d-2}{c-d}=-\dfrac{1}{3}. \\ \dfrac{3c+d-3}{2d-c}=-\dfrac{1}{11}. \end{cases}$

8. $\begin{cases} \dfrac{3}{x-1}+\dfrac{4}{y-1}=0 \\ \dfrac{5}{2x-3}-\dfrac{7}{2y+13}=0. \end{cases}$

9. $\begin{cases} \dfrac{5}{m-2}+\dfrac{7}{2n-3}=0. \\ \dfrac{1}{2m+5}+\dfrac{8}{3n-7}=0. \end{cases}$

10. $\begin{cases} \dfrac{6+a-b}{1-a-b}=-\dfrac{7}{4}. \\ 2a+3b=-1. \end{cases}$

11. $\begin{cases} \dfrac{x+5y}{13}-\dfrac{2y+x}{11}=-1. \\ 3x-y=2. \end{cases}$

12. $\begin{cases} \dfrac{y}{3}-\dfrac{x}{2}=2. \\ \dfrac{3-2x}{5}-\dfrac{4+5y}{11}=4. \end{cases}$

13. $\begin{cases} (m+1)(n+9)-(m+5)(n-7)=112. \\ 2m+3n+9=0. \end{cases}$

14. $\begin{cases} \dfrac{r-s}{2}=\dfrac{25}{6}-\dfrac{r+s}{3}. \\ \dfrac{r+s-9}{2}-\dfrac{s-r-6}{3}=0. \end{cases}$

15. $\begin{cases} \dfrac{w-2}{5}-\dfrac{10-w}{3}-\dfrac{p-10}{4}=0. \\ \dfrac{p+2}{6}-\dfrac{2w+p}{32}-\dfrac{w+13}{16}=0. \end{cases}$

16. $\begin{cases} \dfrac{x-y}{3}-\dfrac{2x+y}{2}=0. \\ \dfrac{x+2y}{2}-\dfrac{x}{4}=-\dfrac{11}{4}. \end{cases}$

17. $\begin{cases} \dfrac{4a+b}{5}-\dfrac{6a-3b}{3}=-3. \\ \dfrac{8a+5b}{2}-\dfrac{10a-b}{7}=-4. \end{cases}$

SIMULTANEOUS LINEAR EQUATIONS

170. Certain equations in which the variables occur in the denominators of fractions may be solved readily without clearing the equations of fractions.

EXAMPLE. Solve the equations
$$\begin{cases} \dfrac{10}{x} - \dfrac{9}{y} = 8. & (1) \\ \dfrac{8}{x} + \dfrac{15}{y} = -1. & (2) \end{cases}$$

SOLUTION: Eliminate the term containing y:

1. M_5 (1): $\qquad \dfrac{50}{x} - \dfrac{45}{y} = 40.$ \hfill (3)

2. M_3 (2): $\qquad \dfrac{24}{x} + \dfrac{45}{y} = -3.$ \hfill (4)

3. Add (4) and (3): $\qquad \dfrac{74}{x} = 37.$ \hfill (5)

$\qquad\qquad\qquad\qquad \therefore 74 = 37\, x \text{ or } x = 2.$ \hfill (6)

4. Substitute 2 for x in (1): $5 - \dfrac{9}{y} = 8.$ \hfill (7)

5. Solve (7) for y: $\qquad y = -3.$

CHECK: Substitute $x = 2$, $y = -3$ in equations (1) and (2).

EXERCISE 104

Solve the following sets of equations:

1. $\begin{cases} \dfrac{9}{a} + \dfrac{10}{b} = -1. \\ \dfrac{6}{a} + \dfrac{15}{b} = +1. \end{cases}$

2. $\begin{cases} \dfrac{10}{c} - \dfrac{9}{d} = 4. \\ \dfrac{8}{c} - \dfrac{15}{d} = \dfrac{9}{2}. \end{cases}$

3. $\begin{cases} 2p + \dfrac{5}{q} = -11. \\ 4p - \dfrac{3}{q} = \dfrac{21}{2}. \end{cases}$

4. $\begin{cases} \dfrac{1}{x} + \dfrac{1}{y} = 5. \\ \dfrac{1}{x} - \dfrac{1}{y} = 1. \end{cases}$

5. $\begin{cases} \dfrac{3}{r} - \dfrac{1}{s} = 9. \\ \dfrac{4}{r} + \dfrac{3}{s} = -1. \end{cases}$

6. $\begin{cases} \dfrac{6}{w} + \dfrac{4}{v} = \dfrac{4}{5}. \\ \dfrac{9}{w} + \dfrac{5}{v} = \dfrac{7}{10}. \end{cases}$

7. $\begin{cases} \dfrac{2}{A} - \dfrac{3}{B} = -1. \\ \dfrac{5}{A} - \dfrac{6}{B} = -\dfrac{1}{2}. \end{cases}$

8. $\begin{cases} \dfrac{4}{r} - \dfrac{3}{t} = 17. \\ \dfrac{5}{r} + \dfrac{6}{t} = -\dfrac{3}{2}. \end{cases}$

9. $\begin{cases} \dfrac{5}{3x} - \dfrac{7}{y} = \dfrac{29}{9}. \\ \dfrac{3}{x} + \dfrac{5}{4y} = -\dfrac{9}{8}. \end{cases}$

10. $\begin{cases} \dfrac{5}{2x} - \dfrac{4}{3y} = \dfrac{1}{2}. \\ \dfrac{2}{3x} - \dfrac{1}{2y} = \dfrac{7}{72}. \end{cases}$

171. In solving problems where two or more letters are used to represent unknown numbers, *as many independent equations* must be obtained from the conditions of the problem *as there are letters used*.

EXAMPLE 1. Four seventeenths of the greater of two numbers exceeds the less number by 5; if the greater be divided by the less, the quotient is 5 and the remainder 10. Find the two numbers.

SOLUTION: 1. Let g = the greater number,
and l = the less number.

2. Then, $\tfrac{4}{17} g = l + 5.$ (1)

3. When the greater is divided by the less, the quotient is 5 and the remainder 10; therefore,

$$g = 5l + 10. \tag{2}$$

4. Solving equations (1) and (2), $g = 85$, $l = 15$.

CHECK: $\tfrac{4}{17}$ of $85 = 20$; $20 - 15 = 5$,
and $85 = 5 \cdot 15 + 10.$

NOTE. In equation (2), use is made of the fact that the dividend equals the divisor times the quotient plus the remainder. Thus, when 17 is divided by 2,
$$17 = 8 \cdot 2 + 1.$$

EXAMPLE 2. If 3 be added to both numerator and denominator of a fraction, its value becomes $\tfrac{2}{3}$; and if 2 be subtracted from both numerator and denominator of the fraction its value becomes $\tfrac{1}{2}$. Required the fraction.

SIMULTANEOUS LINEAR EQUATIONS

SOLUTION: 1. Let $n =$ the numerator,
and $d =$ the denominator.

$$\therefore \frac{n}{d} = \text{the fraction.}$$

2. By the first condition: $\dfrac{n+3}{d+3} = \dfrac{2}{3}.$ (1)

By the second condition: $\dfrac{n-2}{d-2} = \dfrac{1}{2}.$ (2)

3. Solving the equations (1) and (2), $n = 7$, $d = 12$.

Therefore the fraction is $\tfrac{7}{12}$.

CHECK: $\dfrac{7+3}{12+3} = \dfrac{10}{15} = \dfrac{2}{3};\ \dfrac{7-2}{12-2} = \dfrac{5}{10} = \dfrac{1}{2}.$

NOTE. Check the solution by going back to the conditions of the problem.

EXERCISE 105

1. Divide 59 into two parts such that two thirds of the less shall be less by 4 than four sevenths of the greater.

2. Find two numbers such that two fifths of the greater exceeds one half of the less by 2, and four thirds of the less exceeds three fourths of the greater by 1.

3. If 5 be added to the numerator of a certain fraction, the value of the fraction becomes $\tfrac{5}{3}$; and if 5 be subtracted from its denominator, the value of the fraction becomes $\tfrac{5}{2}$. Find the fraction.

4. If 9 be added to both terms of a fraction, its value becomes $\tfrac{6}{7}$; and if 7 be subtracted from both terms of the fraction, its value becomes $\tfrac{2}{3}$. Find the fraction.

5. In 1910, the cost of 3 tons of anthracite coal in Philadelphia exceeded the cost of 4 tons of bituminous coal in Baltimore by $3.10; and the cost of 9 tons of the bituminous coal exceeded the cost of 5 tons of the anthracite by 90¢. Find the cost of the anthracite and of the bituminous coal in 1910.

6. A's age is three fifths of B's age; but in 16 years A's age will be five sevenths of B's age. Find their ages at present.

7. If twice the greater of two numbers be divided by the less, the quotient is 3 and the remainder is 7; if five times the less be divided by the greater, the quotient is 2 and the remainder is 23. Find the numbers.

8. On the tower of the City Hall of Philadelphia is a statue of William Penn. If the total height of the tower and statue be divided by the height of the statue, the quotient is 14 and the remainder is 29; the height of the statue exceeds $\frac{1}{17}$ of the height of the tower by 7 feet. Find the height of the tower and of the statue.

9. If the numerator of a fraction be trebled, and the denominator be increased by 8, the value of the fraction becomes $\frac{9}{8}$; and if the denominator be halved, and the numerator be decreased by 7, the fraction becomes $\frac{1}{4}$. Find the fraction.

10. The City Hall of Philadelphia is said to cover a greater area than any other building in the United States. One fifth of its width exceeds one sixth of its length by 13 feet; and one ninth of its length exceeds one tenth of its width by 7 feet. Find its dimensions.

11. The perimeter of a certain isosceles triangle (see p. 102) is 140 inches. The side exceeds the base by 10 inches. Find the three sides of the triangle.

12. Three years ago A's age was $\frac{4}{3}$ of B's age; but in nine years his age will be $1\frac{1}{9}$ of B's age. Find their present ages.

13. If the age of a university is reckoned from the date of its founding, then, in 1912, the age of Yale exceeded the age of Princeton by 46 years. Four years later, one half of the age of Princeton will exceed one third of the age of Yale by 13 years. Find when each was founded.

14. Twice the shorter side of a parallelogram exceeds the longer side by 5 inches; one third of the sum of the shorter side and 9 exceeds one fifth of the longer side by 3. Find the sides of the parallelogram.

SIMULTANEOUS LINEAR EQUATIONS

15. In 1912 the sum of the ages of the oldest English university, Oxford, and the oldest American university, Harvard, was 1316 years; the age of Oxford exceeded three and three fourths times the age of Harvard by 5 years. Find when each was founded.

16. If one weight is placed 8 inches from the fulcrum of a lever, it balances another weight which is 6 inches from the fulcrum; if the first weight be decreased by 3 pounds, and the second be increased by 4 pounds, the resulting weights will balance if placed 10 feet and 5 feet respectively from the fulcrum. Find the two weights (§ 143).

17. The sum of the reciprocals of two numbers is $\frac{12}{35}$. Twice the reciprocal of the greater number exceeds the reciprocal of the less number by $\frac{3}{35}$. Find the two numbers.

$\left(\text{HINT. The reciprocal of 3 is } \frac{1}{3}; \text{ of } a \text{ is } \frac{1}{a}.\right)$

18. The sum of the reciprocals of two numbers is $\frac{11}{4}$. If twice the reciprocal of the less be increased by four times the reciprocal of the greater, the sum is 8. Find the two numbers.

19. A purse contained $6.55 in quarters and dimes; after 6 quarters and 8 dimes had been taken out, the number of quarters equalled three times the number of dimes. How many of each kind of coin were there?

20. In 7 years, A will be three times as old as B, and 8 years ago he was 6 times as old. What are their present ages?

21. The length of a room exceeds its width by 4 feet. If 2 feet are added to the length, and 3 feet to the width, the area is increased by 103 square feet. Find the dimensions.

SOLUTION: 1.   Let $l =$ the number of feet in the length,
and $w =$ the number of feet in the width.
$\therefore lw =$ the area.

2. $l = w + 4.$ (1)

3. $l + 2 =$ the new length.
$w + 3 =$ the new width.
$\therefore (l+2)(w+3) =$ the new area.
4. $\therefore (l+2)(w+3) = lw + 103.$ (2)
5. Solve the equations (1) and (2), and check.

22. If a rectangular lot were 6 feet longer and 5 feet wider than it is now, it would contain 839 square feet more; if it were 4 feet longer, and 7 feet wider, it would contain 879 square feet more. Find its length and width.

23. If one weight, increased by 10 pounds, be placed 6 feet from the fulcrum, it will balance a second weight, placed $4\frac{1}{2}$ feet from the fulcrum; if the second weight, increased by 10 pounds, be placed $3\frac{1}{2}$ feet from the fulcrum, it will balance the first weight placed 6 feet from the fulcrum. Find the two weights.

24. Will weighs 50 pounds. When Will seats himself 6 feet from the fulcrum and John seats himself 4 feet from the fulcrum on the same side, they exactly balance James, who is sitting $7\frac{1}{4}$ feet from the fulcrum on the other side. When Will and John change places, they find that James must sit $7\frac{3}{4}$ feet from the fulcrum. How much do John and James weigh?

25. A crew can row 10 miles down stream in 50 minutes, and 12 miles up stream in an hour and a half. Find the rate in miles an hour of the current, and of the crew in still water.

(HINT. Review *River Problems*, Exercise 90, § 144; express 50 minutes as $\frac{5}{6}$ hour.)

26. A motor boat which can run at the rate of 15 miles an hour in still water went down stream a certain distance in 4 hours. It took 6 hours for the trip back. What was the distance and the rate of the current?

27. A crew are rowing on a stream the rate of whose current is known to be 2 miles an hour; they find that it takes them

SIMULTANEOUS LINEAR EQUATIONS

one and one third hours to go down, and four hours to come back a certain distance. Find the distance and the rate of the crew in still water.

28. An express train travels 30 miles in 27 minutes less time than a slow train. If the rate of the express train were $\frac{5}{4}$ as great, and if the rate of the slow train were $\frac{4}{5}$ as great, the express train would travel 30 miles in 54 minutes less time than the slow train. Find the rate of each train in miles an hour.

29. If a field is made 5 feet longer and 7 feet wider, its area would be increased by 830 square feet; but if its length is made 8 feet less, and its width 4 feet less, its area is diminished by 700 square feet. Find its length and width.

30. The fore wheel of a carriage makes 8 revolutions more than the hind wheel in going 180 feet; but if the circumference of the fore wheel were $\frac{4}{3}$ as great, and of the hind wheel $\frac{5}{6}$ as great, the fore wheel would make only 5 revolutions more than the hind wheel in going the same distance. Find the circumference of each wheel.

31. A man has $2500 invested from which he receives a total income of $135. Part of the money is invested at 6 % and part at $4\frac{1}{2}$ %. How much is invested in each way?

32. A man has altogether $5000 of savings. He has part invested in a 5 % bond, and the balance invested in a mortgage drawing 6 %. If his total income is $280, how much has he invested in each way?

33. A man has $1200 invested at one rate of interest and $500 at a rate which is 1 per cent greater than the former rate. The income from the first investment exceeds the income from the second investment by $23. Find the rate at which each sum is invested.

34. The simple interest on $800 at 5 % for a certain number of years exceeds the simple interest on $300 at 6 % for a

second period of years by $60. If the second period of years exceeds the first by 4 years, find the number of years each sum is invested.

35. There are two supplementary angles such that $\frac{1}{3}$ of the larger exceeds $\frac{2}{5}$ of the smaller by 5°. Find the angles. (§ 13.)

36. One angle of a triangle is 35°. If the number of degrees in one of the remaining two angles is divided by the number in the other, the quotient is 9 and the remainder is 10. Find the three angles of the triangle. (See § 13.)

37. The fastest train on the Pennsylvania R. R. makes the trip between Chicago and Fort Wayne, Indiana, a distance of 148 miles, in 1 hour and 20 minutes less time than one of the ordinary trains. Its rate is $\frac{3}{2}$ that of the ordinary train. Find the rate of each train.

38. A and B working together can do a piece of work in 6 days; they can also complete the work if A works 10 days and B 3 days. How many days would it take each of them to do the work alone? (See § 142.)

39. A and B working together can do a piece of work in $7\frac{1}{2}$ days. If A works alone for 3 days, and B alone for 6 days, they would complete $\frac{7}{12}$ of the work. Find how long it would take each alone to do the work.

40. A man has a sum of money invested at a certain rate of interest. Another man has a sum greater by $3000, invested at a rate 1 % less, and his income is $45 less than that of the first. A third man has a sum less by $2000 than that of the first, invested at a rate 1 % greater, and his income is $40 greater than that of the first. Find the capital of each man, and the rate at which it is invested.

172. Relations between the Digits of a Number. Integral numbers are written by means of the *digits*.

Thus, 372 is a number of three digits; 3 represents 300 units, 7 represents 70 units, and 2 represents 2 units.

Similarly, if t is the *tens' digit* and u is the *units' digit*, the number is $10\,t + u$.

When the digits of a number are *reversed*, a new number is formed; thus, reversing 52 gives 25. Notice that

$$52 = 10 \times 5 + 2 \text{ and } 25 = 10 \times 2 + 5.$$

Similarly, if x and y are the tens and units digits of a number, the number is $10\,x + y$; if the digits are reversed, the new tens' digit is y, the new units' digit is x, and the new number is $10\,y + x$.

EXERCISE 106

1. Write the number whose units' digit is a, tens' digit b and hundreds' digit c.

2. Write the number represented by reversing the digits in Example 1.

3. Representing the tens' digit of a number by t, and the units' digit by u represent:

(a) the sum of the digits;

(b) the number;

(c) the product of the digits;

(d) the quotient when the number is divided by the sum of the digits.

4. Representing the tens' digit of a number by x, and the units' digit by y:

(a) express the original number;

(b) express the number obtained by reversing the digits;

(c) express the quotient of the new number divided by the old number;

(d) express by an equation the fact that when the original number is divided by the sum of its digits the quotient is 5 and the remainder is 3. (See note, Example 1, § 171.)

238   ALGEBRA

5. The sum of the two digits of a number of two digits is 11; if the digits be reversed, the quotient of the new number divided by the old is 2 and the remainder is 7. Find the number.

SOLUTION: 1. Let $t = $ the tens' digit,
and $u = $ the units' digit.
$$\therefore t + u = 11. \tag{1}$$

2. $\quad 10\,t + u = $ the original number,
and $\quad 10\,u + t = $ the new number.
$$\therefore 10\,u + t = 2(10\,t + u) + 7. \tag{2}$$

3. Solving the pair of equations, (1) and (2), gives $t = 3$, $u = 8$.
∴ the number is 38.

CHECK: The sum of the digits is 11.
$83 \div 38$ gives the quotient 2 and the remainder 7.

6. The tens' digit of a number exceeds its units' digit by 4. If the digits be reversed, the new number is 6 more than one half of the old number. Find the number.

7. The sum of the two digits of a number is 9. If the digits be reversed, the quotient of the new number divided by the units' digit of the given number is 13 and the remainder is 1. Find the number.

8. The sum of the two digits of a number is 16; and if 18 be subtracted from the number, the remainder equals the number obtained by reversing the digits. Find the number.

9. If the digits of a number of two figures be reversed, the sum of the resulting number and twice the given number is 204; and if the given number is divided by the sum of its digits, the quotient is 7 and the remainder is 6. Find the number.

10. If a certain number be divided by the sum of its two digits, the quotient is 4 and the remainder is 3. If the digits be reversed, the sum of the resulting number and 23 is twice the given number. Find the given number.

SIMULTANEOUS LINEAR EQUATIONS

173. Literal Simultaneous Equations. In solving literal simultaneous equations, the addition or subtraction method of elimination is usually the best.

EXAMPLE. Solve for x and y the equations:

$$ax + by = c. \qquad (1)$$
$$rx + sy = t. \qquad (2)$$

SOLUTION: Eliminate y.

1. M_s (1): $\qquad sax + sby = sc. \qquad (3)$
2. M_b (2): $\qquad brx + bsy = bt. \qquad (4)$
3. Subtract (4) from (3): $\qquad sax - brx = sc - bt. \qquad (5)$

$$\therefore (sa - br)x = (sc - bt). \qquad (6)$$
$$\therefore x = \frac{(sc - bt)}{(sa - br)}.$$

Now, going back to (1) and (2), eliminate x.

4. M_r (1): $\qquad rax + rby = rc. \qquad (7)$
5. M_a (2): $\qquad rax + say = ta. \qquad (8)$
6. Subtract (8) from (7): $\qquad (rb - sa)y = (rc - ta).$

$$\therefore y = \frac{(rc - ta)}{(rb - sa)}.$$

The solution is: $\qquad x = \dfrac{sc - bt}{sa - br}; \quad y = \dfrac{rc - ta}{rb - sa} = \dfrac{ta - rc}{sa - br}.$

NOTE. In step 6, when subtracting say from rby, we notice that these are *like terms* since they have the common factor y, and then subtract by multiplying that common factor y by the difference of its coefficients, $(rb - sa)$. Or, we may think of the difference as being $rby - say$, which, factored, becomes $(rb - sa)y$.

EXERCISE 107

1. $\begin{cases} 3x + 4y = 7a. \\ 2x - 5y = 6b. \end{cases}$

2. $\begin{cases} 3x + ay = 5. \\ 2x - by = 6. \end{cases}$

3. $\begin{cases} 4x + my = n. \\ x + py = q. \end{cases}$

4. $\begin{cases} 2ax + y = b. \\ ax - 2y = c. \end{cases}$

5. $\begin{cases} mx + ny = p. \\ cx + dy = e. \end{cases}$

6. $\begin{cases} ax + by = a^2 + 3ab. \\ 2ax - 3by = 2a^2 - 4ab. \end{cases}$

7. $\begin{cases} x + ay = ab - 2\,a. \\ bx + ay = -ab. \end{cases}$

8. $\begin{cases} ax - by = 2\,ab. \\ 2\,bx + 2\,ay = 3\,b^2 - a^2. \end{cases}$

9. $\begin{cases} bx + ay = a^2 + ab. \\ x - y = a + b. \end{cases}$

10. $\begin{cases} 2\,cx + dy = 2\,c^2 + d^2. \\ \dfrac{x+y}{c} = 3. \end{cases}$

11. $\begin{cases} \dfrac{a}{x} + \dfrac{b}{y} = a^2 + b^2. \\ \dfrac{a}{x} - \dfrac{b}{y} = a^2 - b^2. \end{cases}$

12. $\begin{cases} rx + sy = 0. \\ sx + ry = s^2 - r^2. \end{cases}$

13. $\begin{cases} mx - ny = 0. \\ x - y = \dfrac{m^2 - n^2}{mn} \end{cases}$

14. $\begin{cases} x + ay = b. \\ bx + y = a. \end{cases}$

15. Find two numbers whose sum is m and whose difference is n.

16. Divide the number c into two parts so that when the larger is divided by the smaller the quotient is d.

17. Divide the number r into two parts such that when the larger is divided by the smaller the quotient is s and the remainder is t.

18. A and B can do a piece of work together in k days; if A works 3 days and B works 5 days they can do $\frac{1}{2}$ of it. Find how long it would take each alone to do the piece of work.

19. The sum of the digits of a number of two digits is a; the number itself equals b times the units digit. Find the digits of the number.

20. If a be added to the numerator and b be added to the denominator of a certain fraction, its value becomes 1; if b be added to the numerator and a to the denominator, its value becomes 2. Find the fraction.

21. Find two numbers whose sum is c and such that b times the first exceeds a times the second by d.

22. Find two numbers such that the quotient of a divided by the greater exceeds by c the quotient of b divided by the

SIMULTANEOUS LINEAR EQUATIONS

less; and such that the quotient of b divided by the greater exceeds by d the quotient of a divided by the less.

The following two sets of equations arise in the solution of problems in applied mathematics; find T and f:

23. $\begin{cases} mg - T = mf. \\ T = nf. \end{cases}$
24. $\begin{cases} mg - T = mf. \\ T - ng = nf. \end{cases}$

EQUATIONS CONTAINING THREE VARIABLES

174. In the preceding paragraphs equations having two variables have been solved; in each case two equations were given. It is interesting to study equations with more than two variables. For three variables, three equations are necessary.

EXAMPLE. Solve the set of equations,

$$\begin{cases} 2x - y + z = 5. & (1) \\ 3x + 2y + 3z = 7. & (2) \\ 4x - 3y - 5z = -3. & (3) \end{cases}$$

SOLUTION: Eliminate z by combining (1) and (2); the resulting equation will contain only x and y.

1. M_3 (1): $\qquad 6x - 3y + 3z = 15.$ (4)
2. Subtract (2) from (4): $\quad 3x - 5y = 8.$ (5)

Now eliminate z by combining (1) and (3); the resulting equation will contain only x and y.

3. M_5 (1): $\qquad 10x - 5y + 5z = 25.$ (6)
4. Add (3) and (6): $\qquad 14x - 8y = 22.$ (7)

This gives the equations:

$$3x - 5y = 8. \qquad (5)$$
$$14x - 8y = 22. \qquad (7)$$

Solve this set of equations for x and y.

The solution is, $x = 1$, $y = -1$.

Substitute these values of x and y in (1) and obtain z.

$$2 + 1 + z = 5.$$
$$\therefore z = 2.$$

The complete solution is $x = 1$, $y = -1$, $z = 2$.

Check the solution by substituting it in each of the given equations.

EXERCISE 108

1. $\begin{cases} a - 2b + c = 0. \\ a - b + 2c = -11. \\ 2a - b + c = -9. \end{cases}$

2. $\begin{cases} 3x - 2y = 1. \\ 3x + 4z = 5. \\ 5z + 3y = 4. \end{cases}$

3. $\begin{cases} 12m - 4n + p = 3. \\ m - n - 2p = -1. \\ 5m - 2n = 0. \end{cases}$

4. $\begin{cases} 5r - 3s - 4t = -1. \\ 2s + 3t = +9. \\ 4r - t = 3. \end{cases}$

5. $\begin{cases} 3x + 4r + 2t = -5. \\ 2x - 3r - 4t = -10. \\ 4x + 2r + 3t = -21. \end{cases}$

6. $\begin{cases} 6A - 2B - 3C = 3. \\ 2A + 3B + 5C = 0. \\ 8A - 5B - 6C = 1. \end{cases}$

7. $\begin{cases} \dfrac{2}{x} - \dfrac{1}{y} + \dfrac{1}{z} = 5. \\ \dfrac{1}{x} + \dfrac{1}{y} + \dfrac{1}{z} = 9. \\ \dfrac{3}{x} - \dfrac{2}{z} = -2. \end{cases}$

8. $\begin{cases} \dfrac{1}{x} + \dfrac{1}{y} + \dfrac{1}{z} = \dfrac{1}{3}. \\ \dfrac{1}{x} - \dfrac{1}{y} - \dfrac{1}{z} = -\dfrac{5}{3}. \\ \dfrac{1}{y} - \dfrac{1}{z} - \dfrac{1}{x} = \dfrac{25}{3}. \end{cases}$

9. $\begin{cases} x + y + 2z = a. \\ 2x - y + z = b. \\ x - 2y + z = c. \end{cases}$

10. $\begin{cases} \dfrac{1}{x} - \dfrac{1}{y} - \dfrac{1}{z} = a. \\ \dfrac{1}{y} - \dfrac{1}{z} - \dfrac{1}{x} = b. \\ \dfrac{1}{z} - \dfrac{1}{x} - \dfrac{1}{y} = c. \end{cases}$

11. The angle A of a triangle exceeds the angle B by 20°; and the angle C exceeds the angle A by 20°. Find the three angles of the triangle. (See § 13.)

12. The perimeter of a triangle is 175 inches. The side a is 20 inches less than twice the side b; and the side b exceeds the side c by 5 inches. Find the sides of the triangle.

13. The sum of the sides a and b of a triangle is 147 inches; the sum of the sides b and c is 135 inches; and the perimeter is 219 inches. Find the three sides of the triangle.

SIMULTANEOUS LINEAR EQUATIONS

14. The total area of the three largest oceans is 134 million square miles. The area of the Pacific Ocean exceeds twice the area of the Atlantic Ocean by 1 million square miles; and the area of the Atlantic Ocean exceeds the area of the Indian Ocean by 7 million square miles. Find the area of each of the oceans.

15. A recipe for a fondant for candy calls for a total of three and five sixths cups of sugar, water, and glucose; twice the total amount of water and glucose exceeds the amount of sugar by one sixth cup; and three times the amount of glucose and twice the amount of sugar make six cups. How many cups of each ingredient is required for the fondant?

16. The sum of the three digits of a number is 13. If the number, decreased by 8, be divided by the sum of its units and tens' digits, the quotient is 25; and if 99 be added to the number, the digits will be reversed. Find the number.

SOLUTION: 1. Let $x =$ the hundreds' digit,
$y =$ the tens' digit,
and $z =$ the units' digit.

2. Then $100x + 10y + z =$ the number,

3. and $100z + 10y + x =$ the number with its digits reversed.

4. By the conditions of the problem,

$$x + y + z = 13,$$
$$\frac{100x + 10y + z - 8}{y + z} = 25,$$

and $\quad 100x + 10y + z + 99 = 100z + 10y + x.$

5. Solving these questions, $x = 2, y = 8, z = 3.$
Therefore the number is 283.

17. The sum of the three digits of a number is 23; and the digit in the tens' place exceeds that in the units' place by 3. If 198 be subtracted from the number, the digits will be reversed. Find the number.

18. A and B can do a piece of work in 10 days, A and C in 12 days, and B and C in 20 days. In how many days can each of them alone do it?

XIV. SQUARE ROOT AND QUADRATIC SURDS

175. Square Root by Inspection. The square root of a perfect square monomial (§ 90), and of a perfect square trinomial (§ 96) have been found by inspection. Review these paragraphs.

176. Two Square Roots are obtained for each number. They are of equal absolute value, but have opposite signs; they may be written together, by means of the *double sign*, $\pm$.

EXAMPLE 1. $\sqrt{9\,a^4b^2} = \pm\,3\,a^2b$; since $(+\,3\,a^2b)^2 = 9\,a^4b^2$;
and $(-\,3\,a^2b)^2 = 9\,a^4b^2$.

EXAMPLE 2. $\sqrt{9\,a^2 - 12\,ax + 4\,x^2} = \pm(3\,a - 2\,x)$;
since $\{+(3\,a - 2\,x)\}^2 = +(3\,a - 2\,x)^2 = 9\,a^2 - 12\,ax + 4\,x^2$,
and $\{-(3\,a - 2\,x)\}^2 = +(3\,a - 2\,x)^2 = 9\,a^2 - 12\,ax + 4\,x^2$.

177. The square root of a large number may sometimes be obtained by inspection by factoring the number.

EXAMPLE. $\sqrt{1764\,a^4} = \sqrt{4 \cdot 441\,a^4} = \pm\,2 \cdot 21\,a^2 = \pm\,42\,a^2$.

EXERCISE 109

Find the square roots of:

1. $49\,m^4n^6$
2. $64\,x^{12}y^6z^4$
3. $144\,a^4b^8c^2$
4. $225\,r^6s^8t^{10}$
5. $\dfrac{16\,a^{10}}{25\,b^4c^6}$
6. $\dfrac{4\,a^4}{169\,b^6}$
7. $\dfrac{196\,m^8}{256\,n^4}$
8. $\dfrac{169\,x^4y^2}{81\,z^{12}}$
9. $\dfrac{121\,c^4d^6}{144\,x^2y^2}$
10. $\dfrac{225\,s^6t^4}{400\,r^{14}}$

11. When is a trinomial a perfect square?

Find the value of:

12. $\sqrt{a^4 - 6\,a^2b^2 + 9\,b^4}$.
13. $\sqrt{m^6 - 10\,m^3n + 25\,n^2}$.
14. $\sqrt{169\,a^2 - 26\,ar^3 + r^6}$.
15. $\sqrt{4\,x^2 - 20\,xy^4 + 25\,y^8}$.

SQUARE ROOT AND QUADRATIC SURDS

16. $\sqrt{3136}$.   **18.** $\sqrt{4225\,a^2b^2}$.   **20.** $\sqrt{5184\,r^4s^2}$.

17. $\sqrt{2916\,x^4y^2}$.   **19.** $\sqrt{5625\,m^4n^6}$.   **21.** $\sqrt{11025\,x^2y^4z^2}$.

178. Square Root found by Long Division. If it is not possible to factor readily the number under the radical sign, the square root, if there is one, may be found by a process like long division.

EXAMPLE 1. Find the square roots of $a^2 + 2\,ab + b^2$.

SOLUTION: 1. $\sqrt{a^2} = a$. Place a in the root.

2. Square a; subtract.

3. $2 \times a = 2\,a$. Trial divisor.
$2\,ab \div 2\,a = b$. Add b to the trial divisor and to the root. Complete divisor.

4. $b \times (2\,a + b)$; subtract.

$$\begin{array}{r|l}
 & a + b \\ \hline
 & a^2 + 2\,ab + b^2 \\
 & a^2 \\ \hline
2\,a & +2\,ab + b^2 \\
+b & \\ \hline
2\,a + b & \\
 & +2\,ab + b^2 \\
\end{array}$$

The square roots are: $+(a + b)$ and $-(a + b)$.

EXPLANATION: 1. Find the square root of the first term, obtaining a, the first term of the root; place it in the root.

2. Square the first term of the root and subtract it from the given number, obtaining the first remainder, $2\,ab + b^2$.

3. Double the first term of the root, obtaining $2\,a$, the trial divisor. Divide the first term of the remainder by $2\,a$, obtaining b, the second term of the root. Add b to the root and to the trial divisor; the complete divisor is $2\,a + b$.

4. Multiply the complete divisor by b and subtract.

Step 3 is suggested by the process of squaring a binomial. When squaring a binomial, the middle term is obtained by taking twice the product of the first and second terms; this is equivalent to taking twice the first term and multiplying by the second. Reversing the process, the second term, b, will be found, if $2\,ab$ is divided by $2\,a$. After a^2 is subtracted from $a^2 + 2\,ab + b^2$, the remainder $2\,ab + b^2$ equals $b(2\,a + b)$. This suggests adding b to the trial divisor and multiplying the sum by b.

EXAMPLE 2. Find the square root of
$$20\,x^3 - 70\,x + 4\,x^4 + 49 - 3\,x^3.$$

246 ALGEBRA

Solution: 1. Arrange it in the descending powers of x:

2. $\sqrt{4x^4} = 2x^2$.
3. $(2x^2)^2 = 4x^4$. Subtract.
4. $2 \times (2x^2) = 4x^2$.
   $20x^3 \div 4x^2 = 5x$.
5. $5x(4x^2 + 5x)$.
6. $2 \times (2x^2 + 5x)$.
7. $-28x^2 \div 4x^2 = -7$.
8. $-7(4x^2 + 10x - 7)$.

$$\begin{array}{l} 2x^2 + 5x - 7 \\ \overline{4x^4 + 20x^3 - 3x^2 - 70x + 49} \\ 4x^4 \end{array}$$

$4x^2 \,|\, 20x^3 - 3x^2 - 70x + 49$
$\, +5x$
$\overline{4x^2 + 5x} \,|\, 20x^2 + 25x^2$
$4x^2 + 10x \quad | -28x^2 - 70x + 49$
$\, -7$
$\overline{4x^2 + 10x - 7} \,|\, -28x^2 - 70x + 49$

The square roots are: $+(2x^2 + 5x - 7)$ and $-(2x^2 + 5x - 7)$.

Rule. — To find the square root of an algebraic expression:

1. Arrange it according to ascending or descending powers of some letter.

2. Write the positive square root of the first term of the given expression as the first term of the root. Square it and subtract the result from the given expression.

3. Double the root already found, for the trial divisor. Divide the first term of the remainder by the first term of the trial divisor. Add the quotient to the root and also to the trial divisor, obtaining the complete divisor.

4. Multiply the complete divisor by the new term in the square root subtract the product from the remainder obtained in step 2.

5. Continue in this manner: (*a*) double the root already found for a new trial divisor; (*b*) divide the first term of the remainder by the first term of this product for the new term of the root; (*c*) add the new term of the root to the trial divisor, obtaining the complete divisor; (*d*) multiply the complete divisor by the new term of the root; (*e*) subtract.

EXERCISE 110

Find the square roots of the following:

1. $9x^2 + 24xy + 16y^2$.
2. $25m^2 + 30mn + 9n^2$.
3. $36a^2 - 12ab + b^2$.
4. $4x^4 + 4x^3 + 5x^2 + 2x + 1$.
5. $1 - 6a + 11a^2 - 6a^3 + a^4$.
6. $9x^4 - 24x^3 + 4x^2 + 16x + 4$.
7. $49a^2 - 30a^3 + 16 + 9a^4 - 40a$.
8. $25x^4 - 20x^3y - 26x^2y^2 + 12xy^3 + 9y^4$.

SQUARE ROOT AND QUADRATIC SURDS 247

9. $9a^4 + 1 - 4a^3 + 4a^6 - 6a^2 + 12a^5$.

10. $16m^4 + 8m^3x^2 - 23m^2x^4 - 6mx^6 + 9x^9$.

11. $1 - 2x + 3x^2 - 4x^3 + 3x^4 - 2x^5 + x^6$.

12. $x^6 - 4x^4a^2 + 10x^3a^3 + 4x^2a^4 - 20xa^5 + 25a^6$.

13. $9x^2 + 25y^2 + 16z^2 + 30xy - 24xz - 40yz$.

14. $a^2 + b^2 + c^2 - 2ab - 2ac + 2bc$.

15. $20ab^3 + 9a^4 - 26a^2b^2 + 25b^4 - 12a^3b$.

16. $20x^3 - 70x + 4x^4 + 49 - 3x^2$.

17. $49m^4 - 14m^3n - 55m^2n^2 + 8mn^3 + 16n^4$.

18. $m^2 + 8m + 12 - \dfrac{16}{m} + \dfrac{4}{m^2}$.

19. $x^2 - xy - \dfrac{11y^2}{4} + \dfrac{3y^3}{2x} + \dfrac{9y^4}{4x^2}$.

20. $\dfrac{16}{9} + \dfrac{8x}{3a} - \dfrac{13x^2}{3a^2} - \dfrac{4x^3}{a^3} + \dfrac{4x^4}{a^4}$.

179. Square Root of an Arithmetical Number. The square root of 100 is 10; of 10,000 is 100; etc. Hence the square root of a number between 1 and 100 is between 1 and 10; the square root of a number between 100 and 10,000 is between 10 and 100; etc.

That is, the integral part of the square root of a number of one or two figures contains *one* figure; of a number of three or four figures, contains *two* figures; and so on.

Hence, if the given number is divided into groups of two figures each, beginning with the units figure, for each group in the number there will be one figure in the square root. The groups are called **Periods**.

Thus, 2345 becomes 23 45; it has two periods and its square root has two figures, a tens' and a units' figure.

34038 becomes 3 40 38; it has three periods and its square root has three figures. A number having an odd number of figures will always have only one figure in its left-hand period, as in this case.

A decimal number is divided in the same manner, starting from the decimal point in both directions.

Thus, 3257.846 becomes 32 57.84 60. The last decimal period is always completed by annexing a zero. This number has two figures before the decimal point and two after it, in its square root.

180. The first figure of the square root of a number is found by inspection; the remaining figures are found in the same manner as the square root of a polynomial.

EXAMPLE 1. Find the square root of 4624.

SOLUTION. 1. Divide 4624 into periods; this gives 46 24. There are in the square root a tens' and a units' figure.

2. The tens' figure must be 6; 7 is too large for $70^2 = 4900$, which is more than 4624.

3. The rest of the square root is found as follows:

3600 is the largest square less than 4600.
$\sqrt{3600} = 60$; place 60 in the root.
Square 60 and subtract.
Double 60. Trial divisor.
$102 \div 12 = 8^+$. Place 8 in root and add to trial divisor.
Complete divisor
Multiply complete divisor by 8.

$$\begin{array}{r|l} & 60+8 \\ \hline & 46\ 24 \\ & 36\ 00 \\ 120 & 10\ 24 \\ 8 & \\ \hline 128 & 10\ 24 \end{array}$$

The square roots are $+68$ and -68.

It is customary to abbreviate the solution by omitting the zeros as in the following example.

EXAMPLE 2. Find the square root of 552.25.

SOLUTION. The largest square less than 5 is 4; $\sqrt{4} = 2$.
Place 2 in the root.

$2 \times 2 = 4$; annex 0. Trial divisor.
$15 \div 4 = 3^+$; add 3 to the trial divisor.
Complete divisor. Multiply by 3.
$2 \times 23 = 46$; annex 0. Trial divisor.
$230 \div 46 = 5^+$. Add 5 to the trial divisor.
Complete divisor. Multiply by 5.

$$\begin{array}{r|l} & 23.5 \\ \hline & 5\ 52.25 \\ & 4 \\ 40 & 1\ 52 \\ 3 & \\ \hline 43 & 1\ 29 \\ 460 & 23\ 25 \\ 5 & \\ \hline 465 & 23\ 25 \end{array}$$

The square roots are $+23.5$ and -23.5.

SQUARE ROOT AND QUADRATIC SURDS

Rule. — To find the square root of an arithmetical number:

1. Separate the number into periods (§ 179).

2. Find the greatest square number in the left-hand period; write its positive square root as the first figure of the root; subtract the square of the first root figure from the left-hand period, and to the result annex the next period.

3. Form the trial divisor by doubling the root already found and annexing zero.

4. Divide the remainder by the trial divisor, omitting the last figure of each. Annex the quotient to the root already found; add it to the trial divisor for the complete divisor.

5. Multiply the complete divisor by the root figure last obtained and subtract the product from the remainder.

6. If other periods remain, proceed as before, repeating steps 3, 4, and 5 until there is no remainder or until the desired number of decimal places has been obtained for the root.

NOTE 1. It sometimes happens that, on multiplying a complete divisor by the figure of the root last obtained, the product is greater than the remainder. In such cases, the figure of the root last obtained is too great, and the next smaller integer must be substituted for it.

NOTE 2. If any figure of the root is 0, annex 0 to the trial divisor and annex to the remainder the next period.

EXAMPLE 3. Find the square root of 4944.9024.

SOLUTION:
```
              70.32
         | 49 44.90 24
         | 49
         |─────────
   1400  | 44 90
      3  |
   ─────|─────────
   1403  | 42 09
         |─────────
  14060  |  2 81 24
      2  |
   ─────|─────────
  14062  |  2 81 24
```

The square roots are $+\,70.32$ and $-\,70.32$.

The first trial divisor is 140. Since this is greater than 44, the first remainder, annex 0 to the root, obtaining 70.

The second trial divisor is 1400; ($2 \times 70 = 140$; annex 0, 1400). Bring down the next period 90, getting for the second remainder 4490. Divide 44 by 14 gives 3+; annex 3 to the root and add 3 to 1400, etc.

EXERCISE 111

Find the square roots of:

1. 1521.	5. 23409.	9. 462.25.
2. 4489.	6. 54756.	10. 9.8596.
3. 5625.	7. 173889.	11. 11.9716.
4. 8836.	8. 42025.	12. 17.8929.

181. The Approximate Square Root of a number which is not a perfect square is often desired. Obtain usually the first three figures following the decimal point.

EXAMPLE. Find the approximate square root of 2.

SOLUTION:

$$\begin{array}{r|l} & 1.414 \\ \hline & 2.00\ 00\ 00 \\ & 1 \\ 2\ 0\quad & 1\ 00 \\ \underline{4} & \\ 2\ 4\quad & 96 \\ 2\ 8\ 0\quad & 4\ 00 \\ \underline{1} & \\ 2\ 8\ 1\quad & 2\ 81 \\ 2\ 8\ 2\ 0\ & 1\ 19\ 00 \\ \underline{4} & \\ 2\ 8\ 2\ 4\ & 1\ 12\ 96 \\ & 7\ 04 \end{array}$$

The square roots are + 1.414+ and − 1.414+.

NOTE. In order to obtain the desired number of decimal places, annex zeros until there are three periods.

EXERCISE 112

Find the approximate square roots of:

1. 3.	3. 6.	5. 10.	7. 13.	9. 15.	11. 19
2. 5.	4. 7.	6. 11.	8. 14.	10. 17.	12. 21

182. Table of Square Roots. In the remainder of the course it will be necessary to use frequently the square roots of some numbers. Retain some of the square roots as they are

SQUARE ROOT AND QUADRATIC SURDS

found, either in a notebook or in some other convenient place. Make a list of the numbers from 1 to 50, and write their square roots beside them, thus:

Number	Square Root
1	1.000
2	1.414
3	1.732

After working Exercise 112, twelve of the numbers of this table may be tabulated. These roots may be used to obtain the square roots of other numbers.

EXAMPLE 1. Find the square root of 8.

SOLUTION: $\sqrt{8} = \sqrt{4 \times 2} = 2 \times \sqrt{2} = 2 \times (1.414+) = 2.828+$.

EXAMPLE 2. Find the square root of 12.

SOLUTION: $\sqrt{12} = \sqrt{4 \times 3} = 2\sqrt{3} = 2 \times (1.732+) = 3.464+$.

EXERCISE 113

1. Find the following square roots to three decimals:

(a) $\sqrt{18}$.   (b) $\sqrt{20}$.   (c) $\sqrt{24}$.   (d) $\sqrt{27}$.   (e) $\sqrt{28}$.

2. Complete your table of square roots up to 50. Get as many roots as possible by inspection (§ 175); get as many of the remaining roots as possible as in Example 1. Find the others by the long division method (§ 180).

183. The square root of a fraction which is not a perfect square may be found as follows:

$$\sqrt{\frac{3}{2}} = \sqrt{\frac{3 \times 2}{2 \times 2}} = \sqrt{\frac{6}{4}} = \frac{\sqrt{6}}{\sqrt{4}} = \pm \frac{\sqrt{6}}{2}.$$

$$\pm \frac{\sqrt{6}}{2} = \pm \frac{2.449+}{2} = \pm 1.224+.$$

Rule. — To find the square root of a fraction:

1. Change the fraction into an equivalent fraction with a perfect square denominator.

2. The square root of the new fraction equals the square root of its numerator divided by the square root of its denominator.

3. If desired, express the result of step 2 in simplest decimal form, prefixing the double sign, $\pm$.

EXAMPLE. Find the approximate square root of $\frac{3}{8}$.

SOLUTION: 1. The smallest square number into which 8 can be changed is 16; multiply both terms of the fraction by 2.

2. $\sqrt{\frac{3}{8}} = \sqrt{\frac{2 \times 3}{2 \times 8}} = \sqrt{\frac{6}{16}} = \pm \frac{\sqrt{6}}{4} = \pm \frac{2.449^+}{4} = \pm .612^+.$

EXERCISE 114

Find the approximate square roots of:

1. $\frac{3}{4}$.
2. $\frac{5}{9}$.
3. $\frac{7}{16}$.
4. $\frac{1}{3}$.
5. $\frac{1}{2}$.
6. $\frac{2}{5}$.
7. $\frac{3}{7}$.
8. $\frac{5}{8}$.
9. $\frac{5}{6}$.
10. $\frac{4}{7}$.
11. $\frac{9}{5}$.
12. $\frac{3}{10}$.
13. $\frac{7}{11}$.
14. $\frac{5}{18}$.
15. $\frac{2}{27}$.

QUADRATIC SURDS

184. The indicated square root of a number which is not a perfect square is called a **Quadratic Surd**; as, $\sqrt{3}, \sqrt{\frac{5}{3}}, \sqrt{x}, \sqrt{\frac{x}{y}+1}.$

185. Surds should be simplified as in the following examples:

(a) $\sqrt{24} = \sqrt{4 \cdot 6} = 2 \cdot \sqrt{6}$; (b) $\sqrt{\frac{9}{8}} = \sqrt{\frac{9 \cdot 2}{16}} = \frac{3\sqrt{2}}{4}.$

Thus, a quadratic surd is in its simplest form when the number under the radical sign is an integer which does not contain any perfect square factor.

While a quadratic surd has two values, one positive and one negative, it is agreed to consider only the positive root, in order to avoid ambiguity. This root is called the *principal root*.

186. Addition and Subtraction of Surds.

EXAMPLE 1. Find the sum of $\sqrt{20}$ and $\sqrt{45}$.

SOLUTION: 1. $\sqrt{20} + \sqrt{45} = \sqrt{4 \cdot 5} + \sqrt{9 \cdot 5} = 2\sqrt{5} + 3\sqrt{5} = 5\sqrt{5}.$

SQUARE ROOT AND QUADRATIC SURDS

This solution assumes that surds may be added like other numbers. The coefficients of $\sqrt{5}$ are 2 and 3; the sum is found by multiplying $\sqrt{5}$ by the sum of its coefficients (§ 34).

The advantage in adding surds in this way is that fewer square roots need be obtained. Thus, the sum of $\sqrt{20}$ and $\sqrt{45}$ is $5\sqrt{5}$ or $5 \times (2.236^+)$ or 11.180^+. This same result could be obtained by adding the square roots of 20 and 45.

EXAMPLE 2. Simplify $\sqrt{\frac{9}{8}} + \sqrt{\frac{1}{2}}$.

SOLUTION: 1. $\sqrt{\frac{9}{8}} + \sqrt{\frac{1}{2}} = \sqrt{\frac{18}{16}} + \sqrt{\frac{2}{4}} = \frac{3\sqrt{2}}{4} + \frac{\sqrt{2}}{2} = \frac{3\sqrt{2}}{4} + \frac{2\sqrt{2}}{4} = \frac{5\sqrt{2}}{4}.$

2. $\frac{5\sqrt{2}}{4} = \frac{5 \times (1.414^+)}{4} = \frac{7.070^+}{4} = 1.767^+.$

EXAMPLE 3. Simplify $\frac{2}{3} + \sqrt{\frac{1}{3}}$.

SOLUTION: 1. $\frac{2}{3} + \sqrt{\frac{1}{3}} = \frac{2}{3} + \sqrt{\frac{3}{9}} = \frac{2}{3} + \frac{\sqrt{3}}{3} = \frac{2+\sqrt{3}}{3}.$

2. $\frac{2+\sqrt{3}}{3} = \frac{2+1.732^+}{3} = \frac{3.732^+}{3} = 1.244^+.$

NOTE. The results of problems involving surds are often left in the surd form as in step 1 of Examples 2 and 3. There are advantages in finding the approximate decimal value of the result.

EXERCISE 115

Simplify the following:

1. $\sqrt{12} + \sqrt{75}.$
2. $\sqrt{98} - \sqrt{18}.$
3. $\sqrt{80} - \sqrt{20}.$
4. $3\sqrt{27} - \sqrt{48}.$
5. $\sqrt{28} + \sqrt{63}.$
6. $6\sqrt{2} - \sqrt{50} + \sqrt{18}.$
7. $\sqrt{12} + \sqrt{\frac{1}{3}}.$
8. $\sqrt{\frac{2}{5}} + \sqrt{\frac{1}{10}}.$
9. $\sqrt{\frac{2}{3}} + \sqrt{\frac{1}{27}}.$
10. $\sqrt{\frac{3}{8}} - \sqrt{24}.$
11. $\frac{2}{3} + \sqrt{\frac{5}{9}}.$
12. $\frac{1}{2} - \sqrt{\frac{3}{4}}.$
13. $\frac{3}{5} + \sqrt{\frac{2}{25}}.$
14. $-\frac{1}{7} + \sqrt{\frac{2}{49}}.$
15. $-\frac{4}{11} + \sqrt{\frac{1}{121}}.$
16. $+\frac{2}{3} + \sqrt{\frac{4}{3}}.$
17. $-\frac{5}{6} + \sqrt{\frac{1}{6}}.$
18. $-\frac{3}{7} + \sqrt{\frac{2}{7}}.$
19. $-\frac{3}{8} + \sqrt{\frac{5}{8}}.$
20. $\frac{3}{5} - \sqrt{\frac{19}{5}}.$

XV. QUADRATIC EQUATIONS

187. A **Quadratic Equation** is an equation of the second degree (§ 161); it may have one or more unknowns.

188. A **Pure Quadratic Equation** is a quadratic equation having only one unknown, which contains only the second power of the unknown, as, $ax^2 = b$.

EXAMPLE 1. An acre of ground contains 43,560 square feet. How long must the side of a square field be in order that the area of the field shall be one acre?

SOLUTION: 1. Let s = the number of feet in one side.

2. Then s^2 = the number of square feet in the area.

3. Then $\qquad s^2 = 43,560.$

Extract the square root of both members of the equation.

4. Then $\qquad s = \pm\, 208.7^+.$

Since this is a field, only the positive root has meaning; hence the side of the field must be 208.7+ feet.

189. A pure quadratic equation has two roots, because two square roots are obtained in extracting the square roots of the two members of the equation.

Rule. — To solve a pure quadratic equation.

1. Clear the equation of fractions, transpose, and combine terms until the equation takes the form $x^2 =$ a number.

2. Extract the square root of both members of the equation, placing the double sign, $\pm$, before the root in the right member.

NOTE. After extracting the square roots of both members of an equation like $x^2 = a^2$, we get $\pm x = \pm a$. This gives: $+ x = + a$, $+ x = - a$, $- x = + a$, and $- x = - a$.

QUADRATIC EQUATIONS

If both members of the last two equations are multiplied by -1, the equations become $+x = -a$, and $+x = +a$. These are the first two of our four equations. Thus, it is clear that, from $x^2 = a^2$, we get only *two* equations, $x = +a$ and $x = -a$, or $x = \pm a$.

EXAMPLE. Solve the equation $\dfrac{2m}{3} + \dfrac{3}{m} = \dfrac{m}{12} + \dfrac{12}{m}$.

SOLUTION: 1. $\qquad \dfrac{2m}{3} + \dfrac{3}{m} = \dfrac{m}{12} + \dfrac{12}{m}$.

2. $M_{12m}:\qquad 8m^2 + 36 = m^2 + 144$.

3. Simplifying: $\qquad 7m^2 = 108$.

4. $D_7:\qquad m^2 = \tfrac{108}{7}$.

5. $\sqrt{\ }:{}^*\qquad m = \pm \sqrt{\tfrac{108}{7}} = \pm 6\sqrt{\tfrac{3}{7}} = \pm \tfrac{6}{7}\sqrt{21}$.

6. $\sqrt{21} = 4.582:\qquad m = \pm \tfrac{6}{7} \cdot (4.582) = \pm \dfrac{27.492}{7} = \pm 3.927$.

7. $\qquad m_1 = +3.927 \,; \ m_2 = -3.927$.

"m_1" is read "m one." The numeral 1 is called in such cases a subscript. "m_2" is read "m two." These subscripts are used in this case to distinguish between the two roots of the quadratic.

CHECK: In cases such as this, it is better to check by going over the solution a second time. Great care must be taken, however, for it is easy to overlook an error.

NOTE. — Get the result in the radical form first; that is, $m = \pm \tfrac{6}{7}\sqrt{21}$; then it is wise, for many reasons, to get it in decimal form as finally given.

EXERCISE 116

Solve the following equations:

1. $7p^2 - 175 = 0$.
2. $5x^2 - 48 = 80 - 3x^2$.
3. $12c^2 - 140 = 9c^2 - 32$.
4. $\dfrac{2m^2 + 4}{5} - \dfrac{3m^2 - 7}{3} = \dfrac{11}{15}$.
5. $3(m-2) + 2m(m-1) = m$.
6. $3(t+5) - t(t-1) = 4t$.
7. $9a^2 - 7 = 0$.
8. $11a^2 - 3 = 1$.

---

*The symbol "$\sqrt{\ }:$" placed in the left margin will mean, "take the square root of both members of the previous equation."

256   ALGEBRA

Review the statement made at the top of page 187; bear it in mind whenever solving fractional equations.

9. $\dfrac{7}{3 S^2} - \dfrac{11}{9 S^2} = \dfrac{5}{6}.$

10. $\dfrac{2r-3}{4-r} = \dfrac{9+r}{3r+2}.$

11. $\dfrac{x^2+x+1}{x-1} - \dfrac{x^2-x+1}{x+1} = 6.$

12. $\dfrac{3t^2+2}{5} - \dfrac{5t^2-3}{10} = \dfrac{4t^2+1}{25}.$

13. $\dfrac{g+4}{g-4} + \dfrac{g-4}{g+4} = \dfrac{10}{3}.$

14. $\dfrac{r^4 - 3r^2 + 4}{3r^4 + 2r^2 - 4} = \dfrac{r^2 - 3}{3r^2 + 2}.$

15. $a^2 - 2cx^2 = 3b^2.$ Solve for x.

SOLUTION: 1. $\qquad -2cx^2 = 3b^2 - a^2.$

2. $\qquad 2cx^2 = a^2 - 3b^2.$

3. $\qquad x^2 = \dfrac{a^2 - 3b^2}{2c}.$

4. $\qquad x = \pm\sqrt{\dfrac{a^2 - 3b^2}{2c}} = \pm\sqrt{\dfrac{2c(a^2 - 3b^2)}{4c^2}}$

$\qquad\qquad = \pm\dfrac{1}{2c}\sqrt{2a^2c - 6b^2c}.$

Solve for x:

16. $a^2 + x^2 = m.$

17. $a + 2x^2 = c.$

18. $ax^2 = m.$

19. $2cx^2 = d^2.$

20. $\tfrac{1}{2} hx^2 = c.$

21. $3mx^2 - n = p.$

190. A **Right Triangle** is a triangle which has a right angle for one of its angles; as triangle ABC, in which angle B is a right angle.

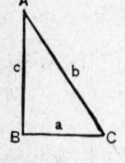

The side opposite the right angle is the *hypotenuse*; as, side AC. The side BC is the *base* and AB is the *altitude*.

In a right triangle, the square of the hypotenuse equals the sum of the squares of the other two sides.

Thus, $\qquad b^2 = a^2 + c^2.$

To verify this fact, draw a right triangle with BC 3 inches and AB 4 inches; measure AC. Substitute the lengths of the sides in the equation $b^2 = a^2 + c^2$.

QUADRATIC EQUATIONS

EXERCISE 117

Carry out all results in this set to one decimal place:

1. Find the altitude of a right triangle whose base is 13 feet and whose hypotenuse is 30 feet.

SOLUTION: 1. Let x = the number of feet in the altitude.
2. Then $$x^2 + 13^2 = 30^2.$$ (why?)
3. Complete the solution.

2. Find the base of a right triangle whose hypotenuse is 45 feet and whose altitude is 25 feet.

3. If the diagonal of a rectangle is 68 inches and the base of the rectangle is three times the altitude, what are the dimensions of the rectangle?

4. If the altitude of a rectangle is a and the base is 4 times the altitude, what is the length of the diagonal?

5. Solve the formula $b^2 = a^2 + c^2$: (a) for a; (b) for c.

In the isosceles triangle ABC, AD, which is perpendicular to BC, is the altitude and BC is the base. BD and DC are equal; this may be verified by measuring them.

6. If AB is 15 inches and BC is 18 inches, find AD.

7. If the equal sides of an isosceles triangle are each 30 inches, and the altitude is 18 inches, find the base.

8. If the equal sides of an isosceles triangle are each $3a$ inches and the base is $2a$ inches, find the altitude?

9. An equilateral triangle is one which has all of its sides equal. Find the altitude of an equilateral triangle whose sides are each 10 inches.

10. (a) Find the altitude of an equilateral triangle whose sides are each s inches; (b) find the area of the triangle.

11. The area of a circle is found by the formula $A = \pi r^2$, where r is the radius, and $\pi = 3\frac{1}{7}$.

Find the area of a circle whose radius is 9 inches.

12. What is the radius of a circle whose area is an acre?
(Express the radius in feet. See § 188.)

Express the results of the following in simplest radical form).

13. Solve the formula $A = \pi r^2$ for r: (a) letting $\pi = 3\frac{1}{7}$; (b) without substituting the value of π.

14. The volume of a circular cylinder is given by the formula $V = \pi r^2 h$; where $r =$ the radius, h the altitude.
Find V when $r = 5$ and $h = 13$.

15. Find r when $V = 759$ and $h = 14$.

16. Solve the cylinder formula for r.

17. Solve the formula $S = 4\pi r^2$ for r.

18. Solve the formula $V = \frac{1}{3}\pi r^2 h$ for r.

19. The distance s in feet through which an object will fall in t seconds is given by the formula $s = \frac{1}{2}gt^2$, where g is 32.
Suppose that a stone is allowed to fall from a tower; how far will it fall in: (a) 3 seconds? (b) 5 seconds?

20. How long will it take a ball to fall 900 feet?

21. Washington's Monument in Washington, D.C., is 555 feet high. How long will it take a ball to fall that distance?

22. Solve the equation $s = \frac{1}{2}gt^2$ for t.

23. Solve the formula $f = \dfrac{mv^2}{r}$ for v.

COMPLETE QUADRATIC EQUATIONS

191. A **Complete Quadratic Equation** is a quadratic equation having only one unknown, which contains the first power of the unknown as well as the second power; as,

$$2x^2 - 3x - 5 = 0.$$

192. Complete quadratic equations have been **Solved by Factoring** in § 108.

QUADRATIC EQUATIONS

EXERCISE 118

Solve by factoring:

1. $x^2 - 5x = 24$.
2. $2m^2 - m - 15 = 0$.
3. $2x^2 + 13x + 20 = 0$.
4. $12y^2 - 7y = 10$.
5. $5w^2 - 7w = 0$.
6. $9x^2 - 49x = 0$.
7. $2x^2 + ax - a^2 = 0$.
   (Solve for x).
8. $8x^2 + 14mx = -3m^2$.
9. $6x^2 - 11xk = 10k^2$.
10. $5x^2 + 15p^2 = 28xp$.
11. $\dfrac{x^2}{3} - \dfrac{x}{2} = \dfrac{35}{6}$.
12. $\dfrac{1}{2} - \dfrac{5}{6x^2} = -\dfrac{7}{12x}$.
13. $\dfrac{1}{8x^2} - \dfrac{13}{24x} = -\dfrac{1}{2}$.
14. $\dfrac{x}{4} + \dfrac{4}{x} = -\dfrac{29}{10}$.
15. $\dfrac{4-t}{1-t} = \dfrac{12}{3-t}$.
16. $\dfrac{7}{s-3} = \dfrac{s-2}{s-4} + \dfrac{1}{2}$.
17. $\dfrac{7}{y-3} - \dfrac{3}{y-4} = \dfrac{1}{2}$.
18. $1 + \dfrac{2}{p-3} - \dfrac{6}{p-8} = 0$.
19. $\dfrac{3}{m+6} - \dfrac{2}{m-5} = \dfrac{5}{4}$.
20. $\dfrac{r+2}{r+3} = \dfrac{36}{(r+3)^2} - 1$.

193. Graphical Solution of Equations With One Variable. Many facts about equations containing one variable can be discovered by the aid of graphical representation.

EXAMPLE 1. Consider the equation $3x - 12 = 0$.

The expression $3x - 12$ has a different value for each value of x:

Thus if $x = 2$, $3x - 12 = -6$; if $x = -3$, $3x - 12 = -21$.

The problem is to find the value of x for which the expression $3x - 12$ will equal zero.

GRAPHICAL SOLUTION: 1. Let $y = 3x - 12$.

2. Find values of y for some values of x:

    if $x = 0$, $y = -12$.   if $x = -2$, $y = -18$.
    if $x = +5$, $y = +3$.   if $x = +6$, $y = +6$.

3. Use these pairs of numbers as coördinates of points and draw the graph.

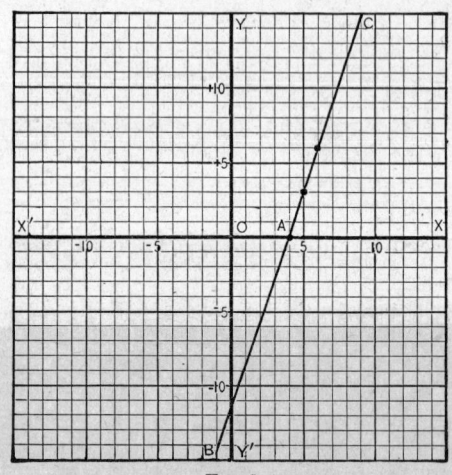

FIG. 9

4. *BC* crosses the *x* axis at point *A*. The coördinates of *A* are: $x = 4$, $y = 0$.

5. Hence when $x = 4$, $3x - 12 = 0$. (*y* is the expression $3x - 12$.)

∴ $x = 4$ is the desired solution of the equation, for we were looking for a value of *x* for which $3x - 12 = 0$.

Rule. — To solve graphically an equation containing one **variable**:

1. Simplify the equation as much as possible.
2. Transpose all terms to the left member.
3. Represent by *y* the expression found in step 2.
4. Find for *y* the values which correspond to selected values of the variable in the equation.
5. Use the pairs of values obtained in step 4 as coördinates of points; plot the points; draw the graph, making the vertical axis the *y* axis.
6. The graph crosses the horizontal axis at points whose ordinates are zero, and whose abscissæ are the desired roots of the equation.

QUADRATIC EQUATIONS

EXAMPLE 2. Solve the equation $x^2 - x = 6$.

SOLUTION: 1. $x^2 - x = 6$, or $x^2 - x - 6 = 0$.

2. Let $y = x^2 - x - 6$.

3. If $x = -4$, $y = (-4)^2 - (-4) - 6 = 16 + 4 - 6 = +14$.

4.

Similarly if $x =$	0	+1	+2	+4	+5	−1	−2	−3	−4
then $y =$	−6	−6	−4	+6	+14	−4	0	+6	+14

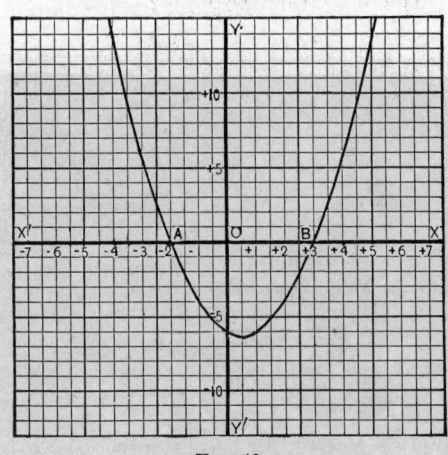

Fig. 10

5. The graph crosses the horizontal axis at the points A and B. According to the rule, the abscissæ of these points are the two roots of the equation.

At A: $\quad x = -2, y = 0$; i.e. $x^2 - x - 6 = 0$.

At B: $\quad x = +3, y = 0$; i.e. $x^2 - x - 6 = 0$.

CHECK: $\quad x = -2$; does $(-2)^2 - (-2) - 6 = 0$? Yes.

$\quad x = +3$; does $(+3)^2 - (+3) - 6 = 0$? Yes.

ALGEBRA

EXERCISE 119

Solve graphically the equations:

1. $x + 3 = 0$.
2. $2x = 7$.
3. $x^2 = 16$.
4. $x^2 - x = 12$.
5. $x^2 - 7x + 6 = 0$.
6. $x^2 + 6x + 5 = 0$.

194. Some quadratic equations cannot be solved readily by factoring; for example, $x^2 - 6x - 2 = 0$, since $x^2 - 6x - 2$ does not have any rational factors. The graphical solution shows that this equation has two roots.

SOLUTION: 1. $x^2 - 6x - 2 = 0$.

2. Let $y = x^2 - 6x - 2$.

When $x =$	-2	-1	0	$+1$	$+2$	$+3$	$+4$	$+6$	$+7$	$+8$
then $y =$	$+14$	$+5$	-2	-7	-10	-11	-10	-2	$+5$	$+14$

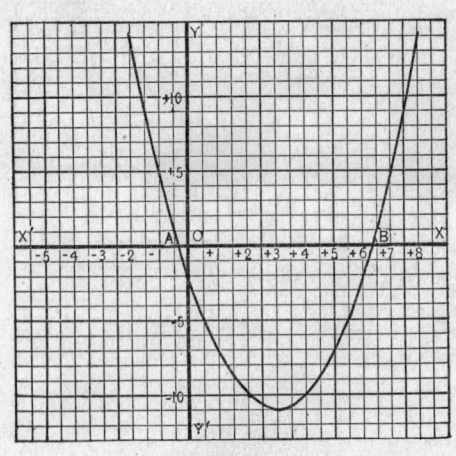

FIG. 11

3. The graph crosses the horizontal axis at the points A and B. The abscissa of A is about $-.3$; the abscissa of B is about $+6.3$.

QUADRATIC EQUATIONS

This indicates that the roots of this equation are approximately $-.3$, and $+6.3$.

There are two methods of solving such equations which give the roots more accurately.

195. Solution by Completing the Square.

DEVELOPMENT 1. Find: (a) $(x-4)^2$; (b) $(x+5)^2$;
(c) $(x-\frac{2}{3})^2$; (d) $(y+\frac{3}{4})^2$.

2. When is a trinomial a perfect square? (See § 96.)

3. Make a perfect square trinomial of $x^2 - 10x$.

SOLUTION: 1. $\frac{1}{2}$ of $10 = 5$; $5^2 = 25$; add 25.
2. The perfect square is $x^2 - 10x + 25$ or $(x-5)^2$.

4. Make perfect square trinomials of the following:
(a) $x^2 - 12x$; (b) $y^2 - 14y$; (c) $z^2 - 20z$.

5. Solve the equation $x^2 - 12x + 20 = 0$.

SOLUTION: 1. S_{20}: $\quad x^2 - 12x = -20$.

2. Make the left member a perfect square by adding 36; therefore add 36 to both members: (§ 41).

A_{36}: $\qquad x^2 - 12x + 36 = 36 - 20$.
or $\qquad\qquad (x-6)^2 = 16$.

3. $\sqrt{\ }$: $\qquad\qquad x - 6 = \pm 4$.

4. $\qquad \therefore x - 6 = +4$, or $x = 6 + 4 = 10$, one root,
and $\qquad x - 6 = -4$, or $x = 6 - 4 = 2$, another root.

CHECK: $x = 10$; does $(10)^2 - 12(10) + 20 = 0$? Yes.
$\qquad x = 2$; does $(2)^2 - 12(2) + 20 = 0$? Yes.

6. Solve the equation $x^2 - 3x - 5 = 0$.

SOLUTION: 1. $x^2 - 3x - 5 = 0$.
2. A_5: $\qquad x^2 - 3x = +5$.
3. $\qquad \frac{1}{2}(-3) = -\frac{3}{2}$; $(-\frac{3}{2})^2 = +\frac{9}{4}$; add $\frac{9}{4}$ to both members.
4. $A_{\frac{9}{4}}$: $\quad x^2 - 3x + \frac{9}{4} = 5 + \frac{9}{4} = \frac{29}{4}$.
5. $\sqrt{\ }$: $\qquad x - \frac{3}{2} = \pm \sqrt{\frac{29}{4}} = \pm \frac{1}{2}\sqrt{29}$.
6. $\qquad \therefore x = \frac{3}{2} \pm \frac{1}{2}\sqrt{29} = \frac{3 \pm \sqrt{29}}{2}$.

7. Radical results, $x_1 = \dfrac{3 + \sqrt{29}}{2}$ and $x_2 = \dfrac{3 - \sqrt{29}}{2}$.

8. Decimal results, $x_1 = \dfrac{3 + 5.385}{2}$ and $x_2 = \dfrac{3 - 5.385}{2}$.

$$= \dfrac{8.385}{2} \qquad\qquad = \dfrac{-2.385}{2}$$

$$= 4.192^{+} \qquad\qquad = -1.192^{+}.$$

CHECK: To check the solution by substituting the roots in either their decimal or their radical form is a long process, with many opportunities for errors. Persons skillful in algebra check by going over the solution carefully.

A quick check, the reason for which will be learned later in algebra, is to find the algebraic sum of the roots; this result should equal the negative of the algebraic coefficient of x in the equation in which the coefficient of x^2 is 1.

Here: $+ 4.192^{+}$ The coefficient of x^2 is 1. The coefficient of x
         $- 1.192^{+}$ is -3. This equals the negative of the algebraic
Sum. $+ 3$ sum of the roots.

If the coefficient of x^2 is not 1, first imagine the equation divided by that coefficient, and *then* select the coefficient of x.

Rule. — To solve a quadratic equation by completing the square:

1. Simplify the equation; transpose all terms containing the unknown number to the left member, and all other terms to the right member so that the equation takes the form

$$ax^2 + bx = c.$$

2. If the coefficient of x^2 is not 1, divide both members of the equation by it, so that the equation takes the form

$$x^2 + px = q.$$

3. Find one half of the coefficient of x; square the result; add the square to both members of the equation obtained in step 2. This makes the left member a perfect square.

4. Write the left member as the square of a binomial; express the right member in its simplest form.

5. Take the square root of both members, writing the double sign, $\pm$, before the square root in the right member.

QUADRATIC EQUATIONS

6. Set the left square root equal to the + root in the right member of the equation in step 5. Solve for the unknown. This gives one root.

7. Repeat the process, using the − root in step 5. This gives the second root of the equation.

8. Express the roots first in simplest radical form, and then, if desired, in simplest decimal form.

EXERCISE 120

Solve by completing the square:

1. $x^2 - 4x - 5 = 0$.
2. $x^2 + 8x - 33 = 0$.
3. $x^2 - 6x - 27 = 0$.
4. $x^2 + 10x + 24 = 0$.
5. $x^2 - 2x - 15 = 0$.
6. $y^2 - 4y = 4$.
7. $a^2 + 6a = 1$.
8. $m^2 - 2m = 1$.
9. $t^2 - 8t = 4$.
10. $z^2 - 10z = 5$.
11. $x^2 + 5x = -4$.
12. $s^2 + 10 = 7s$.
13. $w^2 - 3w = -2$.
14. $m^2 + m = 30$.
15. $r^2 - 13r + 30 = 0$.
16. $z^2 - 6 = 5z$.
17. $g^2 + 9g = 11$.
18. $y^2 - 15y + 16 = 0$.

19. Solve the equation $x^2 - \tfrac{2}{3}x = 1$.

SOLUTION: 1. $\tfrac{1}{2}$ of $\tfrac{2}{3} = \tfrac{1}{3}$. $(\tfrac{1}{3})^2 = \tfrac{1}{9}$.

2. $A_{\tfrac{1}{9}}$: $x^2 - \tfrac{2}{3}x + \tfrac{1}{9} = 1 + \tfrac{1}{9}$.

3. $(x - \tfrac{1}{3})^2 = (\tfrac{10}{9})$.

4. $x - \tfrac{1}{3} = \pm \sqrt{\tfrac{10}{9}} = \pm \tfrac{1}{3}\sqrt{10}$.

5. $x - \tfrac{1}{3} = +\tfrac{1}{3}\sqrt{10}$. $x - \tfrac{1}{3} = -\tfrac{1}{3}\sqrt{10}$.

$$x = \tfrac{1}{3} + \tfrac{1}{3}\sqrt{10} \qquad x = \tfrac{1}{3} - \tfrac{1}{3}\sqrt{10}$$

$$= \frac{1 + \sqrt{10}}{3} \qquad\qquad = \frac{1 - \sqrt{10}}{3}$$

$$= \frac{1 + 3.162}{3} \qquad\qquad = \frac{1 - 3.162}{3}$$

$$= \frac{4.162}{3} = +1.387+. \qquad = \frac{-2.162}{3} = -.720+.$$

ALGEBRA

CHECK: $+1.387$ Coefficient of $x = -\frac{2}{3} = -.6666$.
       $-.720$ $= -.667$.
Sum. $+.667$ $+.667 = -(-.667)$.

20. $x^2 - \frac{4}{3}x = \frac{4}{3}$.
21. $y^2 - \frac{6}{5}y = \frac{8}{5}$.
22. $z^2 + \frac{6}{7}z = 1$.
23. $a^2 - \frac{1}{3}a = \frac{2}{3}$.
24. $m^2 - \frac{3}{5}m = \frac{2}{5}$.
25. $t^2 - \frac{5}{4}t = 7$.

26. Solve the equation $3x^2 - 2x - 1 = 0$.

SOLUTION: 1. D_3: $x^2 - \frac{2}{3}x - \frac{1}{3} = 0$.

2. $A_{\frac{1}{3}}$: $x^2 - \frac{2}{3}x = \frac{1}{3}$.

3. Complete the solution as in Examples 19-25.

27. $3x^2 - 2x - 5 = 0$.
28. $5r^2 + 2r - 3 = 0$.
29. $4t^2 - 8t + 3 = 0$.
30. $3x^2 - 4x - 7 = 0$.
31. $2a^2 - 3a - 9 = 0$.
32. $5p^2 + 3p = 1$.
33. $6w^2 - 5w = 10$.
34. $\frac{3}{5a^2} - \frac{2}{a} - 5 = 0$.
35. $\frac{1}{2p} + 2 - 2p = 0$.
36. $\frac{m}{3} - \frac{2}{m} + 4 = 0$.
37. $\frac{7}{r^2} + \frac{2}{r} - 5 = 0$.

38. $\dfrac{t}{t-3} - \dfrac{3t}{4} = \dfrac{5}{2}$.
39. $\dfrac{x^2}{x-4} + \dfrac{1}{5} = 0$.
40. $\dfrac{3w}{w-7} + \dfrac{2}{w-4} = 0$.
41. $\dfrac{1}{a-5} - \dfrac{2}{a-2} = \dfrac{3}{5}$.
42. $\dfrac{2}{c-2} - \dfrac{1}{c+2} = -\dfrac{15}{8}$.
43. $\dfrac{3}{s-3} - \dfrac{2}{s-2} = 1$.
44. $\dfrac{3}{2y-7} + \dfrac{1}{15} = \dfrac{2}{y-3}$.
45. $\dfrac{2}{w^2-9} - \dfrac{3w}{w+3} = \dfrac{1}{w-3}$.

196. Solution of Literal Quadratic Equations.

EXAMPLE. Solve the equation $ax^2 - 3bx - c = 0$.

SOLUTION: 1. $ax^2 - 3bx - c = 0$.

QUADRATIC EQUATIONS

2. D_a: $\qquad x^2 - \dfrac{3b}{a}x - \dfrac{c}{a} = 0.$

3. $A_{\frac{c}{a}}$: $\qquad x^2 - \dfrac{3b}{a}x = \dfrac{c}{a}.$

4. The coefficient of x is $\left(\dfrac{-3b}{a}\right)$; one half of it is $\left(\dfrac{-3b}{2a}\right)$.

The square of $\left(\dfrac{-3b}{2a}\right)$ is $\left(\dfrac{9b^2}{4a^2}\right)$. Add this to both members of equation 3.

5.
$$x^2 - \dfrac{3b}{a}x + \dfrac{9b^2}{4a^2} = \dfrac{9b^2}{4a^2} + \dfrac{c}{a}.$$
$$\therefore \left(x - \dfrac{3b}{2a}\right)^2 = \dfrac{9b^2 + 4ac}{4a^2}.$$

6. $\qquad x - \dfrac{3b}{2a} = \pm \dfrac{1}{2a}\sqrt{9b^2 + 4ac}.$

7. $\qquad x = \dfrac{+3b \pm \sqrt{9b^2 + 4ac}}{2a}.$

8. $\therefore x_1 = \dfrac{+3b + \sqrt{9b^2 + 4ac}}{2a}$; $x_2 = \dfrac{+3b - \sqrt{9b^2 + 4ac}}{2a}.$

Check: $x_1 + x_2 = \dfrac{+6b}{2a} = +\dfrac{3b}{a}.$ Since this is the negative of the coefficient of x in step 2, the roots are correct.

EXERCISE 121

Solve the following equations for x:

1. $x^2 + 2ax - 3 = 0.$
2. $x^2 + 2ax + b = 0.$
3. $x^2 + 4x - c = 0.$
4. $x^2 + 3x + m = 0.$
5. $2x^2 + 3x - n = 0.$
6. $2x^2 + 4ax + b = 0.$
7. $x^2 + 3ax - 4t = 0.$
8. $x^2 + 2mx = 2m + 1.$
9. $x^2 - 4ax = 9b^2 - 4a^2.$
10. $ax^2 + 2x + 1 = 0.$
11. $rx^2 + 4tx - 5 = 0.$
12. $cx^2 + 2dx + p = 0.$
13. $x^2 + mx + n = 0.$
14. $ax^2 + bx + c = 0.$

197. Solution of Quadratic Equations by a Formula. All quadratic equations having one unknown may be put in the form
$$ax^2 + bx + c = 0.$$

ALGEBRA

This equation may be solved like the equations in Exercise 121. The roots will be found to be

$$x = \frac{-b \pm \sqrt{b^2 - 4ac}}{2a}.$$

This result may be used as a *formula* for solving **any** quadratic equation *of the form* $ax^2 + bx + c$.

EXAMPLE 1. Solve the equation $2x^2 - 3x - 5 = 0$.

SOLUTION: 1. Comparing the equation with $ax^2 + bx + c = 0$:

$$a = 2, \ b = -3, \ c = -5.$$

2. Substitute these values in the formula:

$$x = \frac{-b \pm \sqrt{b^2 - 4ac}}{2a}$$

3. Then
$$x = \frac{-(-3) \pm \sqrt{(-3)^2 - 4(2)(-5)}}{2(2)}$$

$$= \frac{+3 \pm \sqrt{9 + 40}}{4}$$

$$= \frac{3 \pm \sqrt{49}}{4} = \frac{3 \pm 7}{4}.$$

4. $\therefore x_1 = \frac{3+7}{4} = \frac{10}{4} = \frac{5}{2}; \ x_2 = \frac{3-7}{4} = \frac{-4}{4} = -1.$

CHECK: $x_1 = \frac{5}{2}$; does $2(\frac{5}{2})^2 - 3(\frac{5}{2}) - 5 = 0$?
does $2 \cdot \frac{25}{4} - \frac{15}{2} - 5 = 0$?
does $\frac{25}{2} - \frac{15}{2} - 5 = 0$? Yes.

$x_2 = -1$; does $2(-1)^2 - 3(-1) - 5 = 0$?
does $2 + 3 - 5 = 0$? Yes.

EXAMPLE 2. Solve the equation $2x^2 - 3x - 3 = 0$.

SOLUTION: 1. $a = 2, \ b = -3, \ c = -3.$

2. Substituting in the formula, $x = \frac{-b \pm \sqrt{b^2 - 4ac}}{2a}$:

$$x = \frac{3 \pm \sqrt{9 + 24}}{4} = \frac{3 \pm \sqrt{33}}{4} = \frac{3 \pm 5.744+}{4}.$$

$\therefore x_1 = \frac{8.744+}{4} = 2.186+; \ x_2 = \frac{-2.744+}{4} = -.686+.$

QUADRATIC EQUATIONS

CHECK:
2.186^+
$-.686^+$
1.500

The coefficient of x is $-\frac{3}{2}$, when the coefficient of $x^2 = 1$; $1.5 = -(-\frac{3}{2})$.

(For this method of checking, see § 195.)

EXERCISE 122

Solve the equations:

1. $4r^2 - 7r + 3 = 0$.
2. $6t^2 + 13t + 5 = 0$.
3. $y^2 = 6y + 72$.
4. $a^2 - 7a - 30 = 0$.
5. $3x^2 - 2x - 33 = 0$.
6. $3m^2 + 5m + 1 = 0$.
7. $5s^2 = 5s - 1$.
8. $6w^2 - 11w + 2 = 0$.
9. $2x^2 - 3x - 1 = 0$.
10. $x^2 + x - 1 = 0$.
11. $y^2 - 4y + 2 = 0$.
12. $3w^2 - 7w + 2 = 0$.
13. $5c^2 + 8c = 4$.
14. $9x^2 + 16x + 3 = 0$.
15. $15d^2 - 22d - 5 = 0$.
16. $\dfrac{x^2}{3} - \dfrac{x}{2} - \dfrac{3}{2} = 0$.
17. $\dfrac{4}{x} - x - \dfrac{1}{3} = 0$.
18. $\dfrac{3}{5-t} - 2t = 0$.
19. $\dfrac{2}{d-1} - \dfrac{3}{d} = 5$.

198. Summary of Methods of Solving a Quadratic. Four methods of solving a quadratic equation have been given: the graphical, by factoring, by completing the square, and by the formula. The first is useful mainly as a means of illustration; the third is useful mainly in solving the general quadratic $ax^2 + bx + c = 0$, and, thus, in deriving the formula.

HISTORICAL NOTE. Greek mathematicians as early as Euclid were able to solve certain quadratics by a geometric method, about which the student may learn when he studies plane geometry. Heron of Alexandria, about 110 B.C., proposed a problem which leads to a quadratic. His solution is not given, but his result would indicate that he probably solved the equation by a rule which might be obtained from the quadratic by completing its square in a certain manner. Diophantus, 275 A.D., gave many problems which lead to quadratic equations. The rules by which he solved his equations appear to have been derived by completing the square. He considered three separate kinds of quadratics. He gave only one root for a quadratic, even when the equation had two roots.

The Hindu mathematicians, knowing about negative numbers, considered one general quadratic. Cridharra gave a rule much like our formula. The Hindus knew that a quadratic has two roots, but they usually rejected any negative roots.

The Arabians went back to the practice of Diophantus in considering three or more kinds of quadratics. Mohammed Ben Musa, 820 A.D., had five kinds. He admitted two roots when both were positive. Alkarchi gave a purely algebraic solution of a quadratic by completing the square, and refers to this method as being a diophantic method.

In Europe, mathematicians followed the practice of the Arabians, and by the time of Widmann, 1489, had twenty four special forms of equations. These were solved by rules which were learned and used in a mechanical manner. Stifel, 1486-1567, finally brought the study of quadratics back to the point that had been reached by the Hindus one thousand years before. He gave only three normal forms for the quadratic; he allowed double roots when they were both positive. Stevin, 1548-1620, went still farther. He gave only one normal form for the general quadratic, as do we; he solved this in both a geometric and an algebraic manner, giving the method of completing the square. He allowed negative roots.

EXERCISE 123

Miscellaneous Examples

Solve the following equations by any of the preceding methods. As a rule, solve by factoring if possible; otherwise by the formula.

1. $(3x+2)(2x+3) = (x-3)(2x-4)$.
2. $9(y-1)^2 - 4(y-2)^2 = 44$.
3. $\dfrac{30}{m} - \dfrac{30}{m+1} = 1$.
4. $\dfrac{3}{a-6} - \dfrac{2}{a-5} = 1$.
5. $\dfrac{5}{x+4} - \dfrac{3}{x-2} = 6$.
6. $\dfrac{x+2}{x-1} - \dfrac{4-x}{2x} = \dfrac{7}{3}$.
7. $\dfrac{3a}{2a+5} - \dfrac{2}{a-1} = 1$.
8. $\dfrac{2-3t}{4} - \dfrac{4-t}{t-2} = \dfrac{11}{4}$.

QUADRATIC EQUATIONS

9. $\dfrac{3a-5}{2a-5} - \dfrac{2a+5}{3a+5} = 1.$

11. $\dfrac{2w+3}{5} - \dfrac{6-w}{w-4} = 2.$

10. $\dfrac{4v-9}{4v-3} - \dfrac{2v-3}{2v} = 9.$

12. $\dfrac{3r-1}{7-r} - \dfrac{5-4r}{2r+1} = 3.$

13. $\dfrac{1}{x-6} - \dfrac{4}{3(x-1)} = -\dfrac{2}{3x}.$

14. $\dfrac{y+2}{y-2} + \dfrac{y-2}{y+2} = \dfrac{6y+16}{3y}.$

15. $\dfrac{1}{1-t^2} + \dfrac{1}{1+t} - \dfrac{1}{1-t} = -\dfrac{7}{8}.$

16. $\dfrac{3r-6}{5-r} = \dfrac{7}{2} - \dfrac{11-2r}{2(5-2r)}.$

17. $\dfrac{3-2x}{2+x} - \dfrac{2+3x}{2-x} = \dfrac{1}{3} + \dfrac{16x+x^2}{x^2-4}.$

18. $\dfrac{y+1}{y-1} - \dfrac{y+2}{y-2} = \dfrac{2y+13}{y-1}.$

19. $1 + \dfrac{7x}{3x+1} + \dfrac{2x^2}{(3x+1)(7x+1)} = 0.$

20. $\dfrac{1}{(3x+1)(1-5x)} - \dfrac{15x}{2(1-5x)(7x+1)} = \dfrac{x}{(3x+1)(7x+1)}.$

21. Solve the equation $2p^2x^2 - 3pqx - q^2 = 0.$

SOLUTION: 1. $a = 2p^2;\ b = (-3pq);\ c = (-q^2).$

2. Formula: $x = \dfrac{-b \pm \sqrt{b^2 - 4ac}}{2a}.$

$= \dfrac{-(-3pq) \pm \sqrt{(-3pq)^2 - 4(2p^2)(-q^2)}}{2(2p^2)} = \dfrac{+3pq \pm \sqrt{9p^2q^2 + 8p^2q^2}}{4p^2}$

$= \dfrac{+3pq \pm \sqrt{17\,p^2q^2}}{4p^2} = \dfrac{3pq \pm pq\sqrt{17}}{4p^2} = \dfrac{pq(3 \pm \sqrt{17})}{4p^2} = \dfrac{q(3 \pm \sqrt{17})}{4p}.$

272　　ALGEBRA

Solve the following equations for x:

22. $x^2 - 6cx + 5c^2 = 0.$
23. $3x^2 = 2rx + 2r^2.$
24. $x^2 + c^2 - 2xp = 0.$
25. $x^2 - xp + (c^2 - d^2) = 0.$
26. $\frac{1}{2}gx^2 + ax = s.$
27. $2P - 2Px + x^2 = 1.$
28. $x^2 - (a-1)x = a.$
29. $x^2 + ax + bx + ab = 0.$
30. $ax^2 - (a - 2b)x = +2b.$
31. $mx^2 + (2mn - 3n)x - 6n^2 = 0$

EXERCISE 124

Review § 112 before solving this set of examples.

1. Twice the square of a certain number equals the excess of 3 over that number. Find the number.

2. If three times the square of a certain number be increased by the number itself, the sum is 10. Find the number.

3. Find two consecutive integers whose product is 306.

4. If the product of three consecutive integers be divided by each of them in turn, the sum of the three quotients is 74. Find the integers.

5. The sum of the squares of two consecutive integers is 685. Find the integers.

6. The sum of a certain number and its reciprocal is $1\frac{3}{6}$. Find the number.

HINT: The reciprocal of a number is obtained by dividing 1 by the number. The reciprocal of x is $\frac{1}{x}$.

7. Find the dimensions of a rectangle whose area is 357 square feet if its length exceeds its width by 4 feet.

8. The numerator of a certain fraction exceeds its denominator by 3. The fraction exceeds its reciprocal by $\frac{39}{40}$. Find the fraction.

9. The main waiting room of the Union Railway Station in Washington, D.C., has an area of 28,600 square feet. The length exceeds the width by 90 feet. Find the dimensions.

QUADRATIC EQUATIONS

10. Find the base and altitude of a triangle whose area is 63 square inches, if the base exceeds twice the altitude by 4 inches.

11. Find the dimensions of a rectangle whose area equals that of a square of side 24 feet, if the difference of the base and altitude of the rectangle is 14 feet.

12. Find the dimensions of a rectangle if its area equals that of a square of side 35 feet, if the difference of the base and altitude is 24 feet.

13. Find the dimensions of a rectangle whose area is 3750 square feet, if the sum of its base and altitude is 155 feet.

14. Find the dimensions of a rectangle whose area is 1701 square feet, if the sum of its base and altitude is 90 feet.

15. Find the dimensions of a right triangle if its hypotenuse is 20 feet and the base exceeds the altitude by 4 feet.

16. Find the dimensions of a right triangle if its hypotenuse is 26 feet and the sum of whose base and altitude is 34 feet.

17. Find the sides of an isosceles triangle if the perimeter is 35 inches and if the number of inches in the base is the quotient of 75 divided by the number of inches in one of the sides of the triangle.

18. A man travelled 105 miles. If he had gone 9 miles more an hour, he would have performed the journey in $1\frac{1}{2}$ hours less time. Find his rate in miles an hour. (See p. 105.)

19. If a man travels 120 miles by one train and returns on a train whose rate is 10 miles an hour more, he will require 7 hours for the trip. What is the rate of the first train?

20. A crew can row 8 miles downstream and back again in $4\frac{4}{5}$ hours; if the rate of the stream is 4 miles an hour, find the rate of the crew in still water. (See § 144.)

21. A man travels 10 miles by train. He returns by a train which runs 10 miles an hour faster than the first, accomplishing the whole journey in 50 minutes. Find the rate of the first train.

22. A tank can be filled by two pipes running together in 2 hours. The larger pipe by itself will fill it in 3 hours less time than the smaller pipe. How long will it take each pipe to fill the tank alone? (See § 142.)

23. Some boys are canoeing on a river, in part of which the current is 5 miles an hour, and in another part 3 miles an hour. If, when going downstream, they go 4 miles where the current is rapid and 8 miles where it is less rapid in a total time of $1\frac{5}{6}$ hours, what is their rate of rowing in still water?

24. I have a lawn which is 60 by 80 feet. How wide a strip must I cut around it when mowing the grass to have cut half of it?

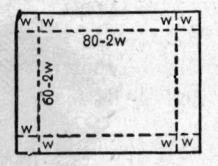

HINT: Referring to the figure, it is clear that if $w =$ the number of feet in the width of the border cut, then the dimensions of the uncut part of the lawn are $(60 - 2w)$ and $(80 - 2w)$.

Hence, $(60 - 2w)(80 - 2w) = \frac{1}{2} \cdot 60 \cdot 80$.

Complete the solution.

25. A farmer is plowing a field whose dimensions are 40 rods and 90 rods. How wide a border must he plow around the field in order to have completed $\frac{5}{6}$ of his plowing?

26. The numerator of a certain fraction is 8 less than the denominator. If the denominator and numerator each be increased by 5, the resulting fraction is twice the fraction obtained by increasing the original denominator by 1. Find the fraction.

27. An automobile made a trip of 50 miles, 10 miles within the city limits and 40 miles outside the city limits. Outside of the city, the rate was increased 15 miles an hour. If the trip took $2\frac{3}{5}$ hours, find the rate at which they travelled within and outside of the city limits.

QUADRATIC EQUATIONS

28. The numerator of a certain fraction exceeds its denominator by 5. If the numerator be decreased by 3 and the denominator be increased by 4, the sum of the new fraction and the original fraction is 3. Find the original fraction.

29. A bicyclist rides a number of hours at a number of miles an hour which exceeds the number of hours by 3; an automobilist, starting 3 hours after him, overtakes him by going two and one half times as fast as he did. Find the rate of each.

30. The circumference of the fore wheel of a carriage is less by 4 feet than the circumference of the hind wheel. In travelling 1200 feet, the fore wheel makes 25 revolutions more than the hind wheel. Find the circumference of each wheel.

IMAGINARY ROOTS IN A QUADRATIC EQUATION

199. EXAMPLE. Solve the equation $x^2 - 2x + 5 = 0$.

SOLUTION: 1. Use the formula method of solving the equation.

$$a = 1, \quad b = -2, \quad c = 5.$$

2. $x = \dfrac{-b \pm \sqrt{b^2 - 4ac}}{2a} = \dfrac{+2 \pm \sqrt{4 - 4 \cdot 1 \cdot 5}}{2}$

3. $= \dfrac{+2 \pm \sqrt{4 - 20}}{2} = \dfrac{2 \pm \sqrt{-16}}{2}.$

The question arises what does $\sqrt{-16}$ mean? Is -4 the square root of -16? No, for $(-4)^2 = +16$. Is $+4$? No, for $(+4)^2 = +16$. Thus, no number with which the student is acquainted will produce -16, when it is squared.

200. No number raised to an even power will produce a negative result; hence an even root of a negative number is impossible up to this point. To avoid this difficulty, a new kind of number is introduced.

An **Imaginary Number** is an indicated square root of a negative number; as $\sqrt{-16}$; $\sqrt{-3}$; $\sqrt{-a^3}$.

The numbers previously studied are called **Real Numbers**.

ALGEBRA

201. Every imaginary number can be expressed as the product of a real number and $\sqrt{-1}$.

$\sqrt{-1}$ is indicated by i, and is called the **Imaginary Unit**.

Thus, $\sqrt{-16} = \sqrt{16(-1)} = \pm 4\sqrt{-1} = \pm 4i.$

$\sqrt{-a^2} = \sqrt{a^2(-1)} = \pm a\sqrt{-1} = \pm ai.$

$\sqrt{-5} = \sqrt{5(-1)} = \pm \sqrt{5} \cdot \sqrt{-1} = \pm i\sqrt{5}.$

HISTORICAL NOTE. The symbol i for $\sqrt{-1}$ was introduced by Euler, one of the greatest mathematicians of the eighteenth century.

EXERCISE 125

Express the following in terms of i:

1. $\sqrt{-49}.$ 2. $\sqrt{-36}.$ 3. $\sqrt{-100}.$ 4. $\sqrt{-81a^2}.$

5. $\sqrt{-25}.$ 6. $\sqrt{-64}.$ 7. $\sqrt{-144}.$ 8. $\sqrt{-121a^2b^2}.$

9. $\sqrt{-\frac{1}{4}}.$ 10. $\sqrt{-\frac{4}{9}}.$ 11. $\sqrt{-\frac{16}{25}}.$ 12. $\sqrt{-\frac{9}{49}}.$

13. $\sqrt{-3}.$ 14. $\sqrt{-32}.$ 15. $\sqrt{-18}.$ 16. $\sqrt{-72}.$

17. $\sqrt{-5}.$ 18. $\sqrt{-27}.$ 19. $\sqrt{-12}.$ 20. $\sqrt{-28}.$

21. Simplify $\sqrt{-\frac{27}{4}}.$

SOLUTION: $\sqrt{-\frac{27}{4}} = \sqrt{\frac{9 \cdot 3 \cdot (-1)}{4}} = \pm \frac{3}{2}\sqrt{3} \cdot \sqrt{-1} = \pm \frac{3i\sqrt{3}}{2}.$

22. $\sqrt{-\frac{2}{9}}.$ 25. $\sqrt{-\frac{8}{9}}.$ 28. $\sqrt{-\frac{32}{25}}.$

23. $\sqrt{-\frac{3}{4}}.$ 26. $\sqrt{-\frac{75}{4}}.$ 29. $\sqrt{-\frac{125}{64}}.$

24. $\sqrt{-\frac{5}{36}}.$ 27. $\sqrt{-\frac{20}{49}}.$ 30. $\sqrt{-\frac{63}{100}}.$

QUADRATIC EQUATIONS

202. Addition and Subtraction of Imaginary Numbers.

EXERCISE 126

1. Add $\sqrt{-4}$ and $\sqrt{-36}$.

SOLUTION: $\sqrt{-4} + \sqrt{-36} = 2i + 6i = 8i$.

NOTE. While every imaginary number, like $\sqrt{-4}$, has two values, one positive and one negative, in problems such as the one in this exercise, only the *principal root*, the positive one, is used, as in the case of surds (§ 185).

2. $\sqrt{-16} + \sqrt{-25}$.

3. $\sqrt{-1} - \sqrt{-49}$.

4. $\sqrt{-81} - \sqrt{-64}$.

5. $\sqrt{-100} + \sqrt{-169}$.

6. $\sqrt{-1} + \sqrt{-49} - \sqrt{-64}$.

7. $\sqrt{-36} + \sqrt{-100} - \sqrt{-81}$.

8. $\sqrt{-a^2} - \sqrt{-4a^2} + \sqrt{-9a^2}$.

9. $\sqrt{-16x^2} - \sqrt{-25x^2} + \sqrt{-49x^2}$.

10. $\sqrt{-3} + \sqrt{-27}$.

11. $\sqrt{-18} - \sqrt{-8}$.

12. $\sqrt{-20} + \sqrt{-45}$.

13. $\sqrt{-28} - \sqrt{-7} + \sqrt{-63}$.

14. $\sqrt{-24} - \sqrt{-54} - \sqrt{-6}$.

15. $\sqrt{-44} + 2\sqrt{-11} - \sqrt{-99}$.

16. Simplify $+\dfrac{5}{2} \pm \sqrt{-\dfrac{27}{4}}$.

SOLUTION: 1. $\dfrac{5}{2} \pm \sqrt{-\dfrac{27}{4}} = \dfrac{5}{2} \pm \dfrac{\sqrt{-27}}{2} = \dfrac{5}{2} \pm \dfrac{3\sqrt{3} \cdot \sqrt{(-1)}}{2}$

$= \dfrac{5}{2} \pm \dfrac{3i\sqrt{3}}{2}$

$= \dfrac{5 \pm 3i\sqrt{3}}{2}$

The numbers in Examples 1–15 are called **Pure Imaginaries**. The sum, or difference, of a pure imaginary and a real number, § 200, as in this exercise, is called a **Complex Number**.

Simplify the following:

17. $\dfrac{1}{2} \pm \sqrt{-\dfrac{3}{4}}.$

18. $\dfrac{2}{3} \pm \sqrt{-\dfrac{4}{9}}.$

19. $\dfrac{3}{4} \pm \sqrt{-\dfrac{5}{16}}.$

20. $\dfrac{3}{5} \pm \sqrt{-\dfrac{28}{25}}.$

21. $\dfrac{7}{10} \pm \sqrt{-\dfrac{27}{100}}.$

22. $\dfrac{6}{13} \pm \sqrt{-\dfrac{75}{169}}.$

203. Meaning of Imaginary Roots of a Quadratic on the Graph.

EXAMPLE. Consider the equation $x^2 + x + 2 = 0$.

SOLUTION: 1. Solve the equation by the formula:

$$a = 1;\ b = 1;\ c = 2.$$

$$x = \frac{-1 \pm \sqrt{1-8}}{2} = \frac{-1 \pm \sqrt{-7}}{2} = \frac{-1 \pm i\sqrt{7}}{2}.$$

$$x_1 = \frac{-1 + i\sqrt{7}}{2};\ x_2 = \frac{-1 - i\sqrt{7}}{2}.$$

2. Solve the equation graphically. (Review rule § 193.)

Let $y = x^2 + x + 2$:

When $x=$	0	+1	+2	+3	−1	−2	−3	−4
then $y=$	+2	+4	+8	+14	+2	+4	+8	+14

3. The graph has the same shape as the graphs obtained when solving other quadratic equations; *but the graph does not cross* the horizontal axis at all. Hence, y or $x^2 + x + 2$ is never zero for any real value of x.

This is characteristic of the graph of a quadratic which has *imaginary* roots.

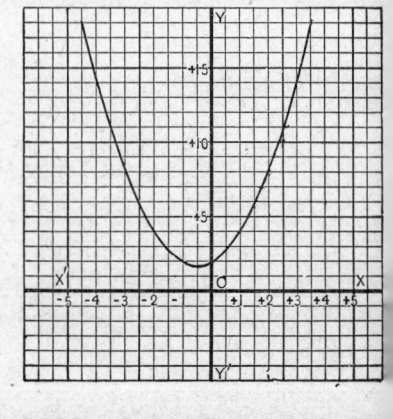

QUADRATIC EQUATIONS

EXERCISE 127

Solve the following equations. Express the roots in simplest form. Draw the graphs for the first three equations.

1. $x^2 + 2x + 3 = 0$.
2. $x^2 + 3x + 4 = 0$.
3. $2x^2 - x + 2 = 0$.
4. $3m^2 - 2m + 5 = 0$.
5. $5c^2 - 7c + 3 = 0$.
6. $8t^2 = 9t - 5$.
7. $11r^2 + 6 = 15r$.
8. $\dfrac{x^2}{5} - \dfrac{3x}{10} + \dfrac{1}{2} = 0$.
9. $\dfrac{2}{x+3} + \dfrac{3x}{5} = 0$.
10. $\dfrac{2x+3}{x-1} = \dfrac{x+7}{x+4}$.
11. $\dfrac{3x}{2} + \dfrac{1}{x} + \dfrac{5}{3} = 0$.
12. $2x^2 - 5ax + 7a^2 = 0$.
13. $3x^2 - 4xw + 2w^2 = 0$.
14. $5x^2 - 7xt + 3t^2 = 0$.

XVI. SPECIAL PRODUCTS AND FACTORING

ADVANCED TOPICS

204. In paragraph 98 is the rule: "The product of the sum and the difference of any two numbers equals the difference of their squares"; thus, $(x+y)(x-y) = x^2 - y^2$ for all numbers x and y.

If $x = 2a$ and $y = 3b$, $(2a+3b)(2a-3b) = 4a^2 - 9b^2$.

If $x = 14$ and $y = 5$, $(14+5)(14-5) = 196 - 25 = 171$.

If $x = (a+b)$ and $y = (c+d)$, then similarly

$$[(a+b)+(c+d)][(a+b)-(c+d)] = (a+b)^2 - (c+d)^2.$$

Likewise, in *any* of the type forms studied in Chapter VIII, the numbers may be general number expressions.

EXAMPLE 1. Multiply $(a+b+c)$ by $(a+b-c)$.

SOLUTION: 1. $(a+b+c)(a+b-c) = \{(a+b)+c\}\{(a+b)-c\}$
2. $\quad\quad\quad\quad\quad = (a+b)^2 - c^2 = a^2 + 2ab + b^2 - c^2$.

Here $x = (a+b)$ and $y = c$.

EXAMPLE 2. Multiply $(r+s+t-n)$ by $(r+s-t+n)$.

SOLUTION: 1. $(r+s+t-n)(r+s-t+n)$
2. $= \{(r+s)+(t-n)\}\{(r+s)-(t-n)\} = (r+s)^2 - (t-n)^2$
3. $= r^2 + 2rs + s^2 - t^2 + 2tn - n^2$.

Here $x = (r+s)$ and $y = (t-n)$.

NOTE. In such examples, the rules for introducing parentheses (§ 50) are used. The various terms of the expressions may be rearranged, if necessary, so that one factor becomes the sum and the other the difference of the *same* two numbers, when the terms are grouped.

SPECIAL PRODUCTS AND FACTORING 281

EXERCISE 128

Find the following products mentally:

1. $\{(a+b)+5\}\{(a+b)-5\}$.
2. $\{(m+n)-2p\}\{(m+n)+2p\}$.
3. $\{10-(r+s)\}\{10+(r+s)\}$.
4. $\{3p-(c+d)\}\{3p+(c+d)\}$.
5. $\{(c+2d)-11a\}\{(c+2d)+11a\}$.
6. $(a-b+c)(a-b-c)$.
7. $(x-y+z)(x-y-z)$.
8. $(a^2+a-1)(a^2-a+1)$.
9. $(a^2+ab+b^2)(a^2-ab+b^2)$.
10. $(a+2b-3c)(a-2b+3c)$.
11. $(3x+4y+2z)(3x-4y-2z)$.
12. $(x^2+x-2)(x^2-x-2)$.
13. $(a+r-c+d)(a+r+c-d)$.
14. $(a-b+m+n)(a-b-m-n)$.
15. $(2x+z-y+w)(2x-z-y-w)$.
16. $\{(a+b)+2(a-b)\}\{(a+b)-3(a-b)\}$.

SOLUTION: Just as $(x+2y)(x-3y) = x^2 - xy - 6y^2$,

so $\{(a+b)+2(a-b)\}\{(a+b)-3(a-b)\}$
$= (a+b)^2 - (a+b)(a-b) - 6(a-b)^2$
$= (a^2+2ab+b^2) - (a^2-b^2) - 6(a^2-2ab+b^2)$
$= a^2 + 2ab + b^2 - a^2 + b^2 - 6a^2 + 12ab - 6b^2$
$= 14ab - 6a^2 - 4b^2$.

Here $x = (a+b)$ and $y = (a-b)$.

17. $\{(m+n)-4\}\{(m+n)-5\}$.
18. $\{(x-y)+8\}\{(x-y)-6\}$.
19. $\{3x-(y+z)\}\{2x-(y+z)\}$.

20. $\{x+3y+15z\}\{x+3y-10z\}$.
21. $\{r+2s-3t\}\{r+2s+7t\}$.
22. $\{3p-4(q+r)\}\{4p-5(q+r)\}$.
23. $\{x^2+2x+1\}\{x^2+2x-5\}$.

24. $[(a+b)-5]^2$.
25. $[6+(m-n)]^2$.
26. $[2a-(c+d)]^2$.
27. $[a+b+c]^2$.
28. $[a+3b-c]^2$.
29. $[a-b+c-d]^2$.
30. $[2r+s-t+x]^2$.
31. $[3a-b+2c-d]^2$.

205. General Problems in Factoring.

EXAMPLE 1. Just as $x^2 - y^2 = (x+y)(x-y)$,
so $(m-n)^2 - 25a^2 = \{(m-n)+5a\}\{(m-n)-5a\}$.

EXAMPLE 2. Just as $x^2 - 3x - 88 = (x-11)(x+8)$,
so $(a-2b)^2 - 3(a-2b) - 88 = \{(a-2b)-11\}\{(a-2b)+8\}$
$= (a-2b-11)(a-2b+8)$.

NOTE. x is $(a-2b)$.

EXERCISE 129

Factor completely the following expressions:

1. $(a+b)^2 - c^2$.
2. $(m-n)^2 - x^2$.
3. $x^2 - (y+z)^2$.
4. $m^2 - (n-p)^2$.
5. $(7x-2y)^2 - y^2$.
6. $(a+b)^2 + 23(a+b) + 60$.
7. $(x-y)^2 + 2(x-y) - 63$.
8. $(x+y)^2 - 5(x+y) - 36$.
9. $(r+s)^2 + 4(r+s)t - 5t^2$.
10. $(p-q)^2 + 8(p-q)r - 20r^2$.
11. $(x^2-4)^2 - (x+2)^2$.
12. $9(m-n)^2 - 12(m-n) + 4$.
13. $(x-y)^2 - (m-n)^2$.
14. $(a^2-2a)^2 + 2(a^2-2a) + 1$.
15. $(1+n^2)^2 - 4n^2$.
16. $(x^2+3x)^2 + 4(x^2+3x) + 4$.

SPECIAL PRODUCTS AND FACTORING

17. $(9a^2+4)^2 - 144a^2$.
18. $(a^2+7a)^2 + 20(a^2+7a) - 96$.
19. $(m+n)^2 + 7(m+n) - 144$.
20. $(x^2+x-9)^2 - 9$.
21. $(x+y)^3 - z^3$.
22. $(r+s)^3 + 8t^3$.
23. $(m+n)^3 - (m-n)^3$.
24. $a^3 + (a+1)^3$.
25. $a^3 - 8(a+b)^3$.
26. $(x+y)^3 + (x-y)^3$.
27. $x^6 - (x^2+1)^3$.
28. $27m^3 - (m-n)^3$.
29. $(2a-b)^3 - (a+2b)^3$.
30. $(x+3y)^3 - (x-3y)^3$.

206. Polynomials Reducible to the Difference of Two Squares. Certain polynomials may be put into the form of the difference of two squares by grouping certain terms.

EXAMPLE 1. Factor $2mn + m^2 - 1 + n^2$.

SOLUTION: 1. $2mn + m^2 - 1 + n^2 = (m^2 + 2mn + n^2) - 1$
2. $ = (m+n)^2 - 1$
3. $ = (m+n+1)(m+n-1)$. **(§ 205)**

EXAMPLE 2. Factor $a^2 - c^2 + b^2 - d^2 - 2cd - 2ab$.

SOLUTION: 1. $a^2 - c^2 + b^2 - d^2 - 2cd - 2ab$
2. $ = (a^2 - 2ab + b^2) - (c^2 + 2cd + d^2)$
3. $ = (a-b)^2 - (c+d)^2$
4. $ = \{(a-b) + (c+d)\}\{(a-b) - (c+d)\}$
5. $ = (a-b+c+d)(a-b-c-d)$

EXERCISE 130

Factor:

1. $a^2 - 2ab + b^2 - c^2$.
2. $m^2 + 2mn + n^2 - p^2$.
3. $a^2 - x^2 - 2xy - y^2$.
4. $x^2 - y^2 - z^2 + 2yz$.
5. $b^2 - 4 + 2ab + a^2$.
6. $2mn - n^2 + 1 - m^2$.
7. $9a^2 - 24ab + 16b^2 - 4c^2$.
8. $16x^2 - 4y^2 + 20yz - 25z^2$.
9. $4n^2 + m^2 - x^2 - 4mn$.
10. $4a^2 - 6b - 9 - b^2$.

11. $10\,xy - 9\,z^2 + y^2 + 25\,x^2$.

12. $a^2 - 2\,ab + b^2 - c^2 + 2\,cd - d^2$.

13. $a^2 - b^2 + x^2 - y^2 + 2\,ax + 2\,by$.

14. $x^2 + m^2 - y^2 - n^2 - 2\,mx - 2\,ny$.

15. $2\,xy - a^2 + x^2 - 2\,ab - b^2 + y^2$.

16. $4\,a^2 + 4\,ab + b^2 - 9\,c^2 + 12\,c - 4$.

17. $16\,y^2 - 36 - 8\,xy - z^2 + x^2 - 12\,z$.

18. $m^2 - 9\,n^2 + 25\,a^2 - b^2 - 10\,am + 6\,bn$.

19. $4\,a^2 - c^2 - 12\,ab + 2\,cd + 9\,b^2 - d^2$.

20. $9\,x^4 - 4\,x^2 + z^2 - 6\,x^2z - 20\,xy - 25\,y^2$.

207. Trinomials Reducible to the Difference of Two Squares.

Type Form: $x^4 + ax^2y^2 + y^4$.

EXAMPLE 1. Factor $a^4 + a^2b^2 + b^4$.

SOLUTION: 1. $a^4 + a^2b^2 + b^4$ may be changed into a perfect square by adding a^2b^2. *Adding and subtracting* a^2b^2:

$$a^4 + a^2b^2 + b^4 = (a^4 + 2\,a^2b^2 + b^4) - a^2b^2.$$

2. $\therefore a^4 + a^2b^2 + b^4 = (a^2 + b^2)^2 - a^2b^2$

3. $\qquad\qquad\qquad = (a^2 + b^2 + ab)(a^2 + b^2 - ab).$ (§ 205)

EXAMPLE 2. Factor $64\,a^4 - 64\,a^2m^2 + 25\,m^4$.

SOLUTION: 1. A perfect square containing $64\,a^4$ and $25\,m^4$ is $64\,a^4 - 80\,a^2m^2 + 25\,m^4$. The given trinomial may be changed into this perfect square by subtracting $16\,a^2m^2$; then

$$64\,a^4 - 64\,a^2m^2 + 25\,m^4 = (64\,a^4 - 80\,a^2m^2 + 25\,m^4) + 16\,a^2m^2.$$

But this is the *sum of two squares* and not factorable in this form.

2. Another perfect square containing $64\,a^4$ and $25\,m^4$ is $64\,a^4 + 80\,a^2m^2 + 25\,m^4$. *Adding and subtracting* $144\,a^2m^2$:

$$64\,a^4 - 64\,a^2m^2 + 25\,m^4 = (64\,a^4 + 80\,a^2m^2 + 25\,m^4) - 144\,a^2m^2.$$

3. $\therefore 64\,a^4 - 64\,a^2m^2 + 25\,m^4 = (8\,a^2 + 5\,m^2)^2 - (12\,am)^2$
$\qquad\qquad\qquad\qquad\qquad = (8\,a^2 + 5\,m^2 + 12\,am)(8\,a^2 + 5\,m^2 - 12\,am)$

SPECIAL PRODUCTS AND FACTORING

EXERCISE 131

Factor the following trinomials:

1. $x^4 + x^2 + 1$.
2. $a^4 + a^2m^2 + m^4$.
3. $c^4 + 6\,c^2 + 25$.
4. $y^4 + 3\,y^2 + 36$.
5. $1 + 2\,t^2 + 9\,t^4$.
6. $1 - r^2 + 16\,r^4$.
7. $x^4 - 12\,x^2y^2 + 4\,y^4$.
8. $9\,m^4 - 19\,m^2 + 1$.
9. $4\,y^4 - 32\,y^2 + 1$.
10. $25\,x^4y^4 - 11\,x^2y^2 + 1$.
11. $4\,a^4 + 11\,a^2b^2 + 9\,b^4$.
12. $9\,m^4 + 14\,m^2n^2 + 25\,n^4$.
13. $4\,r^4 - 32\,r^2t^2 + 49\,t^4$.
14. $9\,m^4n^8 - m^2n^4 + 16$.
15. $4\,p^8 - 24\,p^4r^2 + 25\,r^4$.
16. $9\,a^4 + 17\,a^2b^2 + 49\,b^4$.
17. $4\,x^4 + 7\,x^2y^4 + 16\,y^8$.
18. $9\,t^4 - 31\,t^2x^2 + 25\,x^4$.
19. $16\,m^4n^4 + 15\,m^2n^2 + 25$.
20. $25\,p^4 + 34\,p^2y^2 + 49\,y^4$.
21. $x^4 + 4$.
22. $y^4 + 64$.
23. $x^4 + 4\,y^4$.
24. $4\,x^8 + 1$.

208. Certain polynomials can be *factored by grouping their terms.*

Type Form: $ab + ac + bd + cd = (a+d)(b+c)$.

EXAMPLE 1. Just as $ax + bx = (a+b)x$, (§ 34)
so $\quad a(x+y) + b(x+y) = (a+b)(x+y)$. (§ 34)

EXAMPLE 2. Factor $6\,x^3 - 15\,x^2 - 8\,x + 20$.

SOLUTION:
1. $6\,x^3 - 15\,x^2 - 8\,x + 20 = (6\,x^3 - 15\,x^2) - (8\,x - 20)$ (§ 50)
2. $\qquad = 3\,x^2(2\,x - 5) - 4(2\,x - 5)$ (§ 94)
3. $\qquad = (3\,x^2 - 4)(2\,x - 5)$.

EXERCISE 132

Factor:

1. $2a(x+y) - 3(x+y)$.
2. $5m(r+s) + 2n(r+s)$.
3. $3p(2x-y) - r(2x-y)$.
4. $8(t+w) - m(t+w)$.
5. $a(b+c) - d(b+c)$.
6. $ab + an + bm + mn$.
7. $ax - ay + bx - by$.
8. $ac - ad - bc + bd$.
9. $a^3 + a^2 + a + 1$.
10. $4x^3 - 5x^2 - 4x + 5$.
11. $2 + 3a - 8a^2 - 12a^3$.
12. $3x^3 + 6x^2 + x + 2$.
13. $10mx - 15nx - 2m + 3n$.
14. $a^3x + abcx - a^2by - b^2cy$.
15. $a^2bc - ac^2d + ab^2d - bcd^2$.
16. $30a^3 - 12a^2 - 55a + 22$.
17. $56 - 32x + 21x^2 - 12x^3$.
18. $3ax - ay + 9bx - 3by$.
19. $4x^3 + x^2y^2 - 4y^3 - 16xy$.
20. $rt - rn - sn + st$.
21. $ar + as + br + bs - cr - cs$.
22. $ax + ay - az + bx - bz + by$.
23. $am - bm - cp + ap - cm - bp$.
24. $x^3 - xz^2 + x^2y + xy^2 + y^3 - yz^2$.
25. $2ax + cx + 3by - 2ay - 3bx - cy$.

209. The Sum or the Difference of Two Like Powers.

Type Form: $a^n \pm b^n$.

By actual division, as in § 71:

$$(a^4 - b^4) \div (a - b) = a^3 + a^2b + ab^2 + b^3.$$
$$(a^4 - b^4) \div (a + b) = a^3 - a^2b + ab^2 - b^3.$$
$$(a^5 - b^5) \div (a - b) = a^4 + a^3b + a^2b^2 + ab^3 + b^4.$$
$$(a^5 + b^5) \div (a + b) = a^4 - a^3b + a^2b^2 - ab^3 + b^4.$$

The following rule may be verified in the same manner:

Rule. — I. Letting n represent any positive integer:

1. $a^n - b^n$ is always exactly divisible by $a - b$.

2. $a^n - b^n$ is exactly divisible by $a + b$ when n is even.

3. $a^n + b^n$ is never exactly divisible by $a - b$.

4. $a^n + b^n$ is exactly divisible by $a + b$ when n is odd.

II. In the quotient:

1. The signs are all plus when $a - b$ is the divisor.

2. The signs are alternately plus and minus when $a + b$ is the divisor.

3. The exponent of a in the first term is 1 less than its exponent in the dividend, and decreases by 1 in each succeeding term until it becomes 1.

4. The exponent of b is 1 in the second term, and increases by 1 in each succeeding term until it becomes 1 less than its exponent in the dividend.

EXAMPLE 1. Divide $a^7 - b^7$ by $a - b$.

SOLUTION: 1. By I, 1, $a^7 - b^7$ is exactly divisible by $a - b$.
2. By II, 1, 3, and 4,
$$\frac{a^7 - b^7}{a - b} = a^6 + a^5b + a^4b^2 + a^3b^3 + a^2b^4 + ab^5 + b^6.$$

EXAMPLE 2. Factor $32\,x^5 + 243$.

SOLUTION: 1. $32\,x^5 + 243 = (2\,x)^5 + 3^5$.
2. This expression is of the type $a^n + b^n$, where $a = 2\,x$, $b = 3$, and $n = 5$. By I, 4 and II, 2, 3, and 4,
$$32\,x^5 + 243 = (2\,x + 3)[(2\,x)^4 - (2\,x)^3 \cdot 3 + (2\,x)^2 \cdot 3^2 - (2\,x) \cdot 3^3 + 3^4]$$
$$= (2\,x + 3)(16\,x^4 - 24\,x^3 + 36\,x^2 - 54\,x + 81).$$

CHECK: Let $x = 1$. Then $32\,x^5 + 243 = 32 + 243 = 275$; also,
$(2\,x+3)(16\,x^4-24\,x^3+36\,x^2-54\,x+81) = (2+3)(16-24+36-54+81)$
$= 5 \cdot 55 = 275.$

ALGEBRA

The method of factoring binomials of the form $a^n \pm b^n$ given in this paragraph must be used frequently. However, if the *prime* factors (§ 87) of a binomial of this form are desired, proceed as in:

EXAMPLE 3. $x^6 - y^6 = (x^3 + y^3)(x^3 - y^3)$
$= (x + y)(x^2 - xy + y^2)(x - y)(x^2 + xy + y^2).$

NOTE 1. By § 209, $x^6 - y^6 = (x - y)(x^5 + x^4 y + \cdots + y^5)$.
The second factor is not prime however.

NOTE 2. Whenever the binomial is the difference of two even powers, it may be treated as the difference of two squares.

EXAMPLE 4. $x^9 + y^9 = (x^3)^3 + (y^3)^3 = (x^3 + y^3)(x^6 - x^3 y^3 + y^6)$
$= (x + y)(x^2 - xy + y^2)(x^6 - x^3 y^3 + y^6).$

NOTE 1. By § 209, $x^9 + y^9 = (x + y)(x^8 - x^7 y + x^6 y^2 + \cdots + y^8)$.
The second factor is not prime however.

EXERCISE 133

Find the following quotients:

1. $\dfrac{a^4 - b^2}{a + b}$.

2. $\dfrac{a^4 - b^4}{a - b}$.

3. $\dfrac{x^5 - y^5}{x - y}$.

4. $\dfrac{m^5 - 1}{m - 1}$.

5. $\dfrac{a^6 b^6 - c^6}{ab + c}$.

6. $\dfrac{a^8 - b^8}{a^2 - b^2}$.

7. $\dfrac{x^5 + z^{15}}{x + z^3}$.

8. $\dfrac{1 + a^5}{1 + a}$.

9. $\dfrac{32 - a^5}{2 - a}$.

10. $\dfrac{m^7 - n^7}{m - n}$.

11. $\dfrac{1 - 16 a^4}{1 + 2 a}$.

12. $\dfrac{81 x^4 - y^4}{3 x + y}$.

13. $\dfrac{16 - x^4}{2 - x}$.

14. $\dfrac{a^5 - 243 x^5}{a - 3 x}$.

15. $\dfrac{81 c^4 - 16 d^4}{3 c + 2 d}$.

Factor the following expressions, *if possible*:

16. $27 x^3 - 8 y^3$.
17. $x^4 - y^4$.
18. $x^5 - y^{10}$.
19. $32 - m^5$.
20. $r^6 s^6 - y^6$.
21. $a^7 + b^7$.

SPECIAL PRODUCTS AND FACTORING 289

22. $32 + r^5$.
23. $1 + 32 m^6$.
24. $x^6 + y^6$.
25. $x^{10} - y^{10}$.
26. $x^8 + y^8$.
27. $m^5 - 243$.
28. $64 - x^6$.
29. $x^3 - 256$.
30. $32 a^5 + 243 b^5$.

SUPPLEMENTARY TOPICS

210. The **Remainder Theorem** makes it possible to find the remainder in certain division problems by a short process.

It is known that *dividend = divisor × quotient + remainder*.

Suppose that $x^3 + x^2 - 2$ is divided by $x - 2$; then:

$x^3 + x^2 - 2 = (x - 2) \cdot Q + R$.
Let $x = 2$; then:
$8 + 4 - 2 = 0 \cdot Q + R$.
$\therefore 10 = 0 \cdot Q + R$.
$\therefore 10 = R$.

That is, the remainder is 10.

CHECK: See solution on right.

$$\begin{array}{r} x^2 + 3x + 6 \\ x - 2\overline{\smash{)}x^3 + x^2 - 2} \\ \underline{x^3 - 2x^2} \\ 3x^2 \\ \underline{3x^2 - 6x} \\ 6x - 2 \\ \underline{6x - 12} \\ 10 = R. \end{array}$$

At the left, the correct remainder was obtained by substituting 2 for x in the given expression. This suggests the

Remainder Theorem. If a rational and integral polynomial (§ 115) involving x be divided by $x - a$, the remainder may be found by substituting a for x in the given polynomial.

PROOF: 1. The polynomial (containing x) $= (x - a) \cdot Q + R$.
2. $\therefore$ The polynomial (x replaced by a) $= (a - a) \cdot Q + R$.
3. $\therefore$ The polynomial (x replaced by a) $= 0 \cdot Q + R = R$.

EXAMPLE 1. Find the remainder when $x^4 - 3x + 5$ is divided by $x - 3$.

SOLUTION: 1. Comparing $x - a$ and $x - 3$, a must be 3.
2. Substituting 3 for x in $x^4 - 3x + 5$,
$$R = 3^4 - 3 \cdot 3 + 5 = 81 - 9 + 5 = 77.$$

EXAMPLE 2. Find the remainder when the divisor is $x + 3$.

SOLUTION: 1. Comparing $x - a$ and $x + 3$, a must be -3.
2. Substituting -3 for x in $x^4 - 3x + 5$,
$$R = (-3)^4 - 3 \cdot (-3) + 5 = 81 + 9 + 5 = 95.$$

EXERCISE 134

Find the remainders when:

1. $x^5 + 2x^4 - 7$ is divided by $x - 1$; by $x + 1$.
2. $2x^3 + 3x^2 - 4x + 5$ is divided by $x - 5$; by $x + 5$.
3. $x^4 + 2x^3 - 6$ is divided by $x + 2$; by $x - 2$.
4. $m^3 - 2m^2 - 4$ is divided by $m - 3$; by $m + 4$.
5. $y^4 - y^3 + y^2 - y + 6$ is divided by $y + 3$; by $y - 2$.

211. Synthetic Division is a short process for finding the *quotient* as well as the remainder when a polynomial containing x is divided by a binomial of the form $x - a$.

Consider the two solutions:

SOLUTION (a):
$$\begin{array}{r} 5x^2 + 4x + 6 \\ x - 3 \overline{\smash{)}5x^3 - 11x^2 - 6x - 10} \\ \underline{5x^3 - 15x^2 } \\ 4x^2 - 6x \\ \underline{4x^2 - 12x } \\ 6x - 10 \\ \underline{6x - 18} \\ + 8 \end{array}$$

SOLUTION (b):
$$\begin{array}{r} x + 3 \overline{\smash{)}5x^3 - 11x^2 - 6x - 10} \\ 5 + 15 + 12 + 18 \\ \hline 5 + 4 + 6 \| + 8 \end{array}$$

Quotient: $5x^2 + 4x + 6$.
Remainder: $+ 8$.

The method of performing the solution (b):

(1) -3 of the original divisor is changed to $+3$.

(2) $5x^3 \div x = 5x^2$. Place 5 in the third line.

(3) $+3 \cdot +5 = +15$. Add the product, $+15$, to -11. Place the sum, $+4$, in the third line.

(4) $+3 \cdot +4 = +12$. Add the product, $+12$, to -6. Place the sum, $+6$, in the third line.

(5) $+3 \cdot +6 = +18$. Add the product, $+18$, to -10. Place the sum, $+8$, in the third line.

(6) The numbers 5, $+4$, and $+6$ are the coefficients of the quotient. Since $5x^3 \div x = 5x^2$, the full quotient is $5x^2 + 4x + 6$. The last number of the third line, $+8$, is the remainder.

SPECIAL PRODUCTS AND FACTORING

A partial explanation follows:

(1) In step (1), -3 is changed to $+3$. This permits *addition* in steps (3), (4), and (5) instead of the customary *subtraction*. Thus, in solution (a), when $-15x^2$ is *subtracted* from $-11x^2$, the result is $4x^2$; in solution (b), when $+15x^2$ is *added* to $-11x^2$, the result is again $4x^2$.

(2) In step (3), $+4$ below the line represents, first, the coefficient of the first term of the remainder as in solution (a). When $4x^2$ is divided by x the quotient is $+4x$, so that 4 may properly be considered also the coefficient of the second term of the quotient. Similarly in the case of $+6$ in step (4).

EXAMPLE 2. Divide $7x^4 - 29t^2x^2 - 3t^4$ by $x + 2t$.

SOLUTION. Change $x + 2t$ to $x - 2t$.

$$x - 2t \,\big|\, 7x^4 + 0tx^3 - 29t^2x^2 + 0t^3x - 3t^4$$
$$ \underline{7 \;\; -14t \;\; +28t^2 \;\; +2t^3 \;\; -4t^4}$$
$$ 7 \;\; -14t \;\; -t^2 \;\; +2t^3 \,\|\, -7t^4$$

QUOTIENT: $7x^3 - 14tx^2 - t^2x + 2t^3$.   Remainder: $-7t^4$.

NOTE 1. When powers of x are missing, supply them with coefficients zero, as in this example.

EXERCISE 135

Divide by synthetic division:

1. $x^3 - 2x^2 + 2x - 5$ by $x - 1$.
2. $2x^3 - 4x^2 + 6x - 15$ by $x + 1$.
3. $y^3 - 3y + 10$ by $y - 2$.
4. $z^4 + 5z^3 + 15z^2 - 25$ by $z + 2$.
5. $t^5 - 32$ by $t - 2$.
6. $3m^4 - 25m^2 - 18$ by $m - 3$.
7. $4a^3 + 18a^2 + 50$ by $a + 5$.
8. $6c^4 + 15c^3 + 28c + 5$ by $c + 3$.
9. $3x^3 + 4mx^2 - 2m^2x - 5m^3$ by $x - m$.
10. $4x^4 - 15b^2x^2 - 4b^4$ by $x + 2b$.

NOTE. In §§ 210 and 211, two short processes for finding the remainder in certain division problems are given. Each is important. The second has the further advantage of determining the quotient as well.

ALGEBRA

212. The **Factor Theorem** makes it possible to factor certain polynomials.

EXAMPLE 1. Is $x-1$ a factor of x^3+x^2-2?

SOLUTION: 1. If $x-1$ is a factor, the remainder when x^3+x^2-2 is divided by $x-1$ will be zero.

2. By the remainder theorem, $R = 1 + 1 - 2 = 0$. ($a = 1$.)

3. $\therefore x-1$ is a factor of x^3+x^2-2.

This example illustrates the

Factor Theorem: If a rational and integral polynomial (§ 115) involving x becomes zero when x is replaced by a, then the polynomial has $x-a$ as a factor.

PROOF: Considering the given polynomial the dividend and $x-a$ the divisor, the remainder will be the value of the dividend when x is replaced by a. According to the conditions, this value is zero; hence the remainder will be zero and the division exact. Therefore $x-a$ is a factor of the polynomial.

In applying the factor theorem:

1. Determine mentally, if possible, some number a for which the given polynomial becomes zero. (Factor Theorem.)

2. Divide the polynomial by $x-a$ by synthetic division (§ 211). This division will give further assurance that the remainder is zero, and will also determine the other factor, the quotient. This factor may often be factored.

EXAMPLE 2. Find the factors of $x^3 + 3x^2 - 4x - 12$.

SOLUTION: 1. When $x = 1$, then (mentally) $x^3 + 3x^2 - 4x - 12 = -12$
$\therefore x-1$ is not a factor of the polynomial.

2. When $x = -1$, $x^3 + 3x^2 - 4x - 12 = -6$. $\therefore x+1$ is not a factor.

3. When $x = 2$, $x^3 + 3x^2 - 4x - 12 = -0$. $\therefore x-2$ is a factor.

4. Dividing by synthetic division:
$x+2 \underline{)x^3 + 3x^2 - 4x - 12}$ Remainder $= 0$.
$\underline{\;1\;+2\;\;\;+10\;\;+12}$ $\therefore x-2$ is a factor.
$\;1\;+5\;\;\;+6\;\|\;\;\;0$ The other factor is $x^2 + 5x + 6$.

5. $\therefore x^3 + 3x^2 - 4x - 12 = (x-2)(x^2 + 5x + 6)$
$= (x-2)(x+2)(x+3)$.

SPECIAL PRODUCTS AND FACTORING

EXERCISE 136

Factor by the factor theorem:

1. $x^2 + x - 6$.
2. $x^3 - 2x^2 - x + 2$.
3. $x^3 + x^2 - 4x - 4$.
4. $x^3 - 6x^2 + 11x - 6$.
5. $x^3 - x^2 - 9x + 9$.
6. $2y^3 + y^2 - 3$.
7. $z^3 - 2z^2 + 3$.
8. $r^3 + 4r^2 + 6r + 4$.
9. $t^4 + t^3 - 2t^2 - t + 1$.
10. $m^4 - 5m^3 + 5m^2 + 5m - 6$.

11. $x^3 + mx^2 - 2m^3$.

Let $x = m$; $m^3 + m^3 - 2m^3 = 0$.
$\therefore x - m$ is a factor.
Find the other factor by division.

12. $3x^3 + p^2x - 4p^3$.
13. $x^3 - 5rx^2 + 6r^3$.
14. $x^3 + 3tx^2 - 4t^3$.
15. $x^4 - cx^3 - 7c^2x^2 + c^3x + 6c^4$.

EXERCISE 137

Miscellaneous Examples

In the following list of examples, the types of factoring studied in this chapter will be used. Before taking up the list of examples, review, if necessary, the rules for obtaining the H.C.F. and the L.C.M. of two or more expressions in Chapter IX and for operations with fractions in Chapter X. The examples marked with an *asterisk* (*) depend upon the supplementary topics in § 210 to § 212, and should be omitted if these paragraphs are not studied.

Factor the following expressions:

1. $a^2bc + ac^2d - ab^2d - bcd^2$.
2. $a^2 - (b+c)^2$.
3. $4a^5b^2 + 4a^2b^5$.
4. $x^3 + x^2y + xy^2 + y^3$.
5. $1 - a^8$.
6. $15ac + 18ad - 35bc - 42bd$.
7.* $x^3 + 4x^2 + x - 6$.
8. $3a^6b^2 - 3ab^7$.
9. $a^4 - 22a^2 + 81$.
10. $x^4 - x^2 - 4x - 4$.

11. $(x^2-5x)^2-2(x^2-5x)-24.$
12. $16x^4 - 76x^2y^2 + 81y^4.$
13. $a^6 - 2a^3 + 1.$
14. $9(m+n)^2 - 12(m+n) + 4.$
15. $32x^5 + y^{10}.$
16.* $a^3 - a^2 - 5a - 3.$
17. $9x^2 + 25y^2 - 16z^2 + 30xy.$
18. $a^3b^3 + a^3y^3 - b^3x^3 - x^3y^3.$
19. $m^4 - 625.$
20. $a^6 - 7a^3 - 8.$
21. $128 - m^7.$
22. $2a^2bc - 2b^3c - 4b^2c^2 - 2bc^3.$
23. $x^{10} + 2x^5 + 1.$
24. $a^3 - 5a^2 - 10 + 2a.$
25.* $a^4 - 4a^3 + a^2 - 6a + 8.$
26. $a^{10} - 1.$
27. $a^6 - a^4 + a^2 - 1.$
28. $x^7 + x^4 - x^3 - 1.$
29. $(x^2 - y^2 - z^2)^2 - 4y^2z^2.$
30. $(a^3 + b^3) - 2ab(a+b).$

Find the H. C. F. and the L. C. M. of the following:

31. $3a^3 - 21a^2 - a + 7$, and $a^2 + 6a - 91.$
32. $ac + ad - bc - bd$, and $a^2 - 6ab + 5b^2.$
33. $a^2 + b^2 - c^2 + 2ab$, and $a^2 - b^2 - c^2 + 2bc.$
34. $m^3 - 4m$, $m^3 + 9m^2 - 22m$, $2m^4 - 4m^3 - 3m^2 + 6m.$
35. $3a^3 - a^2b + 3ab - b^2$, $27a^3 - b^3$, $9a^2 - 6ab + b^2.$
36. $16m^4 - n^4$, $16m^4 - 8m^2n^2 + n^4$, $2mx + 2my - nx - ny.$
37. $a^3 - a^2x - ax^2 + x^3$, $3a^3 - 3a^2x + 5ax^2 - 5x^3.$
38.* $x^3 + x - 2$, and $x^2 + x - 2.$
39.* $x^3 - x^2 - x - 2$, and $x^2 + x - 6.$
40. $x^3 + 3ax^2 - a^2x - 3a^3$, and $x^3 + 2ax^2 - a^2x - 2a^3.$

Simplify the following fractional expressions:

41. $\dfrac{x^2 - y^2 + z^2 + 2xz}{x^2 - y^2 - z^2 + 2yz}.$

42. $\dfrac{4m^3 - 10m^2 - 6m + 15}{6m^3 + 8m^2 - 9m - 12}.$

43. $\dfrac{ax - bx - ay + by}{a^2 - b^2}.$

44. $\dfrac{2ac - 2bc - ad + bd}{d^2 - 4c^2}.$

SPECIAL PRODUCTS AND FACTORING

45. $\dfrac{x^2+y^2-z^2+2xy}{x^2+y^2-z^2-2xy} \cdot \dfrac{x^2-y^2+2yz-z^2}{x^2-y^2-2yz-z^2}$.

46. $\dfrac{a^3+b^3}{a-b+c}\left(1-\dfrac{ab+c^2}{a^2-ab+b^2}\right)$.

47. $\dfrac{a^2-b^2-c^2-2bc}{a^2-b^2-c^2+2bc} \div \dfrac{a-b-c}{a+b-c}$.

48. $\dfrac{ar-as+br-bs}{r^2-s^2} \cdot \dfrac{ar+as+br+bs}{a^2+2ab+b^2}$.

49. Solve the equation: $x^2 + ax - 3ab - 3bx = 0$.

SOLUTION: 1. $x^2 + ax - 3ab - 3bx = 0$.
2. Factoring: $x(x+a) - 3b(x+a) = 0$.
$(x-3b)(x+a) = 0$.
3. $\therefore x = 3b$, or $x = -a$. (§ 110)

Solve the following equations:

50. $x^2 + ax - ab - bx = 0$.   **52.** $ax^2 - bx - acx + bc = 0$.

51. $x^2 - 2mn - m^2 - n^2 = 0$.   **53.** $ax^2 - 2dx - 6d + 3ax = 0$.

54. $3anx^2 + 3mnx - apx - mp = 0$.

55. $adx^2 + cdx + aex + ce = 0$.

213. An equation of the first degree, having one unknown, has one root; an equation of the second degree has two roots (§ 109). In general, an equation of the nth degree, having one unknown, has n roots.

The roots of equations of degree higher than the second are not obtained readily, except in particular equations which may be solved partially at least by the factoring method.

EXAMPLE 1. Find the roots of $x^4 - 13x^2 + 36 = 0$.

SOLUTION: 1. Factoring, $(x^2-4)(x^2-9) = 0$.
2. $\therefore x^2 - 4 = 0$; $\therefore x^2 = 4$; $\therefore x = 2$, or $x = -2$.
Also, $x^2 - 9 = 0$; $\therefore x^2 = 9$; $\therefore x = 3$, or $x = -3$.

ALGEBRA

EXAMPLE 2. Solve the equation $y^3 + 2y^2 - 4y + 1 = 0$.

SOLUTION: 1. Factoring by the factor theorem,
$$(y-1)(y^2 + 3y - 1) = 0.$$

2. $\therefore y - 1 = 0$, or $y = 1$.

Also, $y^2 + 3y - 1 = 0$; $\therefore y = \dfrac{-3 \pm \sqrt{9+4}}{2} = \dfrac{-3 \pm \sqrt{13}}{2}$,

$\therefore y = \dfrac{-3 \pm 3.605}{2}$; $y = .302^+$, or -3.302^+.

Hence, $y_1 = 1$; $y_2 = .302^+$; $y_3 = -3.302^+$.

EXERCISE 138

Solve the equations:

1. $x^4 - 26x^2 + 25 = 0$.
2. $m^4 - 11m^2 + 18 = 0$.
3. $y^4 - 15y^2 - 16 = 0$.
4. $4t^4 - 17t^2 + 4 = 0$.
5. $9x^4 + 14x^2 - 8 = 0$.
6.* $x^3 - 7x + 6 = 0$.
7. $x^3 + 2x^2 - 9x - 18 = 0$.
8.* $y^3 - 13y - 12 = 0$.
9.* $m^3 - 19m - 30 = 0$.
10.* $z^3 - z^2 - 3z + 2 = 0$.
11.* $t^3 - 5t - 2 = 0$.
12. $x^3 - 1 = 0$.
13. $y^3 - 8 = 0$.
14. $r^3 - 5r^2 = 5 - r$.
15.* $x^5 - x^4 - 16x + 16 = 0$.
16. $x^4 - x^3 - 5x^2 - x - 6 = 0$.

Solve for x:

17. $x^4 - m^2x^2 - n^2x^2 + m^2n^2 = 0$.
18. $ax^3 + bx^2 - ac^2x - bc^2 = 0$.
19.* $2x^3 - 3a^2x + a^3 = 0$.
20. $x^4 - r^4 = 0$.

REMARK. The graphical solution of equations of higher degree is considered in § 343.

XVII. QUADRATIC EQUATIONS HAVING TWO VARIABLES

GRAPHICAL SOLUTION

214. Graph of a Single Equation.

EXAMPLE 1. Draw the graph of $y - x^2 = 0$.

SOLUTION: 1. Solve the equation for y: $y = x^2$.

2.

When $x =$	0	1	2	3	4	5	-1	-2	-3	-4	-5
then $y =$	0	1	4	9	16	25	$+1$	$+4$	$+9$	$+16$	$+25$

3. This curve is a **Parabola**.

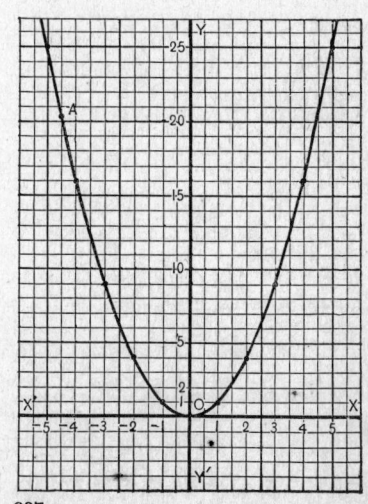

4. The coördinates of any point on the parabola satisfy the equation. The coördinates of A are: $x = -4.5$
and $y = 20+$.

Substituting in $y = x^2$: does $20+ = (-4.5)^2$?

Does $20+ = 20.25$? Yes, approximately. The coördinates should satisfy the equation of the graph. Since the graph cannot be absolutely accurate, and since the coördinates of a point on the graph cannot be read exactly from the graph, the coördinates determined may not exactly satisfy the equation.

298 ALGEBRA

EXAMPLE 2. Draw the graph of $x^2 + y^2 = 25$.

SOLUTION: 1. Solve the equation for y: $y = \pm \sqrt{25 - x^2}$.

2.

When $x =$	0	+1	+2	+3	+4	+5
$y =$	$\pm \sqrt{25}$ ± 5	$\pm \sqrt{24}$ ± 4.8	$\pm \sqrt{21}$ ± 4.5	$\pm \sqrt{16}$ ± 4	$\pm \sqrt{9}$ ± 3	$\pm \sqrt{0}$ 0

3. When x is negative, y has the values given by the corresponding positive values of x. Thus, when x is -3, y is

$$[\pm \sqrt{25 - (-3)^2} = \pm \sqrt{25 - 9} = \pm \sqrt{16} = \pm 4.$$

Notice that for each value of x, y has two values; thus, when x is $+4$, y is either $+3$ or -3. Hence, both $(4, 3)$ and $(4, -3)$ are on the graph.

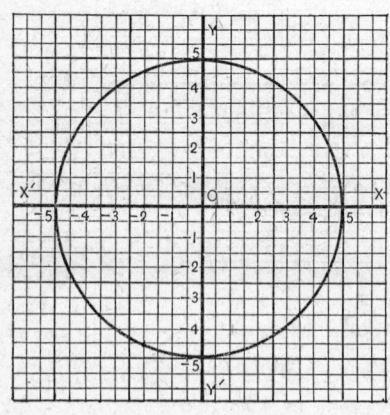

For x greater than 5, y is imaginary; thus, when $x = 6$

$$y = \pm \sqrt{25 - 36} = \pm \sqrt{-11}$$

This means that there are not any points on the graph for values of x greater than 5.

The square roots required in step 2 may be obtained either by the method of § 181, or from the table of square roots constructed in § 182.

4. This curve is a **Circle**. Every equation of the form $x^2 + y^2 = r^2$, is a circle with its center at the origin and its radius equal to r.

EXAMPLE 3. Draw the graph of $9 x^2 + 25 y^2 = 225$.

SOLUTION: $y^2 = \dfrac{225 - 9 x^2}{25}$; $\therefore y = \pm \frac{1}{5} \sqrt{225 - 9 x^2}$.

2. When $x = 2$, $y = \pm \frac{1}{5} \sqrt{225 - 36} = \pm \frac{1}{5} \sqrt{189} = \pm \frac{1}{5} (3 \sqrt{21}) = \pm \frac{1}{5} (3 \times 4.5) = \pm \frac{1}{5} (13.5) = \pm 2.7$.

QUADRATIC EQUATIONS HAVING TWO VARIABLES 299

When $x=$	0	$+1$	$+2$	$+3$	$+4$	$+5$	$+6$
then $y=$	$\pm\dfrac{\sqrt{225}}{5}$	$\pm\frac{1}{5}\sqrt{216}$	$\pm\frac{1}{5}\sqrt{189}$	$\pm\frac{1}{5}\sqrt{144}$	$\pm\frac{1}{5}\sqrt{81}$	$\sqrt{0}$	$\pm\frac{1}{5}\sqrt{-99}$
$=$	$\pm\frac{15}{5}$	$\pm\frac{1}{5}(14.6)$	$\pm\frac{1}{5}(13.5)$	$\pm\frac{12}{5}$	$\pm\frac{9}{5}$	0	imag'y
$=$	± 3	± 2.9	± 2.7	± 2.4	± 1.8	0	imag'y

For negative values of x, y has the values given by the corresponding positive values of x. (See Example 2.)

Notice that for each value of x, there are two values of y.

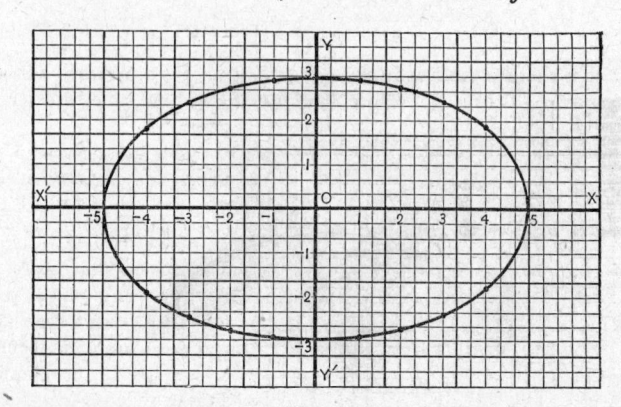

3. This curve is an **Ellipse**. Every equation of the form $ax^2 + by^2 = c$, where a, b, and c are positive, and a not equal to b, has for its graph an ellipse.

EXAMPLE 4. Draw the graph of $9x^2 - 4y^2 = 36$.

SOLUTION: 1. $y^2 = \dfrac{9x^2 - 36}{4}$; $\therefore y = \pm\frac{3}{2}\sqrt{x^2 - 4}$.

2. When $x = 1$, $y = \pm\frac{3}{2}\sqrt{1 - 4} = \pm\frac{3}{2}\sqrt{-3}$; $\therefore y$ is imaginary.

When $x=$	0	$+1$	$+2$	$+3$	$+4$	$+5$	$+6$
then $y=$	$\pm\frac{3}{2}\sqrt{-4}$	$\pm\frac{3}{2}\sqrt{-3}$	$\pm\frac{3}{2}\sqrt{0}$	$\pm\frac{3}{2}\sqrt{5}$	$\pm\frac{3}{2}\sqrt{12}$	$\pm\frac{3}{2}\sqrt{21}$	$\pm\frac{3}{2}\sqrt{32}$
	imag'y	imag'y	0	± 3.3	± 5.1	± 6.8	± 8.4

For negative values of x, y has the values given by the corresponding positive values of x. (See Example 2.)

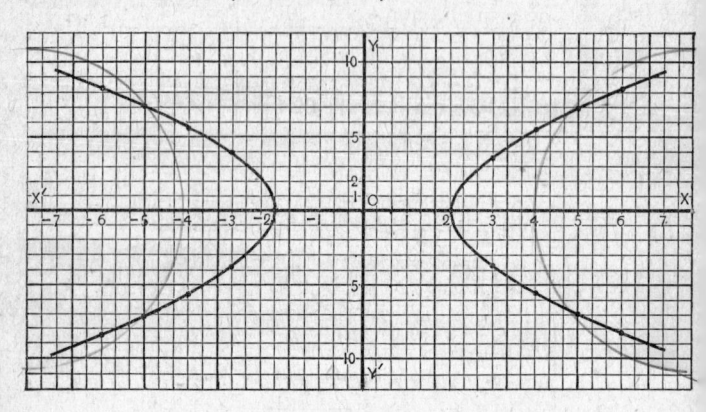

3. This curve is a **Hyperbola**. Every equation of the form $ax^2 - by^2 = c$, where a, b, and c are positive numbers, is a hyperbola.

EXERCISE 139

Draw the graphs for the following equations; name the curves obtained:

1. $x^2 + y^2 = 36$.
2. $y = 3x^2$.
3. $x^2 = 6y$.
4. $x^2 + 4y^2 = 36$.
5. $x^2 - 4y^2 = 36$.
6. $xy = 4$.
7. $x^2 + y^2 = 55$.
8. $4x^2 + y^2 = 16$.

215. Solution of a Pair of Simultaneous Quadratic Equations.

EXAMPLE 1. Solve the pair of equations: $\begin{cases} x^2 + y^2 = 25. & (1) \\ x - y + 1 = 0. & (2) \end{cases}$

SOLUTION: 1. The graph of equation (1) was drawn in Example 2 of § 214; it is the circle of radius 5, with center at the origin.

QUADRATIC EQUATIONS HAVING TWO VARIABLES

2. The graph of equation (2) is found as in § 156. It is a straight line (§ 153). When $x = 0$, $y = 1$; when $x = 2$, $y = 3$.

3. Since points A and B are on both graphs, their coördinates should satisfy both equations.

$A = (3, 4)$; $B = (-4, -3)$. When the coördinates of A and of B are substituted in the equations, it is found that they satisfy the equations.

$\therefore x = 3$, $y = 4$, and $x = -4$, $y = -3$ are solutions of the pair of equations.

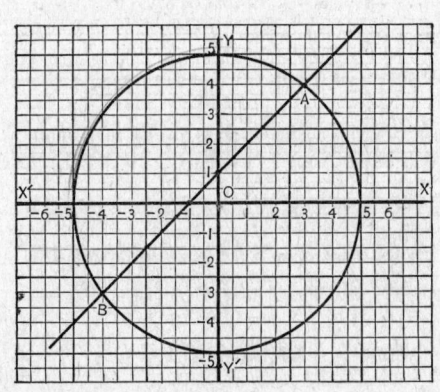

NOTE. Since the graph of every linear equation having two variables is a straight line (§ 153), and since, as the student's subsequent courses in mathematics will show, the graph of every quadratic equation having two variables must be one of the curves discussed in § 214, it is clear that, as a rule, a quadratic and a linear equation with two variables will have two common solutions, for a straight line will, in general, meet such curves in two points.

The straight line might touch the curve at only one point, thus giving only one solution; or it might not touch the curve at all, thus not giving any *real* solution.

EXAMPLE 2. Solve the pair of equations: $\begin{cases} x^2 + y^2 = 25. & (1) \\ x^2 + 2y^2 = 34. & (2) \end{cases}$

SOLUTION: 1. The graph of equation (1) is the circle of radius 5 (see Ex. 2, § 214). The graph of equation (2) is the ellipse of the figure.

2. The points of intersection of the graphs are:

$A: (4, 3)$; $B: (-4, 3)$; $C: (-4, -3)$; $D: (4, -3)$.

302   ALGEBRA

3. Substituting these values of x and y in equations (1) and (2), it becomes clear that the equations have four common solutions.

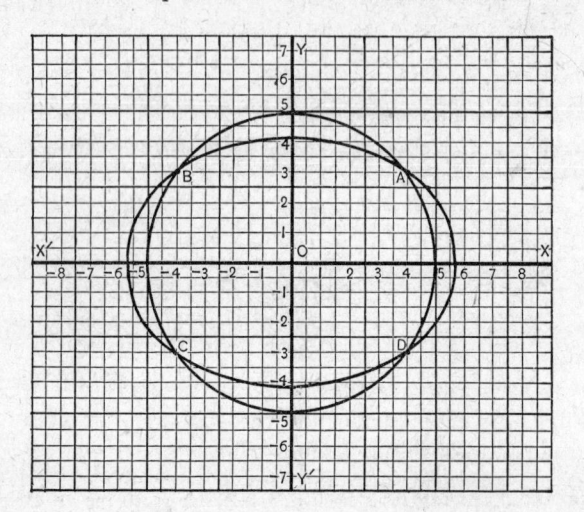

NOTE. Two quadratic equations, having two variables, will have four common solutions, in general. This becomes clear when the graphs of § 214, which result from such equations, are combined in pairs. For example:

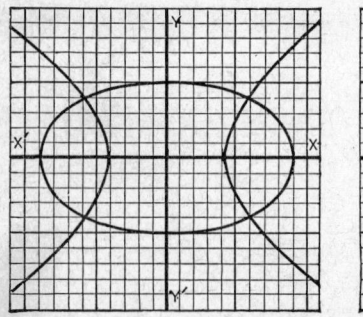

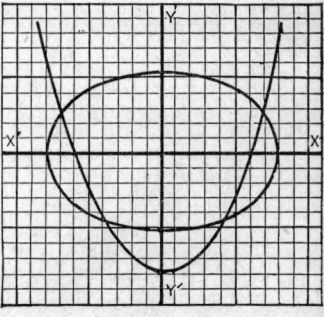

However, there are other possibilities. Thus, the ellipse might intersect only one *branch* of the hyperbola in such manner as to give only two *real* solutions; or it might not intersect it at all, giving no real solutions.

QUADRATIC EQUATIONS HAVING TWO VARIABLES   303

EXERCISE 140

Solve the following pairs of equations graphically

1. $\begin{cases} x^2 + y^2 = 100. \\ x - y + 2 = 0. \end{cases}$

2. $\begin{cases} 4x^2 + y^2 = 61. \\ 2x - y = 1. \end{cases}$

3. $\begin{cases} x^2 - y^2 = -9. \\ 2x - y = 3. \end{cases}$

4. $\begin{cases} x + y = -6. \\ xy = -7. \end{cases}$

5. $\begin{cases} x^2 + y^2 = 50. \\ xy = -7. \end{cases}$

6. $\begin{cases} 3x^2 + 4y^2 = 76. \\ 3y^2 - 11x^2 = 4. \end{cases}$

7. $\begin{cases} x^2 - y^2 = 16. \\ y^2 + x = 4. \end{cases}$

8. $\begin{cases} 4x^2 + y^2 = 36. \\ x^2 - y^2 = -16. \end{cases}$

9. Draw the graph of $\dfrac{x^2}{64} + \dfrac{y^2}{25} = 1$. On the same sheet, draw the three graphs obtained from the equation $x^2 = y + k$, when k is made successively 6, 2, and -6.

REMARK. The four curves studied in this chapter, the circle, the parabola, the ellipse, and the hyperbola are called *conic sections*, for each may be derived by intersecting a circular cone of *two nappes* by a plane. A special study of these curves is made in a later course in mathematics, analytic geometry.

XVIII. SIMULTANEOUS EQUATIONS

INVOLVING QUADRATICS

216. A set of equations having two or more variables are called **Simultaneous Equations** if each equation is satisfied by the same set, or sets, of values of the variables.

217. A set of equations that are solved as simultaneous equations will be called a *system of equations*.

218. A pair of simultaneous linear equations (§ 165) having two variables have one common solution (§ 163). The common solution is readily obtained by the addition or subtraction method (§ 167), or by the substitution method (§ 168) of elimination.

219. Pairs of simultaneous equations occur of which one or both are of degree higher than the first.

Thus, in (*a*) below, equation (1) is of the first degree and (2) is of the second; in (*b*), equation (1) is of the second degree and (2) is of the third.

(*a*) $\begin{cases} 3x + 4y = 5. & (1) \\ 2x^2 - 3xy = 7. & (2) \end{cases}$ (*b*) $\begin{cases} x^2 - 2y^2 = 6. & (1) \\ x^3 + y^3 = 5 & (2) \end{cases}$

Many such combinations, even with two variables, are possible. Only in special cases, however, are the common solutions readily obtained. A few such cases will be considered.

220. CASE I. **One Linear and One Quadratic Equation.**

EXAMPLE. Solve the system: $\begin{cases} x^2 + y^2 + 6x - 16 = 0. & (1) \\ 1 + 2x - y = 0. & (2) \end{cases}$

SOLUTION: 1. From (2), $\qquad\qquad\qquad\qquad y = 2x + 1.$ (3)
2. Substituting in (1), $\qquad x^2 + (2x+1)^2 + 6x - 16 = 0.$ (4)

SIMULTANEOUS EQUATIONS

3. Simplifying (4), $\quad\quad\quad\quad\quad\quad\quad\quad x^2 + 2x - 3 = 0.\quad\quad(5)$
4. Solving for x, $\quad\quad\quad\quad\quad\quad\quad\quad x = 1, \text{ or } x = -3.\quad(6)$
5. Substitute in (2): when $x = 1$, $1 + 2 - y = 0$; $\therefore y = 3$.
    when $x = -3$, $1 - 6 - y = 0$; $\therefore y = -5$.

The solutions are: $x = 1, y = 3$; $x = -3, y = -5$.

The solutions may be checked by substitution.

NOTE. One linear and one quadratic equation having two variables have, in general, two common solutions. The graphical solution of a particular pair of equations of this type is given in Ex. 1, § 215.

EXERCISE 141

march 14

Solve the following systems of equations:

1. $\begin{cases} a^2 + b^2 = 113. \\ a - b = -1. \end{cases}$

2. $\begin{cases} 5x^2 - 3y^2 = -7. \\ y + 2x = 7. \end{cases}$

3. $\begin{cases} 2x^2 - 4xy + 3y^2 = 11. \\ x - 3y = 5. \end{cases}$

4. $\begin{cases} m^2 + mn - n^2 = -19. \\ m - n = -7. \end{cases}$

5. $\begin{cases} x + y = -3. \\ xy = -54. \end{cases}$

6. $\begin{cases} x^2 - xy + y^2 = 63. \\ x - y = -3. \end{cases}$

7. $\begin{cases} x^2 + y^2 = 101. \\ x + y = -9. \end{cases}$

8. $\begin{cases} x^2 + xy + y^2 = 39. \\ x + y = -2. \end{cases}$

9. $\begin{cases} 2y + 2x = 5xy. \\ 2x + 2y = 5. \end{cases}$

10. $\begin{cases} 3c + 2d = -2. \\ cd + 8c = 4. \end{cases}$

11. $\begin{cases} 7a^2 + 10ab = -8. \\ 5a + 4b = -8. \end{cases}$

12. $\begin{cases} x - y = 1. \\ xy = a^2 + a. \end{cases}$

13. $\begin{cases} x^2 + y^2 = 2(a^2 + b^2). \\ x + y = 2a. \end{cases}$

14. $\begin{cases} \dfrac{3}{a} + \dfrac{3}{b} = \dfrac{4}{5}. \\ a + b = 16. \end{cases}$

15. $\begin{cases} \dfrac{x}{3} - \dfrac{y}{4} = -\dfrac{4}{3}. \\ \dfrac{6}{x} + \dfrac{4}{y} = 1. \end{cases}$

16. $\begin{cases} \dfrac{r}{t} + \dfrac{t}{r} = \dfrac{10}{3}. \\ 3r - 2t = -12. \end{cases}$

ALGEBRA

HOMOGENEOUS EQUATIONS

221. An equation is a **Rational Equation** if the variable does not appear under a radical sign.

222. A rational and integral (§ 139) equation is **Homogeneous** if all of its terms are of the same degree (§ 160) with respect to the variables.

Thus: $x^2 - 3xy + y^2 = 0$ is a homogeneous equation; $x^2 - xy + y^2 = 5$ is homogeneous except for the constant term; $x^2 - 3y = 2y^2$ is not homogeneous.

223. CASE II. **Quadratic Equations Homogeneous Except for the Constant Term.**

EXAMPLE 1. Solve the system: $\begin{cases} x^2 + 3y^2 = 28. & (1) \\ x^2 + xy + 2y^2 = 16. & (2) \end{cases}$

SOLUTION: 1. Eliminate the constant terms:

$M_4(1):$* $\qquad 4x^2 + 12y^2 = 112.$ (3)

$M_7(2):$ $\qquad 7x^2 + 7xy + 14y^2 = 112.$ (4)

$(4) - (3):$ $\qquad 3x^2 + 7xy + 2y^2 = 0.$ (5)

2. Solve (5) for x in terms of y:

$$(3x + y)(x + 2y) = 0; \therefore x = -\frac{y}{3}, \text{ or } x = -2y.$$

Substitute $-\frac{y}{3}$ for x in (1): $\quad \therefore \frac{y^2}{9} + 3y^2 = 28.$

$\therefore y^2 + 27y^2 = 9 \cdot 28; \ 28y^2 = 9 \cdot 28; \ y^2 = 9; \ y = \pm 3.$

When $y = 3$: $x = -\frac{y}{3} = -\frac{3}{3} = -1.$ $\therefore x = -1, y = 3$ is a solution.

When $y = -3$: $x = -\frac{y}{3} = -\left(\frac{-3}{3}\right) = 1.$ $\therefore x = 1, y = -3$ is a solution.

3. Substitute $-2y$ for x in (1). $\therefore 4y^2 + 3y^2 = 28.$

$\therefore 7y^2 = 28; \ y^2 = 4; \ y = \pm 2.$

When $y = 2$: $x = -2y = -2 \cdot 2 = -4.$ $\therefore x = -4, y = 2$ is a solution.

When $y = -2$: $x = -2y = -2 \cdot -2 = 4.$ $\therefore x = 4, y = -2$ is a solution.

* See § 167 for $M_4(1)$

SIMULTANEOUS EQUATIONS

CHECK: These four solutions are readily checked by substitution in equations (1) and (2).

NOTE 1. In case one equation does not have a constant term, solve it immediately for one variable in terms of the other as the equation (5) in step 2.

NOTE 2. A system consisting of two quadratic equations has, in general, four solutions.

NOTE 3. The graphical solution of a particular pair of equations of this type is given in Ex. 2, § 215.

EXERCISE 142

Solve the following systems:

1. $\begin{cases} 3\,cd + 2\,d^2 = -7. \\ c^2 - 2\,cd = 30. \end{cases}$

2. $\begin{cases} 2\,x^2 - xy = 2. \\ 4\,x^2 + y^2 = 10. \end{cases}$

3. $\begin{cases} n^2 + 3\,mn = 2. \\ 9\,m^2 + 2\,n^2 = 9. \end{cases}$

4. $\begin{cases} r^2 + rh = 75. \\ h^2 + r^2 = 125. \end{cases}$

5. $\begin{cases} x^2 + xy = -6. \\ xy - y^2 = -35. \end{cases}$

6. $\begin{cases} a^2 + ab + b^2 = 63. \\ a^2 - b^2 = -27. \end{cases}$

7. $\begin{cases} x^2 + 5\,xy - y^2 = -7. \\ x^2 + 3\,xy - 2\,y^2 = -4. \end{cases}$

8. $\begin{cases} 2\,x^2 - xy = 28. \\ x^2 + 2\,y^2 = 18. \end{cases}$

9. $\begin{cases} 2\,x^2 - 3\,xy + 5\,y^2 = 38. \\ 3\,x^2 + xy - 10\,y^2 = 0. \end{cases}$

10. $\begin{cases} m^2 - 2\,mn = 84. \\ 2\,mn - n^2 = -64. \end{cases}$

224. Equivalent Systems. One system of equations is equivalent to another when the common solutions of each system are the solutions of the other system.

225. CASE III. Systems Reducible by Division. A given system may sometimes be reduced by division to an equivalent system in which the equations are of lower degree.

EXAMPLE. Solve the system: $\begin{cases} x^3 - y^3 = 56. & (1) \\ x^2 + xy + y^2 = 28. & (2) \end{cases}$

SOLUTION: 1. Dividing (1) by (2): $x - y = 2$. (3)

2. Form the new system: $\begin{cases} x^2 + xy + y^2 = 28. & (2) \\ x - y = 2. & (3) \end{cases}$

3. Solve the new system by the methods of Case **I**:
$x = 4,\ y = 2$; and $x = -2;\ y = -4$.

ALGEBRA

CHECK: These two solutions are readily checked by substitution in the equations (1) and (2).

NOTE 1. Whenever possible, divide one equation of the given system by the other, member by member, and form a new system consisting of the quotient equation and the divisor equation.

NOTE 2. The full theory underlying this type of example belongs in a more advanced text and is therefore omitted.

226. Number of Solutions. In Case I (§ 220) two solutions and in Case II (§ 223) four solutions are generally obtained. The following rule for determining the number of solutions of any system of equations having two variables is given without proof:

Rule. — Two integral equations, having two variables, whose degrees are *m* and *n* respectively, have in general *mn* common solutions.

Thus, a cubic (third degree) equation and a quadratic equation would have six common solutions. If, however, the system could be reduced to a simpler system, as in the example of § 225, then the number of solutions would be determined by the degrees of the equations forming the new system.

EXERCISE 143

Solve the following systems of equations:

1. $\begin{cases} x^2 - y^2 = 56. \\ x + y = 14. \end{cases}$

2. $\begin{cases} x^4 - y^4 = 240. \\ x^2 + y^2 = 20. \end{cases}$

3. $\begin{cases} x^3 - y^3 = 133. \\ x - y = 7. \end{cases}$

4. $\begin{cases} x^3 - y^3 = 37. \\ x^2 + xy + y^2 = 37. \end{cases}$

5. $\begin{cases} x^3 + y^3 = -217. \\ x + y = -7. \end{cases}$

6. $\begin{cases} a^3 + b^3 = -335. \\ a^2 - ab + b^2 = 67. \end{cases}$

7. $\begin{cases} m^3 - n^3 = -117. \\ m - n = -3. \end{cases}$

8. $\begin{cases} 3c + d = 2. \\ 27c^3 + d^3 = 98. \end{cases}$

9. $\begin{cases} x^3 + y^3 = 9xy. \\ x + y = 6. \end{cases}$

10. $\begin{cases} x^3 + y^3 = 504. \\ x^2 - xy + y^2 = 84. \end{cases}$

SIMULTANEOUS EQUATIONS

11. $\begin{cases} x - y = 3. \\ x^2y - xy^2 = 30. \end{cases}$

12. $\begin{cases} x^3 - 3x^2y = 54. \\ x - 3y = 6. \end{cases}$

13. $\begin{cases} x^2 - xy + 3x = 8. \\ xy - y^2 + 3y = 4. \end{cases}$

14. $\begin{cases} x^3 + y^3 = 26 a^3. \\ x + y = 2a. \end{cases}$

15. $\begin{cases} \dfrac{1}{f^3} + \dfrac{1}{g^3} = 91. \\ \dfrac{1}{f} + \dfrac{1}{g} = 7. \end{cases}$

227. Miscellaneous Types and Methods. Many systems of equations which cannot be solved by the methods already given may be solved by combining the equations so as to obtain a linear equation or an equation of the form $xy = a$ constant.

EXAMPLE 1. Solve the system: $\begin{cases} x^2 + y^2 + 2x + 2y = 23. & (1) \\ xy = 6. & (2) \end{cases}$

SOLUTION: 1. $M_2 (2)$: $\qquad\qquad 2xy = 12.$ (3)

2. Adding (1) and (3): $x^2 + 2xy + y^2 + 2x + 2y = 35.$ (4)

$\therefore (x+y)^2 + 2(x+y) - 35 = 0.$

$\therefore (x+y+7)(x+y-5) = 0.$ (§ 205)

$\therefore x+y = -7,$ or $x+y = 5.$ (§ 110) (5)

3. Form the systems: $A: \begin{cases} x+y = -7. \\ xy = 6. \end{cases}$ $B: \begin{cases} x+y = 5. \\ xy = 6. \end{cases}$

4. Solving A: $x = -1, y = -6$; or $x = -6, y = -1$.

Solving B: $x = 3, y = 2$; or $x = 2, y = 3$.

CHECK: The four solutions check when substituted in equations (1) and (2).

EXAMPLE 2. Solve the system: $\begin{cases} m^2 + mn + n^2 = 7. & (1) \\ m + n = 5 + mn. & (2) \end{cases}$

SOLUTION: 1. Square (2): $m^2 + 2mn + n^2 = 25 + 10mn + m^2n^2.$ (3)

2. Subtract (1) from (3): $\qquad mn = 18 + 10mn + m^2n^2.$ (4)

$\therefore m^2n^2 + 9mn + 18 = 0.$ (5)

$\therefore (mn+6)(mn+3) = 0; \therefore mn = -6,$ or $mn = -3.$ (§ 110)

3. Form the systems: $A: \begin{cases} m+n = 5+mn. \\ mn = -6. \end{cases}$ $B: \begin{cases} m+n = 5+mn. \\ mn = -3. \end{cases}$

ALGEBRA

4. Solving A: $m = 2$, $n = -3$; or $m = -3$, $n = 2$.
   Solving B: $m = 3$, $n = -1$; or $m = -1$, $n = 3$.

CHECK: The four solutions check when substituted in equations (1) and (2).

EXERCISE 144

Solve the following systems:

1. $\begin{cases} xy = 12. \\ x^2 + y^2 = 40. \end{cases}$

2. $\begin{cases} A^2 B^2 + 28\,AB - 480 = 0. \\ 2\,A + B = 11. \end{cases}$

3. $\begin{cases} 2\,w^2 - 5\,t^2 = 13. \\ 15\,t^2 + w^2 = 24. \end{cases}$

4. $\begin{cases} m^2 + p^2 = 1. \\ mp = -\frac{12}{25}. \end{cases}$

5. $\begin{cases} 4\,x^2 + y^2 = 61. \\ 2\,x^2 + 3\,y^2 = 93. \end{cases}$

6. $\begin{cases} 4\,v^2 - 5\,vx = 19. \\ vx + x^2 = 6. \end{cases}$

7. $\begin{cases} 3\,r^2 - 5\,rt + 2\,t^2 = -3. \\ r - t = 1. \end{cases}$

8. $\begin{cases} c^2 + cd + d^2 = 97. \\ c - d = 19. \end{cases}$

9. $\begin{cases} x^3 + y^3 = 756. \\ x^2 - xy + y^2 = 63. \end{cases}$

10. $\begin{cases} p^2 - s^2 = 3. \\ ps = -2. \end{cases}$

11. $\begin{cases} a^2 + 2\,b^2 = 47 + 2\,a. \\ a^2 - 2\,b^2 = -7. \end{cases}$

12. $\begin{cases} xy = a^2 - 1. \\ x + y = 2\,a. \end{cases}$

13. $\begin{cases} \dfrac{m+n}{m-n} + \dfrac{m-n}{m+n} = \dfrac{10}{3}. \\ m^2 + n^2 = 45. \end{cases}$

14. $\begin{cases} x^3 - y^3 = 3\,a^2 + 3\,a + 1. \\ x - y = 1. \end{cases}$

15. $\begin{cases} 7\,v^2 - 5\,vt - 3\,t^2 = 36. \\ v^2 + 3\,vt + t^2 = -4. \end{cases}$

16. $\begin{cases} \dfrac{x+y}{x-y} + \dfrac{2x-y}{x+2y} = \dfrac{15}{4}. \\ x - 3y = -2. \end{cases}$

17. $\begin{cases} p\left(1 + \dfrac{3\,r}{100}\right) = 420. \\ p\left(1 + \dfrac{7\,r}{100}\right) = 480. \end{cases}$

18. $\begin{cases} m - v = -31. \\ mv = -150. \end{cases}$

19. $\begin{cases} x^3 + y^3 = 7\,a^3. \\ x + y = a. \end{cases}$

20. $\begin{cases} x^2 + y^2 = 2\,a^2 - 2\,ab + b^2. \\ 2\,x^2 - y^2 = a^2 + 2\,ab - b^2. \end{cases}$

21. $\begin{cases} x^2 + y^2 = 5(a^2 + b^2). \\ 4\,x^2 - y^2 = 5\,a(3\,a - 4\,b). \end{cases}$

22. $\begin{cases} 8\,x^2 - 11\,y^2 = 8. \\ 12\,x^2 + 13\,y^2 = 248. \end{cases}$

SIMULTANEOUS EQUATIONS

23. $\begin{cases} \dfrac{18}{r-s} + \dfrac{14}{r+s} = 8. \\ r - 2s = 1. \end{cases}$

24. $\begin{cases} x^2 - y^2 = 16. \\ y^2 - 14 = x. \end{cases}$

25. $\begin{cases} x^4 + x^2 y^2 + y^4 = 91. \\ x^2 + xy + y^2 = 13. \end{cases}$

HINT: See § 207.

26. $\begin{cases} a^4 + a^2 b^2 + b^4 = 133. \\ a^2 - ab + b^2 = 7. \end{cases}$

27. $\begin{cases} \dfrac{x^2}{y} + \dfrac{y^2}{x} = -\dfrac{7}{2}. \\ x + y = 1. \end{cases}$

HINT: Clear of fractions; divide (1) by (2).

28. $\begin{cases} m^2 - mn = 27\,n. \\ mn - n^2 = 3\,m. \end{cases}$

HINT: M₃ (2); add; factor.

29. $\begin{cases} x^2 = x + y. \\ y^2 = 3y - x. \end{cases}$

HINT: Find (1)−(2).

30. $\begin{cases} y(x - a) = 2\,ab. \\ x(y - b) = 2\,ab. \end{cases}$

31. $\begin{cases} x^2 y - x = -14. \\ x^4 y^2 + x^2 = 148. \end{cases}$

32. $\begin{cases} 5\,m^2 - 9\,n^2 = -121. \\ 7\,n^2 - 3\,m^2 = 105. \end{cases}$

33. $\begin{cases} mn - (m - n) = 1. \\ m^2 n^2 + (m - n)^2 = 13. \end{cases}$

34. $\begin{cases} a^2 - ab - 12\,b^2 = 8. \\ a^2 + ab - 10\,b^2 = 20. \end{cases}$

35. $\begin{cases} 2\,x^2 - 3\,xy = -4. \\ 4\,xy - 5\,y^2 = 3. \end{cases}$

36. $\begin{cases} t^2 + 5\,tw - w^2 = -7. \\ t^2 + 3\,tw - 2\,w^2 = -4. \end{cases}$

37. $\begin{cases} xy + (x - y) = -5. \\ xy(x - y) = -84. \end{cases}$

38. $\begin{cases} 9\,x^2 - xy - y = 51. \\ -5\,xy + y^2 + 3\,x = 81. \end{cases}$

EXERCISE 145

1. Find two numbers whose sum is 15 and the sum of whose squares is 113.

2. Find two numbers whose difference is 9 and the sum of whose squares is 221.

3. Find two numbers whose difference is 7 and whose sum multiplied by the greater gives 400.

4. The difference of the squares of two numbers is 16 and the product of the numbers is 15. Find the numbers.

5. The sum of the squares of two numbers is 52; the difference of the numbers is one fifth of their sum. Find the numbers.

6. The difference of the cubes of two numbers is 218; the sum of the squares of the numbers increased by the product of the numbers is 109. Find the numbers.

7. If the product of two numbers be multiplied by their sum, the result is -6; and the sum of the cubes of the numbers is 19. Find the numbers.

8. Find two numbers whose difference is 4 and the sum of whose reciprocals (Ex. 6, p. 272) is $\frac{3}{8}$.

9. The sum of the terms of a fraction is 13. If the numerator be decreased by 2, and the denominator be increased by 2, the product of the resulting fraction and the original fraction is $\frac{3}{16}$. Find the fraction.

10. Find the number of two digits in which the units' digit exceeds the tens' digit by 2, and such that the product of the number and its tens' digit is 105. (See § 172.)

11. The sum of the squares of the two digits of a number is 58. If 36 be subtracted from the number, the digits of the remainder are the digits of the original number in reverse order. Find the number.

12. Find the number of two digits such that, if the digits be reversed, the difference of the resulting number and the original number is 9, and their product is 736.

13. The area of a rectangular field is 216 square rods, and its perimeter is 60 rods. Find the length and width of the field.

14. The hypotenuse (§ 190) of a certain right triangle is 10 feet, and the area of the triangle is 24 square feet. Find the base and altitude of the triangle.

SIMULTANEOUS EQUATIONS

15. Find the dimensions of a rectangle whose diagonal is $2\sqrt{10}$ inches and whose area is 12 square inches.

16. A rectangular field contains $2\frac{1}{4}$ acres. If its length were decreased by 10 rods, and its width by 2 rods, its area would be less by one acre. Find its length and width. (See p. 145.)

17. The altitude of a certain rectangle is 2 feet more than the side of a certain square; the perimeter of the rectangle is 7 times the side of the square, and the area of the rectangle exceeds twice the area of the square by 32 square feet. Find the side of the square and the base of the rectangle.

18. If the length of a rectangular field be increased by 2 rods and its width be diminished by 5 rods, its area becomes 24 square rods; if its length be diminished by 4 rods and its width be increased by 3 rods, its area becomes 60 square rods. Find its length and width.

19 A man has two square lots of unequal size, together containing 74 square rods. If the lots were side by side, it would require 38 rods of fence to surround them in a single inclosure of six sides. Find the length of the side of each.

20. A and B working together can do a piece of work in 6 days. It takes B 5 days more than A to do the work. Find the number of days it will take each to do the work alone.

21. Find the sides of a parallelogram if the perimeter is 24 inches and the sum of the squares of the number of inches in the long and short sides is 80.

22. One of two angles exceeds the other by 5°. If the number of degrees in each is multiplied by the number in its supplement, the product obtained from the larger of the given angles exceeds the other product by the square of the number of degrees in the smaller of the given angles. Find the angles.

ALGEBRA

23. Two angles are supplementary. The square of the number of degrees in the larger angle exceeds by 4400 the product of the number of degrees in one angle by the number in the other angle. Find the number of degrees in each angle.

24. The difference in the rates of a passenger train and a freight train is 10 miles per hour. The passenger train requires 1 hour more for a trip of 175 miles than the freight train requires for a trip of 100 miles. Find the rate of each.

25. A crew can row upstream 18 miles in 4 hours more time than it takes them to return. If they row at two thirds of their usual rate, their rate upstream would be 1 mile an hour. Find their rate in still water, and the rate of the stream.

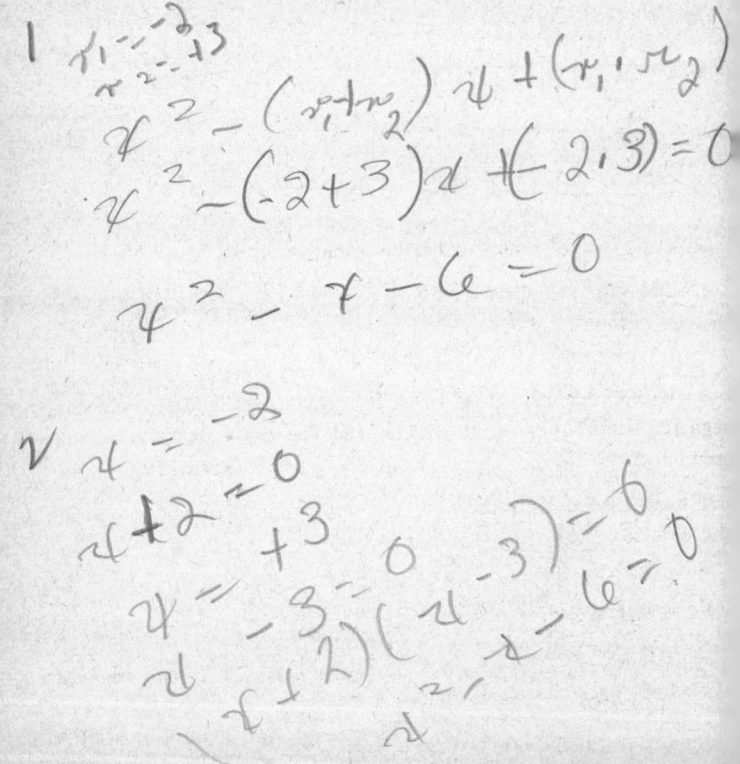

XIX. THE THEORY OF QUADRATIC EQUATIONS

228. The Sum and the Product of the Roots.

The general quadratic equation is:
$$ax^2 + bx + c = 0. \tag{1}$$
Divide both members by a:
$$x^2 + \frac{b}{a} \cdot x + \frac{c}{a} = 0. \tag{2}$$
The roots of (1) are:
$$r_1 = \frac{-b + \sqrt{b^2 - 4ac}}{2a}; \; r_2 = \frac{-b - \sqrt{b^2 - 4ac}}{2a}. \quad (\S\,197) \tag{3}$$
$$r_1 + r_2 = \frac{-2b}{2a} = -\frac{b}{a}. \tag{4}$$
$$r_1 \cdot r_2 = \frac{(-b)^2 - (\sqrt{b^2 - 4ac})^2}{4a^2} = \frac{b^2 - (b^2 - 4ac)}{4a^2} = \frac{4ac}{4a^2} = \frac{c}{a}. \tag{5}$$

Rule. — In the general quadratic equation $ax^2 + bx + c = 0$:

1. The sum of the roots is $-\frac{b}{a}$.   From (4).

2. The product of the roots is $\frac{c}{a}$.   From (5).

3. If the coefficient of x^2 is made 1, the coefficient of x is the negative of the sum of the roots, and the constant term is the product of the roots.   From (2), (4), (5).

EXAMPLE 1. Find the sum and the product of the roots of the equation $2x^2 - 9x - 5 = 0$.

SOLUTION: 1. $a = 2$; $b = -9$; $c = -5$.

2. $\therefore r_1 + r_2 = -\frac{b}{a} = -\frac{-9}{2} = +\frac{9}{2}$; $r_1 r_2 = \frac{c}{a} = \frac{-5}{2}$.

NOTE. The first part of this rule justifies the method of checking solutions of quadratic equations recommended in § 195.

EXERCISE 146

Find by inspection the sum and the product of the roots check examples 1, 2, 3, and 7 by finding the roots:

1. $x^2 + 7x + 6 = 0$.
2. $m^2 - m + 12 = 0$.
3. $3c^2 - c - 6 = 0$.
4. $12y^2 - 4y + 3 = 0$.
5. $9r - 21r^2 + 7 = 0$.
6. $4 - y - 6y^2 = 0$.
7. $2x^2 + 3px - 5p^2 = 0$.
8. $14x^2 + 8tx + 21t^2 = 0$.

9. One root of $4x^2 - x - 5 = 0$ is -1. Find the other root.

SOLUTION: 1. $r_1 = -1$. Let r_2 be the second root.
2. $r_1 + r_2 = +\frac{1}{4}$; $\therefore -1 + r_2 = \frac{1}{4}$, or $r_2 = 1\frac{1}{4} = \frac{5}{4}$.
CHECK: Does $r_1 \cdot r_2 = \frac{-5}{4}$? *i.e.* does $-1 \cdot \frac{5}{4} = \frac{-5}{4}$? Yes.

10. One root of $3x^2 + 7x - 6 = 0$ is $\frac{2}{3}$. Find the other.
11. One root of $7q^2 + 20q + 12 = 0$ is -2. Find the other.
12. One root of $15m^2 + 28m = 32$ is $\frac{4}{5}$. Find the other.
13. One root of $3x^2 - 2kx = 33k^2$ is $-3k$. Find the other.
14. One root of $4p^2 - 15xp - 4x^2 = 0$ is $-4p$. Find the other.

15. Find k so that one root of $x^2 - 5x + k = 0$ may be 7.

SOLUTION: 1. $r_1 + r_2 = 5$; $\therefore r_2 + 7 = 5$, or $r_2 = -2$.
2. $k = r_1 \cdot r_2$; $\therefore k = 7 \cdot -2 = -14$.
CHECK: If $x^2 - 5x - 14 = 0$, then $(x-7)(x+2) = 0$. $\therefore x = 7$, or -2.

16. Find k so that one root of $2x^2 - 3x - k = 0$ may be 3.
17. Find k so that one root of $3x^2 - 7x - 2k = 0$ may be -2.
18. Find n so that one root of $x^2 + 7x + 4n = 0$ may be 5.
19. Find p so that the roots of $x^2 + 3x + p = 0$ shall be equal.

THE THEORY OF QUADRATIC EQUATIONS

20. Find r so that the roots of $3x^2 - 5x + r = 0$ shall be equal.

229. Formation of Equations Having Given Roots. There are two methods of forming a quadratic equation which shall have given roots.

EXAMPLE 1. Form the equation whose roots shall be $\frac{1}{2}$ and $-\frac{3}{4}$.

SOLUTION: 1. Let the coefficient of x^2 be 1; then by § 228 the equation is
$$x^2 - (r_1 + r_2)x + r_1 r_2 = 0.$$

2. $\quad r_1 + r_2 = \frac{1}{2} + \left(-\frac{3}{4}\right) = -\frac{1}{4}; \; r_1 r_2 = \frac{1}{2} \cdot \frac{-3}{4} = \frac{-3}{8}.$

3. ∴ the equation is:
$$x^2 - \left(-\frac{1}{4}\right)x + \left(-\frac{3}{8}\right) = 0, \text{ or } x^2 + \frac{x}{4} - \frac{3}{8} = 0. \quad (\S \, 228)$$

Multiplying both members by 8,
$$8x^2 + 2x - 3 = 0.$$

CHECK: The given roots, if substituted, will satisfy the equation.

EXAMPLE 2. Form the equation whose roots shall be -9 and 2.

SOLUTION: 1. If $x = -9$, then $x + 9 = 0$; if $x = 2$, then $x - 2 = 0$.

2. $\quad \therefore (x+9)(x-2) = 0, \text{ or } x^2 + 7x - 18 = 0.$

It is clear that this equation has the given roots.

NOTE. This second method may be used also to form an equation having three or more roots.

EXERCISE 147

Form the equations whose roots shall be:

1. 2, 3.
2. $-3, -6$.
3. $6, -9$.
4. $12, -5$.
5. $2, \frac{3}{2}$.
6. $1, -\frac{1}{3}$.
7. $\frac{1}{2}, \frac{3}{4}$.
8. $3m, -5m$.
9. $4t, -\frac{3}{5}t$.
10. $-\frac{5}{7}c, \frac{3}{4}c$.
11. $2, 3, -5$.
12. $a + 3m, a - 3m$.
13. $2a - b, 2a + b$.
14. $3 + \sqrt{5}, 3 - \sqrt{5}$.
15. $2 + 3\sqrt{2}, 2 - 3\sqrt{2}$.

DETERMINATION OF THE CHARACTER OF THE ROOTS

230. Classification of Numbers. The numbers considered in this text to this point are:

(*A*) Real numbers.

1. Rational Numbers: (*a*) integers (positive and negative); (*b*) fractions whose terms are integers.

2. Irrational numbers: (*a*) quadratic surds (§ 184); (*b*) surd expressions, such as $2 + \sqrt{3}$.

(*B*) Imaginary Numbers: (*a*) pure imaginaries (§ 202); (*b*) complex numbers (§ 202).

231. It is often necessary to determine the character of the roots of a quadratic.

Thus the roots of $2x^2 - 8x + 3 = 0$ are $\dfrac{4 \pm \sqrt{10}}{2}$.

Since 10 is positive, the roots are real numbers.

Since 10 is not a perfect square, the roots are irrational.

Since $\sqrt{10}$ is added in one root and subtracted in the other, the roots are unequal.

Hence the roots are real, irrational, and unequal.

It is possible to determine the character of the roots however without determining the roots themselves.

For the general quadratic $ax^2 + bx + c = 0$, the roots are

$$r_1 = \frac{-b + \sqrt{b^2 - 4ac}}{2a}; \qquad r_2 = \frac{-b - \sqrt{b^2 - 4ac}}{2a}.$$

Rule 1. — If $b^2 - 4ac$ is positive, the roots are real and unequal. They are rational if $b^2 - 4ac$ is a perfect square, and irrational if $b^2 - 4ac$ is not a perfect square.

2. If $b^2 - 4ac$ equals zero, the roots are real and equal.

3. If $b^2 - 4ac$ is less than zero, the roots are imaginary.

$b^2 - 4ac$ is called the *Discriminant* of the quadratic.

THE THEORY OF QUADRATIC EQUATIONS

EXAMPLE 1. Determine the character of the roots of
$$2x^2 - 5x - 18 = 0.$$

SOLUTION: 1. $b^2 - 4ac = (-5)^2 - 4(2)(-18) = 25 + 144 = 169 = 13^2.$
2. By Rule 1, the roots are real, rational, and unequal.

EXAMPLE 2. Determine the character of the roots of
$$3x^2 + 2x + 1 = 0.$$

SOLUTION: 1. $b^2 - 4ac = 4 - 4 \cdot 3 \cdot 1 = 4 - 12 = -8.$
2. By Rule 3, the roots are imaginary.

EXAMPLE 3. Determine the character of the roots of
$$4x^2 - 12x + 9 = 0.$$

SOLUTION: 1. $b^2 - 4ac = 144 - 4 \cdot 4 \cdot 9 = 144 - 144 = 0.$
2. By Rule 2, the roots are real and equal.

NOTE. This type is most easily understood if the quadratic is solved by factoring. This example becomes $(2x-3)(2x-3) = 0$. The roots are then $\frac{3}{2}$ and $\frac{3}{2}$. It is customary to say that the roots are equal.

EXERCISE 148

Determine by inspection the character of the roots of:

1. $6x^2 + 7x - 5 = 0.$
2. $4x^2 - 20x + 25 = 0.$
3. $3z^2 - 8z + 5 = 0.$
4. $x^2 - 9x + 15 = 0.$
5. $5r^2 + 7r + 3 = 0.$
6. $9s^2 - 1 = 12s.$
7. $5m - 2 = 4m^2.$
8. $4y^2 - y = 6.$
9. $5t^2 + 7 = 8t.$
10. $20x^2 - 41x + 20 = 0.$
11. $7x^2 + 3x = 0.$
12. $16m^2 - 9 = 0.$

XX. EXPONENTS

232. In the preceding chapters, only positive integers have been used as exponents. The fundamental definition when m is a positive integer, is:

$$a^m = a \cdot a \cdot a \cdots a \quad (m \text{ factors}). \qquad (\S\ 15)$$

233. There are five fundamental laws of exponents. When m and n are *positive integers:*

I. Multiplication Law. Just as $a^5 \times a^7 = a^{12}$,
$$\text{so } a^m \times a^n = a^{m+n}.$$

Proof: 1. $a^m = a \cdot a \cdot a \cdots a \quad (m \text{ factors}).$ (§ 232)
2. $\qquad a^n = a \cdot a \cdot a \cdots a \quad (n \text{ factors}).$ (§ 232)
3. $\therefore a^m \cdot a^n = \{a \cdot a \cdot a \cdots a\ (m \text{ factors})\} \cdot \{a \cdot a\ \ a \cdots a\ (n \text{ factors})\}$
$\qquad = a \cdot a \cdot a \cdots a\ \{(m+n) \text{ factors}\}.$
4. $\therefore a^m \cdot a^n = a^{m+n}.$ (§ 232)

II. Division Law. Just as $a^9 \div a^4 = a^5$,
$$\text{so } a^m \div a^n = a^{m-n}. \quad (m \text{ greater than } n.)$$

Proof: 1. $\dfrac{a^m}{a^n} = \dfrac{\cancel{a} \cdot \cancel{a} \cdot \cancel{a} \cdot \cancel{a} \cdots \cancel{a} \cdot a \cdot a \cdots a\ (m \text{ factors})}{\cancel{a} \cdot \cancel{a} \cdot \cancel{a} \cdot \cancel{a} \cdots \cancel{a}\ (n \text{ factors})}.$ (§ 232)
2. $\qquad = a \cdot a \cdots a\ \{(m-n) \text{ factors}\} = a^{m-n}.$ (§ 232)
3. $\therefore a^m \div a^n = a^{m-n}.$

III. Power of a Power. Just as $(a^5)^3 = a^{15}$,
$$\text{so } (a^m)^n = a^{mn}.$$

Proof: 1. $(a^m)^n = a^m \cdot a^m \cdot a^m \cdots a^m \quad (n \text{ factors})$ (§ 232)
2. $\qquad = a^{m+m+m+\cdots+m}\ (n \text{ terms}).$ (Law I)
3. $\therefore (a^m)^n = a^{mn} \quad \{\text{since } m+m+\cdots+m\ (n \text{ terms}) = mn\}.$

IV. Power of a Product. Just as $(ab)^5 = a^5 b^5$,
$$\text{so } (ab)^n = a^n b^n.$$

EXPONENTS

Proof: 1. $(ab)^n = (ab) \cdot (ab) \cdot (ab) \cdots (ab)$ (n factors) (§ 232)

2. $ = \{a \cdot a \cdot a \cdots a(n \text{ factors})\} \cdot \{b \cdot b \cdot b \cdots b\,(n \text{ factors})\}$, (§ 232)

3. $\therefore (ab)^n = a^n \cdot b^n$.

V. Power of a Quotient. Just as $\left(\dfrac{a}{b}\right)^5 = \dfrac{a^5}{b^5}$,

so $\left(\dfrac{a}{b}\right)^n = \dfrac{a^n}{b^n}$.

Proof: 1. $\left(\dfrac{a}{b}\right)^n = \left(\dfrac{a}{b}\right)\left(\dfrac{a}{b}\right)\left(\dfrac{a}{b}\right) \cdots \left(\dfrac{a}{b}\right)$ (n factors) (§ 232)

2. $\phantom{\left(\dfrac{a}{b}\right)^n} = \dfrac{a \cdot a \cdot a \cdots a\,(n \text{ factors})}{b \cdot b \cdot b \cdots b\,(n \text{ factors})}$.

3. $\therefore \left(\dfrac{a}{b}\right)^n = \dfrac{a^n}{b^n}$. (§ 232)

Involution is the name given to the process of finding a power of a number.

EXERCISE 149

Find the results of the indicated operations in the following examples, using the five laws above; the literal exponents denote positive integers.

1. $x^{10} \cdot x$.
2. $m^{12} \cdot m^{11}$.
3. $y^5 \cdot y^n$.
4. $m^{2a} \cdot m^a$.
5. $a^{3n} \cdot a^{2n}$.
6. $b^{r+1} \cdot b^2$.
7. $c^{n-4} \cdot c^5$.
8. $d^{2r+1} \cdot d^r$.
9. $z^{r+1} \cdot z^{r-1}$.
10. $t^{n-2} \cdot t^{n+3}$.
11. $w^{m+n} \cdot w^{m-n}$.
12. $g^{n-r+1} \cdot g^r$.
13. $x^{15} \div x^{13}$.
14. $x^{12} \div x^8$.
15. $y^{5n} \div y^n$.
16. $m^{3c} \div m^c$.
17. $a^{4n} \div a^n$.
18. $b^{r+4} \div b^2$.
19. $c^{n+5} \div c^3$.
20. $d^{2r+3} \div d^r$.
21. $z^{r+4} \div z^{r+2}$.
22. $t^{n+6} \div t^{n-2}$.
23. $w^{m+n} \div w^{m-n}$.
24. $g^{2n-r+1} \div g^r$.
25. $(x^6)^4$.
26. $(y^5)^7$.
27. $(m^4)^8$.
28. $(-a^5 b^3)^5$.
29. $(y^5 z^2 w)^4$.
30. $(m^3 n^2 p^4)^5$.
31. $(a^3)^n$.
32. $(b^m)^2$.
33. $(-c^n d^m)^3$.
34. $(x^4 y^3)^m$.
35. $(r^2 s^6)^t$.
36. $(x^m y^n)^r$.

322 ALGEBRA

37. $\left(\dfrac{x^2}{y^3}\right)^4.$

38. $\left(\dfrac{m^5}{n^3}\right)^p.$

39. $\left(\dfrac{a^5}{b^6}\right)^p.$

40. $\left(\dfrac{r^n}{s^m}\right)^2.$

41. $\left(-\dfrac{x^a}{y^b}\right)^3.$

42. $\left(\dfrac{a^{2n}}{b^{3n}}\right)^2.$

43. $\left(\dfrac{a^n}{b^m}\right)^r.$

44. $\left(\dfrac{x^a}{y^b}\right)^c.$

45. $\left(\dfrac{r^{2n}}{t^{3m}}\right)^k.$

234. Only cube and square roots have been considered in the preceding chapters. More general roots occur in mathematics.

235. Just as $\sqrt[3]{x}$ indicates the *cube root* of x (§ 91), so $\sqrt[n]{x}$ indicates the *n*th *root* of x.

n is called the **Index** of the root.

The nth root of x is the number whose nth power equals x; that is,
$$(\sqrt[n]{x})^n = x.$$

Thus, $\sqrt[4]{x^{12}} = x^3$, since $(x^3)^4 = x^{12}$.

$\sqrt[5]{x^{20}} = x^4$, since $(x^4)^5 = x^{20}$.

$\sqrt[7]{-x^{14}y^{21}} = -x^2y^3$, since $(-x^2y^3)^7 = -x^{14}y^{21}$.

The number under the radical sign is called the **Radicand**.

Rule. — **To find the *n*th root of a perfect *n*th power, divide the exponent of each factor of the radicand by *n*.**

Every number has n nth roots. Unless something is said to the contrary, the *principal root* is denoted by the symbol $\sqrt[n]{\ }$. If n is even, this root is the positive root; if n is odd and the radicand is negative, this root is negative.

Evolution is the name given to the process of finding the root of a number.

HISTORICAL NOTE. A symbol for extracting a root did not appear until the fifteenth century. In Italian mathematics, the first letter of the word Radix, meaning the root, was used to indicate the square root: thus ℞. Presently there were used ℞.2^a, ℞.3^a, etc. to indicate the square, cube, and other roots. Chuquet, a French mathematician of about 1500, used ℞^{2}, ℞^{3}, etc.

EXPONENTS

In Germany, a point was placed before a number to indicate that its square root was to be taken. Two points were used to indicate the fourth root, and three the third root. Reise, 1492–1559, replaced the point by the symbol, $\sqrt{}$, to indicate the square root, and Rudolph, 1515, used the symbol, $\sqrt{\sqrt{}}$, for the fourth root. Stevin, 1548–1620, used the better symbols: $\sqrt{②}$, $\sqrt{③}$, etc. Girard, 1590–1632, used: $\sqrt[2]{}$, $\sqrt[3]{}$, etc. Descartes used the vinculum to indicate what numbers were affected by the root.

EXERCISE 150

Determine:

1. $\sqrt[3]{8}$.
2. $\sqrt[3]{-27}$.
3. $\sqrt[5]{-32}$.
4. $\sqrt[4]{81\,a^4}$.
5. $\sqrt[5]{243\,b^5}$.
6. $\sqrt[4]{m^{20}n^8}$.
7. $\sqrt[4]{\dfrac{x^8}{y^{12}}}$.
8. $\sqrt[5]{\dfrac{-m^{15}}{n^{20}}}$.
9. $\sqrt[6]{\dfrac{x^{18}}{y^{12}}}$.
10. $\sqrt[7]{-\dfrac{t^7}{w^{14}}}$.
11. $\sqrt[6]{64\,a^6b^6}$.
12. $\sqrt[4]{625\,a^8b^4}$.
13. $\sqrt[3]{-27\,m^6n^9}$.
14. $\sqrt[5]{-32\,m^5n^{10}}$.
15. $\sqrt[4]{81\,y^8z^4}$.
16. $\sqrt[7]{-b^{21}c^7d^{14}}$.
17. $\sqrt[4]{\dfrac{m^4}{81}}$.
18. $\sqrt[5]{\dfrac{32\,a^5}{x^{10}}}$.
19. $\sqrt[5]{-\dfrac{243\,m^{15}}{32\,n^5}}$.
20. $\sqrt[6]{\dfrac{x^6y^{12}z^6}{r^{12}s^{24}}}$.
21. $\sqrt{a^{2m}}$.
22. $\sqrt[3]{a^{3r}}$.
23. $\sqrt[4]{b^{4n}c^8}$.
24. $\sqrt[5]{-x^{5t}y^{10s}}$.
25. $\sqrt[6]{a^{12r}b^{18}}$.
26. $\sqrt[n]{a^{2n}b^{3n}}$.
27. $\sqrt[3]{\dfrac{x^{3m}}{8\,y^6}}$.
28. $\sqrt[4]{\dfrac{16\,x^{4m}}{y^{8r}}}$.
29. $\sqrt[n]{\dfrac{a^{3n}}{b^{7n}}}$.
30. $\sqrt[m]{\dfrac{x^{mn}}{y^{pm}}}$.

236. Fractions, zero, and negative numbers are used as exponents. Up to this point the symbols a^{-3} and $a^{\frac{2}{3}}$ do not have any meaning, for the base a cannot be used as a factor *minus three times* or *two thirds times*. (See § 232.)

ALGEBRA

237. Meaning of a Fractional Exponent. If $a^{\frac{2}{3}}$ is to obey the multiplication law (§ 233), then $a^{\frac{2}{3}} \cdot a^{\frac{2}{3}} \cdot a^{\frac{2}{3}} = a^{\frac{6}{3}} = a^2$.

$$\therefore (a^{\frac{2}{3}})^3 = a^2, \text{ or } a^{\frac{2}{3}} = \sqrt[3]{a^2}.$$

This fact suggests the definition: *in a fractional exponent, the denominator denotes the principal root (§ 235) of the power of the base indicated by the numerator.* In symbols,

$$a^{\frac{m}{n}} = \sqrt[n]{a^m}.$$

Thus: $\quad x^{\frac{3}{4}} = \sqrt[4]{x^3}; \ (-27)^{\frac{1}{3}} = \sqrt[3]{-27} = -3.$

EXERCISE 151

Express with radical signs and find the values of:

1. $4^{\frac{1}{2}}$.
2. $27^{\frac{1}{3}}$.
3. $(-8)^{\frac{1}{3}}$.
4. $32^{\frac{1}{5}}$.
5. $81^{\frac{1}{4}}$.
6. $64^{\frac{1}{6}}$.
7. $(-125)^{\frac{1}{3}}$.
8. $256^{\frac{1}{4}}$.
9. $(-1000)^{\frac{1}{3}}$.
10. $(x^6)^{\frac{1}{3}}$.
11. $(y^{12})^{\frac{1}{6}}$.
12. $(z^{10})^{\frac{1}{5}}$.
13. $(-64\,x^3y^3)^{\frac{1}{3}}$.
14. $(32\,a^5b^{20})^{\frac{1}{5}}$.
15. $(81\,x^8y^4)^{\frac{1}{4}}$.

Express with radical signs:

16. $2^{\frac{2}{3}}$.
17. $4^{\frac{3}{4}}$.
18. $5^{\frac{3}{2}}$.
19. $(4\,x)^{\frac{1}{2}}$.
20. $4\,x^{\frac{1}{2}}$.
21. $3\,y^{\frac{2}{3}}$.
22. $2\,ab^{\frac{2}{3}}$.
23. $(2\,ab)^{\frac{2}{3}}$.
24. $m^{\frac{4}{5}}n^{\frac{5}{4}}$.
25. $8\,a^{\frac{1}{6}}b^{\frac{3}{5}}$.

Express with fractional exponents:

26. $\sqrt[5]{a^3}$.
27. $\sqrt[6]{x^5}$.
28. $\sqrt[3]{2\,a}$.
29. $2\sqrt[3]{a}$.
30. $\sqrt[7]{m^5}$.
31. $\sqrt[8]{b^7c^2}$.
32. $2\sqrt[3]{n^2}$.
33. $4\sqrt[5]{y^3}$.
34. $3\,y\sqrt[5]{x^4}$.
35. $a^2\sqrt[3]{b^2}$.

238. Meaning of a Zero Exponent. If a^0 is to obey the multiplication law (§ 233), then $a^m \cdot a^0 = a^{m+0} = a^m$.

$$\therefore a^0 = a^m \div a^m = 1.$$

EXPONENTS

This partially suggests the definition: *the zero power of any number, except zero, is 1.*

Thus: $5^0 = 1$; $x^0 = 1$; $(-65)^0 = 1$.

239. Meaning of a Negative Exponent. If a^{-m} is to obey the multiplication law (§ 233), then $a^{-m} \cdot a^m = a^{-m+m} = a^0 = 1$.

This suggests the definition: $a^{-m} = \dfrac{1}{a^m}$.

Thus:

$$x^{-4} = \frac{1}{x^4};\quad y^{-\frac{2}{3}} = \frac{1}{y^{\frac{2}{3}}} = \frac{1}{\sqrt[3]{y^2}};\quad \left(-\frac{1}{8}\right)^{-\frac{1}{3}} = \frac{1}{(-\frac{1}{8})^{\frac{1}{3}}} = \frac{1}{\sqrt[3]{-\frac{1}{8}}} = \frac{1}{-\frac{1}{2}} = -2.$$

EXERCISE 152

Express with positive exponents and find the values of:

1. 3^{-2}.
2. 2^{-3}.
3. 3^{-3}.
4. 7^0.
5. $3^{-1} \cdot 2^{-4}$.
6. $5^0 \cdot 4^{-2}$.
7. $9 \cdot 6^{-2}$.
8. $100 \cdot 5^{-2}$.
9. $64 \cdot 4^{-3}$.
10. $16^{-\frac{1}{2}}$.
11. $(-27)^{-\frac{1}{3}}$.
12. $81^{-\frac{1}{4}}$.
13. $64^{-\frac{1}{6}}$.
14. $(-125)^{-\frac{1}{3}}$.
15. $(-32)^{-\frac{1}{5}}$.

Write with positive exponents:

16. $a^2 b^{-5}$.
17. $(2a)^{-3}$.
18. $2 a^{-3}$.
19. $(3a)^{-2} b^4$.
20. $3 a^{-2} b^4$.
21. $2^{-2} m^3 n^{-4}$.
22. $4 a^{-6} b^{-3}$.
23. $(2a)^3 \cdot (3b)^{-2}$.

240. Negative Exponents in Fractions.

EXAMPLE 1. $\dfrac{x^{-3} y^2}{z^{-2}} = \dfrac{\frac{1}{x^3} \cdot y^2}{\frac{1}{z^2}} = \dfrac{y^2}{x^3} \cdot \dfrac{z^2}{1} = \dfrac{y^2 z^2}{x^3}$.

This example makes it clear that *a factor may be transferred from one term of a fraction to the other provided the sign of its exponent be changed.*

ALGEBRA

EXAMPLE 2. $\dfrac{5\,x^2y^{-4}z^{-3}}{w^{-2}t} = \dfrac{5\,x^2w^2}{ty^4z^3}.$

EXAMPLE 3. $\dfrac{3\,a^2b}{cd^3} = 3\,a^2bc^{-1}d^{-3}.$

EXERCISE 153

Write with positive exponents:

1. $\dfrac{x^{-4}z}{y^3}.$
2. $\dfrac{2\,a}{b^{-3}}.$
3. $\dfrac{x^2}{2\,y^{-5}}.$
4. $\dfrac{x^2}{5\cdot(2\,y)^{-3}}.$
5. $\dfrac{6\,m^4n^{-3}}{7\,p^{-2}}.$
6. $\dfrac{3\,a^{-3}b^2}{2\,c^{-2}d^4}.$
7. $\dfrac{8\,a^{\frac{3}{4}}b^{-9}}{x^3y^{-\frac{1}{2}}}.$
8. $\dfrac{5\,a^4b^{-\frac{3}{5}}}{6\,c^{-\frac{2}{3}}d^5}.$

Write without any denominator:

9. $\dfrac{3\,x^6}{y^2}.$
10. $\dfrac{b^{\frac{1}{3}}}{c^4}.$
11. $\dfrac{2\,a^2b^5}{c^{-5}}.$
12. $\dfrac{mn^{-6}}{d^3}.$
13. $\dfrac{7\,x^{-7}y}{z^{\frac{1}{6}}}.$
14. $\dfrac{a^{-\frac{2}{5}}}{b^{-4}c^{\frac{3}{5}}}.$
15. $\dfrac{8\,a^{\frac{3}{4}}b^3}{2\,c^{-2}d^{\frac{1}{4}}}.$
16. $\dfrac{4\,a^{\frac{6}{7}}m^{\frac{3}{8}}}{2\,b^5n^{-\frac{5}{3}}}.$

HISTORICAL NOTE. In the note following § 14, credit is given to Herigone for having grasped the idea of an exponent, and for introducing a rather good notation. As early as 1484, another French mathematician, Chuquet, had had some idea of an exponent and had written expressions involving a form of negative exponent and also the zero exponent. His ideas, however, did not spread far. Other attempts to introduce general exponents were made between that time and the time of Newton. To Newton must be given the credit for having finally fixed the present form of writing the various kinds of exponents.

241. The Fundamental Laws of Any Rational Exponent.

The symbol x^n has been defined now (§§ 232, 237, 238, 239) for all rational (§ 230) values of n. The five fundamental laws which have been proved for positive integral exponents (§ 233) apply also for other rational exponents. This fact will be assumed without proof in this text.

EXPONENTS

EXERCISE 154

Law I

EXAMPLE. $a^7 \cdot a^{-5} \cdot a^0 \cdot a^{\frac{1}{2}} = a^{7-5+0+\frac{1}{2}} = a^{2\frac{1}{2}}$.

1. Express Law I in words.

2. Multiply each of the following numbers:
$$r^3; \quad r^7; \quad s^{-4}; \quad r^5 s^2; \quad r^{-3} s^{-6}; \quad r^n s^m$$
by: (a) r^5; (b) r^{-6}; (c) s^3; (d) $r^2 s^3$; (e) $r^{-4} s^{-5}$.

3. Multiply each of the following numbers:
$$x^{\frac{1}{2}}; \quad x^{\frac{1}{4}}; \quad y^{\frac{2}{3}}; \quad x^{\frac{2}{3}} y^{\frac{1}{6}}; \quad x^n y^b;$$
by: (a) $x^{\frac{1}{2}}$; (b) $x^{\frac{1}{3}}$; (c) $y^{\frac{2}{3}}$; (d) $x^{\frac{1}{4}} y^{\frac{1}{6}}$.

4. Multiply each of the following numbers:
$$m^{-\frac{1}{3}}; \quad n^{-\frac{1}{4}}; \quad m^{\frac{1}{5}} n^{-\frac{1}{10}}; \quad m^{-\frac{1}{2}} n^{\frac{1}{8}}; \quad m^{-\frac{1}{6}} n^{-\frac{3}{4}}.$$
by: (a) m; (b) $m^{\frac{1}{2}}$; (c) $n^{-\frac{1}{4}}$; (d) $m^{-1} n^2$.

Multiply:

5. $a^{\frac{2}{3}} + a^{\frac{1}{3}} b^{\frac{1}{3}} + b^{\frac{2}{3}}$ by $a^{\frac{1}{3}} - b^{\frac{1}{3}}$.
6. $2 a^{-1} - 7 - 3 a$ by $4 a^{-1} + 5$.
7. $x^{-\frac{9}{4}} + 2 x^{-\frac{3}{2}} + 4 x^{-\frac{3}{4}} + 8$ by $x^{-\frac{3}{4}} - 2$.
8. $x^{\frac{2}{3}} + x^{\frac{1}{6}} y^{\frac{1}{6}} + y^{\frac{2}{3}}$ by $x^{\frac{2}{3}} - x^{\frac{1}{6}} y^{\frac{1}{6}} + y^{\frac{2}{3}}$.

Find:

9. $(a^{-\frac{1}{2}} + b^{\frac{1}{2}})(a^{-\frac{1}{2}} - b^{\frac{1}{2}})$.
10. $(x^{-\frac{1}{3}} - y^{-\frac{1}{3}})^2$.
11. $(r^n - s^m)^2$.
12. $(x^{\frac{1}{2}} - 6)(x^{\frac{1}{2}} + 13)$.
13. $(r^{\frac{3}{2}} - s^{\frac{5}{2}})^2$.
14. $(a^{\frac{3}{5}} + 7 b^{-1})(a^{\frac{3}{5}} - 8 b^{-1})$.

Law II

Example. $m^{2\frac{1}{2}} \div m^{-\frac{1}{4}} = m^{2\frac{1}{2}-(-\frac{1}{4})} = m^{2\frac{3}{4}}.$

15. Express Law II in words.

16. Divide each of the following numbers:
$$t^{10};\quad t^{-12};\quad t^a;\quad t^{\frac{1}{2}};\quad t^{-\frac{1}{4}};\quad t^{2\frac{1}{2}};$$
by: (a) t^3; (b) t^{-4}; (c) $t^{\frac{1}{2}}$; (d) $t^{-\frac{1}{8}}.$

17. Divide each of the following numbers:
$$c^{-5}d^4;\quad c^x d^6;\quad c^{\frac{1}{5}}d^{-\frac{1}{3}};\quad c^{2\frac{1}{4}}d^{3\frac{1}{2}};$$
by: (a) cd; (b) $c^{-2}d^{-1}.$

18. Divide $a^{-3}+a^{-2}+a^{-1}$ by $a^{-4}.$

19. Divide $4x^{-6}+6x^{-4}+12x^{-2}$ by $2x^{-2}.$

20. Divide $a^4+a^3+a^2+a$ by $a^{\frac{1}{2}}.$

21. Divide a^2+b^2 by $a^{\frac{2}{3}}+b^{\frac{2}{3}}.$

22. Divide $a-1$ by $a^{\frac{1}{2}}+1.$

23. Divide $a-4a^{\frac{3}{4}}+6a^{\frac{1}{2}}-4a^{\frac{1}{4}}+1$ by $a^{\frac{1}{2}}-2a^{\frac{1}{4}}+1.$

Law III

Example. $(x^{-\frac{3}{2}})^{\frac{4}{5}} = x^{-\frac{3}{2}\cdot\frac{4}{5}} = x^{-\frac{6}{5}}.$

24. Indicate and find the values of the following numbers:
$$(x^6)^n;\quad (y^{-12})^n;\quad (z^{\frac{6}{5}})^n;\quad (r^{-\frac{1}{2}})^n;\quad (t^{2.4})^n;$$
when n is: (a) 2; (b) -3; (c) $\frac{1}{2}$; (d) $-\frac{1}{3}$; (e) $-\frac{3}{2}.$

Laws IV and V

Example 1. $(x^{-5}y^{\frac{5}{3}})^{-\frac{1}{5}} = x^{-5\cdot-\frac{1}{5}}y^{\frac{5}{3}\cdot-\frac{1}{5}} = xy^{-\frac{1}{3}}.$

Example 2. $\left(\dfrac{r^{-\frac{3}{2}}}{s^{2\frac{1}{2}}}\right)^{-2} = \dfrac{r^{-\frac{3}{2}\cdot-2}}{s^{2\frac{1}{2}\cdot-2}} = \dfrac{r^3}{s^{-5}} = r^3 s^5.$

EXPONENTS

25. Express Law IV in words.

26. Express Law V in words.

27. Indicate and find the values of:

$$(a^2 b^{-3})^n; \quad (m^{-3} p^{\frac{1}{2}})^n; \quad (x^{-\frac{3}{4}} y^{-\frac{3}{8}})^n; \quad (r^{-a} s^{-b})^n;$$

when n is: (a) 2; (b) -4; (c) $\frac{1}{6}$; (d) $-\frac{1}{3}$.

Find the values of:

28. $(-8)^{\frac{2}{3}}$.

SOLUTION: $(-8)^{\frac{2}{3}} = [(-8)^{\frac{1}{3}}]^2 = [\sqrt[3]{-8}]^2 = (-2)^2 = 4$.

29. $25^{\frac{3}{2}}$.   **32.** $81^{\frac{3}{4}}$.   **35.** $(4 x^2)^{\frac{7}{2}}$.   **38.** $(-32)^{\frac{7}{5}}$.

30. $9^{\frac{5}{2}}$.   **33.** $49^{\frac{3}{2}}$.   **36.** $(243 x^5)^{\frac{3}{5}}$.   **39.** $(64 x^6 y^{12})^{\frac{5}{6}}$.

31. $8^{\frac{7}{3}}$.   **34.** $(-27)^{\frac{2}{3}}$.   **37.** $(16 m^4)^{\frac{5}{4}}$.   **40.** $(-125)^{\frac{4}{3}}$.

41. $(-64 a^3 b^6)^{\frac{2}{3}}$.   **43.** $(256 x^4 y^8)^{\frac{3}{4}}$.

42. $(-128 m^7)^{\frac{3}{7}}$.   **44.** $16^{1.25}$.

45. Simplify $\dfrac{10^{1.5} \times 10^2}{10^{1.25}}$.

SOLUTION: $\dfrac{10^{1.5} \times 10^2}{10^{1.25}} = 10^{1.5+2-1.25} = 10^{2.25}$.

46. Multiply each of the following numbers:

$$10^{1.75}; \quad 10^{2.23}; \quad 10^{3.47}; \quad 10^{9.32}; \quad 10^{9.86};$$

by (a) 10; (b) 100; (c) $10^{1.25}$.

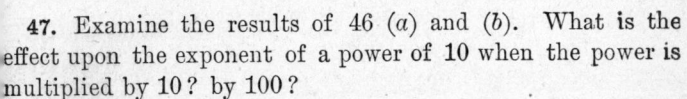

47. Examine the results of 46 (a) and (b). What is the effect upon the exponent of a power of 10 when the power is multiplied by 10? by 100?

48. Replace the word "multiply" in Example 46 by "divide" and solve the resulting exercises.

Simplify:

49. $\dfrac{a^{2m-3n} \cdot a^{-5m-n}}{a^{3m-4n}}$.   **50.** $\dfrac{a^n \cdot (a^{n-1})^n}{a^{n+1} \cdot a^{n-1}}$.

XXI. RADICALS

242. A **Radical** is a root of a number indicated by a radical sign; as, $\sqrt{5}$, $\sqrt[3]{a}$, $\sqrt[4]{x+1}$.

If the indicated root can be obtained, the radical is a *rational* number; if it cannot be obtained, it is an *irrational* number (cf. § 230).

243. The *index* (§ 235) determines the *order* of the radical. Thus, $\sqrt[3]{x+1}$ is a radical of the *third* order.

244. An introduction to radicals of the *second order* (square roots) has been given in Chapter XIV. In § 186, a means of simplifying radical expressions in order to find their approximate values is illustrated. Some methods of simplifying more complicated radical expressions will be given in this chapter. These methods, like the one in § 186, lead to more economical and often to more accurate methods of finding the approximate arithmetical values of the expressions.

It will be of interest also to find that radicals, like integers and fractions, can be added, subtracted, divided, etc.

245. Radicals of the second order will be emphasized. *Where the final expression involves only square roots of arithmetical numbers, the approximate arithmetical value should be found as in the examples solved in the text.*

246. Two principles are used frequently in this chapter:

(*A*) $(\sqrt[n]{x})^n = x$ (§ 235). Thus, $(\sqrt{2})^2 = 2$. From this it follows that $\sqrt{2^2} = 2$. Similarly $\sqrt[5]{3^5} = 3$.

(*B*) $\sqrt[n]{ab} = \sqrt[n]{a} \cdot \sqrt[n]{b}$. Thus, $\sqrt[4]{7 \cdot 9} = \sqrt[4]{7} \cdot \sqrt[4]{9}$.

RADICALS

This principle may be expressed: *the nth root of the product of two numbers is equal to the product of the nth roots of the numbers.*

REDUCTION OF A RADICAL TO ITS SIMPLEST FORM

247. Reducing a Radical to a Radical of Lower Order.

EXAMPLE 1. $\sqrt[6]{125} = \sqrt[6]{5^3} = (5^3)^{\frac{1}{6}} = 5^{\frac{3}{6}} = 5^{\frac{1}{2}} = \sqrt{5}.$
$$\therefore \sqrt[6]{125} = \sqrt{5} = 2.23^+.$$

EXAMPLE 2. $\sqrt[9]{64} = (2^6)^{\frac{1}{9}} = 2^{\frac{6}{9}} = 2^{\frac{2}{3}} = \sqrt[3]{2^2} = \sqrt[3]{4}.$

∴ the ninth root of 64 may be found by obtaining the cube root of 4. In the chapter on *logarithms*, a method for determining a higher root of any number will be given.

EXERCISE 155

Reduce to radicals of lower order; see § 245:

1. $\sqrt[4]{25}.$
2. $\sqrt[4]{100}.$
3. $\sqrt[6]{8}.$
4. $\sqrt[4]{36}.$
5. $\sqrt[6]{27}.$
6. $\sqrt[6]{343}.$
7. $\sqrt[8]{16}.$
8. $\sqrt[8]{81}.$
9. $\sqrt[10]{32}.$
10. $\sqrt[6]{49}.$
11. $\sqrt[8]{25}.$
12. $\sqrt[10]{9}.$
13. $\sqrt[12]{64}.$
14. $\sqrt[14]{4}.$
15. $\sqrt[15]{216}.$
16. $\sqrt[12]{100}.$
17. $\sqrt[15]{243}.$
18. $\sqrt[4]{121\,a^2b^2}.$
19. $\sqrt[6]{125\,x^3y^3}.$
20. $\sqrt[10]{32\,m^5}.$
21. $\sqrt[8]{81\,w^4}.$
22. $\sqrt[12]{8\,x^9m^6}.$
23. $\sqrt[6]{27\,a^6x^3}.$
24. $\sqrt[12]{256\,a^4x^8}.$

248. Removing a Factor from the Radicand.

EXAMPLE 1. $\sqrt{75} = \sqrt{25 \cdot 3} = \sqrt{25} \cdot \sqrt{3} = 5 \cdot \sqrt{3}.$
$$\therefore \sqrt{75} = 5(1.732^+) = 8.66^+. \quad \text{(See also § 182.)}$$

EXAMPLE 2. $\sqrt[5]{96\,a^5b^{12}c^8} = \sqrt[5]{32\,a^5b^{10}c^5} \cdot \sqrt[5]{3\,b^2c^3}$
$$= 2\,ab^2c\sqrt[5]{3\,b^2c^3}.$$

ALGEBRA

Rule. — To simplify a radical by removing factors from the radicand:

1. Resolve the radicand into two factors, the second of which contains no factor which is a perfect power of degree corresponding to the order of the radical.

2. Find the required root of the first factor; multiply it by the indicated root of the second factor.

EXERCISE 156

Simplify by removing factors from the radicand; see § 245:

1. $\sqrt{28}$.
2. $\sqrt{12}$.
3. $\sqrt{80}$.
4. $\sqrt{63}$.
5. $\sqrt{98}$.
6. $\sqrt{96}$.
7. $\sqrt{112}$.
8. $\sqrt{108}$.
9. $\sqrt{125}$.
10. $\sqrt{99\,a^2}$.
11. $\sqrt{60\,x^2y^4}$.
12. $\sqrt{200\,m^3n^2}$.
13. $\sqrt[3]{40\,a^3}$.
14. $\sqrt[3]{54\,m}$.
15. $\sqrt[3]{375\,x^6}$.
16. $\sqrt[3]{108\,a^5}$.
17. $\sqrt[3]{128\,xy^4}$.
18. $\sqrt[3]{1125\,m^3n^4}$.
19. $\sqrt[4]{162}$.
20. $\sqrt[4]{64\,a^6b^9}$.
21. $\sqrt[5]{64\,a^6c^7}$.
22. $\sqrt[5]{243\,n^6p^5}$.
23. $\sqrt[6]{128\,x^6y^5}$.
24. $\sqrt[7]{128\,x^3y^8}$.
25. $\sqrt{(a^2-4\,b^2)(a-2\,b)}$.
26. $\sqrt{27\,a^3b - 36\,a^2b^2 + 12\,ab^3}$.
27. $\sqrt{5\,x^3 + 30\,x^2 + 45\,x}$.
28. $\sqrt{(x^2-x-6)(x^2+2\,x-15)}$.

29. $\sqrt[3]{\dfrac{5}{8}} = \sqrt[3]{\dfrac{5}{2^3}} = \dfrac{\sqrt[3]{5}}{\sqrt[3]{2^3}} = \dfrac{\sqrt[3]{5}}{2}$.

30. $\sqrt[3]{\dfrac{2}{27\,m^6}}$.
31. $\sqrt[3]{\dfrac{4\,a^2}{125}}$.
32. $\sqrt[4]{\dfrac{7\,m}{16\,a^4}}$.
33. $\sqrt[4]{\dfrac{5\,y}{81\,x^4}}$.
34. $\sqrt[5]{\dfrac{3\,d}{32\,c^5}}$.
35. $\sqrt[5]{\dfrac{5\,rs}{x^5y^{10}}}$.
36. $\sqrt[6]{\dfrac{3\,y^2}{64\,x^6}}$.
37. $\sqrt[7]{\dfrac{5}{128\,m^7n^{14}}}$.

249. Changing a Fractional to an Integral Radicand. Review § 183 and Exercise 114. The method of § 183 applies to radicals of higher order.

EXAMPLE. $\sqrt[3]{\dfrac{27}{4\,a^4}} = \sqrt[3]{\dfrac{3^3 \cdot 2\,a^2}{(2\,a^2)^2 \cdot 2\,a^2}} = \dfrac{3}{2\,a^2}\sqrt[3]{2\,a^2}$.

RADICALS

Rule. — To change a fractional to an integral radicand:

1. Multiply both numerator and denominator of the fraction by such a number as will make the denominator a perfect power of degree corresponding to the order of the radical.

2. Simplify the resulting radical as in § 248.

EXERCISE 157

Express with integral radicands; see § 245:

1. $\sqrt{\dfrac{2}{3}}$.

2. $\sqrt{\dfrac{7}{5}}$.

3. $\sqrt{\dfrac{5}{3}}$.

4. $\sqrt{\dfrac{5}{2}}$.

5. $\sqrt{\dfrac{3}{11}}$.

6. $\sqrt{\dfrac{5}{12\,a}}$.

7. $\sqrt{\dfrac{9\,a^2}{8\,b}}$.

8. $\sqrt{\dfrac{13\,m^3}{20\,n^2}}$.

9. $\sqrt[3]{\dfrac{1}{4}}$.

10. $\sqrt[3]{\dfrac{3}{2}}$.

11. $\sqrt[3]{\dfrac{2}{5}}$.

12. $\sqrt[3]{\dfrac{7}{2\,a}}$.

13. $\sqrt[3]{\dfrac{5\,b^3 c}{9}}$.

14. $\sqrt[3]{\dfrac{8\,a^3 c^4}{25}}$.

15. $\sqrt[3]{\dfrac{5\,x^3}{16\,y^2}}$.

16. $\sqrt[4]{\dfrac{1}{8}}$.

17. $\sqrt[4]{\dfrac{2}{27}}$.

18. $\sqrt[4]{\dfrac{3}{64}}$.

19. $\sqrt[4]{\dfrac{a}{125\,b}}$.

20. $\sqrt[4]{\dfrac{5\,m^3}{9\,n^3}}$.

21. $\sqrt[4]{\dfrac{11\,a^3}{16\,c^4 d^3}}$.

22. $\sqrt[5]{\dfrac{1}{27}}$.

23. $\sqrt[5]{\dfrac{3\,a}{16}}$.

24. $\sqrt[5]{\dfrac{4}{125\,b^3}}$.

25. $\sqrt[6]{\dfrac{3\,a^6 b}{16\,c^5}}$.

26. $\sqrt[7]{\dfrac{7\,n^4}{32\,m^3}}$.

27. $\sqrt{\dfrac{a+b}{a-b}}$.

28. $\sqrt{a^2 - \left(\dfrac{a}{2}\right)^2}$.

250. To Introduce the Coefficient of a Radical under the Radical Sign.

EXAMPLE. $2\,a\sqrt[3]{3\,x^2} = \sqrt[3]{(2\,a)^3} \cdot \sqrt[3]{3\,x^2} = \sqrt[3]{8\,a^3 \cdot 3\,x^2} = \sqrt[3]{24\,a^3 x^2}$.

Rule. — To introduce a factor under the radical sign:

1. Raise the factor to the power denoted by the index.

2. Multiply the radicand by the result of step 1.

EXERCISE 158

Introduce under the radical sign the coefficients of:

1. $5\sqrt{2}$.
2. $8\sqrt{3}$.
3. $4\sqrt[3]{5}$.
4. $5\sqrt[3]{4}$.
5. $2\sqrt[4]{5}$.
6. $3\sqrt[5]{2}$.
7. $4a\sqrt{8a}$.
8. $7x^2\sqrt{6x^3}$.
9. $3ab\sqrt[3]{5a^2}$.
10. $x^3y^2\sqrt[3]{x^2y^4}$.
11. $3m^2\sqrt[4]{2m}$.
12. $2a^5\sqrt[7]{7a^3}$.

13. $(1+a)\sqrt{\dfrac{1-a}{1+a}}$.

14. $(x-1)\sqrt{\dfrac{2}{x-1}+1}$.

15. $\dfrac{a-b}{a+b}\sqrt{\dfrac{a+b}{a-b}}$.

16. $\dfrac{x^2-1}{x^2+1}\sqrt{1-\dfrac{2x}{(x+1)^2}}$.

251. Similar Radicals are radicals which, in their simplest form, do not differ at all or differ only in their coefficients; thus, $2\sqrt[3]{ax^2}$ and $3\sqrt[3]{ax^2}$ are similar radicals.

252. Addition and Subtraction of Radicals. Review § 186 and Exercise 115. The methods of § 186 apply to radicals of a higher order.

EXAMPLE. $\sqrt[3]{\tfrac{1}{4}} - \sqrt[3]{24} + \sqrt[3]{54} = \sqrt[3]{\tfrac{2}{8}} - \sqrt[3]{8\cdot 3} + \sqrt[3]{27\cdot 2}$
$= \tfrac{1}{2}\sqrt[3]{2} - 2\sqrt[3]{3} + 3\sqrt[3]{2} = 3\tfrac{1}{2}\sqrt[3]{2} - 2\sqrt[3]{3}$.

Rule. — To add or subtract radicals:

1. Reduce them to their simplest form.

2. Combine similar radicals (see § 186) and indicate the addition or subtraction of those which are dissimilar.

EXERCISE 159

Simplify the following expressions; see § 245:

1. $\sqrt{98} - \sqrt{32}$.
2. $2\sqrt{80} + \sqrt{180}$.
3. $3\sqrt{24} - \sqrt{150}$.
4. $\sqrt[3]{54} + \sqrt[3]{16}$.
5. $\sqrt[3]{192\,m} - \sqrt[3]{3\,m}$.
6. $\sqrt[3]{27\,x^2} + \sqrt[3]{24\,x^2}$.
7. $\sqrt[4]{32} - \sqrt[4]{162}$.
8. $\sqrt[5]{64} - \sqrt[5]{2}$.
9. $\sqrt[6]{3} + \sqrt[6]{192}$.

RADICALS

10. $m^2\sqrt[3]{32\,m^2} + m\sqrt[3]{108\,m^5} - \sqrt[3]{500\,m^8}$.

11. $x^2\sqrt{150\,x} + \sqrt{96\,x^3} - \sqrt{54\,x^5} - x\sqrt{24\,x^3}$.

12. $\sqrt{\frac{9}{2}} + \sqrt{\frac{25}{8}}$.

13. $\sqrt{\frac{2}{27}} + \sqrt{\frac{8}{3}}$.

14. $\sqrt[3]{\frac{2}{9}} + \sqrt[3]{\frac{1}{36}}$.

15. $\sqrt{\frac{8}{5}} + \sqrt{\frac{9}{10}} - \sqrt{\frac{5}{8}}$.

16. $\sqrt[4]{\frac{a^4}{8}} + \sqrt[4]{\frac{b^8}{8}}$.

17. $\sqrt[5]{m} + \sqrt[5]{\frac{m}{16}}$.

18. $\sqrt[6]{2\,m^7} + \sqrt[6]{\frac{2}{m^5}}$.

19. $\sqrt[7]{\frac{3}{a^5}} - \sqrt[7]{\frac{a^2}{b^4}}$.

20. $\sqrt{\frac{a+b}{a-b}} - \sqrt{\frac{a-b}{a+b}} + \frac{2\,a}{a^2 - b^2}\sqrt{a^2 - b^2}$.

253. Reduction of Radicals of Different Orders to Equivalent Radicals of the Same Order.

EXAMPLE. Reduce $\sqrt{2}$, $\sqrt[3]{3}$, and $\sqrt[4]{5}$ to equivalent radicals of the same order. Determine which is the greatest number.

SOLUTION: 1. By § 237, $\sqrt{2} = (2)^{\frac{1}{2}} = 2^{\frac{6}{12}} = \sqrt[12]{2^6} = \sqrt[12]{64}$.

2. $\sqrt[3]{3} = (3)^{\frac{1}{3}} = 3^{\frac{4}{12}} = \sqrt[12]{3^4} = \sqrt[12]{81}$.

3. $\sqrt[4]{5} = (5)^{\frac{1}{4}} = 5^{\frac{3}{12}} = \sqrt[12]{5^3} = \sqrt[12]{125}$.

4. ∴ $\sqrt[4]{5}$ is the greatest number.

Rule. — To reduce radicals to equivalent radicals of the same order:

1. Express the radicals with fractional exponents.

2. Reduce the exponents to a common denominator.

3. Rewrite the resulting expressions with radical signs.

EXERCISE 160

Reduce to equivalent radicals of the same order:

1. $\sqrt{3}$ and $\sqrt[3]{5}$.
2. $\sqrt{2}$ and $\sqrt[5]{3}$.
3. $\sqrt[3]{a^2b}$ and $\sqrt[5]{a^4b^3}$.
4. $\sqrt{2}$ and $\sqrt[7]{12}$.
5. $\sqrt[3]{4}$ and $\sqrt[4]{6}$.
6. $\sqrt{xy}$, $\sqrt[4]{yz}$, and $\sqrt[5]{xz}$.
7. $\sqrt[3]{2a}$, $\sqrt[4]{2b}$, and $\sqrt[6]{6c}$.
8. $\sqrt[3]{2}$, $\sqrt[6]{8}$, and $\sqrt[9]{13}$.
9. $\sqrt[4]{1-x}$, and $\sqrt[6]{1+x}$.
10. $\sqrt[8]{a+b}$ and $\sqrt[6]{a-b}$.

Arrange in order of magnitude:

11. $\sqrt[3]{2}$ and $\sqrt[4]{3}$.
12. $\sqrt[3]{11}$ and $\sqrt{5}$.
13. $\sqrt[5]{10}$ and $\sqrt[3]{4}$.
14. $\sqrt{3}$ and $\sqrt[5]{15}$.
15. $\sqrt{3}$, $\sqrt[3]{5}$, and $\sqrt[4]{7}$.
16. $\sqrt[3]{14}$, $\sqrt{6}$, and $\sqrt[6]{175}$.

MULTIPLICATION OF RADICALS

254. Multiplication of Radicals of the Second Order.

EXAMPLE. $2\sqrt{3} \cdot \sqrt{6} = 2\sqrt{3 \cdot 6} = 2\sqrt{3^2 \cdot 2} = 2 \cdot 3\sqrt{2} = 6\sqrt{2}$

$\therefore 2\sqrt{3} \cdot \sqrt{6} = 6\sqrt{2} = 6(1.414^+) = 8.484^+.$

EXERCISE 161

Find the products; see § 245:

1. $\sqrt{2} \cdot \sqrt{10}$.
2. $\sqrt{3} \cdot \sqrt{12}$.
3. $\sqrt{7} \cdot \sqrt{14}$.
4. $\sqrt{5} \cdot \sqrt{15}$.
5. $2\sqrt{3} \cdot \sqrt{21}$.
6. $3\sqrt{20} \cdot \sqrt{10}$.
7. $2\sqrt{5} \cdot 3\sqrt{5}$.
8. $(3\sqrt{3})^2$.
9. $(5\sqrt{2})^2$.
10. $(2\sqrt{7})^3$.
11. $5\sqrt{6x} \cdot 2\sqrt{3x}$.
12. $3\sqrt{3m^2} \cdot 2\sqrt{15m}$.
13. $\sqrt{x+1} \cdot \sqrt{x-1}$.
14. $(\sqrt{x-5})^2$.
15. $(3\sqrt{x+2})^2$.

RADICALS

16. Multiply $2\sqrt{3} + 3\sqrt{2}$ by $3\sqrt{3} - \sqrt{2}$.

SOLUTION:
$$2\sqrt{3} + 3\sqrt{2}$$
$$3\sqrt{3} - \sqrt{2}$$
$$\overline{18 + 9\sqrt{6}\phantom{-2\sqrt{6}-6}}$$
$$\phantom{18+9\sqrt{6}} -2\sqrt{6} - 6$$
$$\overline{18 + 7\sqrt{6} - 6} = 12 + 7\sqrt{6}.$$

$\therefore (2\sqrt{3} + 3\sqrt{2})(3\sqrt{3} - \sqrt{2}) = 12 + 7(2.44) = 12 + 17.08 = 29.08.$

Find the following products:

17. $(5 - \sqrt{3})(5 + \sqrt{3})$.

18. $(2a - \sqrt{b})(2a + \sqrt{b})$.

19. $(\sqrt{3} + 7)(\sqrt{3} - 8)$.

20. $(2 + 3\sqrt{3})(6 - \sqrt{3})$.

21. $(\sqrt{2} - 4)(3\sqrt{2} - 5)$.

22. $(4 + \sqrt{5})^2$.

23. $(2 - 3\sqrt{7})^2$.

24. $(\sqrt{2} - 7)(\sqrt{2} + 7)$.

25. $(2\sqrt{3} + 5)(2\sqrt{3} - 5)$.

26. $(\sqrt{a} - \sqrt{b})(\sqrt{a} + \sqrt{b})$.

27. $(\sqrt{x+1} + 1)^2$.

28. $(\sqrt{a-3} - 4)^2$.

29. $(\sqrt{x} - \sqrt{x+5})^2$.

30. $(\sqrt{x+1} - \sqrt{x-1})^2$.

255. Multiplication of Radicals of Any Order.

EXAMPLE 1. $\sqrt[5]{4x^2} \cdot \sqrt[5]{8x^4} = \sqrt[5]{32x^6} = 2x\sqrt[5]{x}.$

EXAMPLE 2. $\sqrt{2a} \cdot \sqrt[3]{4a^2} = \sqrt[6]{(2a)^3} \cdot \sqrt[6]{(4a^2)^2}$
$$= \sqrt[6]{2^3 \cdot a^3 \cdot 4^2 \cdot a^4} = \sqrt[6]{2^3 \cdot 2^4 \cdot a^7}$$
$$= 2a\sqrt[6]{2a}.$$

Rule. — To multiply monomial radicals:

1. Reduce the radicals, if necessary, to equivalent radicals of the same order. (§ 253.)

2. Multiply together the radicands obtained in step 1 for the radicand of the product; place it under the common root. (§ 246, B.)

3. Simplify the result of step 2 as in §§ 248 and 249.

EXERCISE 162

Find the products:

1. $\sqrt[3]{4} \cdot \sqrt[3]{2}$.
2. $2\sqrt[3]{3} \cdot \sqrt[3]{18}$.
3. $5\sqrt[3]{9x^2} \cdot \sqrt[3]{3x^2}$.
4. $\sqrt[4]{9} \cdot \sqrt[4]{27}$.
5. $\sqrt[5]{8} \cdot 3\sqrt[5]{12}$.
6. $\sqrt[6]{16x^3} \cdot \sqrt[6]{12x^4}$.
7. $6\sqrt[7]{x^6y^3} \cdot \sqrt[7]{xy^5}$.
8. $\sqrt{a} \cdot \sqrt[8]{a}$.
9. $\sqrt[3]{b^2} \cdot \sqrt[6]{b}$.
10. $\sqrt{m} \cdot \sqrt[4]{m^3}$.
11. $\sqrt[3]{2} \cdot \sqrt[6]{8}$.
12. $\sqrt{10} \cdot \sqrt[4]{4}$.
13. $\sqrt[3]{9a^2} \cdot \sqrt{15a}$.
14. $\sqrt[4]{4c^2} \cdot \sqrt[3]{2c}$.
15. $5\sqrt[3]{m^2n} \cdot \sqrt[9]{6m^3n^6}$.

DIVISION OF RADICALS

256. Division of Monomial Radicals of the Same Order.

EXAMPLE 1. $\sqrt{6} \div \sqrt{2} = \sqrt{\dfrac{6}{2}} = \sqrt{3}$. $\therefore \sqrt{6} \div \sqrt{2} = 1.732^+$.

EXAMPLE 2. $\sqrt{12} \div \sqrt{15} = \sqrt{\dfrac{12}{15}} = \sqrt{\dfrac{4}{5}} = \sqrt{\dfrac{4 \cdot 5}{5^2}} = \dfrac{2\sqrt{5}}{5}$.

$\therefore \sqrt{12} \div \sqrt{15} = \dfrac{2(2.236^+)}{5} = \dfrac{4.472^+}{5} = .894^+$.

EXAMPLE 3. $\sqrt[3]{8} \div \sqrt[3]{18} = \sqrt[3]{\dfrac{8}{18}} = \sqrt[3]{\dfrac{4}{9}} = \sqrt[3]{\dfrac{4 \cdot 3}{3^3}} = \dfrac{1}{3}\sqrt[3]{12}$.

Rule. — To divide monomial radicals of the same order.

1. Divide the radicand of the dividend by the radicand of the divisor, and write the result under the common radical sign.

2. Simplify the result as in §§ 248 and 249.

RADICALS 339

EXERCISE 163

Perform the indicated divisions; see § 245:

1. $\sqrt{8} \div \sqrt{2}$.
2. $\sqrt{14} \div \sqrt{7}$.
3. $\sqrt{12\,m} \div \sqrt{4\,m}$.
4. $6\sqrt{15} \div 2\sqrt{5}$.
5. $2\,a\sqrt{72} \div a\sqrt{18}$.
6. $\sqrt{2} \div \sqrt{\tfrac{1}{2}}$.
7. $15\sqrt{ab^3} \div 5\sqrt{ab}$.
8. $6\sqrt{18\,r^3 s} \div 2\sqrt{6\,r^2 s}$.
9. $4\,c\sqrt{12\,c^3 d^3} \div \sqrt{2\,d}$.
10. $\sqrt{15} \div \sqrt{\tfrac{1}{5}}$.
11. $11\sqrt{xy} \div \sqrt{\tfrac{1}{4}\,y}$.
12. $\sqrt{5} \div \sqrt{2}$.
13. $\sqrt{10} \div \sqrt{6}$.
14. $\sqrt{12} \div \sqrt{7}$.
15. $\sqrt{33} \div \sqrt{15}$.
16. $(8\sqrt{12} - 6\sqrt{3}) \div 2\sqrt{3}$.
17. $(15\sqrt{2\,a} + 25\sqrt{6\,a}) \div 5\sqrt{2\,a}$.
18. $(\sqrt{8} + 2\sqrt{10}) \div \sqrt{3}$.
19. $(3\sqrt{15} - 4\sqrt{18}) \div \sqrt{6}$.
20. $\sqrt[3]{135} \div \sqrt[3]{5}$.
21. $\sqrt[3]{63} \div \sqrt[3]{7}$.
22. $\sqrt[5]{26\,a^3} \div \sqrt[5]{39\,a^2}$.
23. $\sqrt[4]{192\,m^6} \div \sqrt[4]{3\,m^2}$.
24. $\sqrt[8]{125\,a^2 b^2} \div \sqrt[8]{25\,b^2 c}$.
25. $2\,a\sqrt[7]{12\,xy} \div a\sqrt[7]{6\,xy^2}$.
26. $3\,ab\sqrt[6]{xy^2 z} \div a\sqrt[6]{xy^5 z}$.
27. $6\,m^2 n\sqrt[5]{ab^3} \div 2\,mn\sqrt[5]{ab^7}$.
28. $\sqrt[m]{5\,r^8 s} \div \sqrt[m]{r^6 s}$.
29. $\sqrt[n]{ax^6 y} \div \sqrt[n]{ax^5 y}$.

257. Division of Monomial Radicals of Any Order.

EXAMPLE 1. $\dfrac{2}{\sqrt[3]{4}} = \dfrac{\sqrt[3]{2^3}}{\sqrt[3]{4}} = \sqrt[3]{\dfrac{8}{4}} = \sqrt[3]{2}$.

EXAMPLE 2. $\dfrac{\sqrt{3}}{\sqrt[3]{9}} = \dfrac{\sqrt[6]{3^3}}{\sqrt[6]{9^2}} = \sqrt[6]{\dfrac{27}{81}} = \sqrt[6]{\dfrac{1}{3}} = \sqrt[6]{\dfrac{3^5}{3^6}} = \dfrac{1}{3}\sqrt[6]{243}$.

Rule. — To divide one radical by another:

1. Reduce the radicals, if necessary, to equivalent radicals of the same order.

2. Divide the radicand of the dividend by the radicand of the divisor for the radicand of the quotient and write the result under the common radical sign. Simplify the result.

EXERCISE 164

Find the quotients:

1. $2 \div \sqrt[3]{2}$.
2. $3 \div \sqrt[4]{3}$.
3. $3 \div \sqrt[3]{6}$.
4. $5 \div \sqrt[4]{25}$.
5. $a \div \sqrt[5]{a}$.
6. $\sqrt{2} \div \sqrt[3]{2}$.
7. $\sqrt{3} \div \sqrt[4]{3}$.
8. $\sqrt[3]{3} \div \sqrt[6]{9}$.
9. $\sqrt{8x} \div \sqrt[4]{32x}$.
10. $\sqrt[3]{12a^2} \div \sqrt{2a}$.
11. $\sqrt[5]{\frac{4}{9}} \div \sqrt{\frac{2}{3}}$.
12. $\sqrt[3]{81 x^2 y} \div \sqrt[6]{9 xy}$.
13. $\sqrt[12]{\frac{27}{5}} \div \sqrt[4]{\frac{3}{5}}$.
14. $\sqrt[3]{20} \div \sqrt[9]{125}$.
15. $\sqrt[3]{2 x^2 y} \div \sqrt[6]{2 xy^2}$.

258. Division by a Binomial Quadratic Surd.

EXAMPLE 1.

$$\frac{1}{2+\sqrt{3}} = \frac{(2-\sqrt{3})}{(2+\sqrt{3})(2-\sqrt{3})} = \frac{2-\sqrt{3}}{4-3} = \frac{2-\sqrt{3}}{1}.$$

$\therefore 1 \div (2+\sqrt{3}) = 2 - 1.732^+ = .267^+$.

NOTE. $2+\sqrt{3}$ is multiplied by $2-\sqrt{3}$, thus giving the product of the sum and the difference of two numbers. The product is the difference of their squares. $2+\sqrt{3}$ and $2-\sqrt{3}$ are called Conjugate Surds.

In general, the product of two conjugate surd expressions is a rational number, for $(a+\sqrt{b})(a-\sqrt{b})$ equals $a^2 - (\sqrt{b})^2 = a^2 - b$.

Rule. — To divide a number by a binomial quadratic surd:

1. Multiply both dividend and divisor by the conjugate surd of the divisor, and simplify the result.

RADICALS

EXAMPLE 2.

$$\frac{3\sqrt{2}+1}{2\sqrt{2}-1} = \frac{(3\sqrt{2}+1)(2\sqrt{2}+1)}{(2\sqrt{2}-1)(2\sqrt{2}+1)} = \frac{12+5\sqrt{2}+1}{8-1}.$$

$$\therefore \frac{3\sqrt{2}+1}{2\sqrt{2}-1} = \frac{13+5(1.414^+)}{7} = \frac{20.07^+}{7} = 2.86^+.$$

NOTE. Since in this method of division the original fraction is changed into an equivalent fraction with a *rational* (§ 242) denominator, the process is referred to as "Rationalizing the Denominator."

EXERCISE 165

Perform the indicated divisions; see § 245:

1. $\dfrac{6}{3+\sqrt{5}}.$

2. $\dfrac{1}{\sqrt{6}-2}.$

3. $\dfrac{4}{3-\sqrt{5}}.$

4. $\dfrac{5}{\sqrt{3}-4}.$

5. $\dfrac{6}{3+2\sqrt{5}}.$

6. $\dfrac{2+\sqrt{3}}{1+\sqrt{3}}.$

7. $\dfrac{3-\sqrt{2}}{4+\sqrt{2}}.$

8. $\dfrac{\sqrt{a}+b}{\sqrt{a}-b}.$

9. $\dfrac{\sqrt{x}-\sqrt{y}}{\sqrt{x}+\sqrt{y}}.$

10. $\dfrac{\sqrt{5}-\sqrt{2}}{\sqrt{5}+\sqrt{2}}.$

11. $\dfrac{2\sqrt{2}+3}{3\sqrt{2}+2}.$

12. $\dfrac{5\sqrt{2}+6}{3\sqrt{2}-6}.$

13. $\dfrac{\sqrt{x-2}+1}{\sqrt{x-2}+2}.$

14. $\dfrac{\sqrt{a-b}+\sqrt{a}}{\sqrt{a-b}-\sqrt{a}}.$

15. $\dfrac{\sqrt{1+a}-\sqrt{1-a}}{\sqrt{1+a}+\sqrt{1-a}}.$

259. Involution and Evolution of Radicals is accomplished in the case of monomials by the use of exponents.

EXAMPLE 1. $(\sqrt[6]{12})^3 = (12^{\frac{1}{6}})^3 = 12^{\frac{3}{6}} = 12^{\frac{1}{2}} = \sqrt{12} = 2\sqrt{3}.$

$\therefore (\sqrt[6]{12})^3 = 2(1.732^+) = 3.464^+.$

EXAMPLE 2. $\sqrt[3]{(\sqrt[5]{27\,x^3})} = \{(27\,x^3)^{\frac{1}{5}}\}^{\frac{1}{3}} = \{(3\,x)^3\}^{\frac{1}{15}} = (3\,x)^{\frac{1}{5}}.$

$\therefore \sqrt[3]{(\sqrt[5]{27\,x^3})} = \sqrt[5]{3\,x}.$

EXERCISE 166

Simplify the following expressions; see § 245:

1. $(\sqrt[4]{5})^2$.
2. $(\sqrt[6]{8})^2$.
3. $(\sqrt[8]{128})^3$.
4. $(\sqrt[8]{6})^4$.
5. $(\sqrt[3]{16})^2$.
6. $(2\,a\sqrt[3]{b})^5$.
7. $(\sqrt[9]{7\,a^4})^3$.
8. $(\sqrt[8]{50\,xy})^4$.
9. $(\sqrt[6]{3})^7$.
10. $(5\,m\sqrt[10]{96\,m^6})^2$.
11. $(\sqrt[7]{3\,a-2})^3$.
12. $(\sqrt[12]{48\,x^3y^5})^3$.
13. $\sqrt[5]{(\sqrt{32})}$.
14. $\sqrt[3]{(\sqrt{27})}$.
15. $\sqrt{(\sqrt[3]{25})}$.
16. $\sqrt[5]{(\sqrt[6]{32\,a^5})}$.
17. $\sqrt{(\sqrt[5]{49})}$.
18. $\sqrt[4]{(\sqrt{10})}$.
19. $\sqrt[5]{(\sqrt[4]{2\,xy^3})}$.
20. $\sqrt[3]{(\sqrt[4]{9\,a^7})}$.
21. $\sqrt{(\sqrt[4]{x^2-6\,x+9})}$.

260. Square Roots of a Binomial Quadratic Surd. It is possible to find the square roots of some binomial surds by inspection.

$$(\sqrt{2}-\sqrt{3})^2 = 2 - 2\sqrt{6} + 3 = 5 - 2\sqrt{6}.$$

Notice that the square of the binomial surd is a binomial; that 5 is the sum of the two radicands 2 and 3 and that the radicand 6 is the product of the radicands of the given binomial. This example suggests the

Rule. — To find the square root of a binomial surd (§ 184):

1. Reduce the surd term so that its coefficient is 2.

2. Separate the rational term into two numbers whose product shall be the radicand obtained in step 1.

3. Extract the square roots of the two numbers of step 2 and connect them by the sign of the surd term (§ 96).

EXAMPLE. Find the square roots of $22 - 3\sqrt{32}$.

SOLUTION: 1. $\sqrt{22 - 3\sqrt{32}} = \sqrt{22 - \sqrt{9\cdot 8\cdot 4}} = \sqrt{22 - 2\sqrt{72}}$.

2. $22 = 18 + 4$ and $18 \times 4 = 72$.

3. $\therefore \sqrt{22 - 3\sqrt{32}} = \pm(\sqrt{18} - \sqrt{4}) = \pm(3\sqrt{2} - 2)$. (§ 176.)

CHECK: $(3\sqrt{2}-2)^2 = 18 - 12\sqrt{2} + 4 = 22 - 3\sqrt{16\cdot 2} = 22 - 3\sqrt{32}$.

RADICALS

EXERCISE 167

Find the square roots of:

1. $11 + 2\sqrt{28}$.
2. $17 - 2\sqrt{72}$.
3. $11 - 2\sqrt{30}$.
4. $8 - \sqrt{60}$.
5. $6 + \sqrt{32}$.
6. $6 - \sqrt{20}$.
7. $9 - 3\sqrt{8}$.
8. $8 + 4\sqrt{3}$.
9. $20 - 6\sqrt{11}$.

IMAGINARY NUMBERS

261. An introduction to imaginary numbers was given in Chapter XV. Review, if necessary, paragraphs 199 to 202 inclusive.

262. Powers of the Imaginary Unit i.

By § 201, i is $\sqrt{-1}$; therefore $i^2 = -1$. (§ 235.)

$i^3 = i^2 \cdot i = (-1) i = -i.$
$i^4 = i^3 \cdot i = (-i) i = -i^2 = -(-1) = 1.$
$i^5 = i^4 \cdot i = 1 \cdot i = i.$

Thus, the first four positive integral powers of i are $i, -1, -i,$ and 1; and for higher powers, these numbers recur in the same order. Find, for example, $i^6, i^7,$ and i^8.

263. Multiplication of Imaginary Numbers.

EXAMPLE 1.

$\sqrt{-2} \cdot \sqrt{-3} = i\sqrt{2} \cdot i\sqrt{3} = i^2\sqrt{6} = (-1) \cdot \sqrt{6} = -\sqrt{6}.$

Note that each number is expressed in terms of the unit i, and that the fact that $i^2 = -1$ is used.

EXAMPLE 2. Find the product $(2 - \sqrt{-3})(5 + \sqrt{-3})$.

SOLUTION: $(2 - \sqrt{-3})(5 + \sqrt{-3}) = (2 - i\sqrt{3})(5 + i\sqrt{3}).$

$$\begin{array}{r} 2 - i\sqrt{3} \\ 5 + i\sqrt{3} \\ \hline 10 - 5 i\sqrt{3} \\ + 2 i\sqrt{3} - i^2 \cdot 3 \\ \hline 10 - 3 i\sqrt{3} - (-1)3 = 13 - 3 i\sqrt{3} \end{array}$$

ALGEBRA

EXERCISE 168

Find the products:

1. $\sqrt{-4} \cdot \sqrt{-9}$.
2. $\sqrt{-3} \cdot \sqrt{-12}$.
3. $\sqrt{-6} \cdot \sqrt{-3}$.
4. $\sqrt{-5} \cdot \sqrt{-15}$.
5. $\sqrt{-9a^2} \cdot \sqrt{-16a^2}$.
6. $2\sqrt{-3} \cdot 3\sqrt{-3}$.
7. $5\sqrt{-2} \cdot 4\sqrt{-2}$.
8. $a\sqrt{-b} \cdot c\sqrt{-b}$.
9. $m\sqrt{-r} \cdot n\sqrt{-s}$.
10. $\sqrt{-a} \cdot -\sqrt{-b}$.
11. $(2+\sqrt{-1}) \cdot (2-\sqrt{-1})$.
12. $(3+\sqrt{-5})(3-\sqrt{-5})$.
13. $(7+\sqrt{-6})(7+2\sqrt{-6})$.
14. $(9-\sqrt{-3})(11+\sqrt{-3})$.
15. $(-1+\sqrt{-3})(-1-\sqrt{-3})$.
16. $(4-\sqrt{-5})^2$.
17. $(x+\sqrt{-y})(x-\sqrt{-y})$.
18. $\{\frac{1}{2}(-1+\sqrt{-3})\}^2$.
19. $\{\frac{1}{2}(-1-\sqrt{-3})\}^2$.
20. $\{\frac{1}{2}(-1-\sqrt{-3})\}^3$.

264. Division of Imaginary Numbers.

EXAMPLE 1. $\dfrac{\sqrt{-12}}{\sqrt{-3}} = \dfrac{i\sqrt{12}}{i\sqrt{3}} = \dfrac{\sqrt{12}}{\sqrt{3}} = \sqrt{4} = 2.$

EXAMPLE 2.
$$\dfrac{10}{\sqrt{-2}} = \dfrac{10}{i\sqrt{2}} = \dfrac{10 \cdot i\sqrt{2}}{i^2 \cdot \sqrt{2} \cdot \sqrt{2}} = \dfrac{10\, i\sqrt{2}}{-2} = -5\, i\sqrt{2}.$$

EXAMPLE 3. $\dfrac{2}{1+\sqrt{-3}} = \dfrac{2}{1+i\sqrt{3}} = \dfrac{2(1-i\sqrt{3})}{(1+i\sqrt{3})(1-i\sqrt{3})}$

$$= \dfrac{2(1-i\sqrt{3})}{1-i^2 \cdot 3} = \dfrac{2(1-i\sqrt{3})}{1+3} = \dfrac{1-i\sqrt{3}}{2}.$$

NOTE. As in division of real radicals, rationalize the divisor, by multiplying by the *conjugate imaginary*. Thus, to rationalize $3-\sqrt{-5}$, multiply it by $3+\sqrt{-5}$; the product will be $3^2 - (\sqrt{-5})^2$, or $9-(-5)$, which is 14.

RADICALS

EXERCISE 169

Find the quotients:

1. $\sqrt{-25} \div \sqrt{-5}$.
2. $\sqrt{-32} \div \sqrt{-8}$.
3. $\sqrt{42} \div \sqrt{-6}$.
4. $\sqrt{63} \div \sqrt{-7}$.
5. $\sqrt{-ab} \div \sqrt{-bc}$.
6. $\sqrt{-a} \div \sqrt{-a^3}$.
7. $2\sqrt{-75} \div \sqrt{-3}$.
8. $12\sqrt{-18} \div 4\sqrt{-2}$.
9. $a\sqrt{-108} \div \sqrt{-4}$.
10. $\sqrt{-40\,x^3} \div \sqrt{-5\,x^2}$.
11. $\dfrac{2}{1-\sqrt{-3}}$.
12. $\dfrac{1+\sqrt{-1}}{1-\sqrt{-1}}$.
13. $\dfrac{5+4\sqrt{-6}}{5-4\sqrt{-6}}$.
14. $\dfrac{7-6\sqrt{-3}}{3+2\sqrt{-3}}$.

265. Application of Radicals. In Chapters XV and XVIII irrational (§ 242) roots were found for quadratic equations. Checking by substitution in such cases was not recommended at that time.

EXAMPLE. Solve the equation $x^2 + x - 1 = 0$.

SOLUTION: 1. By the formula (§ 197), $\quad x = \dfrac{-1 \pm \sqrt{1+4}}{2}$.

2. $\quad \therefore r_1 = \dfrac{-1+\sqrt{5}}{2};\ r_2 = \dfrac{-1-\sqrt{5}}{2}$.

CHECK: Does $\left(\dfrac{-1+\sqrt{5}}{2}\right)^2 + \left(\dfrac{-1+\sqrt{5}}{2}\right) - 1 = 0$?

Does $\dfrac{1-2\sqrt{5}+5}{4} + \dfrac{-1+\sqrt{5}}{2} - 1 = 0$?

Does $\dfrac{1-2\sqrt{5}+5-2+2\sqrt{5}-4}{4} = 0$? Yes.

EXERCISE 170

1. Check the second root r_2 above by substitution.

Solve and check the following equations:

2. $x^2 - x - 1 = 0$.

3. $x^2 - 2x - 2 = 0$.

4. $y^2 - 3y + 1 = 0$.

5. $x^2 + x + 1 = 0$.

6. $x^3 + 1 = 0$. (See § 213.)

7. $x^3 - 8 = 0$.

8. In a higher course in mathematics (trigonometry) certain six numbers occur, five of them bearing the following indicated relations to the sixth; calling the numbers s, c, t, S, C, T:

(a) $c = \sqrt{1 - s^2}$.

(b) $t = \dfrac{s}{\sqrt{1 - s^2}}$.

(c) $S = \dfrac{1}{\sqrt{1 - s^2}}$.

(d) $C = \dfrac{1}{s}$.

(e) $T = \dfrac{\sqrt{1 - s^2}}{s}$.

If $s = \dfrac{1}{\sqrt{2}}$, find c, t, S, C, and T in simplest radical form.

9. If $s = \dfrac{\sqrt{3}}{2}$, find c, t, S, C, and T in simplest radical form.

10. When factoring expressions in Chapters VIII and XVI, only factors involving rational numbers were permitted. Factor the following expressions, using irrational or imaginary numbers, if necessary:

(a) $x^2 - 2$.
(b) $x^2 - 5$.
(c) $x^2 + 9$.
(d) $x^2 + 2$.
(e) $x^2 + 4$.
(f) $3x^2 - 4$.
(g) $5x^2 - 9$.
(h) $2x^2 - 5$.
(i) $ax^2 - b$.

IRRATIONAL EQUATIONS

266. An **Irrational Equation** is one in which the unknown number appears under a radical sign or with a fractional exponent.

RADICALS

267. It is agreed that the radical sign or fractional exponent shall denote the principal root (§ 235); thus the square root shall always denote the positive root.

268. The following examples illustrate the methods of solution of irrational equations.

EXAMPLE 1. Solve the equation $x - 1 - \sqrt{x^2 - 5} = 0$.

SOLUTION: 1. Transposing, $x - 1 = \sqrt{x^2 - 5}$.

2. Squaring both members, $x^2 - 2x + 1 = x^2 - 5$.

3. $\therefore -2x = -6$, or $x = 3$.

CHECK: Does $3 - 1 = \sqrt{3^2 - 5}$? Does $2 = \sqrt{4}$? Yes. (See § 267.)

NOTE. When a single radical occurs in an equation, transpose the terms until the radical is on one side by itself and the remaining terms are on the other side. Then, if the radical is a square root, square both members of the equation; if it is a cube root, cube both members.

EXAMPLE 2. Solve the equation $x - 1 + \sqrt{x^2 - 5} = 0$.

SOLUTION: 1. Transposing, $\sqrt{x^2 - 5} = 1 - x$.

2. Squaring both members, $x^2 - 5 = x^2 - 2x + 1$.

3. $\therefore 2x = 6$, or $x = 3$.

CHECK: Does $3 - 1 + \sqrt{3^2 - 5} = 0$? Does $2 + \sqrt{4} = 0$? No. (§ 267.)

Therefore 3 is not a root of the equation. Recall that in solving an equation a number is sought which will satisfy the equation. The equation may, however, impose an impossible relation upon some numbers, as in this case, and then it is impossible to find a solution.

What is the explanation of the solution $x = 3$? If the original equation is compared with the equation of Example 1, it is noticed that the only difference is in the sign of the radical; also that in step 2, after squaring both members in both examples, the resulting equation is the same. In each example, *if the equation of step 1 has a root*, that number is a root of the equation of step 2; but, since the equation of step 2 is the same in each solution, it cannot be asserted in advance whether its root or roots are roots of the equation of Example 1 or of Example 2. When finally the solution $x = 3$ is obtained, the question arises, is 3 a root of the equation in Example 1 or in Example 2? The root $x = 3$ satisfies the equation of Example 1; it does not satisfy the equation of Example 2. It is customary to say that, in Example 2, the *extraneous root 3 is introduced by the method of solution*.

This example makes clear the necessity of checking the solutions of equations.

EXAMPLE 3. Solve the equation $\sqrt{x-2}+\sqrt{2x+5}=3$.

SOLUTION: 1. Transposing, $\sqrt{x-2}=3-\sqrt{2x+5}$.

2. Squaring, $x-2=9-6\sqrt{2x+5}+2x+5$.

3. $\therefore 6\sqrt{2x+5}=x+16$.

4. Squaring, $36(2x+5)=x^2+32x+256$.

5. $\therefore x^2-40x+76=0$. $\therefore x=2$, or 38. (§ 110.)

CHECK: Does $\sqrt{2-2}+\sqrt{2\cdot 2+5}=3$? Does $\sqrt{0}+\sqrt{9}=3$? Yes. Does $\sqrt{38-2}+\sqrt{2\cdot 38+5}=3$? Does $\sqrt{36}+\sqrt{81}=3$? No. (See § 267.)

Therefore $x=2$ is the only solution of this equation.

NOTE 1. It will be found that the extraneous root 38 will satisfy the equation $\sqrt{2x+5}-\sqrt{x-2}=3$.

NOTE 2. When there are two radicals in an equation, arrange the terms so that one radical appears alone in one member of the equation.

EXERCISE 171

Solve and check the following equations:

1. $\sqrt{3x-5}-2=0$.
2. $\sqrt[3]{6x+9}+8=5$.
3. $\sqrt{9x^2+5}-3x=1$.
4. $\sqrt{y}-\sqrt{y-12}=2$.
5. $\sqrt{t+4}+\sqrt{t}=3$.
6. $\sqrt[3]{8x^3-12x^2}+1=2x$.
7. $\sqrt{s+11}+\sqrt{s+6}=5$.
8. $\sqrt{m}+\sqrt{m+4}=\dfrac{2}{\sqrt{m}}$.
9. $\sqrt{z-6}+\sqrt{z}=\dfrac{3}{\sqrt{z-6}}$.
10. $\dfrac{\sqrt{3r+1}+\sqrt{3r}}{\sqrt{3r+1}-\sqrt{3r}}=4$.
11. $\dfrac{\sqrt{x+a}+\sqrt{x-a}}{\sqrt{x+a}-\sqrt{x-a}}=2$.
12. $\dfrac{\sqrt{2x-3}}{\sqrt{3x+2}}=\dfrac{\sqrt{4x-4}}{\sqrt{6x+1}}$.
13. $\sqrt{10+x}-\sqrt{10-x}=2$.
14. $\sqrt{6+10a-3a^2}=2a-3$.

RADICALS

15. $\sqrt{c+2} + \sqrt{3c+4} = 2.$
16. $\sqrt{w-1} + \sqrt{3w+3} = 4.$
17. $\sqrt[3]{x^3 + 8x^2 + 16x - 1} = x + 3.$
18. $\sqrt{y+3} - \sqrt{y+8} = -\sqrt{y}.$
19. $\sqrt{x^2 - \sqrt{2x+1}} = x - 1.$
20. $\sqrt{5+x} + \sqrt{5-x} = \dfrac{12}{\sqrt{5-x}}.$
21. $\dfrac{\sqrt{t}}{\sqrt{t+2}} - \dfrac{\sqrt{t+2}}{\sqrt{t}} = \dfrac{5}{6}.$

Solve for x:

22. $\sqrt{x - 12\,ab} = \dfrac{9a^2 - b^2}{\sqrt{x}}.$
23. $\sqrt{a+x} - \sqrt{a-x} = \sqrt{x}.$
24. $\sqrt{(x-2b)(x+8b)} = x + 4b.$
25. $\sqrt{3x+2a} - \sqrt{4x-6a} = \sqrt{2a}.$
26. Solve the equation $t = \pi\sqrt{\dfrac{l}{g}}$:
    (a) for l; (b) for g.
27. Solve the equation $V = \sqrt{2gs}$:
    (a) for g; (b) for s.

XXII. LOGARITHMS

269. Logarithms are exponents.

Every positive number may be expressed, exactly or approximately, as a power of 10. The exponent corresponding to a number so expressed is called its **Logarithm to the Base 10.**

Thus, $10^2 = 100$; therefore 2 is the logarithm of 100 to the base 10. This is written: $\log_{10} 100 = 2$, or more briefly $\log 100 = 2$.

Similarly $\log_{10} 35$ is read "logarithm of 35 to the base 10."

270. Much difficult computation may be simplified by the use of logarithms. To make this fact clear, the *approximate* values of some powers of 10 will be computed and some examples will be solved.

1. $10^0 = 1$; $10^1 = 10$; $10^2 = 100$; $10^3 = 1000$.

2. $10^{.5} = 10^{\frac{1}{2}} = \sqrt{10} = 3.1623$.
   $10^{1.5} = 10^1 \times 10^{.5} = 10 \times 3.1623 = 31.623$.
   $10^{2.5} = 10^1 \times 10^{1.5} = 10 \times 31.623 = 316.23$.

3. $10^{.25} = (10^{.5})^{\frac{1}{2}} = \sqrt{3.1623} = 1.7782$.
   $10^{1.25} = 10^1 \times 10^{.25} = 10 \times 1.7782 = 17.782$.
   $10^{2.25} = 10^1 \times 10^{1.25} = 10 \times 17.782 = 177.82$.

4. $10^{.75} = (10^{1.5})^{\frac{1}{2}} = \sqrt{31.623} = 5.6234$.
   $10^{1.75} = 10 \times 10^{.75} = 10 \times 5.6234 = 56.234$.
   $10^{2.75} = 10 \times 10^{1.75} = 10 \times 56.234 = 562.34$.

$1.0000 = 10^{0.00}$
$1.7782 = 10^{0.25}$
$3.1623 = 10^{0.50}$
$5.6234 = 10^{0.75}$
$10.0000 = 10^{1.00}$
$17.7820 = 10^{1.25}$
$31.6230 = 10^{1.50}$
$56.2340 = 10^{1.75}$
$100.0000 = 10^{2.00}$
$177.8200 = 10^{2.25}$
$316.2300 = 10^{2.50}$
$562.3400 = 10^{2.75}$
$1000.0000 = 10^{3.00}$

LOGARITHMS

EXAMPLE 1. Find 3.1623×17.782.

SOLUTION: 1. 3.1623×17.782
2. $= 10^{.50} \times 10^{1.25} = 10^{1.75}$
3. $\therefore 3.1623 \times 17.782 = 56.234.$

This is approximately correct.

CHECK:
```
        3.1623
       17.782
       ──────
       63246
      252984
      221361
     221361
      31623
     ───────
      56.232+
```

EXAMPLE 2. Find $1000 \div 56.234$.

SOLUTION: 1. $1000 \div 56.234$
2. $= 10^3 \div 10^{1.75} = 10^{3-1.75} = 10^{1.25}.$
3. $\therefore 1000 \div 56.234 = 17.782$

The solution is correct.

CHECK:
```
               17.78
       56.234)1000.00000
              562 34
              ──────
              437 660
              393 638
              ───────
               44 0220
               39 3638
               ───────
                4 65820
                4 49872
```

EXAMPLE 3. Find $(5.6234)^2 \times 316.23 \div 177.82$.

SOLUTION: 1. $(5.6234)^2 \times 316.23 \div 177.82$
2. $\qquad = (10^{.75})^2 \times 10^{2.50} \div 10^{2.25}$
3. $\qquad = 10^{1.50 + 2.50 - 2.25} = 10^{1.75}.$
4. $\therefore (5.6234)^2 \times 316.23 \div 177.82 = 56.234.$

This example also may be checked by ordinary computation.

271. From the examples of § 270 it is clear that a more complete list of exponents (logarithms) and ability to use them must be of great advantage, for in each case the solution by exponents is the simpler. The following paragraphs teach the methods of using logarithms.

272. Logarithms of numbers to the base 10 are called **Common Logarithms**, and form, collectively, the **Common System of Logarithms**.

ALGEBRA

273. If a number is not an exact power of 10, its logarithm can be given only approximately; a **four-place logarithm** is one given correct to four decimal places.

Thus the logarithm of 13 is 1.1139; *i.e.* $13 = 10^{1.1139}$, approximately.

The integral part of the logarithm is called the **Characteristic** and the decimal part, the **Mantissa**.

The characteristic of log 13 is 1 and the mantissa is .1139.

NOTE 1. The plural of *mantissa* is *mantissæ*.

NOTE 2. A negative number does not have a logarithm.

274. The Characteristic of the Logarithm of a Number Greater than 1. It is known that $3.53 = 10^{.5478}$, or $\log 3.53 = .5478$

Multiplying both members of $3.53 = 10^{.5478}$ by 10,

$$35.3 = 10^{.5478} \times 10^1 = 10^{1.5478}, \text{ or } \log 35.3 = 1.5478.$$

Similarly, $353 = 10^1 \times 10^{1.5478} = 10^{2.5478}$, or $\log 353 = 2.5478$.

The numbers 3.53, 35.3, and 353 have the same *significant figures*; they differ only in the location of the decimal point. Their logarithms differ only in the characteristics. These two facts indicate a connection between the location of the decimal point and the characteristic.

3.53 has **one** figure to the left of the decimal point; its logarithm has as characteristic **1 less than 1, or 0**.

35.3 has **two** figures to the left of the decimal point; its logarithm has as characteristic **1 less than 2, or 1**.

353 has **three** figures to the left of the decimal point; its logarithm has as characteristic **1 less than 3, or 2**.

Rule. — **The characteristic of the common logarithm of a number greater than 1 is one less than the number of significant figures to the left of the decimal point.**

Thus, the characteristic of log 357.83 is 2; of log 70390.5 is 4.

LOGARITHMS

EXERCISE 172

What are the characteristics of the logarithms of:

1. 365.
2. 2000.
3. 50698.
4. 7.
5. 16.1.
6. 123.05.
7. 6.35.
8. 60907.03.
9. 500.005.
10. 300506.7.
11. 300.506.
12. 1000000.

Tell the number of significant figures preceding the decimal point when the characteristic of the logarithm is:

13. 4. 14. 2. 15. 0. 16. 1. 17. 3. 18. 5.

275. The Characteristic of the Logarithm of a Number less than 1.
Dividing both members of $3.53 = 10^{.5478}$ (§ 274) by 10,

$.353 = 10^{.5478} \div 10^1 = 10^{.5478-1}$. ∴ $\log .353 = .5478 - 1$.

Dividing both members of $.353 = 10^{.5478-1}$, by 10,

$.0353 = 10^{.5478-1} \div 10^1 = 10^{.5478-2}$. ∴ $\log .0353 = .5478 - 2$.

Similarly, $.00353 = 10^{.5478-3}$. ∴ $\log .00353 = .5478 - 3$.

Between the decimal point and the first significant figure of:

.353 there are no zeros; the characteristic of log .353 is -1.
.0353 there is one zero; the characteristic of log .0353 is -2.
.00353 there are two zeros; the characteristic of log .00353 is -3.

Rule. — The characteristic of the common logarithm of a number less than 1 is negative; numerically it is one more than the number of zeros between the decimal point and the first significant figure.

Thus, the characteristic of log .0045 is -3; of log .00027, is -4.

EXERCISE 173

What are the characteristics of the logarithms of:

1. .05.
2. .0032.
3. .00064.
4. .0586.
5. .00007.
6. .08375.
7. .3.
8. .33759.

Tell the number of zeros preceding the first significant figure when the characteristic of the logarithm is:

9. -3. 10. -1. 11. -5. 12. -2. 13. -4.

276. Method of Writing a Negative Characteristic.

In § 275 log .353 = .5478 − 1. Actually, therefore, log .353 is −.4522, a negative number. For many reasons, however, the positive mantissa and the negative characteristic are retained.

.5478 − 1 is written: 9.5478 − 10. Numerically the two expressions have equal value. Note that 9 − 10 = −1.

The process in general is to decide upon the characteristic by the rule in § 275; then, if it is −1, write it 9 − 10; if −2, write it 8 − 10; etc.

Thus, log .02 is .3010 − 2, or 8.3010 − 10.

NOTE. The negative characteristic is often written thus: log .02 = $\bar{2}$.3010; again, log .353 = $\bar{1}$.5478. The minus sign is written over the characteristic to indicate that it alone is negative, the mantissa being positive.

EXERCISE 174

1–12. Tell how each of the characteristics of the examples of Exercise 173 should be written.

277. Mantissa of a Logarithm.

From §§ 274 and 275:

log 3.53 = .5478;   log .353 = 9.5478 − 10;
log 35.3 = 1.5478; log .00353 = 7.5478 − 10.

The numbers 3.53, 35.3, .353, and .00353 have the same significant figures. Their common logarithms have the same mantissæ. This is an example of the

Rule. — The common logarithms of all numbers having the same significant figures have the same mantissæ.

Thus, the logarithms of 2506, 2.506, 250.6, etc., all have the same mantissæ.

278.

A **Table of Logarithms** consists of the mantissæ of the logarithms of certain numbers. The characteristics of the logarithms may be determined by the rules given in §§ 274 and 275. The table given on pages 356 and 357 gives the mantissæ of all integers from 100 to 999 inclusive, calculated

LOGARITHMS

to four decimal places. The decimal point is omitted. Such a table is called a *four-place table*. While a five or six place table would be more accurate, this table is sufficiently accurate for all ordinary purposes.

279. To find the Logarithm of a Number of Three Significant Figures.

EXAMPLE 1. Find the logarithm of 16.8.

SOLUTION: 1. In the column headed "No." find 16. On the horizontal line opposite 16, pass over to the column headed by the figure 8. The mantissa 2253 found there, is the required mantissa.

2. The characteristic is 1, by the rule in § 274.

3. ∴ log 16.8 is 1.2253.

Rule. — To find the logarithm of a number of three figures:

1. Look in the column headed "No." for the first two figures of the given number. The mantissa will be found on the horizontal line opposite these two figures and in the column headed by the third figure of the given number.

2. Prefix the characteristic according to §§ 274 and 275.

EXAMPLE 2. Find log .304.

SOLUTION: 1. Opposite 30 in the column headed by 4 is the mantissa .4829. The characteristic is − 1 or 9 − 10. (§§ 275 and 276.)

2. ∴ log .304 = 9.4829 − 10.

NOTE. The logarithm of a number of one or two significant figures may be found by using the column headed 0. Thus the mantissa of log 8.3 is the same as the mantissa of log 8.30; of log 9, the same as of log 900.

EXERCISE 175

Find the logarithms of:

1. 235.	5. 72.	9. 56.2.	13. .00465.
2. 769.	6. 8.	10. 7.83.	14. 8690.
3. 843.	7. 3.2.	11. .924.	15. 24700.
4. 900.	8. 620.	12. .0326.	16. 60.7.

ALGEBRA

No.	0	1	2	3	4	5	6	7	8	9
10	0000	0043	0086	0128	0170	0212	0253	0294	0334	0374
11	0414	0453	0492	0531	0569	0607	0645	0682	0719	0755
12	0792	0828	0864	0899	0934	0969	1004	1038	1072	1106
13	1139	1173	1206	1239	1271	1303	1335	1367	1399	1430
14	1461	1492	1523	1553	1584	1614	1644	1673	1703	1732
15	1761	1790	1818	1847	1875	1903	1931	1959	1987	2014
16	2041	2068	2095	2122	2148	2175	2201	2227	2253	2279
17	2304	2330	2355	2380	2405	2430	2455	2480	2504	2529
18	2553	2577	2601	2625	2648	2672	2695	2718	2742	2765
19	2788	2810	2833	2856	2878	2900	2923	2945	2967	2989
20	3010	3032	3054	3075	3096	3118	3139	3160	3181	3201
21	3222	3243	3263	3284	3304	3324	3345	3365	3385	3404
22	3424	3444	3464	3483	3502	3522	3541	3560	3579	3598
23	3617	3636	3655	3674	3692	3711	3729	3747	3766	3784
24	3802	3820	3838	3856	3874	3892	3909	3927	3945	3962
25	3979	3997	4014	4031	4048	4065	4082	4099	4116	4133
26	4150	4166	4183	4200	4216	4232	4249	4265	4281	4298
27	4314	4330	4346	4362	4378	4393	4409	4425	4440	4456
28	4472	4487	4502	4518	4533	4548	4564	4579	4594	4609
29	4624	4639	4654	4669	4683	4698	4713	4728	4742	4757
30	4771	4786	4800	4814	4829	4843	4857	4871	4886	4900
31	4914	4928	4942	4955	4969	4983	4997	5011	5024	5038
32	5051	5065	5079	5092	5105	5119	5132	5145	5159	5172
33	5185	5198	5211	5224	5237	5250	5263	5276	5289	5302
34	5315	5328	5340	5353	5366	5378	5391	5403	5416	5428
35	5441	5453	5465	5478	5490	5502	5514	5527	5539	5551
36	5563	5575	5587	5599	5611	5623	5635	5647	5658	5670
37	5682	5694	5705	5717	5729	5740	5752	5763	5775	5786
38	5798	5809	5821	5832	5843	5855	5866	5877	5888	5899
39	5911	5922	5933	5944	5955	5966	5977	5988	5999	6010
40	6021	6031	6042	6053	6064	6075	6085	6096	6107	6117
41	6128	6138	6149	6160	6170	6180	6191	6201	6212	6222
42	6232	6243	6253	6263	6274	6284	6294	6304	6314	6325
43	6335	6345	6355	6365	6375	6385	6395	6405	6415	6425
44	6435	6444	6454	6464	6474	6484	6493	6503	6513	6522
45	6532	6542	6551	6561	6571	6580	6590	6599	6609	6618
46	6628	6637	6646	6656	6665	6675	6684	6693	6702	6712
47	6721	6730	6739	6749	6758	6767	6776	6785	6794	6803
48	6812	6821	6830	6839	6848	6857	6866	6875	6884	6893
49	6902	6911	6920	6928	6937	6946	6955	6964	6972	6981
50	6990	6998	7007	7016	7024	7033	7042	7050	7059	7067
51	7076	7084	7093	7101	7110	7118	7126	7135	7143	7152
52	7160	7168	7177	7185	7193	7202	7210	7218	7226	7235
53	7243	7251	7259	7267	7275	7284	7292	7300	7308	7316
54	7324	7332	7340	7348	7356	7364	7372	7380	7388	7396
No.	0	1	2	3	4	5	6	7	8	9

LOGARITHMS

No.	0	1	2	3	4	5	6	7	8	9
55	7404	7412	7419	7427	7435	7443	7451	7459	7466	7474
56	7482	7490	7497	7505	7513	7520	7528	7536	7543	7551
57	7559	7566	7574	7582	7589	7597	7604	7612	7619	7627
58	7634	7642	7649	7657	7664	7672	7679	7686	7694	7701
59	7709	7716	7723	7731	7738	7745	7752	7760	7767	7774
60	7782	7789	7796	7803	7810	7818	7825	7832	7839	7846
61	7853	7860	7868	7875	7882	7889	7896	7903	7910	7917
62	7924	7931	7938	7945	7952	7959	7966	7973	7980	7987
63	7993	8000	8007	8014	8021	8028	8035	8041	8048	8055
64	8062	8069	8075	8082	8089	8096	8102	8109	8116	8122
65	8129	8136	8142	8149	8156	8162	8169	8176	8182	8189
66	8195	8202	8209	8215	8222	8228	8235	8241	8248	8254
67	8261	8267	8274	8280	8287	8293	8299	8306	8312	8319
68	8325	8331	8338	8344	8351	8357	8363	8370	8376	8382
69	8388	8395	8401	8407	8414	8420	8426	8432	8439	8445
70	8451	8457	8463	8470	8476	8482	8488	8494	8500	8506
71	8513	8519	8525	8531	8537	8543	8549	8555	8561	8567
72	8573	8579	8585	8591	8597	8603	8609	8615	8621	8627
73	8633	8639	8645	8651	8657	8663	8669	8675	8681	8686
74	8692	8698	8704	8710	8716	8722	8727	8733	8739	8745
75	8751	8756	8762	8768	8774	8779	8785	8791	8797	8802
76	8808	8814	8820	8825	8831	8837	8842	8848	8854	8859
77	8865	8871	8876	8882	8887	8893	8899	8904	8910	8915
78	8921	8927	8932	8938	8943	8949	8954	8960	8965	8971
79	8976	8982	8987	8993	8998	9004	9009	9015	9020	9025
80	9031	9036	9042	9047	9053	9058	9063	9069	9074	9079
81	9085	9090	9096	9101	9106	9112	9117	9122	9128	9133
82	9138	9143	9149	9154	9159	9165	9170	9175	9180	9186
83	9191	9196	9201	9206	9212	9217	9222	9227	9232	9238
84	9243	9248	9253	9258	9263	9269	9274	9279	9284	9289
85	9294	9299	9304	9309	9315	9320	9325	9330	9335	9340
86	9345	9350	9355	9360	9365	9370	9375	9380	9385	9390
87	9395	9400	9405	9410	9415	9420	9425	9430	9435	9440
88	9445	9450	9455	9460	9465	9469	9474	9479	9484	9489
89	9494	9499	9504	9509	9513	9518	9523	9528	9533	9538
90	9542	9547	9552	9557	9562	9566	9571	9576	9581	9586
91	9590	9595	9600	9605	9609	9614	9619	9624	9628	9633
92	9638	9643	9647	9652	9657	9661	9666	9671	9675	9680
93	9685	9689	9694	9699	9703	9708	9713	9717	9722	9727
94	9731	9736	9741	9745	9750	9754	9759	9763	9768	9773
95	9777	9782	9786	9791	9795	9800	9805	9809	9814	9818
96	9823	9827	9832	9836	9841	9845	9850	9854	9859	9863
97	9868	9872	9877	9881	9886	9890	9894	9899	9903	9908
98	9912	9917	9921	9926	9930	9934	9939	9943	9948	9952
99	9956	9961	9965	9969	9974	9978	9983	9987	9991	9996
No.	0	1	2	3	4	5	6	7	8	9

ALGEBRA

280. To find the Logarithm of a Number of More than Three Significant Figures.

EXAMPLE 1. Find log 327.5.

SOLUTION: 1. From the table: $\left. \begin{array}{l} \log 327 = 2.5145 \\ \log 327.5 = ? \\ \log 328 = 2.5159 \end{array} \right\}$ Difference = .0014.

2. Since 327.5 is between 327 and 328, its logarithm must be between their logarithms. An increase of one unit in the number (from 327 to 328) produces an increase of .0014 in the mantissa. It is *assumed* therefore that an increase of .5 in the number (from 327 to 327.5) produces an increase of .5 of .0014, or of .0007, in the mantissa.

3. ∴ log 327.5 = 2.5145 + .5 × .0014
   = 2.5145 + .0007 = 2.5152.

This result is obtained in practice as follows. The difference between any mantissa and the next higher mantissa as written in the table (neglecting the decimal point) is called the *tabular difference*. The tabular difference for this example is 14(5159−5145). .5 of the tabular difference is 7. Adding this to 5145 gives 5152, the required mantissa of log 327.5.

Similarly to find log 327.25, the tabular difference is 14. .25 × 14 = 3.5. Hence the mantissa of log 327.25 is 5145 + 3.5 or 5148.5. ∴ log 327.25 = 2.5149.

NOTE 1. The process of determing a mantissa which is between two mantissæ of the table is called Interpolation.

NOTE 2. The assumption made in step 2 is not warranted by the facts. Nevertheless, for ordinary purposes, the results obtained in this manner are sufficiently correct. This is the common method of interpolating.

NOTE 3. When interpolating, it is customary to cut down all decimals so that the mantissa will again be a four-place decimal. Thus 3.5 is called 4. 3.4 would be called 3.

Rule. — To find the logarithm of a number of more than three significant figures:

1. Find the mantissa for the first three figures, and the tabular difference for that mantissa.

2. Multiply the tabular difference by the remaining figures of the given number, preceded by a decimal point.

3. Add the result of step 2 to the mantissa obtained in step 1.

4. Prefix the proper characteristic by §§ 274 and 275.

LOGARITHMS

EXAMPLE 2. Find log 34.652.

SOLUTION: 1. Mantissa of log 346 = 5391.
Mantissa of log 347 = 5403.

2. Tabular difference = 12. .52 × 12 = 6.24 = 6.
3. ∴ Mantissa for log 34652 = 5391 + 6 = 5397.
4. ∴ log 34.652 = 1.5397.

EXAMPLE 3. Find log .021508.

SOLUTION: 1. Mantissa of log 215 = 3324.
Mantissa of log 216 = 3345.

2. Tabular difference = 21. .08 × 21 = 1.68 = 2.
3. ∴ mantissa of log 21508 = 3324 + 2 = 3326.
4. ∴ log .021508 = .3326 − 2, or 8.3326 − 10.

EXERCISE 176

Find the tabular difference when the mantissa is:

1. 3222.	3. 6590.	5. 8982.	7. 7076.	9. 4728.
2. 4166.	4. 7364.	6. 5340.	8. 8692.	10. 7435.

Find the logarithms of:

11. 325.5.	16. 32.16.	21. 327.11.	26. 3.1416.
12. 263.1.	17. 1.608.	22. 243.25.	27. 1.0453.
13. 786.3.	18. 7.961.	23. 62.721.	28. .22735.
14. 492.2.	19. .8462.	24. 803.75.	29. .063457.
15. 703.4.	20. .05375.	25. 6.2534.	30. .004062.

281. To find the Number Corresponding to a Given Logarithm.

EXAMPLE 1. Find the number whose logarithm is 1.6571.

SOLUTION: 1. Find the mantissa 6571 in the table.

2. In the column headed "No." on the line with 6571 is 45. These are the first two figures of the number. At the head of the column containing 6571 is 4, the third figure of the number. Hence the number sought has the figures 454.

3. The characteristic being 1, the number must have two figures to the left of the decimal point. (§ 274.)

∴ the number is 45.4.

Rule — To find the number corresponding to a given logarithm when the mantissa appears in the table:

1. Find the three figures corresponding to this mantissa, as in the example.

2. Place the decimal point according to the rules in §§ 274 and 275.

EXERCISE 177

Find the numbers whose logarithms are:

1. 2.6138.
2. 1.3365.
3. 3.6972.
4. 2.9542.
5. 3.9289.
6. 0.8162.
7. 1.7404.
8. 4.7024.
9. 0.8893.
10. 9.8000 − 10.
11. 8.5378 − 10.
12. 7.4133 − 10.

EXAMPLE 2. Find the number whose logarithm is 1.3934.

SOLUTION: 1. The mantissa 3934 does not appear in the table.

The next less mantissa is 3927, and the next greater is 3945.
The corresponding numbers are 247 and 248. That is:

mantissa of log 247 = 3927 ⎫ Diff. ⎫ Tabular
mantissa of log x = 3934 ⎬ = 7. ⎬ difference
mantissa of log 248 = 3945 ⎭   ⎭ = 18.

2. Since an increase of 18 in the mantissa produces an increase of 1 in the number, it is *assumed* that an increase of 7 in the mantissa must produce an increase of $\frac{7}{18}$ or .38 in the number. Hence the number has the figures 247.38.

3. Since the characteristic is 1, the number must be 24.738.

Rule. — To find the number corresponding to a given logarithm when the mantissa does not appear in the table:

1. Find in the table the next less mantissa. Find the corresponding number of three figures, and the tabular difference.

2. Subtract the next less mantissa from the given mantissa and divide the remainder by the tabular difference.

LOGARITHMS

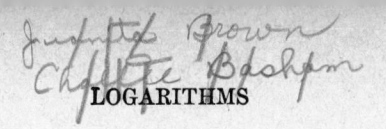

3. Annex the quotient to the number of three figures obtained in step 1.

4. Place the decimal point according to the rules in §§ 274 and 275.

EXERCISE 178

Find the numbers whose logarithms are:

1. 1.8079.
2. 3.3565.
3. 2.6639.
4. 0.7043.
5. 2.5524.
6. 0.8744.
7. 9.9108 − 10.
8. 8.8077 − 10.
9. 7.5862 − 10.
10. 8.2998 − 10.
11. 2.5369.
12. 9.7022 − 10.
13. 2.4644.
14. 3.1634.
15. 2.9310.

PROPERTIES OF LOGARITHMS

282. The preceding discussion relates entirely to the Common System of Logarithms. (§ 272.) Certain properties of logarithms to any base will be considered now.

NOTE. The base may be any positive number different from 1.

283. Just as $\log_{10} 3.053 = .4847$ means that $10^{.4847} = 3.053$, so $\log_a N = x$ means that $N = a^x$.

$\log_a N$ is read "the logarithm of N to the base a."

284. Logarithm of a Product.

Assume that $\left.\begin{array}{l}a^x = M \\ a^y = N\end{array}\right\}$; then $\begin{cases} x = \log_a M, \\ y = \log_a N. \end{cases}$

Also $a^x \cdot a^y = MN$, or $a^{x+y} = MN$. ∴ $\log_a MN = x + y$. (§ 283)
Therefore $\log_a MN = \log_a M + \log_a N$.

Rule. — In any system, the logarithm of a product is equal to the sum of the logarithms of its factors.

EXAMPLE 1. Given $\log 2 = .3010$, and $\log 3 = .4771$, find $\log 72$.

ALGEBRA

SOLUTION: **1.** $\log 72 = \log 2 \cdot 2 \cdot 2 \cdot 3 \cdot 3$.
2. $= \log 2 + \log 2 + \log 2 + \log 3 + \log 3$.
3. $\therefore \log 72 = 3 \log 2 + 2 \log 3 = 3(.3010) + 2(.4771)$
$= .9030 + .9542 = 1.8572$.

EXERCISE 179

Given $\log 2 = .3010$, $\log 3 = .4771$, and $\log 7 = .8451$. Find the following logarithms as in Example 1; check the solutions by finding the same logarithms in the table:

1. $\log 21$.
2. $\log 42$.
3. $\log 36$.
4. $\log 126$.
5. $\log 128$.
6. $\log 252$.
7. $\log 324$.
8. $\log 378$.
9. $\log 168$.

10. Find by logarithms the value of $35.2 \times 2.35 \times 6.43$.

SOLUTION: **1.** Let $v = 35.2 \times 2.35 \times 6.43$. | $\log 35.2 = 1.5465$
2. $\therefore \log v = \log 35.2 + \log 2.35 + \log 6.43$. | $\log 2.35 = 0.3711$
3. $\therefore \log v = 2.7258$. | $\log 6.43 = \underline{0.8082}$
4. $\therefore \quad v = 531.87$. (§ 281.) | $\quad\quad\quad\quad 2.7258$

Find by logarithms the values of:

11. 32.5×27.8.
12. 2.49×65.7.
13. $.289 \times 365$.
14. 34.55×29.9.
15. 678.1×37.
16. 1.732×580.
17. 3.142×6039.
18. 541.2×1.523.
19. 43.65×865.25.

20. Find by logarithms the value of $.0631 \times 7.208 \times .51272$.

SOLUTION: **1.** $\log v = \log .0631 + \log 7.208 + \log .51272$.
2.
$\log .0631 = 8.8000 - 10$
$\log 7.208 = 0.8578$
$\log .51272 = \underline{9.7099 - 10}$
$19.3677 - 20 = 9.3677 - 1$

3. $\therefore \log v = 9.3677 - 10$. $\therefore v = .2332$. (§ 281.)

NOTE. If the sum of the logarithms is a negative number, the result should be written so that the negative part of the characteristic is -10.

Find by logarithms the values of:

21. $.0235 \times 3.14$.

22. $.5638 \times .0245$.

23. $.7783 \times 6.282$.

24. $84.75 \times .00368$.

25. $.0273 \times .00569 \times .684$.

26. $.2908 \times .0305 \times .0062$.

285. Logarithm of a Quotient.

Assume that $\left.\begin{array}{l}a^x = M \\ a^y = N\end{array}\right\}$; then $\begin{cases} x = \log_a M, \\ y = \log_a N. \end{cases}$

Also, $a^x \div a^y = M \div N$, or $a^{x-y} = M \div N$.

$\therefore \log_a (M \div N) = x - y$.

Therefore, $\log_a (M \div N) = \log_a M - \log_a N$.

Rule. — In any system, the logarithm of the quotient of two numbers is equal to the logarithm of the dividend minus the logarithm of the divisor.

EXAMPLE 1. Given $\log 2 = .3010$ and $\log 3 = .4771$, find $\log \frac{3}{2}$.

SOLUTION: 1. $\log \frac{3}{2} = \log 3 - \log 2 = .4771 - .3010 = .1761$.

EXAMPLE 2. Find $\log \frac{8}{9}$.

SOLUTION: 1. $\log \frac{8}{9} = \log \frac{2 \cdot 2 \cdot 2}{3 \cdot 3}$.

2. $= (\log 2 + \log 2 + \log 2) - (\log 3 + \log 3)$.
3. $= 3(.3010) - 2(.4771) = .9030 - .9542$.
4. $\therefore \log \frac{8}{9} = 9.9488 - 10$.

$\begin{array}{r} .9030 = 10.9030 - 10 \\ .9542 = .9542 \\ \hline 9.9488 - 10 \end{array}$

NOTE 1. To find the logarithm of a fraction, add the logarithms of the factors of the numerator, and from the result subtract the sum of the logarithms of the factors of the denominator.

NOTE 2. To subtract a greater logarithm from a less, or to subtract a negative logarithm from a positive, increase the characteristic of the minuend by 10, writing — 10 after the mantissa to compensate. Thus, in this example, .9542 is greater than .9030; therefore, .9030 is written 10.9030 — 10, after which the subtraction is performed.

ALGEBRA

EXERCISE 180

Given $\log 2 = .3010$, $\log 3 = .4771$, and $\log 7 = .8451$, find:

1. $\log \tfrac{7}{3}$.
2. $\log 1\tfrac{4}{3}$.
3. $\log \tfrac{9}{7}$.
4. $\log 1\tfrac{2}{7}$.
5. $\log \tfrac{49}{27}$.
6. $\log 2\tfrac{1}{8}$.
7. $\log \tfrac{7}{6}$.
8. $\log 2\tfrac{1}{32}$.

Find by logarithms the values of:

9. $255 \div 48$.
10. $376 \div 83$.
11. $299 \div 99$.
12. $630.5 \div 402$.
13. $300.25 \div 3.14$.
14. $230.56 \div 1.06$.
15. $2865 \div 1.045$.
16. $7.835 \div 23.75$.
17. $9.462 \div 85.64$.

18. $\dfrac{3.14 \times 25}{365}$.

19. $\dfrac{23.5 \times 1.05}{3785}$.

20. $\dfrac{24.75 \times .0058}{1.41}$.

21. $\dfrac{16.08 \times 256}{17}$.

22. $\dfrac{.0036 \times 2.35}{.0084}$.

23. $\dfrac{287.5 \times .096}{3.1416}$.

24. $\dfrac{25.6 \times .738 \times .0535}{265 \times 432}$.

25. $\dfrac{1.405 \times 207 \times .00392}{508 \times .6354}$.

286. The Logarithm of a Power of a Number.

Assume that $a^x = M$; then $x = \log_a M$.

Also, $(a^x)^p = M^p$, or $a^{px} = M^p$. $\therefore \log M^p = px$.

Therefore, $\log M^p = p \log_a M$.

Rule.—In any system, the logarithm of any power of a number is equal to the logarithm of the number multiplied by the exponent indicating the power.

EXAMPLE 1. Given $\log 7 = .8451$, find $\log 7^5$.

SOLUTION: $\log 7^5 = 5 \log 7 = 5 \times .8451 = 4.2255$.

EXAMPLE 2. Find by logarithms 1.04^{10}.

SOLUTION: 1. $\log 1.04^{10} = 10 \log 1.04 = 10 \times .0170 = .1700$.

2. The number whose logarithm is .1700 is 1.479. (§ 281)

3. $\therefore 1.04^{10} = 1.479$.

LOGARITHMS

EXAMPLE 3. Find by logarithms $\sqrt[3]{365}$.

SOLUTION: 1. $\log \sqrt[3]{365} = \log 365^{\frac{1}{3}} = \frac{1}{3} \log 365$.

2. ∴ $\log \sqrt[3]{365} = \frac{1}{3} \times 2.5623 = 0.8541$.
3. The number whose logarithm is 0.8541 is 7.146.   (§ 281)
4. ∴ $\sqrt[3]{365} = 7.146$.

When finding a cube root, the logarithm of the radicand is divided by 3; when finding a square root, the logarithm of the radicand is divided by 2. This suggests the

Rule. — In any system, the logarithm of a root of a number is the logarithm of the radicand divided by the index of the root.

EXAMPLE 4. Find by logarithms $\sqrt[4]{.0359}$.

SOLUTION: 1. $\log \sqrt[4]{.0359} = \frac{1}{4} \log .0359 = \frac{1}{4}(8.5551 - 10)$.

2. ∴ $\log \sqrt[4]{.0359} = \frac{1}{4}(38.5551 - 40)$. (See note.)
3. ∴ $\log \sqrt[4]{.0359} = 9.6387 - 10$.
4. The number whose logarithm is $9.6387 - 10$ is .4352.   (§ 281)
5. ∴ $\sqrt[4]{.0359} = .4352$.

NOTE. To divide a negative logarithm, write it in such form that the negative part of the characteristic may be divided exactly by the divisor, and give -10 as quotient.

Thus $8.5551 - 10$ is changed to $38.5551 - 40$ since the divisor is 4. If the divisor were 3, it would be changed to $28.5551 - 30$.

EXERCISE 181

Given $\log 2 = .3010$, $\log 3 = .4771$, and $\log 7 = .8451$; find:

1. $\log 3^7$.
2. $\log 2^5$.
3. $\log 7^4$.
4. $\log 27^3$.
5. $\log (21)^{\frac{1}{3}}$.
6. $\log \sqrt[4]{7}$.
7. $\log \sqrt[5]{6}$.
8. $\log \sqrt[3]{14}$.

Find by logarithms the values of the following:

9. 235^2.
10. 2.045^3.
11. $\sqrt[3]{6.35}$.
12. $\sqrt[4]{9.863}$.
13. 3.1416×18^2.
14. 7.795^4.
15. 12^2.
16. $\frac{4}{3} \times 3.1416 \times 5^3$.
17. $\sqrt{\frac{276.8}{940}}$.
18. $\sqrt{25 \times 19.6 \times 17.3}$.
19. $\sqrt[3]{3} \times \sqrt[5]{5}$.
20. $\left(\frac{4400}{6937}\right)^2$.

ALGEBRA

21. The volume of a right circular cylinder is given by the formula $V = \pi R^2 H$.

Find the volume (by logarithms):

(a) if $R = 10.5$ and $H = 26.5$.

(b) if $R = 8.2$ and $H = 33.1$.

22. The volume of a sphere is given by the formula $V = \frac{4}{3}\pi R^3$. Find the volume:

(a) if $R = 12$;   (b) if $R = 6.2$.

23. The interest on P dollars at $r\%$ for t years is given by the formula $I = \dfrac{Prt}{100}$. Find I

(a) if $P = \$765$, $r = 5$, and $t = 6.5$ years.

(b) if $P = \$1250$, $r = 4.5$, and $t = 8$ years and 3 months.

24. The amount to which P dollars will accumulate at $r\%$ compound interest in n years is given by the formula,

$$A = P\left(1 + \frac{r}{100}\right)^n. \quad \text{Find } A:$$

(a) if $P = \$250$, $r = 4$, and $n = 10$.

(b) if $P = \$75$, $r = 3.5$, and $n = 15$.

25. A cylindrical cistern has for its diameter 5 feet. Find the number of barrels of water this cistern has in it when the water is 9 feet deep. (One cubic foot of water is about $7\frac{1}{2}$ gallons; one barrel contains $31\frac{1}{2}$ gallons.)

HISTORICAL NOTE. Logarithms were introduced by John Napier (1550–1617), a Scotch gentleman who studied mathematics and science as a pastime. The Napier logarithms were not the common logarithms. Briggs (1556–1631), an English mathematician, computed the first table of Common Logarithms.

XXIII. PROGRESSIONS

ARITHMETIC PROGRESSION

287. An **Arithmetic Progression** (A. P.) is a sequence of numbers, called *terms*, each of which after the first is derived from the preceding by adding to it a fixed number, called the **Common Difference**.

Thus, 1, 3, 5, 7, ⋯ is an A. P. Each term is derived from the preceding by adding 2. The next two terms are 9 and 11. 2 is the common difference.

Again, 9, 6, 3, ⋯ is an A. P. The common difference is -3. The next two terms are 0 and -3.

NOTE. The common difference may be found by subtracting any term from the one following it.

EXERCISE 182

Determine which of the following are arithmetic progressions; determine the common difference and the next two terms of the arithmetic progressions:

1. 4, 7, 10, 13, ⋯.
2. 1, 3, 7, 9, 15, ⋯.
3. 10, 7, 4, 1, ⋯.
4. 25, 20, 15, 10, ⋯.
5. $2\frac{1}{2}, 3\frac{1}{4}, 4, 4\frac{3}{4}, \cdots$.
6. $5\,m, 7.5\,m, 10\,m, \cdots$.
7. $4\,p, 1.5\,p, -p, \cdots$.
8. 1.06, 1.12, 1.18, ⋯.
9. $a+b, a+2\,b, a+3\,b, \cdots$.
10. $5\,r+6\,s, 6\,r+4\,s, 7\,r+2\,s, \cdots$.

Write the first five terms of the A. P. in which:

	11	12	13	14	15
the first term is	15	25	7.5	x	a
the common difference is	6	-8	3.5	-4	d

ALGEBRA

288. The nth Term of an Arithmetic Progression. It is possible to determine a particular term of an arithmetic progression without finding all of the preceding terms.

Given the first term a, the difference d, and the number of the term n, of an arithmetic progression, find the nth term l.

The progression is $a, a+d, a+2d, a+3d, \cdots$. The coefficient of d in each term is 1 less than the number of the term. Thus, the 10th term would be $a+9d$. Therefore the coefficient of d in the nth term must be $(n-1)$.

$$\therefore l = a + (n-1)d.$$

EXAMPLE. Find the 10th term of $8, 5, 2, \cdots$.

SOLUTION: 1. $a = 8$; $d = -3$; $n = 10$; $l = ?$
2. $l = a + (n-1)d.$ $\therefore l = 8 + (10-1)(-3) = 8 - 27 = -19.$

EXERCISE 183

Find:

1. The 12th term of $3, 9, 15, \cdots$; also the 20th.

2. The 15th term of $16, 12, 8, \cdots$; also the 25th.

3. The 13th term of $-7, -12, -17, \cdots$; also the 31st.

4. The 16th term of $2, 2\frac{1}{2}, 3, \cdots$; also the 51st.

5. The 11th term of $1.05, 1.10, 1.15, \cdots$; also the 26th.

6. What term of the progression $5, 8, 11, \cdots$ is 86?

SOLUTION: 1. $a = 5$; $d = 3$; $l = 86$; find n.
2. $l = a + (n-1)d.$ $\therefore 86 = 5 + (n-1)3.$
3. Solving for n, $n = 28.$ $\therefore$ 86 is the 28th term.

7. What term of the progression $8, 5, 2, \cdots$ is -70?

8. What term of the progression $\frac{1}{3}, \frac{5}{6}, \frac{4}{3}, \cdots$ is $20\frac{1}{3}$?

9. What term of the progression $-75, -67, -59, \cdots$ is 197?

10. What term of the progression $1, 1.05, 1.10, \cdots$ is 2?

PROGRESSIONS

11. If the first term of an A.P. is 15, and the 11th term is 35, what is the common difference?

HINT: $35 = 15 + (11-1)d$.

Find the common difference:

12. If the first term is 5 and the 22d term is 173.

13. If the first term is -20 and the 33d term is -4.

14. If the first term is 325 and the 31st term is 25.

15. Find the 10th term of the arithmetic progression whose first term is 7 and whose 16th term is 97.

16. A man is paying for a lot on the installment plan. His payments the first three months are $10.00, $10.05, and $10.10. What will his 20th and 25th payments be?

289. The terms of an arithmetic progression between any two other terms are called the **Arithmetic Means** of those two terms.

Thus, the three arithmetic means of 2 and 14 are 5, 8, 11, since 2, 5, 8, 11, 14 form an arithmetic progression.

A single arithmetic mean of two numbers is particularly important. It is called **The Arithmetic Mean** of the numbers.

When two numbers are given, any specified number of arithmetic means may be inserted between them.

EXAMPLE. Insert five arithmetic means between 13 and -11.

SOLUTION: 1. There results an arithmetic progression of 7 terms, in which $a = 13$, $l = -11$, and $n = 7$. Find d.

2. $l = a + (n-1)d$. ∴ $-11 = 13 + 6d$, or $d = -4$.

3. The progression is: 13, 9, 5, 1, -3, -7, -11.

CHECK: There is an A.P. with five terms between 13 and -11.

EXERCISE 184

1. Insert three arithmetic means between 3 and 19.

2. Insert four arithmetic means between -10 and 20.

3. Insert nine arithmetic means between 3 and 28.

4. Insert five arithmetic means between $\frac{1}{2}$ and 5.

5. Insert five arithmetic means between $-\frac{5}{4}$ and -5.

6. Find the arithmetic mean of 7 and 15.

7. Find the arithmetic mean of $\sqrt{2}$ and $\sqrt{18}$.

8. Find the arithmetic mean of $x+7$ and $x-7$.

9. Find the arithmetic mean of a and b. From the result, make a rule for finding the arithmetic mean of any two numbers.

NOTE. The arithmetic mean of two numbers is commonly called their *average*.

10. Find the common difference if two arithmetic means are inserted between r and s.

11. Find the common difference if k arithmetic means are inserted between m and p.

290. The Sum of the First n Terms of an Arithmetic Progression.

Given the first term a, the nth term l, and the number of terms n; find the sum of the terms S.

SOLUTION: 1. $S = a + (a+d) + (a+2d) + \cdots + (l-2d) + (l-d) + l.$ (1)

2. Writing the terms in reverse order,
$$S = l + (l-d) + (l-2d) + \cdots + (a+2d) + (a+d) + a. \quad (2)$$

3. Adding the equations (1) and (2), term for term,
$$2S = (a+l) + (a+l) + (a+l) + \cdots + (a+l) + (a+l) + (a+l). \quad (3)$$

4. There were n terms in the right member of (1); from each, there results a sum $(a + l)$ in (3).

$$\therefore 2S = n(a+l), \text{ or } S = \frac{n}{2}(a+l). \quad (4)$$

PROGRESSIONS

5. In § 288, $l = a + (n-1)d$; substituting this value of l in (4),

$$S = \frac{n}{2}\{a + (a + (n-1)d)\}, \text{ or } S = \frac{n}{2}\{2a + (n-1)d\}. \quad (5)$$

EXAMPLE 1. Find the sum of the first 15 terms of the arithmetic progression, of which the first term is 5 and the 15th term is 45.

SOLUTION: 1. $a = 5$; $l = 45$; $n = 15$.

2. $S = \frac{n}{2}(a + l)$. $\therefore S = \frac{15}{2}(5 + 45) = 15 \cdot 25 = \mathbf{375}.$

EXAMPLE 2. Find the sum of the first 12 terms of the progression 8, 5, 2, ···.

SOLUTION: 1. $a = 8$; $d = -3$; $n = 12$.

2. $S = \frac{n}{2}\{2a + (n-1)d\}$. $\therefore S = 6\{16 + 11 \cdot (-3)\} = 6\{16 - 33\}.$

$$\therefore S = 6(-17) = \mathbf{-102}.$$

EXERCISE 185

Find the sum of:

1. 12 terms of 3, 9, 15, ···.
2. 15 terms of $-7, -12, -17, \cdots$.
3. 16 terms of $-69, -62, -55, \cdots$.
4. 10 terms of $1.06, $1.12, $1.18, ···.

Find the sum of the terms of an arithmetic progression if:

5. The number is 12, the first is 5, and the last is 50.
6. The number is 31, the first is 40, and the last is 0.
7. The number is 18, the first is -18, and the last is 22.
8. The number is 8, the first is $-\frac{3}{5}$, and the last is $\frac{7}{10}$.
9. Find the sum of the numbers 1, 2, 3, ···, 100.
10. Find the sum of the even numbers from 2 to 100.
11. Find the sum of the odd numbers from 1 to 99.

12. Find the sum of all even integers, beginning with 2 and ending with 250.

13. If a boy earns $360 during his first year of work, and is given an increase of $50 per year for each succeeding year, what is his salary during his 10th year, and how much has he earned altogether during the 10 years?

14. If at the beginning of each of 10 years a man invests $100 at 6% simple interest, to what does the principal and interest amount at the end of the 10th year?

15. How many poles will there be in a pile of telegraph poles if there are 25 in the first layer, 24 in the second, etc., and 1 in the last?

16. A man has a debt of $3000, upon which he is paying 6% interest. At the end of each year he plans to pay $300 and the interest on the debt which has accrued during the year. How much interest will he have paid when he has freed himself of the debt?

17. A man is paying for a $300 piano at the rate of $10 per month with interest at 6%. Each month he pays *the total interest which has accrued on that month's payment.* How much money, including principal and interest, will he have paid when he has freed himself from the debt?

18. It has been learned that, if a marble, placed in a groove on an *inclined plane*, passes over a distance D in one second, then in the second second it will pass over the distance $3D$, in the third, over the distance $5D$, etc. Over what distance will it pass in the 10th second? in the tth second.

19. Through what total distance does it pass in 5 seconds? in 10 seconds? in t seconds?

PROGRESSIONS

20. Experiment has shown that an object will fall during successive seconds the following distances:

1st second, 16.08 ft.;   3d second, 80.40 ft.;
2d second, 48.24 ft.;   4th second, 112.56 ft.

Find the distance through which the object will fall during the 7th second; the tth second.

21. Find the total distance through which the object falls in 5 seconds; in t seconds.

22. Substitute g for 32.16 in the final result of Example 21 and simplify the result.

291. In an arithmetic progression, there are five elements, a, d, l, n, S. Two *independent* formulæ connect these elements, the formula for the sum and the formula for the term l. Hence if any three of the elements are known, the other two may be found.

NOTE. Remember that the formula for the sum is given in *two* ways.

EXAMPLE 1. Given $a = -\frac{5}{3}$, $n = 20$, $S = -\frac{5}{3}$; find d and l.

SOLUTION: 1. $S = \frac{n}{2}(a + l)$. $\therefore -\frac{5}{3} = 10\left(-\frac{5}{3} + l\right)$; whence $l = \frac{3}{2}$.

2. $l = a + (n-1)d$. $\therefore \frac{3}{2} = -\frac{5}{3} + (19) \cdot d$; whence $d = \frac{1}{6}$.

EXAMPLE 2. Given $a = 7$, $d = 4$, $S = 403$; find n and l.

SOLUTION: 1. $S = \frac{n}{2}\{2a + (n-1)d\}$. $\therefore 403 = \frac{n}{2}\{14 + (n-1) \cdot 4\}$.

2. $\therefore 806 = n\{4n + 10\}$; $4n^2 + 10n - 806 = 0$; $2n^2 + 5n - 403 = 0$.

$\therefore n = \dfrac{-5 \pm \sqrt{25 + 3224}}{4} = \dfrac{-5 \pm \sqrt{3249}}{4} = \dfrac{-5 \pm 57}{4} = -\dfrac{62}{4}$, or $+13$.

Since n is the number of terms, n must be 13.

3. $l = a + (n-1)d$. $\therefore l = 7 + 12 \cdot 4 = 55$.

NOTE. A *negative* or a *fractional* value of n is inapplicable, and must be rejected together with all other values depending upon it.

ALGEBRA

EXAMPLE 3. The sixth term of an arithmetic progression is 10 and the 16th term is 40. Find the 10th term.

SOLUTION: 1. By the formula $l = a + (n-1)d$:
$$a + 5d = 10.$$
$$a + 15d = 40.$$

2. Solving the system of equations in step 1, $d = 3$ and $a = -5$.

3. The 10th term: $l = -5 + 9 \cdot 3 = -5 + 27 = 22$.

EXERCISE 186

1. Given $d = 5$, $l = 71$, $n = 15$; find a and S.

2. Given $a = -9$, $n = 23$, $l = 57$; find d and S.

3. Given $a = \frac{1}{4}$, $l = \frac{35}{4}$, $S = \frac{315}{2}$; find d and n.

4. Given $a = \frac{1}{2}$, $l = -\frac{5}{11}$, $d = -\frac{1}{22}$; find n and S.

5. Given $d = \frac{1}{2}$, $n = 17$, $S = 17$; find a and l.

6. Given $a = \frac{3}{4}$, $n = 15$, $S = \frac{405}{8}$; find d and l.

7. Given $a = -\frac{5}{2}$, $l = -\frac{23}{2}$, $S = -91$; find d and n.

8. Given $a = \frac{15}{2}$, $d = -\frac{3}{4}$, $S = \frac{135}{4}$; find n and l.

9. Given a, l, and n; derive a formula for d.

10. Given a, d, and l; derive a formula for n.

11. Given a, n, and S; derive a formula for l.

12. Given d, n, and S; derive a formula for a.

13. Given d, l, and n; derive formulæ for a and S.

14. The 8th term of an arithmetic progression is 10, and the 14th term is -14. Find the 23d term.

15. The 7th term of an arithmetic progression is $-\frac{1}{6}$, the 16th term is $\frac{7}{3}$, and the last term is $\frac{13}{2}$. Find the number of terms.

16. The sum of the 2d and 6th terms of an arithmetic progression is $-\frac{5}{2}$, and the sum of the 5th and 9th terms is -10. Find the first term.

17. Find four numbers in arithmetic progression such that the sum of the first two shall be 12, and the sum of the last two -20.

PROGRESSIONS

18. Find five numbers in arithmetic progression such that the sum of the second, third, and fifth shall be 10, and the product of the first and fourth -36.

19. Find three numbers in arithmetic progression such that the sum of their squares is 347, and one half the third number exceeds the sum of the first and second by $4\frac{1}{2}$.

20. Find three integers in arithmetic progression such that their sum shall be 12, and their product -260.

GEOMETRIC PROGRESSION

292. A **Geometric Progression** (G. P.) is a sequence of numbers, called *terms*, each of which, after the first, is derived by multiplying the preceding term by a fixed number called the **Ratio**.

Thus, 2, 6, 18, 54, ⋯ is a geometric progression. Each term is obtained by multiplying the preceding term by 3. The ratio is 3.

Again, 15, -5, $+\frac{5}{3}$, $-\frac{5}{9}$, ⋯ is a G. P. The ratio is $-\frac{1}{3}$. The next two terms are $+\frac{5}{27}$ and $-\frac{5}{81}$.

NOTE. The ratio may be found by dividing any term by the one preceding it.

EXERCISE 187

Determine which of the following are geometric progressions; determine the ratio and also the next two terms of the geometric progressions:

1. 4, 8, 16, 32, ⋯.
2. 200, 50, 25, 10, ⋯.
3. 81, 27, 9, ⋯.
4. -2, $+6$, -18, $+54$, ⋯.
5. $5m$, $\dfrac{5m}{2}$, $\dfrac{5m}{4}$, ⋯.
6. $3x$, $6x^2$, $12x^3$, ⋯
7. 2, -4, -8, 16, -32, ⋯.
8. $(1+r)$, $(1+r)^2$, $(1+r)^3$, ⋯
9. $\dfrac{1}{m}$, $\dfrac{1}{m^2}$, $\dfrac{1}{m^3}$, ⋯.
10. $\dfrac{10}{x}$, $\dfrac{2}{x^2}$, $\dfrac{2}{5x^3}$, ⋯.

ALGEBRA

Write the first five terms of the G. P. in which:

	11	12	13	14	15
The first term is:	-5	100	$\frac{1}{3}$	$\frac{1}{2}x$	a
The ratio is:	-2	$\frac{1}{5}$	2	$\frac{1}{3}$	r

293. The nth Term of a Geometric Progression. It is possible to determine a particular term of a geometric progression without finding all of the preceding terms.

Given the first term a, the ratio r, and the number of terms n, of a geometric progression, determine the nth term l.

The progression is a, ar, ar^2, ar^3, $\cdots$.

The exponent of r in each term is 1 less than the number of the term. Hence the 10th term would be ar^9. Therefore the exponent of r in the nth term must be $(n-1)$.

$$\therefore l = ar^{n-1}.$$

EXAMPLE. What is the 7th term of 9, 3, 1, $\cdots$?

SOLUTION: 1. $a = 9$; $r = \frac{1}{3}$; $n = 7$; $l = ?$

2. $l = ar^{n-1}$. $\therefore l = 9\left(\dfrac{1}{3}\right)^6 = 3^2 \cdot \dfrac{1}{3^6} = \dfrac{1}{3^4} = \dfrac{1}{81}$.

EXERCISE 188

1. Find the 6th term of 1, 3, 9, $\cdots$.

2. Find the 7th term of 6, 4, $\frac{8}{3}$, $\cdots$.

3. Find the 5th term of -2, 10, -50, $\cdots$.

4. Find the 9th term of 3, $\frac{3}{2}$, $\frac{3}{4}$, $\cdots$.

5. Find the 10th term of $-\frac{5}{2}$, $+5$, -10, $\cdots$.

6. Find the 8th term of $\dfrac{x}{32}, \dfrac{x^2}{16}, \dfrac{x^3}{8}, \cdots$.

7. Indicate the 11th term of 1, $(1+r)$, $(1+r)^2$, $\cdots$.

PROGRESSIONS

8. Indicate the 15th term of $1, \frac{1}{2}, \frac{1}{4}, \frac{1}{8}, \cdots$; also the kth term.

9. Indicate the 13th term of $m, \dfrac{m^2}{3}, \dfrac{m^3}{9}, \dfrac{m^4}{27}, \cdots$; also the $(n+1)$th term.

10. What term of the progression $3, 6, 12, 24, \cdots$ is 384?

11. What term of the progression $5, 10, 20, \cdots$ is 160?

12. What term of the progression $18, 6, 2, \cdots$ is $\frac{2}{27}$?

13. If the first term of a geometric progression is 5, and the 6th term is $\frac{5}{32}$, what is the ratio?

Find the ratio of the geometric progression if:

14. The first term is $\frac{1}{18}$ and the fifth term is $\frac{9}{2}$.

15. The first term is $\frac{3}{8}$, and the 7th term 24.

294. The terms of a geometric progression between any two other terms are called the **Geometric Means** of those two terms.

Thus, the three geometric means of 2 and 162 are 6, 18, and 54, since 2, 6, 18, 54, 162, form a geometric progression.

A single geometric mean of two numbers is particularly important. It is called **The Geometric Mean** of the numbers. When two numbers are given, any specified number of geometric means may be inserted between them.

EXAMPLE. Insert three geometric means between 9 and $\frac{16}{9}$.

SOLUTION: 1. There results a geometric progression of 5 terms, in which $a = 9$, $l = \frac{16}{9}$, and $n = 5$. Find r.

2. $l = ar^{n-1}$. $\therefore \dfrac{16}{9} = 9 \cdot r^4$, or $r^4 = \dfrac{16}{81}$. $\therefore r = \sqrt[4]{\dfrac{16}{81}} = \pm \dfrac{2}{3}$.

3. The progression is: $9, 6, 4, \frac{8}{3}, \frac{16}{9}$, or $9, -6, 4, -\frac{8}{3}, \frac{16}{9}$.

CHECK: There is a G. P. with three terms between 9 and $\frac{16}{9}$.

ALGEBRA

EXERCISE 189

1. Insert 4 geometric means between 3 and 729.
2. Insert 5 geometric means between 2 and 128.
3. Insert 2 geometric means between $\frac{1}{9}$ and 3.
4. Find the geometric mean of 8 and 32.
5. Find the geometric mean of $3\,t$ and $\dfrac{1}{12\,t}$.
6. Find the geometric mean between $2\,x$ and $8\,x^5$.
7. Find the geometric mean between $\dfrac{m}{x}$ and $\dfrac{x}{m}$.
8. Find the geometric mean between a and b.
9. Insert 3 geometric means between 3 and 12.
10. Insert 2 geometric means between a and b.

295. The Sum of the First n Terms of a Geometric Progression

Given the first term a, the ratio r, and the number of terms n, of a geometric progression, find the sum of the terms S.

SOLUTION: 1. $S = a + ar + ar^2 + \cdots + ar^{n-2} + ar^{n-1}.$ (1)

2. Multiplying both members of (1) by r,

$$rS = ar + ar^2 + ar^3 + \cdots + ar^{n-1} + ar^n. \tag{2}$$

3. Subtracting equation (2) from equation (1),

$$S - rS = a - ar^n, \text{ or } S(1-r) = a - ar^n. \tag{3}$$

4. $$\therefore S = \frac{a - ar^n}{1 - r}. \tag{4}$$

5. Since $l = ar^{n-1}$, then $rl = ar^n$. Substituting rl for ar^n in equation (4),

$$S = \frac{a - rl}{1 - r}. \tag{5}$$

EXAMPLE. Find the sum of the first 6 terms of 2, 6, 18 $\cdots$.

SOLUTION: $a = 2, r = 3, n = 6.$ Find S.

2. $S = \dfrac{a - ar^n}{1 - 3}.\ \ \therefore S = \dfrac{2 - 2\cdot 3^6}{1 - 3} = \dfrac{2 - 1458}{-2} = \dfrac{-1456}{-2} = 728.$

PROGRESSIONS

EXERCISE 190

Find the sum of the first:

1. Eight terms of the progression 5, 10, 20, ⋯.
2. Six terms of the progression 24, 12, 6, ⋯.
3. Seven terms of the progression 5, − 15, + 45, ⋯.
4. Seven terms of the progression $\frac{1}{18}$, − $\frac{1}{6}$, $\frac{1}{2}$, ⋯.
5. Five terms of the progression − 2, 10, − 50, ⋯.
6. Fifteen terms of the progression $3\,m$, $3\,m^3$, $3\,m^5$, ⋯.
7. Ten terms of the progression 1, m^2, m^4, m^6, ⋯
8. Find the sum of 15 terms of 1, $(1+r)$, $(1+r)^2$, ⋯.
9. Find the sum of the first 10 powers of 2.
10. Find the sum of the first 10 powers of 3.

11. Each year a man saves half as much again as he saved the preceding year. If he saved $128 the first year, to what sum will his savings amount at the end of seven years?

12. Find the sum of the terms from the 11th to the 15th inclusive in the progression $\frac{1}{16}$, $\frac{1}{8}$, $\frac{1}{4}$, ⋯.

13. A father agrees to give his son 5 ¢ on his fifth birthday, 10 ¢ on his sixth, and each year up to the 21st inclusive to double the gift of the preceding year. How much will he have given him altogether after his 21st birthday?

296. Infinite Geometric Progression. By an infinite geometric progression is meant one the number of whose terms increases indefinitely. If the ratio is greater than one, the terms become larger and larger. For example, the progression 3, 6, 12, 24, ⋯. If S_n represents the sum of the first n terms of a progression, then, when r is greater than 1, S_n increases indefinitely as n increases indefinitely.

Thus, in the progression 3, 6, 12, ⋯, as n increases indefinitely,

380   ALGEBRA

S_n increases indefinitely. Hence the sum of an infinite number of terms of the progression must be an indefinitely large number.

When the numerical value of the ratio is less than 1, the progression has special interest.

EXAMPLE 1. Consider the progression $5, \frac{5}{3}, \frac{5}{9}, \ldots$.

SOLUTION: 1. The ratio r is $\frac{1}{3}$.

2.

When n is:	$l = ar^{n-1}$ is:	$S_n = \dfrac{a - rl}{1 - r}$ is:
4	$5(\frac{1}{3})^3 = \frac{5}{27}$	$\dfrac{5 - \frac{1}{3} \cdot (\frac{5}{27})}{1 - \frac{1}{3}} = \dfrac{5 - \frac{5}{81}}{1 - \frac{1}{3}}$
10	$5(\frac{1}{3})^9 = \frac{5}{19683}$	$\dfrac{5 - \frac{1}{3} \cdot \frac{5}{19683}}{1 - \frac{1}{3}} = \dfrac{5 - \frac{5}{59049}}{1 - \frac{1}{3}}$

3. Clearly, as n increases, l decreases; also the term rl of S_n decreases. If n increases indefinitely, l will become approximately zero, the term r will become approximately zero, and S_n will become approximately

$$\frac{5}{1 - \frac{1}{3}} = \frac{5}{\frac{2}{3}} = \frac{15}{2}.$$

Consider now *any* geometric progression in which r is less than 1 in absolute value (§ 21). The sum of the first n terms is:
$$S_n = \frac{a - ar^n}{1 - r}.$$

Now as n increases indefinitely, r^n decreases indefinitely, becoming approximately zero. Hence the term $a \cdot r^n$ becomes approximately zero. a, and $1 - r$ remain the same.

$\therefore S_n$ becomes approximately $\dfrac{a - 0}{1 - r}$ or $\dfrac{a}{1 - r}$.

Hence, the sum of an infinite number of terms of a geometric progression in which r is numerically less than 1, is given by the formula $S = \dfrac{a}{1 - r}.$

PROGRESSIONS

EXAMPLE. Find the sum to infinity of the progression
$$4, -\tfrac{8}{3}, \tfrac{16}{9}, \cdots.$$

SOLUTION: 1. $a = 4$; $r = -\tfrac{2}{3}$.

2. Since r is numerically less than 1, $S = \dfrac{a}{1-r}$.

$$\therefore S = \frac{4}{1+\tfrac{2}{3}} = \frac{4}{\tfrac{5}{3}} = \frac{12}{5} = 2.4.$$

EXERCISE 191

Find the sums to infinity of:

1. $6, 2, \tfrac{2}{3}$.

2. $1, \tfrac{1}{2}, \tfrac{1}{4}, \cdots$.

3. $16, 4, 1, \cdots$.

4. $5, \tfrac{5}{10}, \tfrac{5}{100}, \cdots$.

5. $1, .1, .01, .001, \cdots$.

6. $x, \dfrac{x}{2}, \dfrac{x}{4}, \cdots$.

7. $a, \dfrac{a}{10}, \dfrac{a}{100}, \cdots$.

8. $1, -\tfrac{1}{5}, +\tfrac{1}{25}, \cdots$.

9. $-\tfrac{5}{3}, -\tfrac{10}{9}, -\tfrac{20}{27}, \cdots$.

10. $\tfrac{1}{8}, -\tfrac{1}{18}, +\tfrac{2}{81}, \cdots$.

11. Find the value of the *repeating* decimal $.8181\cdots$.

SOLUTION: 1. $.8181\cdots = \tfrac{81}{100} + \tfrac{81}{10000} +$ etc. $\cdots$.

2. This is a G. P. in which $a = \tfrac{81}{100}$; $r = \tfrac{1}{100}$. The value of the decimal if an infinite number of decimal places is considered is given by the formula

$$S = \frac{a}{1-r} \quad (\S\,296).$$

$$\therefore S = \frac{\tfrac{81}{100}}{1-\tfrac{1}{100}} = \frac{81}{100} \times \frac{100}{99} = \frac{81}{99} = \frac{9}{11}.$$

Find the values of the following repeating decimals:

12. $.3333\cdots$.

13. $.7777\cdots$.

14. $.5333\cdots$.

15. $.6444\cdots$.

16. $.212121\cdots$.

17. $.151515\cdots$.

XXIV. THE BINOMIAL THEOREM

297. The **Binomial Theorem** is a formula for determining by inspection the expansion of any power of a binomial.

By actual multiplication:

$(a + x)^2 = a^2 + 2\,ax + x^2.$ (1)
$(a + x)^3 = a^3 + 3\,a^2x + 3\,ax^2 + x^3.$ (2)
$(a + x)^4 = a^4 + 4\,a^3x + 6\,a^2x^2 + 4\,ax^3 + x^4.$ (3)

Rule. — To expand any power of a binomial, like $(a + x)^n$:

1. The exponent of a in the first term is n and decreases by 1 in each succeeding term until it becomes 1. The last term does not contain a.

2. The first term does not contain x. The exponent of x in the second term is 1 and increases by 1 in each succeeding term until it is n in the last term.

3. The coefficient of the first term is 1; of the second is n.

4. If the coefficient of any term be multiplied by the exponent of a in that term, and the product be divided by the number of the term, the quotient is the coefficient of the next term.

NOTE 1. The number of terms is $n + 1$.

NOTE 2. The coefficients of terms "equidistant from the ends" are the same; for example, the second and the next to the last.

EXAMPLE 1. Expand $(a + x)^5$.

SOLUTION: 1. The exponents of a are 5, 4, 3, 2, 1. The exponents of x, starting with 1 in the second term, are 1, 2, 3, 4, and 5. Writing the terms without the coefficients gives:

$$a^5 + a^4x + a^3x^2 + a^2x^3 + ax^4 + x^5.$$

2. The coefficient of the first term is 1, and of the second term is 5 (Rule 3). Multiplying 5, the coefficient of the second term, by 4, the

THE BINOMIAL THEOREM

exponent of a in the second term, and dividing by 2, the number of the term, gives 10, the coefficient of the third term; and so on.

Filling in the coefficients in this manner gives:

$$(a+x)^5 = a^5 + 5\,a^4x + 10\,a^3x^2 + 10\,a^2x^3 + 5\,ax^4 + x^5.$$

EXAMPLE 2. Expand $\left(2 - \dfrac{m}{3}\right)^6$.

SOLUTION: 1. In this example, a is 2 and x is $\left(-\dfrac{m}{3}\right)$.

2. $\therefore \left(2 - \dfrac{m}{3}\right)^6 = 2^6 + 6 \cdot 2^5 \left(-\dfrac{m}{3}\right) + 15 \cdot 2^4 \left(-\dfrac{m}{3}\right)^2 + 20 \cdot 2^3 \cdot \left(-\dfrac{m}{3}\right)^3$
$+ 15 \cdot 2^2 \cdot \left(-\dfrac{m}{3}\right)^4 + 6 \cdot 2 \cdot \left(-\dfrac{m}{3}\right)^5 + \left(-\dfrac{m}{3}\right)^6$

3. $= 64 - 6 \cdot 32 \cdot \dfrac{m}{3} + 15 \cdot 16 \cdot \dfrac{m^2}{9} - 20 \cdot 8 \cdot \dfrac{m^3}{27} + 15 \cdot 4 \cdot \dfrac{m^4}{81}$
$- 12 \cdot \dfrac{m^5}{243} + \dfrac{m^6}{729}.$

4. $= 64 - 64\,m + \dfrac{80}{3}\,m^2 - \dfrac{160}{27}\,m^3 + \dfrac{20}{27}\,m^4 - \dfrac{4}{81}\,m^5 + \dfrac{m^6}{729}.$

NOTE 1. When the second term of the binomial is negative, the terms of the expansion are alternately positive and negative.

NOTE 2. When the terms of the binomial are complicated monomials, place each in parentheses, and afterwards simplify as in steps 3 and 4.

EXERCISE 192

Expand the following:

1. $(x+y)^4$.
2. $(m-n)^5$.
3. $(c+1)^4$.
4. $(r-2)^5$.
5. $(m+n)^6$
6. $(a^2-b^2)^4$.
7. $(2\,a+1)^5$.
8. $(a-3\,b)^4$.
9. $(1+x^2)^6$.
10. $(1-x)^8$.
11. $(a-\tfrac{1}{2})^5$.
12. $(\tfrac{1}{3}+x)^4$.
13. $(2\,m^2-1)^6$.
14. $(a^2+b^2c)^4$.
15. $(3+x^3)^5$.

Find the first three terms of:

16. $(a-3)^{15}$.
17. $(m^2+2\,n)^{20}$.
18. $(a-\tfrac{1}{2})^{16}$.
19. $(a^2-b^3)^{10}$.
20. $(x^3+3\,y^5)^{12}$.
21. $(m^2-4\,n^2)^{11}$.

22. $\left(\dfrac{1}{a}+\dfrac{1}{b}\right)^7$.

23. $\left(\dfrac{1}{a}-a\right)^6$.

24. $\left(\dfrac{a}{b}+\dfrac{b}{a}\right)^8$.

25. $(a^{-1}+b^{-2})^5$.

26. $(a^{\frac{1}{2}}-b^{\frac{1}{3}})^7$.

27. $(\sqrt{2}-\sqrt{3})^6$.

28. Write the first 4 terms of $(a+x)^n$.

298. The rth or General Term of $(a+x)^n$. Following the rules of § 297,

$$(a+x)^n = a^n + n \cdot a^{n-1}x + \frac{n(n-1)}{1\cdot 2}\cdot a^{n-2}x^2$$

$$+ \frac{n(n-1)(n-2)}{1\cdot 2\cdot 3} a^{n-3}x^3 + \cdots.$$

Note the fourth term. The exponent of x is 1 less than the number of the term; the exponent of a is n minus the exponent of x; the last factor of the denominator equals the exponent of x; in the numerator there are as many factors as there are factors in the denominator. Hence,

Rule.— In the rth term of $(a+x)^n$:

1. **The exponent of x is $r-1$.**

2. **The exponent of a is $n-$ the exponent of x,** i.e., $n-r+1$.

3. **The denominator of the coefficient is $1\cdot 2\cdot 3 \cdots (r-1)$,** the last factor being the same as the exponent of x.

4. **The numerator of the coefficient is $n(n-1)\cdots$ etc., until there are as many factors as in the denominator.**

∴ The rth term is $\dfrac{n(n-1)\cdots(n-r+2)}{1\cdot 2\cdots(r-1)} \cdot a^{n-r+1} \cdot x^{r-1}$.

EXAMPLE. Find the 8th term of $(3\,a^{\frac{1}{2}}-b)^{11}$.

2. SOLUTION: 1. $(3\,a^{\frac{1}{2}}-b)^{11} = \{(3\,a^{\frac{1}{2}})+(-b)\}^{11}$.

In the 8th term, the exponent of $(-b)$ will be 7 (Rule 1); the exponent of $(3\,a^{\frac{1}{2}})$ will be $11-7$, or 4; the last factor of the denominator will be 7, and there will be 7 factors in the numerator starting with $11\cdot 10$, etc.

THE BINOMIAL THEOREM

8. $\therefore$ The 8th term is $\dfrac{11\cdot 10\cdot \overset{3}{\cancel{9}}\cdot \cancel{8}\cdot \cancel{7}\cdot \cancel{6}\cdot \cancel{5}}{1\cdot \cancel{2}\cdot 3\cdot \cancel{4}\cdot \cancel{5}\cdot \cancel{6}\cdot \cancel{7}}\cdot (3\,a^{\frac{1}{2}})^4(-b)^7$,

or $\qquad 330(81\,a^2)(-b^7) = -26730\,a^2 b^7$.

NOTE. If the second term of the binomial is negative, it should be inclosed, sign and all, in parentheses, before applying the rules. Also, if either term has an exponent or coefficient other than 1, the term should be inclosed in parentheses before applying the rules.

EXERCISE 193

Find the:

1. 4th term of $(a+x)^8$.
2. 9th term of $(m-n)^{11}$.
3. 5th term of $(g+2)^9$.
4. 10th term of $(q-x)^{16}$.
5. 8th term of $(m^2-n^3)^{12}$.
6. 6th term of $(a^3+3\,x^5)^{10}$.
7. 7th term of $(c-\tfrac{1}{2})^{15}$.
8. 5th term of $(2\,x^2-3)^{10}$.
9. 6th term of $(x^m-y^n)^{12}$.
10. 7th term of $\left(\dfrac{a}{b}-b\right)^{15}$.
11. 4th term of $\left(\dfrac{x^2}{y}-\dfrac{y^2}{x}\right)^{12}$.
12. 8th term of $(x^{-1}-2\,y^{\frac{1}{2}})^{13}$.

299. The Binomial Formula has not been proved in this chapter; it has been written down from observation of the results in certain special cases. The formula has been applied only for positive integral values of n.

The proof of the formula for positive integral exponents will be found in § 335.

In more advanced courses in mathematics, the formula is proved to be correct (with certain limitations) not only for positive integral values of n but also for negative and fractional values.

HISTORICAL NOTE. The binomial theorem was formulated by Newton.

XXV. RATIO, PROPORTION, AND VARIATION

300. The **Ratio** of one number to another is the quotient of the first divided by the second.

Thus, the ratio of a to b is $\dfrac{a}{b}$; it is also written $a:b$. The numerator is called the **Antecedent** and the denominator is called the **Consequent**.

All ratios are fractions and are subject to the usual rules for operations with fractions.

301. The ratio of two concrete quantities may be found if they are of the same kind and are measured in terms of the same unit.

Thus, the ratio of 3 lb. to 2 lb. is $\frac{3}{2}$; and the ratio of 350 lb. to 2 tons is $\frac{350}{4000}$ or $\frac{7}{80}$.

EXERCISE 194

Express the following ratios and simplify them:

1. 3 to 9.
2. 12 to 2.
3. $5x$ to $2x$.
4. $6a^2$ to $15a^3$.
5. $\frac{5}{8}$ to $\frac{3}{16}$.
6. $\frac{2}{15}$ to $\frac{1}{3}$.
7. 25 to 375.
8. $a^2 - b^2$ to $a^3 - b^3$.

9. A line 15 inches long is divided into two parts which have the ratio $2:3$. Find the parts.

SOLUTION: 1. Let $x =$ the short part.

2. Then $15 - x =$ the long part.

3. Then $\dfrac{x}{15 - x} = \dfrac{2}{3}$.

Complete the solution.

10. Divide a line 63 inches long into two parts whose ratio is $3:4$.

RATIO, PROPORTION, AND VARIATION

11. Divide 36 into two parts such that the ratio of the greater diminished by 4 to the less increased by 3 shall be $3:2$.

12. The ratio of the height of a tree to the length of its shadow on the ground is $17:20$. Find the height of the tree if the length of the shadow is 110 feet.

13. Divide 99 into three parts which are as $2:3:4$.

HINT: Let the parts be $2x$, $3x$, and $4x$.

14. Divide a farm consisting of 720 acres into parts which are as $3:5$.

15. Divide $1000 into 3 parts which are as $5:3:2$.

302. A Proportion is a statement that two ratios are equal. The statement that the ratio of a to b is equal to the ratio of c to d is written either

$$\frac{a}{b} = \frac{c}{d}, \text{ or } a:b = c:d.$$

This proportion is read "a is to b as c is to d."

Thus 3, 9, 5 and 15 form a proportion since $\frac{3}{9} = \frac{5}{15}$.

HISTORICAL NOTE. Leibnitz, 1646–1716, was instrumental in establishing the use of the form $a:b = c:d$.

303. The first and fourth terms of a proportion are called the **Extremes**, and the second and third the **Means**.

In the proportion $a:b = c:d$, a and d are the extremes, and b and c are the means; a and c are the antecedents, and b and d are the consequents.

EXERCISE 195

Find the value of the literal number in the first six of the following exercises and of x in the remaining ones:

1. $\dfrac{x}{3} = \dfrac{5}{27}$.

2. $\dfrac{2}{y} = \dfrac{3}{10}$.

3. $\dfrac{7}{16} = \dfrac{c}{5}$

4. $\dfrac{9}{24} = \dfrac{3}{z}$.

5. $\dfrac{2-x}{3} = \dfrac{5}{2}$

6. $\dfrac{3-t}{4+t} = \dfrac{5}{2}$

7. $\dfrac{a}{b} = \dfrac{x}{c}.$

8. $\dfrac{a}{2b} = \dfrac{x}{3c}.$

9. $\dfrac{r^2}{sx} = \dfrac{r}{t}.$

10. $\dfrac{m}{np} = \dfrac{c}{nx}.$

11. $\dfrac{a-x}{x} = \dfrac{a}{b}.$

12. $\dfrac{a}{x-m} = \dfrac{n}{x}.$

304. A **Mean Proportional** between two numbers a and b is the number x in the proportion $a : x = x : b$.

A mean proportional between 2 and 3 is x in: $\dfrac{2}{x} = \dfrac{x}{3}.$

$$\therefore x^2 = 6\,;\ x = \pm\sqrt{6}.$$

Thus, there are two mean proportionals between any numbers. Generally the positive one is used.

305. The **Third Proportional** to two numbers a and b is the number x in the proportion $a : b = b : x$.

Thus, the third proportional to 2 and 3 is x in: $\dfrac{2}{3} = \dfrac{3}{x}$;

$$\therefore 2x = 9 \text{ and } x = 4.5.$$

306. The **Fourth Proportional** to three numbers a, b, and c is the number x in the proportion $a : b = c : x$.

Thus, the fourth proportional to 2, 3, and 4 is the number x in: $\dfrac{2}{3} = \dfrac{4}{x}$;

$$\therefore 2x = 12 \text{ and } x = 6.$$

NOTE. The numbers must be placed in the proportion in the order in which they are given, as in the illustrative examples.

EXERCISE 196

Find the fourth proportional to:

1. 2, 5, and 4.
2. 5, 4, and 2.
3. 7, 3, and 14.
4. 35, 20, and 14.
5. $6\,a$, $2\,b$, and c.
6. x, y, and xy.

Find the mean proportionals between:

7. 18 and 50.
8. $2\frac{1}{3}$ and $\frac{3}{5}$.
9. $2\,a$ and a.
10. $12\,m^2n$ and $3\,mn^2$.

RATIO, PROPORTION, AND VARIATION

11. $\dfrac{a^2-a-6}{a+4}$ and $\dfrac{a^2+a-12}{a+2}$. **12.** x^3-y^3 and $\dfrac{x^2+xy+y^2}{x-y}$.

13–16. Find the third proportional to the numbers in examples 7, 8, 9, and 10.

17. Find the third proportional to a^2-9 and $a-3$.

18. Find the third proportional to $10\,x$ and $3\,y$.

19. Find the fourth proportional to:

$$\frac{2\,x^2-2\,y^2}{a+b},\ \frac{x^3-y^3}{a^2-b^2},\ \text{and}\ \frac{ax-by+ay-bx}{x^2+xy+y^2}.$$

20. Find the mean proportionals between:

$$\frac{ax-ay-bx+by}{x^2+xy+y^2}\ \text{and}\ \frac{x^3-y^3}{(a-b)^3}.$$

PROPERTIES OF PROPORTIONS

307. *In a proportion, the product of the means is equal to the product of the extremes.*

This property of a proportion is proved as follows:

If $\dfrac{a}{b}=\dfrac{c}{d}$, then $ad=bc$, by clearing of fractions.

EXAMPLE. Since $\tfrac{2}{3}=\tfrac{6}{9}$, $2 \cdot 9$ should equal $3 \cdot 6$. Does it?

308. *If the product of two numbers is equal to the product of two other numbers, one pair may be made the means and the other the extremes of a proportion.*

If $mn=xy$, then $\dfrac{m}{x}=\dfrac{y}{n}$.

Prove this by dividing both members of the given equation by nx.

Prove that the following proportions also are true:

(a) $\dfrac{m}{y}=\dfrac{x}{n}$ (divide by ny).   (b) $\dfrac{x}{m}=\dfrac{n}{y}$.   (c) $\dfrac{n}{x}=\dfrac{y}{m}$.

EXAMPLE 1. Since $3 \cdot 8 = 6 \cdot 4$, $\tfrac{3}{6}$ should equal $\tfrac{4}{8}$. Does it?

EXAMPLE 2. Write three other proportions which should be true according to the property given in this paragraph.

ALGEBRA

309. *In any proportion, the terms are in proportion by* **Alternation**; *that is, the first term is to the third as the second is to the fourth.*

If $\dfrac{a}{b}=\dfrac{c}{d}$, prove $\qquad \dfrac{a}{c}=\dfrac{b}{d}.$

SUGGESTION. Use § 307 and then divide both members of the equation by cd.

EXAMPLE. Since $\tfrac{2}{6}=\tfrac{4}{12}$, then $\tfrac{2}{4}$ should equal $\tfrac{6}{12}$. Does it?

310. *In any proportion, the terms are in proportion by* **Inversion**; *that is, the second term is to the first as the fourth is to the third.*

If $\dfrac{a}{b}=\dfrac{c}{d}$, prove $\qquad \dfrac{b}{a}=\dfrac{d}{c}.$

SUGGESTION. Use § 307, and then divide both members of the equation by ac.

EXAMPLE. Since $\tfrac{2}{6}=\tfrac{4}{12}$, then $\tfrac{6}{2}$ should equal $\tfrac{12}{4}$. Does it?

311. *In any proportion, the terms are in proportion by* **Composition**; *that is, the sum of the first two terms is to the second as the sum of the last two terms is to the fourth.*

If $\dfrac{a}{b}=\dfrac{c}{d}$, prove $\qquad \dfrac{a+b}{b}=\dfrac{c+d}{d}.$

SUGGESTION. Add 1 to both members of the given equation.

EXAMPLE. Since $\dfrac{2}{6}=\dfrac{4}{12}$, then $\dfrac{2+6}{6}$ should equal $\dfrac{4+12}{12}$. Does it?

312. *In any proportion, the terms are in proportion by* **Division**; *that is, the difference of the first two terms is to the second, as the difference of the last two is to the fourth.*

If $\dfrac{a}{b}=\dfrac{c}{d}$, prove $\qquad \dfrac{a-b}{b}=\dfrac{c-d}{d}.$

SUGGESTION. Subtract 1 from both members of the equation.

EXAMPLE. Since $\dfrac{10}{2}=\dfrac{15}{3}$, then $\dfrac{10-2}{2}$ should equal $\dfrac{15-3}{3}$. Does it?

RATIO, PROPORTION, AND VARIATION

313. *In any proportion, the terms are in proportion by **Composition** and **Division**; that is, the sum of the first two terms is to their difference as the sum of the last two terms is to their difference.*

If $\dfrac{a}{b} = \dfrac{c}{d}$, prove $\dfrac{a+b}{a-b} = \dfrac{c+d}{c-d}$.

PROOF. 1. Since $\dfrac{a}{b} = \dfrac{c}{d}$, then $\dfrac{a+b}{b} = \dfrac{c+d}{d}$. (Composition)

2. Since $\dfrac{a}{b} = \dfrac{c}{d}$, then $\dfrac{a-b}{b} = \dfrac{c-d}{d}$. (Division)

3. Divide the members of the equation in step 1 by those of the equation in step 2:

$$\dfrac{a+b}{b} \div \dfrac{a-b}{b} = \dfrac{c+d}{d} \div \dfrac{c-d}{d}.$$

4. Simplifying step 3: $\dfrac{a+b}{a-b} = \dfrac{c+d}{c-d}$.

EXAMPLE. Since $\dfrac{10}{2} = \dfrac{15}{3}$, then, $\dfrac{10+2}{10-2}$ should equal $\dfrac{15+3}{15-3}$. Does it?

314. *In a series of equal ratios, the sum of the antecedents is to the sum of the consequents as any antecedent is to its consequent.*

If $\dfrac{a}{b} = \dfrac{c}{d} = \dfrac{e}{f}$, etc., prove $\dfrac{a+c+e+\text{etc.}}{b+d+f+\text{etc.}} = \dfrac{a}{b}$.

PROOF. 1. Let $v =$ the common value of the equal ratios $\dfrac{a}{b}$, $\dfrac{c}{d}$, $\dfrac{e}{f}$, etc.

2. Then since $\dfrac{a}{b} = v$, $a = bv$

$\dfrac{c}{d} = v$, $c = dv$.

$\dfrac{e}{f} = v$, $e = fv$.

3. Then $(a+c+e) = bv + dv + fv = v(b+d+f)$.

4. $D_{(b+d+f)}$: $\dfrac{a+c+e}{b+d+f} = v$. $\therefore \dfrac{a+c+e}{b+d+f} = \dfrac{a}{b}$ or $\dfrac{c}{d}$ or $\dfrac{e}{f}$.

EXAMPLE. Since $\dfrac{1}{2} = \dfrac{3}{6} = \dfrac{5}{10}$, $\dfrac{1+3+5}{2+6+10}$ should equal $\dfrac{1}{2}$. Does it?

HISTORICAL NOTE. All of these properties of a proportion were known to Euclid, 300 B.C.

392 ALGEBRA

315. There are several other properties of a proportion which follow directly from properties of an equation or of a fraction.

(a) If $\dfrac{a}{b} = \dfrac{c}{d}$, then $\dfrac{a^3}{b^3} = \dfrac{c^3}{d^3}$. Raise both members to the third power.

(b) If $\dfrac{a}{b} = \dfrac{c}{d}$, then $\dfrac{\sqrt[3]{a}}{\sqrt[3]{b}} = \dfrac{\sqrt[3]{c}}{\sqrt[3]{d}}$. Extract the cube root of both members.

(c) If $\dfrac{a}{b} = \dfrac{c}{d}$, then $\dfrac{ma}{mb} = \dfrac{nc}{nd}$. Multiply numerator and denominator of the first ratio by m, and of the second by n.

(d) If $\dfrac{a}{b} = \dfrac{c}{d}$, then $\dfrac{ma}{nb} = \dfrac{mc}{nd}$. Multiply both members of the equation by $\dfrac{m}{n}$.

316. In the preceding paragraphs, some of the simple properties of a proportion have been given. There are many others which may be derived by means of these simple properties.

EXAMPLE. If $\dfrac{a}{b} = \dfrac{c}{d}$, prove $\dfrac{2a+3b}{2c+3d} = \dfrac{2a-3b}{2c-3d}$.

PROOF. 1. Since $\dfrac{a}{b} = \dfrac{c}{d}$, then $\dfrac{2a}{3b} = \dfrac{2c}{3d}$. (§ 315, d)

2. Then $\dfrac{2a+3b}{2a-3b} = \dfrac{2c+3d}{2c-3d}$. (By § 313)

3. Then $\dfrac{2a+3b}{2c+3d} = \dfrac{2a-3b}{2c-3d}$. (By § 309)

EXERCISE 197

1. Write by inversion:

(a) $\dfrac{3}{4} = \dfrac{15}{20}$. (b) $\dfrac{2}{5} = \dfrac{m}{x}$. (c) $\dfrac{a}{b} = \dfrac{x}{y}$.

2. Write these same three proportions by alternation.

3. Write these same three proportions by composition.

4. Write these same three proportions by division.

5. Write the proportion (c) in Example 1:

(a) by inversion and the result by composition;

(b) by alternation and the result by division;
(c) by composition and the result by alternation;
(d) by division and the result by inversion.

6. If $\dfrac{m}{n} = \dfrac{x}{y}$, prove that $\dfrac{m+n}{x+y} = \dfrac{n}{y}$.

7. If $\dfrac{r}{s} = \dfrac{a}{b}$, prove that $\dfrac{s+r}{r} = \dfrac{b+a}{a}$.

8. If $\dfrac{a}{b} = \dfrac{c}{d}$, prove that $\dfrac{a-b}{c-d} = \dfrac{b}{d}$.

9. If $\dfrac{x}{u} = \dfrac{w}{t}$, prove that $\dfrac{x^2 + u^2}{u^2} = \dfrac{w^2 + t^2}{t^2}$.

10. If $\dfrac{a}{b} = \dfrac{c}{d}$, prove that $\dfrac{2a - 3b}{b} = \dfrac{2c - 3d}{d}$.

EXERCISE 198

Proportion in Geometry

1. In a triangle in which DE is parallel to BC, $m:r = n:s$.

To test this truth: (a) measure m, n, r, and s; (b) find the value of the ratio $m:r$ and of $n:s$; (c) compare these two ratios.

This truth may be tested in any triangle. It may be expressed thus: *the upper segment on one side is to the lower segment on that side as the upper segment on the other is to the lower segment on the other.*

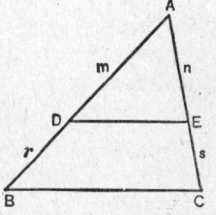

2. Write the proportion $\dfrac{m}{r} = \dfrac{n}{s}$ by alternation. Express the resulting proportion in words as in Example 1.

3. Write the proportion of Example 1 by composition and express it in words.

4. Write the proportion of Example 1 by inversion and express it in words.

5. If $AD = 7$, $DB = 4$, and $AE = 8$, find EC.

6. If $AB = 12$, $AD = 5$, and $AC = 14$, find AE.

Hint. Let $AE = x$, and $CE = 14 - x$.

7. If $AD = DB$, how does AE compare with EC?

8. If $AD = 20$, $DB = 8$, and $AC = 30$, find AE and EC.

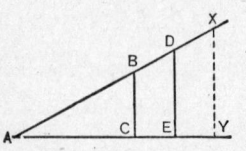

9. If two perpendicular lines BC and DE are drawn from one side of an angle to the other, then $BC : AC = DE : AE$.

Test this statement by measuring the lines in the figure and finding the value of the ratios.

10. Draw any other perpendicular, as XY. Find the ratio of XY to AY and compare the ratio with those found in Example 9. What do you conclude about all ratios obtained by dividing the length of the perpendicular by the distance from A to the foot of the perpendicular (like AY)?

11. Using the fact stated in Example 9, tell how to find the height of the tree in the figure, if the height of the rod and the lengths on the shadows of the tree and the rod are as indicated.

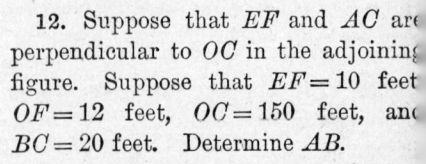

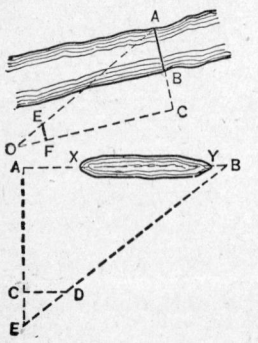

12. Suppose that EF and AC are perpendicular to OC in the adjoining figure. Suppose that $EF = 10$ feet, $OF = 12$ feet, $OC = 150$ feet, and $BC = 20$ feet. Determine AB.

13. Suppose that CD and AB are perpendicular to AE in the adjoining figure; that $AX = 5$ feet, $YB = $ feet, $AE = 750$ feet, $CE = 25$ feet, and $CD = 30$ feet. Find XY.

RATIO, PROPORTION, AND VARIATION

VARIATION

317. Some quantities change or **vary** and are called **Variable Quantities.**

Thus, the distance between a moving train and its destination *varies*, — that is, it decreases; the age of an individual *varies* from moment to moment, — that is, it increases.

318. A quantity which is fixed in any given problem is called a **Constant.**

Thus, if a workman receives a fixed sum per day, the total wages due him changes from day to day if he works and remains unpaid. His daily wage is a constant; his total wages is a variable.

319. A change or **Variation** in one quantity usually produces a variation in one or more other quantities. Such variables are called **Related Variables.** For each value of one variable there is a corresponding value of the other variable, or variables.

Thus, if the side of a square is increased, the perimeter and the area of the square are also increased.

320. Variation is the study of some of the laws connecting related variables. Instead of the quantities themselves, their measures in terms of certain units of measure are used.

Thus, distance is expressed as a *number* of miles, rods, or other units of length; weight is expressed as a *number* of units of weight; area is expressed as a *number* of units of area.

321. One quantity **varies directly** as another when the ratio of any value of the one to the corresponding value of the other is constant.

Thus, the ratio of the perimeter of a square to the side of the square is always 4, because the perimeter is 4 times the length of the side; therefore the perimeter varies directly as the side of the square.

322. The symbol, $\propto$, is read "varies as"; thus, $a \propto b$ is read "a varies as b."

If $x \propto y$, then $\dfrac{x}{y} = m$, where m is a constant, expresses the relation between any two corresponding values of x and y. (See § 321.)

Since $\dfrac{x}{y} = m$, then $x = my$.

Either equation may be used to express direct variation.

323. One quantity is said to **vary inversely** as another when the product of any value of the one and the corresponding value of the other is constant.

Thus, the time and rate of a train going a distance d are connected by the equation $rt = d$. If the distance remains fixed, then the time varies inversely as the rate; for example, if the rate is doubled, the time is halved.

If x varies inversely as y, then $xy = m$, where m is a constant, expresses the relation between them.

If $xy = m$, then also $x = \dfrac{m}{y}$. Either equation may be used to express inverse variation.

324. One quantity is said to **vary jointly** as two others when it varies directly as their product. If x varies jointly as y and z, then $\dfrac{x}{yz} = m$, where m is a constant, expresses the relation between the variables.

Thus, the wages of a workman varies jointly as the amount he receives per day and the number of days he works; for, letting W equal his total wages, w his daily pay, and n the number of days he works, then $W = nw$. Here $m = 1$.

Again, the formula for the area of a triangle is

$$A = \tfrac{1}{2} ab.$$

This shows that the area of a triangle varies jointly as the base and altitude. (Here $m = \tfrac{1}{2}$.)

325. One quantity may vary directly as a second and inversely as a third. Let x vary directly as y and inversely as z; then

$$x = \frac{my}{z}$$

expresses the relation between the variables. Notice that this combines the equation for direct variation of y and inverse variation of z.

326. Variation of more complicated related variables needs to be expressed sometimes.

EXAMPLE 1. $x \propto y^2$ may be written $x = my^2$.

EXAMPLE 2. $x^3 \propto y^2$ may be written $x^3 = my^2$.

EXAMPLE 3. The volume of a circular cylinder varies jointly as the altitude and as the square of the radius. This may be expressed: $v \propto ar^2$, or $v = kar^2$.

EXAMPLE 4. a varies directly as q, and inversely as d^2. This may be expressed: $a = \dfrac{kq}{d^2}$.

EXERCISE 199

Express the following relations both by means of the symbol $\propto$ and by an equation:

1. The area of a rectangle varies jointly as the base and altitude.

2. The area of a circle varies as the square of the diameter.

3. The volume of a rectangular prism varies jointly as the length, width, and height.

4. The distance a body falls from a position of rest varies as the square of the number of seconds in which it falls.

5. The interest varies jointly as the principal, the rate, and the time.

ALGEBRA

Express the following relations by means of equations.

6. The rate of a train varies inversely as the time, if the distance is constant.

7. The rate of gain varies inversely as the capital invested, if the total gain is constant.

8. The weight of an object above the surface of the earth varies inversely as the square of the distance from the center of the earth.

9. The per capita cost of instruction for pupils in a school room varies directly as the salary of the teacher and inversely as the number of the pupils.

10. The volume of a circular cone varies jointly as the altitude and the square of the radius.

11. If z varies jointly as x and y, and equals $\frac{2}{5}$ when $y = \frac{4}{5}$ and $x = \frac{3}{4}$, find z when $y = \frac{5}{4}$ and $x = \frac{4}{3}$.

SOLUTION. 1. According to the conditions $z = mxy$.

2. $\therefore \dfrac{2}{5} = m \cdot \dfrac{3}{4} \cdot \dfrac{4}{5}$, or $m = \dfrac{2}{3}$, since $z = \frac{2}{5}$ when $x = \frac{3}{4}$ and $y = \frac{4}{5}$.

3. $\therefore z = \frac{2}{3} xy$, substituting $\frac{2}{3}$ for m.

4. $\therefore z = \frac{2}{3} \cdot \frac{4}{3} \cdot \frac{5}{4} = \frac{10}{9}$, when $x = \frac{4}{3}$ and $y = \frac{5}{4}$.

NOTE. In such problems, first find the constant, as in step 2.

12. If $y \propto x$ and is equal to 40 when $x = 5$, what is its value when $x = 9$?

13. If $y \propto x^3$ and is equal to 40 when $x = 4$, what is the equation for y in terms of x?

14. If x varies inversely as y and is equal to $\frac{2}{3}$ when $y = \frac{3}{4}$, what is the value of y when x is $\frac{3}{2}$?

15. If $(5x + 8) \propto (6y - 1)$ and $x = 6$ when $y = -3$, what is the value of x when $y = 7$?

16. The distance fallen by a body, from a position of rest varies as the square of the number of seconds in which the

RATIO, PROPORTION, AND VARIATION

body falls. If it falls 256 feet in 4 seconds, how far will it fall in 6 seconds?

17. The interest on a sum of money varies jointly as the rate of interest and the principal. If the interest is $375 when the rate is 5% and the principal is $3000, what is the interest when the rate is 6% and the principal is $2500?

18. The principal varies directly as the interest and inversely as the rate. If the principal, $4000, produces $250 interest at 4%, what principal must be invested for the same time to yield $500 at 5%?

19. The number of tiles required to cover a given area varies inversely as the length and width of the tile. If it takes 270 tiles 2 inches by 5 inches in size to cover a certain area, how many tiles 3 inches by 6 inches will be required for the same area?

20. The number of posts required for a fence varies inversely as the distance between them. If it takes 80 posts when they are placed 12 feet apart, how many will be required when they are placed 15 feet apart?

XXVI. SUPPLEMENTARY TOPICS

CUBE ROOT

327. Cube Root of a Polynomial. By the binomial formula (§ 297), $(a+b)^3 = a^3 + 3a^2b + 3ab^2 + b^3$. Any polynomial which may be put in this form is a perfect cube. Its cube root may be found by inspection.

EXAMPLE. Find $\sqrt[3]{8r^3 + 36r^2 + 54r + 27}$.

SOLUTION: 1. $8r^3 + 36r^2 + 54r + 27 = (2r)^3 + 3(2r)^2 \cdot 3 + 3(2r) \cdot 3^2 + 3^3$.

2. $\therefore \sqrt[3]{8r^3 + 36r^2 + 54r + 27} = 2r + 3$.

Notice that "a" is $2r$ and "b" is 3.

NOTE. If b is negative, the form is $a^3 - 3a^2b + 3ab^2 - b^3$.

EXERCISE 200

Find by inspection the cube roots of:

1. $8x^3 + 12x^2 + 6x + 1$.
2. $1 - 12a + 48a^2 - 64a^3$.
3. $27m^6 + 1 + 27m^4 + 9m^2$.
4. $8t^6 - 60t^4 - 125 + 150t^2$.
5. $\dfrac{a^3}{8} - \dfrac{a^2b}{4} + \dfrac{ab^2}{6} - \dfrac{b^3}{27}$.

328. The cube root, exact or approximate, of a polynomial may be found by a division process.

The perfect cube polynomial $a^3 + 3a^2b + 3ab^2 + b^3$ may be put in the form $a^3 + b(3a^2 + 3ab + b^2)$. This expression suggests the

Rule. — To find the cube root of a polynomial:

1. **Arrange the polynomial according to the powers of some letter (§ 37).**

SUPPLEMENTARY TOPICS

2. Write the cube root of the first term as the first term of the root. Cube the first term of the root and subtract it from the given expression.

3. For the trial divisor, take three times the square of the first term of the root. Divide the first term of the remainder (step 2) by the trial divisor. Write the quotient as the next term of the root.

4. For the complete divisor, add to the trial divisor three times the product of the new term of the root by the part obtained previously, and also the square of the new term of the root.

5. Multiply the complete divisor by the new term of the root and subtract the result from the remainder (step 2).

6. Continue in this manner until the cube root or the desired number of terms has been obtained: (*a*) for the trial divisor, take three times the square of the part of the root already found; (*b*) divide the first term of the last remainder by the first term of the trial divisor for the new term of the root; (*c*) form the complete divisor as in step 4; (*d*) multiply and subtract as in step 5.

EXAMPLE 1. Find $\sqrt[3]{8 x^6 - 36 x^4 y + 54 x^2 y^2 - 27 y^3}$.

SOLUTION:
1. $a = \sqrt[3]{8 x^6} = 2 x^2$.
2. $a^3 = 8 x^6$; subtract.
3. Trial divisor: $3 a^2 = 12 x^4$.
$b = -36 x^4 y \div 12 x^4 = -3 y$.
Complete divisor:
$\quad 3 a^2 = 12 x^4$
$\quad 3 ab = -18 x^2 y$
$\quad b^2 = 9 y^2$
$3 a^2 + 3 ab + b^2 = 12 x^4 - 18 x^2 y + 9 y^2$
4. Multiply by $-3 y$. Subtract.

Root / work (displayed to the right):

$2 x^2 - 3 y$

$8 x^6 - 36 x^4 y + 54 x^2 y^2 - 27 y^3$
$8 x^6$

$-36 x^4 y + 54 x^2 y^2 - 27 y^3$

$-36 x^4 y + 54 x^2 y^2 - 27 y^3$

402 ALGEBRA

EXAMPLE 2. Find $\sqrt[3]{28\,x^3-54\,x+x^6+3\,x^4-9\,x^2-27-6\,x^5}$.

SOLUTION: 1. $a=\sqrt[3]{x^6}=x^2$.
2. $a^3=x^6$; subtract.
3. Trial divisor: $3\,a^2=3\,x^4$. $\quad -6\,x^5+3\,x^4=-2\,x$
   Complete divisor:
   $$3\,a^2=3\,x^4$$
   $$3\,ab=-6\,x^3$$
   $$b^2=4\,x^2$$
   $$3\,a^2+3\,ab+b^2=3\,x^4-6\,x^3+4\,x^2$$
4. Multiply by $-2\,x$. Subtract.
5. Trial divisor: $3\,a^2=3(x^2-2\,x)^2=3\,x^4-12\,x^3+12\,x^2$
   $b=-9\,x^4+3\,x^4=-3$.
   $$3\,ab=3(x^2-2\,x)(-3)=-9\,x^2+18\,x$$
   $$b^2=(-3)^2\qquad\qquad\qquad +9$$
   Complete divisor: $\quad 3\,x^4-12\,x^3+3\,x^2+18\,x+9$
6. Multiply by -3. Subtract.

$$\begin{array}{l}
x^2-2\,x-3 \\
\hline
x^6-6\,x^5+3\,x^4+28\,x^3-9\,x^3-54\,x \\
x^6 \\
\hline
-6\,x^5+3\,x^4+28\,x^3 \\[4pt]
-6\,x^5+12\,x^4-8\,x^3 \\
\hline
-9\,x^4+36\,x^3-9\,x^2-54\,x \\[4pt]
-9\,x^4+36\,x^3-9\,x^2-54
\end{array}$$

EXERCISE 201

Find the cube roots of:

1. $c^3+3\,c^2d+3\,cd^2+d^3$.
2. $r^3-3\,r^2s+3\,rs^2-s^3$.
3. $a^6+12\,a^4b+48\,a^2b^2+64\,b^3$.
4. $27\,m^3+135\,m^2n+225\,mn^2+125\,n^3$.
5. $x^6-6\,x^5+9\,x^4+4\,x^3-9\,x^2-6\,x-1$.
6. $8\,a^6+36\,a^5+66\,a^4+63\,a^3+33\,a^2+9\,a+1$.
7. $30\,y^3+27\,y^6+12\,y-45\,y^4-8-35\,y^3+27\,y^5$.
8. $9\,a^3-36\,a+a^6+21\,a^4-9\,a^5-8-42\,a^2$.

329. Cube Root of an Arithmetical Number. The cube root of 1000 is 10; of 1,000,000 is 100; etc. Hence the cube root of a number between 1 and 1000 is between 1 and 10; the cube root of a number between 1000 and 1,000,000 is between 10 and 100; etc.

That is, the integral part of the cube root of a number of one, two, or three figures contains one figure; of a number of four, five, or six figures, contains two figures; and so on.

Hence if the given number is divided into periods (§ 179) of three figures each, beginning with the units' figure, for each period in the number there will be one figure in the cube root.

330. The first figure of the cube root of a number is found by inspection; the remaining figures are found in the same manner as the cube root of a polynomial.

EXAMPLE 1. Find the cube root of 157464.

SOLUTION: 1. 157464 has two periods: 157 464. There are in the cube root two figures, a tens' and a units' figure. $50 + 4$

2. 125000 is the largest cube in 157000. | 157 464
$a = \sqrt[3]{125000} = 50$. Place 50 in the root. | 125 000

Subtract,   32 464

3. Trial divisor: $3 a^2 = 3(50)^2 = 7500$
$b = 324 \div 75 = 4^+$. Place 4 in the root.

4. Complete divisor: $3 ab = 3 \cdot 50 \cdot 4 = 600$
                                    $b^2 = 4^2 = 16$

5. Multiply 4. $3 a^2 + 3 ab + b^2 = \overline{8116}$ 32 464

Rule. — To find the cube root of an arithmetical number:

1. Separate the number into periods (§ 179) of three figures each.

2. Find the greatest cube number in the left hand period; write its cube root as the first figure of the root; subtract the cube of the first root figure from the left hand period, and to the result annex the next period.

3. Form the trial divisor by taking three times the square of the part of the root already found annexing two zeros.

4. Divide the remainder (step 2) by the trial divisor and annex the integral part of the quotient to the root already found.

5. Form the complete divisor by adding to the trial divisor three times the product of the new root figure by the part of the root

already found, with one zero annexed, and also the square of the new root figure.

6. Multiply the complete divisor by the new root figure and subtract the product from the remainder.

7. Continue in this manner until the cube root or the desired number of decimal places for the root has been obtained.

NOTE 1. Note 1, p. 249, applies with equal force to the above rule.

NOTE 2. If any root figure is zero, annex two zeros to the trial divisor and annex the next period to the remainder.

EXAMPLE 2. Find the cube root of 8144.865728.

The solution may be arranged as follows:

```
                    20.12
           8 144.865 728
           8
 120000   | 144 865
    600
      1
 120601   | 120 601
12120300  | 24 264 728
  12060
      4
12132364  | 24 264 728
```

Since 1200 is not contained in 144, the second root figure is zero; we then annex two zeros to the trial divisor 1200, and annex to the remainder the next period.

EXERCISE 202

Find the cube roots of the following numbers:

1. 19683.
2. 148877.
3. 59.319.
4. 2515456.
5. 857.375.
6. 46.268279.
7. 187149.248.
8. 444.194947.
9. 788889.024.

DETACHED COEFFICIENTS

331. Detached Coefficients. Solutions of examples in "long" multiplication and division may be abbreviated as in the following examples.

EXAMPLE 1. Multiply $3x^3 + 2x - 4$ by $3x - 2$.

SOLUTION: (a)

$$\begin{array}{l}3x^3 + 0 \cdot x^2 + 2x - 4 \\ 3x - 2 \\ \hline 9x^4 + 0 \cdot x^3 + 6x^2 - 12x \\ - 6x^3 - 0 \cdot x^2 - 4x + 8 \\ \hline 9x^4 - 6x^3 + 6x^2 - 16x + 8\end{array}$$

SOLUTION: (b)

$$\begin{array}{l}3x^3 + 0 \cdot x^2 + 2x - 4 \\ 3x - 2 \\ \hline 9 +0 +6 -12 \\ -6 -0 -4 +8 \\ \hline 9 -6 +6 -16 +8\end{array}$$

$\therefore$ Result $= 9x^4 - 6x^3 + 6x^2 - 16x + 8$.

Note that in solution (b) only the coefficients are written in the partial and total products; that the multiplier and multiplicand are arranged in the same order of powers of x; that 0 is supplied for the missing powers.

Solution (b) is by "detached coefficients."

EXAMPLE 2. Divide $12a^3 - 25a - 3$ by $2a - 3$.

SOLUTION: (a)

$$\begin{array}{r}6a^2 + 9a +1 \\ 2a - 3 \overline{)12a^3 + 0 \cdot a^2 - 25a - 3} \\ \underline{12a^3 - 18a^2} \\ 18a^2 - 25a \\ \underline{18a^2 - 27a} \\ 2a - 3 \\ \underline{2a - 3}\end{array}$$

SOLUTION: (b)

$$\begin{array}{r}6 +9 +1 \\ 2a - 3 \overline{)12a^3 + 0 - 25a - 3} \\ \underline{12 - 18} \\ 18 - 25 \\ \underline{18 - 27} \\ 2 - 3 \\ \underline{2 - 3}\end{array}$$

$\therefore$ Result $= 6a^2 + 9a + 1$.

Solution (b) is by "detached coefficients."

EXERCISE 203

Solve by detached coefficients:

1–5. Examples 21–25 on page 73.

6–10. Examples 21–25 on page 94.

NOTE. The same device may be used to abbreviate addition and subtraction exercises.

ALGEBRA

PROOFS OF THE RULES FOR THE DIVISIBILITY OF $a^n \pm b^n$

332. In § 209, the rules for the divisibility of $a^n \pm b^n$ were determined by inspection. These rules may be proved by means of the factor theorem.

PROOF OF I, 1. If b be substituted for a in $a^n - b^n$, the result is $b^n - b^n$, or 0. Then, by § 212, $a^n - b^n$ has $a - b$ as a factor.

PROOF OF I, 2. If $-b$ be substituted for a in $a^n - b^n$, the result is $(-b)^n - b^n$. When n is even, $(-b)^n - b^n = b^n - b^n = 0$. Then, by § 212, $a^n - b^n$ has $a - (-b)$ or $a + b$ as a factor, *when n is even*.

PROOF OF I, 3. If b be substituted for a in $a^n + b^n$, the result is $b^n + b^n$, or $2\,b^n$. This result is not zero unless b is zero. Then, by § 212, $a^n + b^n$ never has $a - b$ as a factor.

PROOF OF I, 4. If $-b$ be substituted for a in $a^n + b^n$, the result is $(-b)^n + b^n$. When n is odd, $(-b)^n + b^n = -b^n + b^n = 0$. Then, by § 212, $a^n + b^n$ has $a - (-b)$ or $a + b$ as a factor, *when n is odd*.

333. The Highest Common Factor of Polynomials which cannot be Readily Factored. The rule in arithmetic for finding the H. C. F. of two numbers is :

1. Divide the greater number by the less.

2. If there is a remainder, divide the divisor by it. Continue thus to make the remainder the divisor and the preceding divisor the dividend, until there is no remainder.

3. The last divisor is the H. C. F. required.

EXAMPLE. Find the H. C. F. of 169 and 546.

```
169)546(3
    507
    ───
    39)169(4
       156
       ───
       13)39(3
          39
          ──
```

∴ the H.C.F. of 169 and 546 is 13.

A similar process serves for polynomials.

Let A and B be two polynomials, the degree (§ 115) of A being equal to or greater than that of B.

Suppose that B is contained in A p times, with a remainder C; that C is contained in B q times, with a remainder D; and that D is contained in C exactly r times.

```
B) A(p
   pB
   ──
   C) B(q
      qC
      ──
      D) C(r
         rD
         ──
          0
```

Then D is a common factor of A and B.

Proof. Since *dividend = divisor × quotient + remainder:*

$$A = pB + C. \quad (1) \qquad B = qC + D. \quad (2) \qquad C = rD.$$

Substitute the value of C in (2); then,

$$B = qrD + D = D(qr + 1). \tag{3}$$

Substitute the values of B and C in (1); then,

$$A = pD(qr + 1) + rD = D(pqr + p + r). \tag{4}$$

From (3) and (4), D is a common factor of A and B.

Further, every common factor of A and B is a factor of D.

Proof. Let F be any common factor of A and B; and let

$$A = mF \text{ and } B = nF.$$

Then: from (1) $\quad C = A - pB = mF - pnF,$ \hfill (5)

from (2) $\quad D = B - qC.$ \hfill (6)

Substituting in (6) the values of B and C,

$$D = nF - q(mF - pnF) = F(n - qm + qpn). \tag{7}$$

Hence F is a factor of D.

Then, since every common factor of A and B is a factor of D, and since D itself is a common factor of A and B, it follows that D is the *highest* common factor of A and B.

In applying the process to polynomials the following notes should be observed.

NOTE 1. Each division should be continued until the remainder is of a lower degree than that of the divisor.

NOTE 2. If the terms of one expression have a common factor which is not a common factor of the terms of the other expression, the factor may be removed, for it evidently cannot form part of the common factor of the two expressions. In like manner, any remainder may be divided by a factor which is not a factor of the preceding divisor.

NOTE 3. If the given expressions have a common factor which may be seen by inspection, remove it and find the H. C. F. of the resulting expressions. The result multiplied by the common factor that has been removed is the H. C. F. of the given expressions.

NOTE 4. If the first term of the dividend, or of any remainder, is not divisible by the first term of the divisor, it may be made so by multiplying the dividend by any number which is not a factor of the divisor.

EXAMPLE 1. Find the H. C. F. of

$$6x^3 - 25x^2 + 14x \text{ and } 6ax^2 + 11ax - 10a.$$

SOLUTION: 1. Remove x from the first expression and a from the second. (See Note 2.) Then continue as below.

Divide by 12. (Note 2.)

$$\begin{array}{r|l}
6x^2 - 25x + 14 & 6x^2 + 11x - 10 \underline{\,|\,1\,} \\
 & 6x^2 - 25x + 14 \\ \hline
 & 12\,|\,36x - 24 \\
\end{array}$$

$$\begin{array}{r|l}
3x - 2 & 6x^2 - 25x + 14 \underline{\,|\,2x - 7\,} \\
 & 6x^2 - 4x \\ \hline
 & -21x + 14 \\
 & -21x + 14 \\
\end{array}$$

$\therefore 3x - 2$ is the H. C. F.

SUPPLEMENTARY TOPICS

EXAMPLE 2. Find the H.C.F. of $2m^3 - 3m^2 - 8m - 3$,
and $\qquad 3m^4 - 7m^3 - 5m^2 - m - 6.$

SOLUTION: Since $3m^4$ does not contain $2m^3$, multiply the second expression by 2. (See Note 4.)

$$\begin{array}{r}
3m^4 - 7m^3 - 5m^2 - m - 6 \\
2
\end{array}$$

$$2m^3 - 3m^2 - 8m - 3 \,\big)\, 6m^4 - 14m^3 - 10m^2 - 2m - 12 \,\big(\, 3m$$
$$\underline{6m^4 - 9m^3 - 24m^2 - 9m}$$
$$-5m^3 + 14m^2 + 7m - 12$$
$$-2$$
$$\overline{10m^3 - 28m^2 - 14m + 24}\,\big(\,5$$
$$\underline{10m^3 - 15m^2 - 40m - 15}$$
$$-13 \,\big|\, -13m^2 + 26m + 39$$
$$m^2 - 2m - 3$$

$$m^2 - 2m - 3 \,\big)\, 2m^3 - 3m^2 - 8m - 3 \,\big(\, 2m - 1$$
$$\underline{2m^3 - 4m^2 - 6m}$$
$$m^2 - 2m - 3$$
$$m^2 - 2m - 3$$

∴ $m^2 - 2m - 4$ is the H.C.F.

Notice that $-5m^3$ of the first remainder does not contain $2m^3$, and that the remainder is therefore multiplied by -2. Notice also that the divisor -13 is removed from the second remainder, thus making the first term of the new divisor positive.

EXERCISE 204

Find the H.C.F. of:

1. $x^2 + 5x - 24$ and $x^3 + 4x^2 - 26x + 15$.
2. $3x^2 - 4x - 4$ and $3x^4 - 7x^3 + 6x^2 - 9x + 2$.
3. $2m^4 + 5m^3 - 2m^2 + 3m$ and $6m^3n - 7m^2n + 5mn - 2n$.
4. $x^2y - 6xy - 27y$ and $x^3y - 2x^2y - 8xy + 21y$.
5. $4x^2y - 15xy^2 + 9y^3$ and $8x^4 - 18x^3y + 25x^2y^2 - 12xy^3$.
6. $3n^3 + 8n^2 - 9n + 2$ and $6n^4 + 23n^3 + 2n^2 - 13n + 2$.

ALGEBRA

7. $6 a^6 + 5 a^5 - 6 a^4 - 3 a^3 + 2 a^2$ and $9 a^4 + 18 a^3 + 5 a^2 - 8 a - 4$.
8. $3 b^4 - 13 b^3 + 3 b^2 + 4 b$ and $9 b^3 + 12 b^2 - 8 b - 5$.
9. $12 a^3 - 5 a^2 x - 11 a x^2 + 6 x^3$ and $15 a^3 + 11 a^2 x - 8 a x^2 - 4 x^3$.
10. $2 x^3 - 3 x^2 + 2 x - 8$ and $3 x^3 - 7 x^2 + 4 x - 4$.

334. The L. C. M. of Two Polynomials which cannot be Readily Factored. Let A and B be two polynomials; let F be their H. C. F. and M their L. C. M. Let $A = aF$ and $B = bF$.

Since F is the highest common factor of aF and bF, a and b cannot have any common factors. Hence, the L. C. M. of aF and bF is abF

That is, $M = abF = a(bF) = aB;$
or $M = abF = b(aF) = bA.$

Rule. — To find the L. C. M. of two polynomials:

Divide one of the polynomials by their H. C. F. and multiply the quotient by the other polynomial.

EXERCISE 205

Find the L. C. M. of:

1. $3 a^2 - 13 a + 4$ and $3 a^2 + 14 a - 5$.
2. $6 a^2 + 25 ab + 24 b^2$ and $12 a^2 + 16 ab - 3 b^2$.
3. $12 m^2 - 21 m - 45$ and $4 m^3 - 11 m^2 - 6 m + 9$.
4. $2 a^3 - 5 a^2 - 18 a - 9$ and $3 a^3 - 14 a^2 - a + 6$.
5. $6 x^3 - 7 x^2 + 5 x - 2$ and $4 x^4 - 5 x^2 + 4 x - 3$.

335. Proof of the Binomial Theorem for Positive Integral Powers. In § 299 attention is directed to the fact that the binomial theorem was not proved in § 297. Assume now, as there, that

$$(a+x)^n = a^n + na^{n-1}x + \frac{n(n-1)}{1\cdot 2}a^{n-2}x^2 + \frac{n(n-1)(n-2)}{1\cdot 2\cdot 3}a^{n-3}x^3 + \cdots \quad (1)$$

Multiply both members of (1) by $a + x$. Then

$$(a+x)^{n+1} = a^{n+1} + na^n x + \frac{n(n-1)}{1\cdot 2}a^{n-1}x^2 + \frac{n(n-1)(n-2)}{1\cdot 2\cdot 3}a^{n-2}x^3 + \cdots$$
$$+\ a^n x\ +\ \frac{n}{1}a^{n-1}x^2 +\ \frac{n(n-1)}{1\cdot 2}a^{n-2}x^3 + \cdots.$$

$$\therefore (a+x)^{n+1} = a^{n+1} + (n+1)a^n x + n\left[\frac{n-1}{2}+1\right]a^{n-1}x^2 + \frac{n(n-1)}{1\cdot 2}\left[\frac{n-2}{3}+1\right]a^{n-2}x^3 + \cdots$$

$$= a^{n+1} + (n+1)a^n x + n\cdot\frac{n+1}{2}a^{n-1}x^2 + \frac{n(n-1)}{1\cdot 2}\cdot\frac{n+1}{3}a^{n-2}x^3 + \cdots$$

$$= a^{n+1} + (n+1)a^n x + \frac{(n+1)\cdot n}{1\cdot 2}a^{n-1}x^2 + \frac{(n+1)\cdot n\cdot(n-1)}{1\cdot 2\cdot 3}a^{n-2}x^3 + \cdots$$

It will be observed that the expansion on the right is in accordance with the rules of § 297. This proves that if the rules of § 297 are assumed for any particular positive integer, n, they hold true, also, for the next greater integer, $n + 1$.

But the rules are known to be satisfactory in the case of $(a+x)^4$; hence they hold for $(a+x)^5$. Since they hold for $(a+x)^5$, then they hold also for $(a+x)^6$; and so on.

Therefore the binomial theorem is true for any positive integer.

NOTE. The above method of proof is known as mathematical induction.

INDETERMINATE FORMS

336. The fraction $\dfrac{x+5}{x-3}$ becomes $\dfrac{8}{0}$ for $x = 3$; $\dfrac{x^2-9}{x-3}$ becomes $\dfrac{0}{0}$. Neither has any meaning, for division by zero is not allowed (§ 64). Results like these, however, must be interpreted at times. The following paragraphs show how to give the interpretation.

337. A *constant* is a number which always has the same value in a particular mathematical discussion.

412　ALGEBRA

A *variable* is a number which assumes different values in a particular mathematical discussion.

Thus n may assume the values .1, .01, .001, ..., etc.

A *limit of a variable* is a constant the difference between which and the variable may be made to become and remain less than any assigned positive number, however small.

Thus, the variable n above is evidently approaching the value 0; or, the *limit of n is zero*.

The symbol $\doteq$ is read "approaches the limit." Thus, $n \doteq 0$ means "n approaches the limit zero."

338. If a number becomes and remains greater than any positive number which may be assigned, it is said to *become infinitely large* or to *approach infinity as limit*.

The symbol ∞ is called "infinity."

Thus, if n represents any positive integer (assuming therefore the values 1, 2, 3, ..., etc.), it approaches infinity as limit; *i.e.* limit of $n = \infty$, or $n \doteq \infty$.

NOTE. ∞ is not a symbol for some definite value. It is a symbol for the limit of a number which "becomes and remains larger than any assigned positive number."

Evidently as $n \doteq \infty$, also $n^2 \doteq \infty$. $\underset{n \doteq \infty}{\text{Limit}}\, n^2 = \infty$ is read "the limit of n^2 as n approaches ∞ is infinity."

339. Interpretation of $\dfrac{a}{0}$. To determine the meaning of $\dfrac{1}{0}$, replace $\dfrac{1}{0}$ by $\dfrac{1}{x}$ and consider limit $\dfrac{1}{x}$ as $x \doteq 0$.

If x becomes .1, .01, .001, ..., etc, $\dfrac{1}{x}$ becomes 10, 100, 1000, ..., etc.

Evidently, then, $\dfrac{1}{x}$ increases indefinitely. That is, $\underset{x \doteq 0}{\text{limit}}\, \dfrac{1}{x} = \infty$. Then, to the *otherwise meaningless* form $\dfrac{1}{0}$, give the value ∞.

SUPPLEMENTARY TOPICS 413

In general, $\dfrac{a}{0}$, where a is constant, is given the value ∞ with the meaning:

If the numerator of a fraction remains constant, while the denominator $\doteq 0$, the value of the fraction $\doteq \infty$.

Thus, $\dfrac{x+5}{x-3}$ for $x=3$ is $\dfrac{8}{0}$ or ∞; *i.e.* $\displaystyle\lim_{x \doteq 3}\left(\dfrac{x+5}{x-3}\right) = \infty$.

340. Interpretation of $\dfrac{a}{\infty}$. To determine the meaning of $\dfrac{1}{\infty}$, replace $\dfrac{1}{\infty}$ by $\dfrac{1}{x}$ and consider limit $\dfrac{1}{x}$ as $x \doteq \infty$.

If x becomes 10, 100, 1000, ..., etc., $\dfrac{1}{x}$ becomes .1, .01, .001, ..., etc. Evidently $\displaystyle\lim_{x \doteq \infty}\dfrac{1}{x} = 0$. Then, to the otherwise meaningless form $\dfrac{1}{\infty}$ assign the value 0.

In general, $\dfrac{a}{\infty}$, where a is constant, is given the value 0, with the meaning:

If the numerator of a fraction remains constant, while the denominator $\doteq \infty$, the value of the fraction $\doteq 0$.

Thus, the value of $\dfrac{2}{n^2}$ for $n = \infty$ is $\dfrac{2}{\infty}$, or 0.

341. Consider $\dfrac{x^2-9}{x-3}$. For $x=3$, the fraction becomes $\dfrac{0}{0}$. Since $x - 3 = 0$ for $x = 3$, the fraction may not be reduced to lower terms by dividing numerator and denominator by $x - 3$. However, for x not equal to 3, the numerator and denominator may be divided by $x - 3$, giving the simpler form $x + 3$. Consider now $\displaystyle\lim_{x \doteq 3}(x+3)$. $\displaystyle\lim_{x \doteq 3}(x+3) = 3 + 3 = 6$. Then for $x = 3$, assign to $\dfrac{x^2-9}{x-3}$ the value 6.

414　　　　ALGEBRA

In general, if any expression involving one variable assumes an indeterminate form when the variable is assigned some particular value, reduce the expression to its simplest form, find the limit of the result as the variable approaches that particular value, and assign the limit as the value of the expression for the particular value of the variable.

EXAMPLE 2.　$\dfrac{x^2-25}{x-5}$, for $x = 5$, has the value $\dfrac{0}{0}$.

For x not equal to 5, $\dfrac{x^2-25}{x-5} = x + 5$.　$\underset{x \doteq 5}{\text{limit}}\,(x+5) = 10$.

Hence for $x = 5$, give to $\dfrac{x^2-25}{x-5}$ the value 10.

EXAMPLE 3.　Find the value of $\dfrac{2x^2+2x-5}{x^2+1}$ as $x \doteq \infty$.

For any *finite* value of x,　$\dfrac{2x^2+2x-5}{x^2+1} = \dfrac{2+\dfrac{2}{x}-\dfrac{5}{x^2}}{1+\dfrac{1}{x^2}}$.

$$\underset{x \doteq \infty}{\text{limit}} \left\{ \dfrac{2+\dfrac{2}{x}-\dfrac{5}{x^2}}{1+\dfrac{1}{x^2}} \right\} = \dfrac{2+0-0}{1+0} = \dfrac{2}{1} = 2.$$

Hence the value of $\dfrac{2x^2+2x-5}{x^2+1}$ as $x \doteq \infty$ is 2.

Direct substitution here gives the value $\dfrac{\infty}{\infty}$. This is another indeterminate form.

342. The form $\dfrac{0}{0}$. The form $\dfrac{0}{0}$ arises in the first two examples of § 341. In one case this form is given the value 6, and in the other it is given the value 10. In general, the value of $\dfrac{0}{0}$ is determined by the limiting process.

SUPPLEMENTARY TOPICS

EXERCISE 206

Find the values of the following as $x \doteq 0$:

1. $\dfrac{3}{x}$.
2. $\dfrac{5}{x^2}$.
3. $\dfrac{1}{\left(\dfrac{1}{x}\right)}$.
4. $\dfrac{2x}{x(x+5)}$.
5. $\dfrac{x^2}{x(x+1)}$.

Find the values of the following as $x \doteq \infty$:

6. x^2.
7. 2^x.
8. $\dfrac{3}{x}$.
9. $2 + \dfrac{5}{x}$.
10. $\dfrac{1}{2^x}$.

Find the values of the following:

11. $\displaystyle\lim_{x \doteq 2}\left(\dfrac{x^2-4}{x^2-5x+6}\right)$.

12. $\displaystyle\lim_{y \doteq \infty}\left(\dfrac{y^2+5}{y}\right)$.

13. $\displaystyle\lim_{y \doteq \infty}\left(\dfrac{y+5}{y^2}\right)$.

14. $\displaystyle\lim_{x \doteq 3}\left(\dfrac{x^2-x-6}{x^2-3x}\right)$.

15. $\displaystyle\lim_{n \doteq 0}\left(\dfrac{1}{n} + \dfrac{5}{n(n-5)}\right)$.

16. $\displaystyle\lim_{x \doteq \infty}\left(\dfrac{x^2+2x-7}{x^2-1}\right)$.

17. The equations $y = 2x+3$ and $y = 2x+5$ have no common solution according to § 158. Consider $y = 2x+3$ and $y = ax+5$. Solve them as simultaneous equations, and find the values of x and y as $a \doteq 2$.

18. Solve $2x+3y=6$ and $4x+by=7$ as simultaneous equations, and find the values of x and y as $b \doteq 6$.

§ 343. Graphical Solution of Equations.

In § 213, the statement was made that an equation of the nth degree, having one unknown, has n roots, but that these roots are not readily found for equations of degree above the second. Such equations may be solved graphically as in § 193.

EXAMPLE. Solve the equation $x^3 - 4x^2 - 2x + 8 = 0$.

SOLUTION: 1. Let $y = x^3 - 4x^2 - 2x + 8$.

When $x =$	0	1	2	3	4	5	-1	-2	-3
then $y =$	8	3	-4	-7	0	23	5	-12	-49

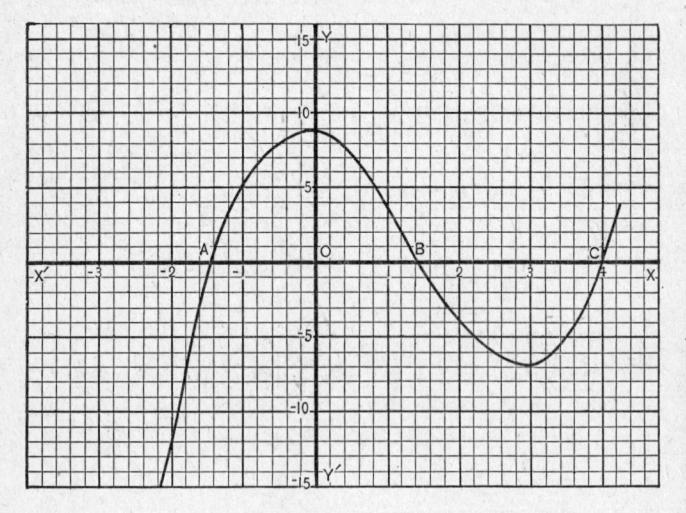

2. The curve crosses the horizontal axis at points A, B, and C. Hence its roots are, approximately, -1.42, $+1.42$, and $+4$.

CHECK: This equation may be solved as in § 213. Using the factor theorem: $x^3 - 4x^2 - 2x + 8 = (x - 4)(x^2 - 2) = 0$.

∴ $x = 4$; also $x^2 = 2$, or $x = \pm \sqrt{2} = \pm 1.414$.

Clearly the results ± 1.42 obtained graphically are close to the roots ± 1.414.

EXERCISE 207

Solve the following equations graphically:

1. $x^3 - 3x^2 - x + 3 = 0$.
2. $x^3 - 4x^2 - 7x + 10 = 0$.
3. $x^3 + x^2 - 6x = 0$.
4. $x^4 - 10x^2 + 9 = 0$.
5. $x^3 + x^2 - 10x - 10 = 0$.
6. $x^3 - x^2 - 8x + 8 = 0$.

DETERMINANTS

§ 344. The symbol $\begin{vmatrix} 3 & 4 \\ 2 & 7 \end{vmatrix}$ is called a *determinant*. Its value is defined to be $3 \cdot 7 - 2 \cdot 4$ which equals $21 - 8$, or 13.

In general $\begin{vmatrix} a & c \\ b & d \end{vmatrix}$ is called a **Determinant of the Second Order** and is defined thus: $\begin{vmatrix} a & c \\ b & d \end{vmatrix} = ad - bc$.

The numbers a, b, c, and d are called the *terms* of the determinant.

Clearly, any difference such as $rs - mn$ may be arranged as a determinant: thus $rs - mn = \begin{vmatrix} r & n \\ m & s \end{vmatrix}$.

EXAMPLE 1. $\begin{vmatrix} 2 & -5 \\ 4 & +3 \end{vmatrix} = 2 \cdot 3 - 4(-5) = 6 + 20 = 26.$

EXAMPLE 2. $26 - 15 = 2 \cdot 13 - 3 \cdot 5 = \begin{vmatrix} 2 & 5 \\ 3 & 13 \end{vmatrix}.$

EXERCISE 208

Find the values of:

1. $\begin{vmatrix} 6 & 5 \\ 4 & 2 \end{vmatrix}.$
2. $\begin{vmatrix} 5 & 3 \\ 2 & -7 \end{vmatrix}.$
3. $\begin{vmatrix} 4 & -2 \\ 6 & 9 \end{vmatrix}.$
4. $\begin{vmatrix} 3 & -4 \\ -2 & 7 \end{vmatrix}.$
5. $\begin{vmatrix} -5 & 3 \\ 2 & 6 \end{vmatrix}.$
6. $\begin{vmatrix} 3a & 4 \\ 2c & 1 \end{vmatrix}.$
7. $\begin{vmatrix} 2m & -p \\ 2n & r \end{vmatrix}.$
8. $\begin{vmatrix} 3a & 4d \\ 2c & 5e \end{vmatrix}.$

Express as determinants:

9. $mn - xy.$
10. $2ab - cd.$
11. $33 - 14.$
12. $6c - 5d.$
13. $cd + pq.$
14. $3mn + 2rs.$

§ 345. Determinants make it possible to solve simultaneous linear equations by inspection. Solving the following pair of equations,

$$ax + by = c \brace dx + ey = f,$$

$$x = \frac{ce - bf}{ae - bd} \text{ and } y = \frac{af - cd}{ae - bd}.$$

$$\therefore x = \frac{\begin{vmatrix} c & b \\ f & e \end{vmatrix}}{\begin{vmatrix} a & b \\ d & e \end{vmatrix}} \text{ and } y = \frac{\begin{vmatrix} a & c \\ d & f \end{vmatrix}}{\begin{vmatrix} a & b \\ d & e \end{vmatrix}}.$$

Notice that the two solutions may be expressed as the quotients of determinants whose terms are the coefficients of the equations.

Rule: To solve two simultaneous linear equations having two unknowns by determinants:

1. Arrange the equations in the form: $\begin{cases} ax + by = c. \\ dx + ey = f. \end{cases}$

2. The value of x is a fraction: its denominator is the determinant formed by the coefficients of x and y, $\begin{vmatrix} a & b \\ d & e \end{vmatrix}$; its numerator is the determinant obtained by replacing the coefficients of x in the denominator determinant by the corresponding absolute terms, $\begin{vmatrix} c & b \\ f & e \end{vmatrix}$.

3. The value of y is a fraction with the same denominator as x; its numerator is the determinant obtained by replacing the coefficients of y in the denominator determinant by the absolute terms, $\begin{vmatrix} a & c \\ d & f \end{vmatrix}$.

Example. Solve the pair of equations: $\begin{cases} 2x - 5y = -16. \\ 3x + 7y = 5. \end{cases}$

Solution: $$x = \frac{\begin{vmatrix} -16 & -5 \\ 5 & 7 \end{vmatrix}}{\begin{vmatrix} 2 & -5 \\ 3 & 7 \end{vmatrix}} = \frac{-16 \cdot 7 - 5(-5)}{2 \cdot 7 - 3(-5)} = \frac{-112 + 25}{14 + 15} = \frac{-87}{29} = -3.$$

$$y = \frac{\begin{vmatrix} 2 & -16 \\ 3 & 5 \end{vmatrix}}{\begin{vmatrix} 2 & -5 \\ 3 & 7 \end{vmatrix}} = \frac{10 - 3(-16)}{2 \cdot 7 - 3(-5)} = \frac{10 + 48}{14 + 15} = \frac{58}{29} = 2.$$

SUPPLEMENTARY TOPICS

Check:

In (1): Does $2(-3) - 5(2) = -16$? Does $-6 - 10 = -16$? Yes.
In (2): Does $3(-3) + 7(2) = 5$? Does $-9 + 14 = 5$? Yes.

EXERCISE 209

1–10. Solve by means of determinants examples 1–10 of Exercise 101. Check the solutions.

§ 346. Determinants are especially useful in solving simultaneous linear equations with more than two unknowns.

$$\begin{vmatrix} a_1 & a_2 & a_3 \\ b_1 & b_2 & b_3 \\ c_1 & c_2 & c_3 \end{vmatrix}$$

is called **a determinant of the third order.** Its value is defined to be:

$$a_1 b_2 c_3 + a_2 b_3 c_1 + a_3 c_2 b_1 - c_1 b_2 a_3 - b_1 a_2 c_3 - a_1 b_3 c_2.$$

The adjoining diagram aids in recalling this value. Take the product $a_1 b_2 c_3$ along the diagonal and add to it the two products formed by starting with a_2 and a_3 respectively and following the arrows which point in the direction of this diagonal; then subtract the product $c_1 b_2 a_3$ along the other diagonal, and also subtract the two other products formed by starting with b_1 and a_1 respectively and following the arrows which point in the direction of this second diagonal.

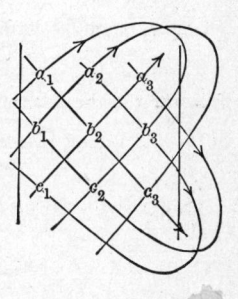

Example.
$$\begin{vmatrix} 1 & 5 & 2 \\ 4 & 7 & 3 \\ 2 & -3 & 6 \end{vmatrix} = 1 \cdot 7 \cdot 6 + 5 \cdot 3 \cdot 2 + 2(-3) \cdot 4$$
$$- 2 \cdot 7 \cdot 2 - 4 \cdot 5 \cdot 6 - 1 \cdot 3 \cdot (-3)$$
$$= 42 + 30 - 24 - 28 - 120 + 9$$
$$= -91.$$

ALGEBRA

EXERCISE 210

Find the values of:

1. $\begin{vmatrix} 1 & 2 & 3 \\ 2 & 1 & 2 \\ 3 & 3 & 1 \end{vmatrix}$. **2.** $\begin{vmatrix} 2 & 4 & 6 \\ 3 & -2 & 3 \\ 1 & 5 & 4 \end{vmatrix}$. **3.** $\begin{vmatrix} 2 & 2 & 3 \\ -2 & -4 & -11 \\ 5 & -6 & 2 \end{vmatrix}$.

4. Solve the equations: $\begin{cases} 3x + y - z = 14. \\ x + 3y - z = 16. \\ x + y - 3z = -10. \end{cases}$

SOLUTION: A rule similar to that of § 345 applies for linear equations with more than two unknowns. Hence:

$$x = \frac{\begin{vmatrix} 14 & 1 & -1 \\ 16 & 3 & -1 \\ -10 & 1 & -3 \end{vmatrix}}{\begin{vmatrix} 3 & 1 & -1 \\ 1 & 3 & -1 \\ 1 & 1 & -3 \end{vmatrix}} = \frac{-126 + 10 - 16 - 30 + 48 + 14}{-27 - 1 - 1 + 3 + 3 + 3} = \frac{-100}{-20} = 5.$$

$$y = \frac{\begin{vmatrix} 3 & 14 & -1 \\ 1 & 16 & -1 \\ 1 & -10 & -3 \end{vmatrix}}{\begin{vmatrix} 3 & 1 & -1 \\ 1 & 3 & -1 \\ 1 & 1 & -3 \end{vmatrix}} = \frac{-120}{-20} = 6. \qquad z = \frac{\begin{vmatrix} 3 & 1 & 14 \\ 1 & 3 & 16 \\ 1 & 1 & -10 \end{vmatrix}}{\begin{vmatrix} 3 & 1 & -1 \\ 1 & 3 & -1 \\ 1 & 1 & -3 \end{vmatrix}} = \frac{-140}{-20} = 7.$$

CHECK: The solution checks when substituted in the three equations.

NOTE. The equations must be arranged first in the form $ax + by + cz = d$. Thus the equation $2x - 3z = 7$ would be written $2x + 0y - 3z = 7$.

Solve the following equations by determinants:

5. $\begin{cases} x + y - z = 24. \\ 4x + 3y - z = 61. \\ 6x - 5y - z = 11. \end{cases}$

6. $\begin{cases} 5x - y + 4z = -5. \\ 3x + 5y + 6z = -20. \\ x + 3y - 8z = -27. \end{cases}$

7. $\begin{cases} 4a - 5b - 6c = 22. \\ a - b + c = -6. \\ 9a + c = 22. \end{cases}$

8. $\begin{cases} 4x - 3y = 1. \\ 4y - 3z = -15. \\ 4z - 3x = 10. \end{cases}$

9. $\begin{cases} 9x + 5z = -7. \\ 3x + 5y = 1. \\ 9y + 3z = 2. \end{cases}$

10. $\begin{cases} 2x + 5y + 3z = -7. \\ 2y - 4z = 2 - 3x. \\ 5x + 9y = 5 + 7z. \end{cases}$

INDEX

A, the symbol, 48.
Abscissa, 212.
Absolute value, 26.
Algebraic expression, 17; value of an, 17.
Angle, 15; right, 15; straight, 15.
Angles, complementary, 15; sum of, in a triangle, 17; supplementary, 16.
Arithmetic, means, 369; progression, 367.
Ascending powers, 39.
Axis, horizontal, 211; vertical, 211.

Base, 17.
Binomial, 38; square of a, 117; theorem, 382.
Braces, 55.
Brackets, 55.

Cancellation, in an equation, 98; in a fraction, 161.
Changing signs, in an equation, 99; in a fraction, 163.
Characteristic, 352.
Clearing of fractions, 185.
Coefficient, 34; detached, 405; numerical, 34.
Common, difference, 367; logarithm, 351.
Complement of an angle, 15.
Complex number, 277.
Conditional equation, 96.
Coördinates, 212.

Cube, of a monomial, 111; perfect, 112; root, 112, 400.

D, the symbol, 48.
Degree, of a monomial, 154; of an angle, 15; of an equation, 221; of a polynomial, 154.
Descending powers, 39.
Discriminant, 318.
Division, synthetic, 290.

Elimination, by addition or subtraction, 223; by substitution, 225.
Ellipse, 299.
Equation, 7, 96; cancelling terms in an, 98; changing signs in an, 99; complete quadratic, 258; conditional, 96; degree of, 221; fractional, 185; graphical solution of an, 259; homogeneous, 306; identical, 96; indeterminate, 222; integral, 185; linear, 221; literal, 200; members of an, 7; of first degree, 97; properties of an, 97; pure quadratic, 254; rational, 306; simple, 97; solving an, 7; transposition, in an, 98.
Equations, dependent, 222; formation of, 317; inconsistent, 222; independent, 222; simultaneous, 222, 304; system of, 304.
Equivalent systems, 307.
Evolution, 322.

INDEX

Exponent, 18; fractional, 324; negative, 325; zero, 324.
Exponents, law of division of, 87; law of multiplication of, 65; laws of, 326.
Expression, algebraic, 17.
Extremes, 387.

Factor, 3; common, 11; highest common, 155, 406; to, 110; theorem, 292.
Factors, prime, 110.
Formula, 19.
Formulæ, deriving, 202.
Fourth proportional, 388.
Fractions, 160; clearing of, 185; equivalent, 167.
Fulcrum, 193.
Fundamental operations, 18.

Geometric, mean, 377; progression, 375.
Graph, of an equation with two variables, 216, 297.
Graphical representation, 206.
Graphical solution of equations with one variable, 259, 415.
Graphs, 206.
Grouping, symbols of, 55; factoring by, 285.

Homogeneous equations, 306.
Horizontal axis, 211.
Hyperbola, 300.

Identity, 96.
Imaginary number, 275.
Imaginary numbers, addition and subtraction of, 277; multiplication of, 343; division of, 344.
Imaginary roots in a quadratic equation, 275; meaning of, on graphs 278.
Imaginary unit, 276.
Inconsistent equations, 220, 222.
Independent equations, 218, 222.
Indeterminate, equations, 216, 222; forms, 411.
Index, 113, 322.
Infinite geometric progression, 379.
Infinity, 412.
Integral equations, 185.
Involution, 321.
Irrational, equation, 346; number, 318.

Left member of an equation, 7.
Lever, 193.
Like terms, 35.
Limit, 412.
Linear equation, 221.
Literal, equation, 200; numbers, 2.
Logarithm, 350; common, 351.
Lowest common multiple, 157.

M, the symbol, 48.
Mantissa, 352.
Members of an equation, 7.
Minuend, 41.
Monomial, 34; cube of a, 111; cube root of a, 112; square of a, 110; square root of a, 112.
Monomials, addition of, 35; multiplication of, 67.

Negative numbers, 26; addition of, 27; division of, 86; multiplication of, 30; powers of, 32; subtraction of, 43.
Negative, term, 34; exponent, 325.
Number, complex, 277; imaginary, 275, 318; irrational, 318; literal,

INDEX

2; **negative, 26**; positive, 26; prime, 110; rational, 318; real, 275, 318; unknown, 7.

Numerical, coefficient, 34; value, 17.

Opposite quantities, 23.

Order, of determinant, **417**; of radical, 330.

Ordinate, 212.

Origin, 211.

Parabola, 297.

Parallelogram, 20.

Parentheses, 4; inclosing terms in, 59; removing 55.

Perfect, cube, 112; square, 112; square trinomial, 120.

Periods, 247.

Polynomial, 38; arranging a, 39.

Polynomials, addition of, 38; division of, 91; multiplication of, 72; square root of, 245; subtraction of, 45; factoring of, 285.

Positive number, 26; quantity, 24; term, 34.

Power, 17.

Powers, ascending, 39; descending, 39.

Prime number, 110.

Progression, arithmetic, **367**; geometric, 375.

Proportion, 387; by alternation, 390; by composition, 390; by division, 390; by composition and division, 391; by inversion, 390.

Proportional, fourth, **388**; mean, 388; third, 388.

Pure quadratic, 254.

Pyramid, 22.

Quadratic equation, 148, 254; solution of, by completing the square, 263; by factoring, 148, 258; by formula, 267; complete, 258; graph of, 259; having two unknowns, 304; imaginary roots in a, 275; pure, 254.

Quadratic surd, 252.

Quantities, opposite, 23; signed, 24.

Quantity, negative, 24; positive, 24.

Radical, 330; index of, 113; order of, 330.

Radicals, addition of, 252, 334; similar, 334.

Radicand, 322.

Ratio, 386; of a geometric progression, 375.

Rational, equation, 306; number, 318.

Rationalizing the denominator, 341.

Remainder theorem, 289.

Right, angle, 15; member, 7; triangle, 256.

Root, cube, 112, 400; square, of a fraction, 251; of an equation, 97; principal, 252, 322; square, 112.

Roots, imaginary, 275; of a quadratic, 148, 254.

S, the symbol, 48.

Signed, numbers, 26; quantities, 24

Signs, change of, in an equation, 99; law of, in addition, 27; in a fraction, 163; in division, 86; in multiplication, 31.

Similar terms, 35.

Simultaneous equations, 218, 222, 304.

Square root, approximate, 250; by division, 245; by inspection, 244; of a monomial, 112; of a number,

247; of a polynomial, 245; of a trinomial, 120.
Straight angle, 15.
Supplement, 16.
Supplementary angles, 16.
Surd, conjugate, 340; quadratic, 252; addition of, 252, 334.
Symbols of grouping, 55.
Synthetic division, 290.
System of equations, 304.

Table, of square roots, 250; of logarithms, 354.
Term, 34; degree of, 154; negative, 34; positive, 34.

Terms, dissimilar, 35; like, 35; similar, 35; unlike, 35.
Theorem, binomial, 382; factor, 292; remainder, 289.
Transposition, 98.
Triangle, altitude of, 21; area of, 21; base of, 21.

Unit, imaginary, 276.
Unknown number, 7.
Unlike terms, 35.

Variables, 216.
Vertical axis, 211.
Vinculum, 55.

ANSWERS TO WELLS AND HART'S NEW HIGH SCHOOL ALGEBRA

EXERCISE 5. Page 11.

18. 73.09 lb.   **19.** $214\frac{2}{7}$ lb.   **20.** 150 lb.

EXERCISE 7. Page 14.

16. C, $16; B, $32; A, $48.   **17.** $839.
18. 8; 40; 72.   **19.** 12; 168; 180.
20. 2d, $75; 1st, $150; 3d, $300.   **21.** 60 in.; 80 in.; 100 in.
22. 22 in.; 44 in.   **23.** 40 rd.; 120 rd.
24. AB, 20 in.; CD, 40 in.; AD, 60 in.; BC, 100 in.
25. Philadelphia, 90 mi.; Chicago, 900 mi.

EXERCISE 10. Pages 20-22.

1. *b.* Equal to it. *c.* A rectangle; b; a; ab. *d.* ab square units. *e.* The area of a parallelogram equals the product of the base and altitude. *g.* 240. *h.* 375. *i.* 12.5. *j.* 24. *k.* 50. *l.* 30.

2. *b.* A parallelogram; b; a; ab. *c.* $\frac{1}{2}$ of it. *d.* $\frac{1}{2}ab$. *e.* The area of a triangle equals one half of the product of the base and altitude. *g.* 85. *h.* 300. *i.* 13. *j.* 40.

3. *a.* $V = abc$. *b.* 120. *c.* 378. *d.* 8.

4. *a.* $V = \frac{1}{3}ab$. *b.* 90. *c.* 20. *d.* 90.

5. *a.* The circumference of a circle equals twice the product of π and the radius of the circle. *b.* 62.832 inches. *c.* 100 inches.

6. *a.* The area of a circle equals π times the square of the radius. *b.* 314.16 sq. in. *c.* 78.54 sq. ft.

7. 294.72.   **8.** 2915.1.   **9.** 113.1 cu. ft.
10. 314.16 sq. ft.

EXERCISE 16. Page 33.

14. -6.   **15.** 4.   **16.** -40.
17. -132.   **18.** -8.   **19.** 2.
20. -20.   **21.** -24.   **22.** -62.
23. -16.   **24.** -15.   **25.** -11.

EXERCISE 19. Pages 40–41.

1. $A - 2B$.
2. $-2t^2 + 6n^3$.
3. $-am + 4bn$.
4. $-b^2$.
5. $-4r^3 + r^2s + 9rs^2 - 10$.
6. $-2x^3 + x^2y - 5xy^2 + y^3$.
7. $-7m^3 - 2m^2n - 5mn^2 + 2n^3$.
8. $8a + 3b + 3c$.
9. $12k - 7 - m$.
10. $-2a + 5b - 2c + 9d$.
11. $35r + 4s - 4t$.
12. $10xy$.
13. $10n^2$.
14. $2a^3 + 6ab^2$.
15. $6x^2 + xy - 7y^2$.
16. $12a^3 + 24a^2 - 9a - 8$.
17. $2x^5 + 2x^3y^2 + x^2y^3 + 2xy^4$.
18. $19x^3 + 8x^2 - 23x - 7$.
19. $3A^3 + 11A^2B + 8AB^2 + 6B^3$.
20. $\frac{3}{4}a + \frac{1}{6}b - \frac{1}{10}c$.
21. $2\frac{1}{3}m - \frac{1}{5}n$.
22. $2\frac{1}{4}a - \frac{2}{3}b + \frac{1}{14}c$.
23. $.7A - 10.4B + 1.5C$.
24. $.75x^2 - .75xy + .8y^2$.
25. $3.5m + .7n + 2.4$.
26. $5a^2 - 8ab - 2b^2$.
27. $3x^3 - x - 4$.
28. $x^3 - 8x^2y - 2xy^2 - 3y^3$.
29. $3a^3 - 5a^2 + 4a - 2$.
30. $a^3 + 21x^3$.

EXERCISE 22. Pages 45–47.

1. $4a^2 - 3a - 20$.
2. $8a - 15x + 5y$.
3. $-3m + 4n + 11p$.
4. $a + 3b$.
5. $3ab - 6bc + ac$.
6. $4x^2 + 7x - 6$.
7. $7r^3 + 2r^2s - 2rs$.
8. $-x^3 + 3x^2 - 6x + 5$.
9. $6a^2b - ab^2 + 3b^3$.
10. $x^4y - xy^4$.
11. $-4xy$.
12. $2x^2y + 2y^3$.
13. $-6b + 8c$.
14. $-10m^2 + 3mn - 5n^2$.
15. $2bc$.
16. $x^3 - x^2 + 6x - 7$.
17. $-3x + 3y - 3z$.
18. $4B - 14C$.
19. $7x^3 + 11x^2 + 2x - 5$.
20. $2y^2$.
21. $6a - 12b + 21c + 2d$.
22. $-9a^3 + 8a^2 - 4a + 3$.
23. $4a - 2a^2 - 2a^3$.
24. $10x^3 - 6x^2 + 9x - 12$.
25. $9a^3 + 3a^2b - 12ab^2 - 8b^3$.
26. $7a - b - 8c - 4d$.
27. $5 - 4x + 7x^2 - 20x^3 - 5x^4$.
28. $4a^5 + 10a^4 - 11a^3 - 16a^2 - 8a + 1$.
29. $x^5 - 5x^4y + 6x^3y^2 + 11x^2y^3 - 15xy^4 + y^5$.

ANSWERS

30. $25n^3 - 21n^2 + 3n - 4$.
31. $2x^3 - 5x^2y + xy^2$.
32. $-26x^3 + 2x^2 + x - 5$.
33. $\frac{1}{4}m + n - \frac{1}{14}p$.
34. $1\frac{1}{6}a - \frac{5}{12}b - \frac{7}{10}c$.
35. $1\frac{1}{15}v + \frac{1}{2}w + \frac{3}{14}x$.
36. $56b^2 - 6ab - 5a^2$.
37. $5a - 7b + 4c$.
38. $3a - 2b + c$.
39. $5a + 4b - 5$.
40. $4a^2 - 4ab$.
41. $2a^2 - 6ab + 10b^2$.
42. $-5x^3 + 10x^2 - 2x - 1$.
43. $x - 12y - z$.
44. $-5a + 9b - 3c - 3d$.
45. $2.5x - 2y + 2z$.

EXERCISE 24. Pages 51-52.

7. James, 15 yr.; John, 30 yr.
8. A, 20 yr.; B, 10 yr.; C, 30 yr.
9. 35°; 140°.
10. 71 rd.
11. 32,000 sq. mi.
12. 20,400 ft.
13. Nile, 3500 mi.; Mississippi, 4200 mi.
14. Highest, 102 mi. per hr.; lowest, 4 mi. per hr.
15. Mobile, 62 in.; Yuma, 3.1 in.

EXERCISE 25. Page 54.

15. $37,500.
16. $3\frac{3}{4}$ yr.
17. 4%.
18. 1.04 P; 1.06 P; 1.07 P.
19. 1.08 P dollars; 1.15 P dollars.
20. $2800.
21. $6\frac{2}{3}$ yr.
22. $16\frac{2}{3}$ yr.
24. 6 yr.
25. $23.8 + \%$.

EXERCISE 26. Page 58.

21. $6 - 2c$.
22. $-3a$.
23. $-a + 3b$.
24. $2a$.
25. $3x - 2$.
26. $-b - 16$.
27. $3x$.
28. $7x^2 - x + 6$.
29. $-r + s$.
30. $-4q$.
31. $8m - 7n$.
32. $13r - 2s - t$.
33. $-2x - y$.
34. $4a - 1$.
35. $8b + 11$.
36. $12r$.
37. $5x + 12a - 4$.
38. $6ab + 17$.
39. $-4c + 2$.
40. $-6m + n$.

EXERCISE 29. Pages 62-64.

1. 17.
2. 20.
3. 18.
4. 2.
5. −19.
6. −8.
7. 1.
8. 9.
9. 1.
10. 0.
11. 13, 17.
12. A, 51 yr.; B, 64 yr.
13. 28, 95.
14. A, 64 yr.; B, 38 yr.
15. 58, 35.
16. 14 ft.; 21 ft.; 29 ft.
17. 840 ft.
18. $3800, gold leaf, $5000, appropriation of 1800.
19. 2, nearer; 5, farther.
20. 17, 18.
21. 35, 36, 37.
22. 53, 54, 55, 56.
23. 97, 99.
24. 76.
25. 42°, 126°, 116°, 76°.
26. 105°, angle; 75°, supplement.
27. 35°, angle; 55°, complement.
28. 75°.
29. Nitrogen, 20 lb.; phosphoric acid, 30 lb.; potash, 50 lb.
30. Rhode Island, 1248 sq. mi.; Texas, 265,896 sq. mi.

EXERCISE 34. Page 71.

15. $7x^2 - 35x$.
16. $-60 a^3b + 42 ab^3$.
17. $x^6y - 4 x^4y^3 + x^2y^5$.
18. $-r^3s + r^2s^2 - rs^3$.
19. $-3 a^3b + 6 a^2b^2 - 3 ab^3$.
20. $48 x^8 - 40 x^6 - 96 x^5$.
21. $-12 a^5b^3 + 8 a^4b^4 + 16 a^3b^5$.
22. $-40 m^8 + 5 m^6 + 15 m^4$.
24. $50 a + 7 b$.
25. $-5 ay$.
26. $x^2 - 2xy - y^2$.
27. $16 m + 12$.
28. $-6 cm - 36 c$.
29. $r^3 - s^3$.
30. $x + 1$.
31. $-m$.
32. $18 r - 5$.
33. $2 - 20 s$.
34. $x^3 - 2x + 3$.
35. $3 x^2 - xy + 2 y^2$.
36. $t + 7$.
37. $14 x - 10$.
38. $-3 x + 2$.
39. $-7 m$.
40. $-x^6 + 8 x^4 - 5 x^2$.
41. $\frac{1}{8} m^3n - \frac{1}{12} m^2n^2 + \frac{1}{18} mn^3$.

ANSWERS

EXERCISE 35. Pages 73-74.

1. $x^2 + 8x + 15$.
2. $r^2 - 11r + 28$.
3. $2s^2 - 11s + 15$.
4. $3m^2 - 10m - 8$.
5. $4t^2 + 3t - 27$.
6. $6x^2 + 23x + 21$.
7. $10m^2 + 23m - 5$.
8. $12p^2 + 36p - 21$.
9. $30y^2 - 46y + 8$.
10. $28z^2 + 5z - 50$.
11. $2a^2 + 3ab + b^2$.
12. $6c^2 - cd - 2d^2$.
13. $15r^2 + 8rs - 12s^2$.
14. $15x^2 - 26xy + 8y^2$.
15. $24m^2 + 18mp - 15p^2$.
16. $42y^2 + 2yz - 72z^2$.
17. $66a^2 - 14ad - 20d^2$.
18. $96p^2 - 28pq - 49q^2$.
19. $2x^4 - 7x^2y^2 + 3y^4$.
20. $99w^4 - 50w^2v - 21v^2$
21. $m^3 + 2m^2 - 6m - 9$.
22. $10a^3 + 33a^2 - 52a + 9$.
23. $x^3 - 5x^2y + 9xy^2 - 9y^3$.
24. $x^3 + y^3$.
25. $x^3 - 64y^3$.
26. $m^4 + m^2n^2 + n^4$.
27. $a^5 - 6a^3 + 6a^2 - 7a + 6$.
28. $2a^4 - 7a^3 - 18a^2 - a + 3$.
29. $6x^4 + 13x^3 - 70x^2 + 71x - 20$.
30. $8n^4 - 50n^2 + 32$.
31. $63r^4 + 114r^3y + 49r^2y^2 - 16ry^3 - 20y^4$.
32. $12a^4 - 47a^3b - 8a^2b^2 + 107ab^3 + 56b^4$.
33. $a^2 - 2ab + b^2 - c^2$.
34. $r^2 - s^2 - 2st - t^2$.
35. $4n^4 - 5m^2n^2 + m^4$.
36. $a^5 - 5a^4b + 10a^3b^2 - 10a^2b^3 + 5ab^4 - b^5$.
37. $m^5 + 243$.
38. $8a^2 + 40ac - 18b^2 + 50c^2$.
39. $x^5 - 32$.
40. $a^3 - 3abc - b^3 - c^3$.
41. $\frac{1}{9}a^2 - \frac{1}{16}b^2$.
42. $\frac{1}{4}m^2 - \frac{1}{9}n^2$.
43. $\frac{1}{16}x^2 - \frac{1}{81}y^2$.
44. $2a^2 + \frac{2}{3}ab - \frac{1}{6}b^2$.
45. $x^2 - \frac{145}{72}xy + y^2$.
46. $9x^2 - 30x + 25$.
47. $8m^3 - 36m^2n + 54mn^2 - 27n^3$.
48. $64r^3 + 240r^2 + 300r + 125$.
49. $16x^4 - 96x^3 + 216x^2 - 216x + 81$.
50. $27a^3 - 108a^2b + 144ab^2 - 64b^3$.
51. $a^3 + a^2 - 14a - 24$.
52. $2m^3 - 5m^2 - 37m + 60$.
53. $x^6 - y^6$.
54. $m^4 - n^4$.
55. $x^6 - y^6$.

ALGEBRA

EXERCISE 36. Page 75.

1. $11 a^2 - 111$.
2. $12 m$.
3. $2 a^2 - 12 x^2$.
4. $29 b^2 - 28 ab$.
5. $h^2 + 3 h + 18$.
6. $2 x^2 - 12 x - 2$.
7. $12 x^2 - 3 x - 6$.
8. $10 a^2 - 76 a - 36$.
9. $2 x^2 + 79 x + 22$.
10. $2 ab^2 + 2 a^2 b$.

EXERCISE 37. Pages 76–77.

1. 13.
2. 7.
3. 9.
4. 1.
5. 2.
6. 2.
7. 3.
8. 4.
9. 6.
10. 5.
11. 7.
12. 9.
13. -13.
14. 2.
15. 10.
16. 32, 43.
17. 42, 58.
18. Paris, 4020 mi.; London, 3740 mi.
19. 40, 47.
20. 25, 35.
21. 24, 56.
22. Length, 470 ft.; width, 340 ft.
23. 15, 16.
24. $-21, -20$.
25. Chicago, 2,185,283; Philadelphia, 1,549,008; New York, 4,766,883.

EXERCISE 39. Pages 79–81.

1. A, 45 yr.; B, 5 yr.
2. Father, 27 yr.; son, 3 yr.
3. Father, 40 yr.; son, 15 yr.
4. A, 45 yr.; B, 9 yr.
5. A, 42 yr.; B, 84 yr.
6. 8 yr.
7. 17 yr.
9. 15 lb. at 70 ¢; 35 lb. at 40 ¢.
10. $31\frac{1}{4}$ lb. at 36 ¢; $68\frac{3}{4}$ lb. at 20 ¢.
11. $33\frac{1}{3}$ lb. clover seed; $166\frac{2}{3}$ lb. blue grass seed.
12. 6 quarters; 13 dimes.
13. 5 half-dollars; 15 dimes.
14. 7 quarters; 9 nickels.
15. 8 $2 bills; 13 fifty-cent pieces; 24 dimes.

ANSWERS

EXERCISE 40. Page 82.

1. 5.
2. 4.
3. 2.
4. 12.
5. 2.
6. 10.
7. −21.
8. −20.
9. 7.
10. 3.
11. 18.
12. 10.
13. 4.
14. $\frac{1}{2}$.
15. $\frac{3}{5}$.
16. 6.
17. $\frac{3}{4}$.
18. $\frac{3}{5}$.
19. 13.
20. $\frac{5}{7}$.

EXERCISE 41. Pages 83-84.

1. 40.
2. 15, 20, 30.
3. 30.
4. 42.
5. 56.
6. 750.
7. 20.
8. 105.
9. 90°, 60°, 30°.
10. 90°, 45°, 45°.
11. 12, 13, 14.
12. 12 dimes, 3 dollars, 15 cents.
13. Length, 450 ft.; width, 250 ft.
14. Michigan, 1800 ft.; Huron, 1000 ft.; Superior, 900 ft.
15. Length, 760 ft.; width, 130 ft.
16. 1820, 9.6 million; 1910, 92.2 million.
17. Phosphoric acid, 12 lb.; potash, 60 lb.; nitrogen, 27 lb.
18. Length, $751\frac{1}{3}$ ft.; width, 350 ft.
19. $20.50.
20. Water, 3740 mi.; rail, 3250 mi.

EXERCISE 46. Pages 94-95.

15. $n^2 - 10$.
16. $x - 12\,a$.
17. $a - 6\,b$.
18. $x + 5\,z$.
19. $x^2 + 8\,y$.
20. $xy - 12$.
21. $5\,x - 7$.
22. $3\,a - 7$.
23. $2\,a - 3$.
24. $5\,x - 8$.
25. $8\,x - 3\,y$.
26. $5\,m + 4\,n$.
27. $x^2 + x - 12$.
28. $3\,a^2 + 2\,a - 4$.
29. $2\,x^2 - 3\,xy + 4\,y^2$.
30. $3\,a^2 - 2\,ab - b^2$.

31. $x^2 + 2xy + y^2$.
32. $n+2$; remainder, 2.
33. $4x - 3$.
34. $a^2 + a - 1$; remainder, 20.
35. $m^2 - 3m - 4$.
36. $x^2 + xy + y^2$.
37. $x^2 - 2x + 4$.
38. $x^3 + 2x^2 + 4x + 8$.
39. $x^3 - x^2y + xy^2 - y^3$.
40. $x^3 + x^2y + xy^2 + y^3$.
41. $x^4 - x^3y + x^2y^2 - xy^3 + y^4$.
42. $x^4 + x^3y + x^2y^2 + xy^3 + y^4$; rem. $2y^5$.
43. $x^4 - 2x^3 + 4x^2 - 8x + 16$.
44. $1 - 2a + 4a^2 - 8a^3$.
45. $n - 2$.
46. $2x^2 + 9x - 5$.
47. $4m^2 - 2mn^2 + n^4$.
48. $7x^2 + 8x + 4$; rem. **40**.
49. $x^3 + 2x^2 - 6x + 5$.
50. $4a^2 + ab - 5b^2$.
51. $x - \tfrac{1}{2}$.
52. $x - 3$.
53. $3x + \tfrac{1}{3}$.
54. $\tfrac{1}{2}a + 2$.

EXERCISE 47. Pages 99–100.

1. 7.
2. -5.
3. 1.
4. 3.
5. -3.
6. 5.
7. 2.
8. 4.
9. $\tfrac{4}{5}$.
10. $\tfrac{2}{3}$.
11. -5.
12. -10.
13. $-\tfrac{7}{2}$.
14. $\tfrac{1}{2}$.
15. 2.
16. $-\tfrac{7}{5}$.
17. -1.
18. 6.
19. -12.
20. 7.

EXERCISE 48. Pages 100–103.

1. 31, 13.
2. -5.
3. 9, 10.
4. 24, 14.
5. Father, 35 yr.; son, 7 yr.
6. 15, 17, 19.
7. A, $7.50; B, $5.25; C, $9.25.
8. 35, 14.
9. Width, 430 ft.; length, 780 ft.
10. 10 in.; 20 in.; 15 in.
11. 27, 107.
12. 278 ft. below sea level.
13. B, $36; A, $12.
14. 8 quarters, 5 nickels, 16 half-dollars, 13 dimes.
15. Pink variety, 300; yellow variety, 200; scarlet variety, 800.
16. 55°, 55°, 70°.

ANSWERS

17. 285 in.; 285 in.
18. 55° below zero.
19. Virginia, 42,627 sq. mi.; Nebraska, 77,520 sq. mi.; California, 158,297 sq. mi.
20. Girls, 516,536; boys, 398,525.
22. $700, at 5%; $2000, at 6%.
23. $5000.
24. $9000.
25. U. S. Steel Stock, $3000; Chicago Edison Bonds, $15,000.

EXERCISE 49. Pages 105–106.

11. $7\frac{1}{2}$ hr.
12. 9 hr.
13. $12\frac{1}{2}$ hr.
14. 6 hr.
15. 21 mi. per hr.
16. 15 mi. per hr.
17. A, 29 mi. per hr.; B, 21 mi. per hr.
18. 6 mi.
19. $45\frac{5}{17}$ mi.
20. 5 hr.
21. 24 mi. per hr.
22. $33\frac{1}{3}$ mi. an hr.
23. 1 hr. 52 min.

EXERCISE 50. Pages 108–109.

1. a, 27°; b, 45°; c, 90°; d, 180°.
2. b, 86°; c, 131°; d, 14°.
5. $459\frac{2}{3}$° below zero.
6. Tin, $449\frac{3}{5}$°; iron, 2192°; mercury, $-38\frac{1}{5}$°; paraffine, 131°.
7. Fahrenheit, $\frac{7}{5}$°; Faraday, $-151\frac{3}{5}$°; Dewar, $-439\frac{3}{5}$°; Onnes, $-452\frac{1}{5}$°.
8. a, 10°; b, $-11\frac{1}{3}$°; c, $-22\frac{2}{9}$°.
9. Alcohol, 78°; turpentine, 160°.
10. $-295\frac{3}{5}$°.

EXERCISE 63. Pages 134–135.

1. $2x^2 + 8x + 6$.
2. $2x^2 + 7x + 6$.
3. $2x^2 + 7x + 3$.
4. $6x^2 + 11x + 3$.
5. $6x^2 + 13x + 6$.
6. $6a^2 - 7a + 2$.
7. $3a^2 - 10a + 8$.
8. $3a^2 - 13a + 12$.

ALGEBRA

9. $6a^2 - 19a + 15$.
10. $8a^2 - 30a + 25$.
11. $6r^2 + 7r - 5$.
12. $8r^2 + 2r - 21$.
13. $20r^2 + 6r - 8$.
14. $21r^2 + 4r - 12$.
15. $32r^2 + 12r - 27$.
16. $18s^2 - 3s - 10$.
17. $40s^2 - 18s - 7$.
18. $55s^2 - 16s - 48$.
19. $36s^2 - 3s - 60$.
20. $45s^2 - 30s - 40$.
21. $18a^2b^2 - 24ab - 10$.
22. $42m^2n^2 - 45mn + 12$.
23. $72r^4 + 5r^2 - 12$.
24. $65x^6 - 4x^3 - 21$.
25. $24p^4 - 10p^2 - 21$.
26. $55m^4 + 46m^2 - 24$.
27. $54c^6 - 3c^3 - 2$.
28. $150n^6 + 5n^3 - 12$.
29. $28x^4 + 4x^2 - 5$.
30. $48t^6 + 5t^3 - 18$.
31. $70r^2s^2 - 3rs - 27$.
32. $8a^2 - 2ab - 15b^2$.
33. $42m^2 + 11ms - 20s^2$.
34. $72t^2 - 35tx + 3x^2$.
35. $x^2 - 25y^2$.
36. $4x^2 - 9y^2$.
37. $4m^2 - 20mn + 25n^2$.
38. $9t^2 + 24nt + 16n^2$.
39. $27a^2b^2 + 33abc - 20c^2$.
40. $30x^2y^2 + xyz - 42z^2$.
41. $56r^4 + r^2s - 72s^2$.
42. $110x^6 - x^3y^3 - 132y^6$.
43. $54m^2n^4 - 3mn^2 - 12$.
44. $6 + 31x + 18x^2$.
45. $30 + 3t^2 - 63t^4$.
46. $80 - 2z^3 - 12z^6$.
47. $35 + 12xy - 36x^2y^2$.
48. $36 - 53xy^2 + 11x^2y^4$.
49. $90a^4b^2 - 74a^2bc + 12c^2$.
50. $60x^4 - 13x^2y - 28y^2$.
51. $63t^4 + 10t^2x^2 - 25x^4$.
52. $32m^4 + 4m^2n - 45n^2$.
53. $35x^4 + x^2y^2 - 6y^4$.
54. $44c^4 - 75c^2d + 25d^2$.
55. $135p^4 - 12p^2q - 4q^2$.
56. $160a^2 + 4ab - 21b^2$.
57. $90m^2 + 63mn - 10n^2$.
58. $24m^2 + 4m + \frac{1}{6}$.
59. $72x^2 - 10xy + \frac{1}{3}y^2$.
60. $120a^2 - \frac{4}{3}ab - \frac{4}{9}b^2$.

EXERCISE 65. Page 138.

9. 8.
10. $3\frac{1}{3}$.

EXERCISE 68. Pages 142–143.

1. $12x^2 - xy - 6y^2$.
2. $1\frac{9}{21}x^2 - 36y^2$.
3. $a^6 - 1$.
4. $4a^2 - 4ab + b^4$.
5. $21a^4 - 53a^2b^2 - 8b^4$.
6. $a^4 - b^4$.

ANSWERS

7. $9x^2 + 7xy - 2y^2$.
8. $3a^2x - 3b^2x$.
9. $25a^2 - 50ab^2 + 24b^4$.
10. $3m^5 - 12m^3n^2 + 6mn^4$.
11. $7n^7 - 7n$.
12. $3a^3 - 3a$.
13. $a^4 - 3a^2y - 108y^2$.
14. $x^6 - y^6$.
15. $x^2 - \frac{3}{2}xy + \frac{9}{16}y^2$.
16. $m^2 - \frac{3}{4}m + \frac{1}{8}$.
17. $6x^3 - 22x^2 - 8x$.
18. $B^4 - 10AB^2C + 24A^2C^2$.
19. $a^7 - 9a$.
20. $10a^2 + 5ab - 15b^2$.
21. $30y + 3y^2 - 9y^3$.
22. $21m^2 - 119m - 42$.
23. $x^6 - y^4$.
24. $x^2y^2 + 12xy - 64$.
25. $2x^2 - 16xy + 32y^2$.
26. $x^4 - 4x^2 + 3$.
27. $x^3 + \frac{1}{8}$.
28. $\frac{4}{25}x^4 - \frac{9}{16}$.
29. $4n^2 - 2n + \frac{1}{4}$.
30. $x^2 - \frac{1}{8}x - \frac{15}{32}$.

EXERCISE 69. Page 145.

13. 11, 9.
14. 3, 4, 5, 6.
15. 7, 8.
16. 125, 126.
17. 6 mi. per hr.; 6 hr.

EXERCISE 70. Pages 145-147.

1. *a.* 600 sq. in.; *b.* 300 sq. in.; *c.* 600 sq. in.
2. *a.* $2x(x-5)$ sq. in.; *b.* $x(x-5)$ sq. in.; *c.* $2x(x-5)$ sq. in.
3. *a.* $y(y+4)$ sq. in.; *b.* $\frac{y(y+4)}{2}$ sq. in.; *c.* $y(y+4)$ sq. in.
4. *a.* s^2 sq. in.; *b.* base, $(s+4)$ in.; altitude, $(s-3)$ in.; *c.* $(s+4)(s-3)$ sq. in.; *d.* $(s+4)(s-3) = s^2 + 50$.
5. *a.* Altitude, a in.; base, $(2a+5)$ in.; area, $a(2a+5)$ sq. in. *b.* altitude, $(a+3)$ in.; base, $(2a+9)$ in.; area, $\frac{(a+3)(2a+9)}{2}$ sq. in.; *c.* $a(2a+5) = \frac{(a+3)(2a+9)}{2} + 25$.
6. Altitude, 6 in.; base, 14 in.
7. Altitude, 79 ft.; base, 96 ft.
8. Width, 40 ft.; length, 50 ft.
9. Upper square, 34 ft.; lower square, 55 ft.
10. 144 trees.

EXERCISE 71. Page 149.

1. $4, 8$.
2. $11, -5$.
3. $7, -9$.
4. $6, 12$.
5. $10, 11$.
6. $1, -2$.
7. $1, 6$.
8. $7, -3$.
9. $+\frac{2}{3}, -\frac{2}{3}$.
10. $+\frac{5}{8}, -\frac{5}{8}$.
11. $0, 5$.
12. $0, \frac{2}{3}$.
13. $1, -\frac{3}{8}$.
14. $\frac{3}{2}, -\frac{7}{2}$.
15. $\frac{7}{6}, -\frac{5}{4}$.
16. $\frac{1}{2}, \frac{3}{2}$.
17. $-\frac{1}{2}, -\frac{2}{3}$.
18. $-5, \frac{2}{3}$.
19. $3, \frac{1}{3}$.
20. $-2, -\frac{1}{2}$.

EXERCISE 72. Pages 150–151.

1. $-7a, 5a$.
2. $+\frac{3}{4}b, -\frac{3}{4}b$.
3. $-13m, -10m$.
4. $+\frac{3}{5}c, -\frac{3}{5}c$.
5. $-3a, -\frac{1}{2}a$.
6. $b, \frac{2}{7}b$.
7. $\dfrac{c}{2}, -\dfrac{5c}{3}$.
8. $-t, \dfrac{14t}{13}$.
9. $-v, \dfrac{13v}{9}$.
10. $\dfrac{k}{7}, -6k$.
11. $-a, 3a$.
12. $-10p, 2p$.
13. $3c, +12c$.
14. $4n, 12n$.
15. $8b, -\dfrac{b}{2}$.
16. $-\dfrac{m}{10}, \dfrac{5m}{3}$.
17. $a, -\dfrac{3a}{8}$.
18. $5t, -\dfrac{t}{3}$.
19. $-2r, \dfrac{11r}{3}$.
20. $-\dfrac{5s}{6}, \dfrac{3s}{2}$.

EXERCISE 73. Pages 152–153.

1. -3, or $\frac{5}{2}$.
2. $3, 4, 5\ ;\ -1, 0, 1$.
3. $11, 7$.
4. $5, 2$.
5. Altitude, 3 ft.; base, 10 ft.
6. Length, $2\frac{1}{2}$ mi.; width, $\frac{1}{2}$ mi.
7. $75, or $25.
8. Length, 30 rd.; width, 10 rd.
9. Chicago lot: length, 125 ft.; width, 25 ft. Indianapolis lot length, 130 ft.; width, 35 ft.
10. 5 ft.

ANSWERS

EXERCISE 75. Page 156.

21. $m^2 + 2m + 4$.
22. $3a^2b$.
23. $a + 4$.
24. $x - 5y$.
25. $3a + 2b$.

EXERCISE 76. Pages 158–159.

5. $3 \cdot 5 \cdot 7 \cdot 11$.
6. $3 \cdot 3 \cdot 3 \cdot 2 \cdot 2 \cdot 5$.
20. $6(r+s)(r-s)(r-t)$.
21. $(a-4)(a-3)(a-5)$.
22. $(1-x)^3(1+x)$.
23. $3(2-3x)^2(2+3x)^2$.
24. $(2-x)(3-x)(4-x)$.
26. $(r-4)(r+4)(r+7)$.
27. $(a+x)^2(a^2-ax+x^2)$.
28. $yz(2x-1)(4x^2+2x+1)(11x+1)$.
29. $(b-7)(b-5)(b+9)(b-12)$.
30. $(2x-5)^2(2x+5)$.
31. $12(m-6)^2(m+8)(m+4)$.
32. $(3n-8)(3n-1)(n+2)$.
33. $(1+3x)(1-3x+9x^2)(1-8x)$
34. $(x+7)(x-6)(x+5)$.
35. $a(a^2-1)(a-10)$.

EXERCISE 78. Page 164.

1. $\dfrac{2y+x}{3y-2x}$.
2. $-\dfrac{3}{2x+y}$.
3. $-\dfrac{a+4}{a+6}$.
4. $-\dfrac{3(m+n)}{5m+n}$.
5. $\dfrac{x-2}{5-x}$.
6. $\dfrac{t^2+3t+9}{t+3}$.
7. $\dfrac{x+4}{x^2+4x+16}$.
8. $-\dfrac{r+s}{2(3r+s)}$.
9. $\dfrac{3c(d-c)}{5(d+c)}$.
10. $-\dfrac{2m(3x+2y)}{3n(9x^2+6xy+4y^2)}$.

EXERCISE 79. Page 166.

9. $3y + 1 + \dfrac{6}{3y-1}$.
10. $4p - 6 + \dfrac{21}{2p+3}$.
11. $x^2 + xy + y^2 + \dfrac{3y^3}{x-y}$.
12. $a^2 + 2ab + 4b^2 + \dfrac{16b^3}{a-2b}$.
13. $x^3 + x^2y + xy^2 + y^3 + \dfrac{2y^4}{x-y}$.
14. $x^2 + 3xy + 6y^2 + \dfrac{18y^3}{x-2y}$.
15. $3a + 2 + \dfrac{7}{4a-1}$.
16. $3a + 14 + \dfrac{37a+35}{a^2-2a-3}$.

EXERCISE 81. Pages 172–175.

23. $\dfrac{2b^2 - ab + 3a^2}{a^2b^2}.$

24. $\dfrac{st + 2rt - 3rs}{rst}.$

25. $\dfrac{axz + byz - cxy}{xyz}.$

26. $\dfrac{5an^2 - 10bmn - 2cm^3}{10m^2n^2}.$

27. $\dfrac{14a - 5}{6a}.$

28. $\dfrac{3y^2 - 6x^2}{2x^2y^2}.$

29. $-\dfrac{3x + 4z}{6xz}.$

30. $\dfrac{ac + bc + ab}{abc}.$

33. $\dfrac{m^2 + 1}{m^2 - 1}.$

34. $\dfrac{2r^2}{r^2 - 9}.$

35. $\dfrac{13 - 4m}{(5m - 2)(2m + 3)}.$

36. $\dfrac{38b}{(3a - 4)(5a + 6)}.$

37. $\dfrac{2x^2 - 9y^2}{(3y - x)(2x - 3y)}.$

38. $\dfrac{3x^2 - xy + 2y^2}{6(x^2 - y^2)}.$

39. $\dfrac{29}{(3a - 7)(6a + 15)}.$

40. $\dfrac{29p - 12}{6(2p - 3)(5p - 4)}.$

41. $\dfrac{8x}{x^2 - 4}.$

42. $\dfrac{4p}{4p^2 - 1}.$

43. $\dfrac{2ab}{8a^3 + b^3}.$

44. $\dfrac{6x(x + 3)}{x^3 - 27}.$

45. $\dfrac{8}{x + 2}.$

46. $0.$

47. $\dfrac{a^3 - 2x^3}{(a + x)(a^3 - x^3)}.$

48. $0.$

49. $\dfrac{20 - 3x}{(x - 2)(x - 3)(x + 5)}.$

50. $\dfrac{a^2 + 2a - 2}{(a - 1)(a + 2)(a - 3)}.$

51. $\dfrac{2a^2 + 18a + 3}{(2a - 1)(a + 2)(3a + 1)}.$

52. $\dfrac{r^2 + 6ar + 3a^2}{(r - 3a)^2(r + 7a)}.$

53. $\dfrac{-11}{(x + 1)(x - 2)(x + 3)}.$

54. $\dfrac{a - 3}{a^2 - a + 1}.$

56. $\dfrac{2a + 15}{9 - a^2}.$

57. $\dfrac{x + y}{xy(y - x)}.$

58. $\dfrac{10x + 1}{12(x - 2)}.$

59. $\dfrac{4a}{m(16-m^2)}$.

60. $\dfrac{12}{1-a^2}$.

61. $\dfrac{r^2}{r^2-4}$.

62. $\dfrac{a-b}{a+b}$.

63. $\dfrac{x^2-x}{(x+5)(x-2)(x+3)}$.

64. $\dfrac{208}{15}$.

65. $\dfrac{3a^2-a+2}{3a}$.

66. $\dfrac{2x}{x+y}$.

67. $\dfrac{2b}{5a+b}$.

68. $\dfrac{6a^2-6}{2a-3}$.

69. 0.

70. $\dfrac{32}{4-3m}$.

71. $\dfrac{r^3-s^3}{r+s}$.

EXERCISE 82. Pages 176–177.

3. $\dfrac{ay}{x^2}$.

4. $\dfrac{5b}{4a}$.

5. $\tfrac{1}{2}$.

6. 1.

7. $2abc$.

8. $\dfrac{9xy}{8mn^2}$.

9. $\dfrac{2(x-a)}{3x}$.

10. $\dfrac{2m-1}{m-4}$.

11. $\dfrac{a-5}{3a^2}$.

12. $\dfrac{3p-3r}{4(p-9)}$.

13. $\dfrac{2(a-3)}{(a-6)^2}$.

14. $\dfrac{x(x-1)}{(x+1)(x+2)}$.

15. $\dfrac{y^2(x-2y)}{x^2(x-y)}$.

16. $\dfrac{1}{3a}$.

17. $\dfrac{3r-2s}{3r+2s}$.

18. $\dfrac{m-3}{2(m-2)}$.

19. $\dfrac{5(x+y)}{2}$.

20. $\dfrac{2x-3}{3x-2}$.

21. $\dfrac{m+1}{2}$.

22. a.

23. $-\tfrac{3}{2}$.

24. $\dfrac{-2x}{a+x}$.

25. -1.

ALGEBRA

EXERCISE 83. Page 179.

7. $\dfrac{3(x+3)}{2(x-2)}$.

8. $\dfrac{r(2r+5v)}{v(4r-3v)}$.

9. $\dfrac{2e^2}{e-1}$.

10. $\dfrac{(c+d)^2}{c-d}$.

11. $\dfrac{4(r+s)}{r-s}$.

12. $\dfrac{t(t+2s)}{s}$.

13. $\dfrac{a(a+7)}{m^2(a-3)^2}$.

14. $\dfrac{w(w-2)}{w+5}$.

15. $\dfrac{(a+2b)(a-5b)}{(a+8b)(a+4b)}$.

16. $\dfrac{1}{m}$.

17. 1.

18. $\dfrac{a}{x-b}$.

19. $\dfrac{20\,r(r+s)(2r-3s)}{3s(2r+3s)(r+2s)}$.

20. $m-n$.

EXERCISE 84. Page 181.

1. 12.

2. 9.

3. $\dfrac{1}{x+y}$.

4. a.

5. $\dfrac{2b-3a}{2b+3a}$.

6. $\dfrac{ad-bc}{ad+bc}$.

7. $\dfrac{3b}{4b^2+2ab+a^2}$.

8. $\dfrac{3(2a-5b)}{5(4a+3b)}$.

9. $\dfrac{b+a}{b}$.

10. $2ab(a-2b)$.

11. $\dfrac{2x+y}{x+2y}$.

12. $\dfrac{x-1}{4x-3}$.

13. $\dfrac{a-b}{a+b}$.

14. $\dfrac{a+6}{a+1}$.

15. $\dfrac{2r^2}{r-s}$.

16. $\dfrac{3x+4}{x+1}$.

17. $\tfrac{3}{4}$.

18. $\dfrac{1}{vx}$.

19. $\dfrac{a}{a-1}$.

20. 3.

EXERCISE 85. Pages 183–184.

1. $-\tfrac{1}{17}$.

2. $\tfrac{2}{5}$.

3. $\tfrac{15}{4}$.

4. $\tfrac{20}{27}$.

5. $1\tfrac{3}{3}$.

6. $\dfrac{x}{2a}$.

7. $\dfrac{3}{x-y}$.

8. $\dfrac{3x}{x+2}$.

9. $\dfrac{2}{2m-1}$.

10. $\dfrac{2}{2a-1}$.   11. $\dfrac{p^2+p+1}{p}$.   12. $\dfrac{1+x^2}{x}$.

13. $\dfrac{ad-bc}{ad+bc}$.   14. $\dfrac{2x-3y}{6}$.   15. $\dfrac{x+5}{x+2}$.

16. $\dfrac{x^2-x-6}{x}$.   17. $\dfrac{a^2-4b^2}{a^2-b^2}$.   18. $\dfrac{x-2y}{y}$.

19. $\dfrac{m(m^2+n^2)}{n(m^2+2mn-n^2)}$.   20. $a-1$.   21. $\dfrac{a-b}{a+b}$.

22. $\dfrac{x+3y}{3x-y}$.   23. $\dfrac{3x-2}{x+1}$.   24. x

25. $\dfrac{2a^2+3b^2}{5ab}$.

EXERCISE 86. Pages 186–189.

1. 3.   2. 2.   3. 5.   4. −2.   5. 7.   6. 6.
7. 15.   8. 1.   9. −5.   10. 10.   11. −3.   12. −4.
13. 3.   14. −1.   15. $\tfrac{1}{2}$.   17. 3.   18. 4.   19. $\tfrac{1}{2}$.
20. 2.   21. −4.   22. 1.   23. −1.   24. −$\tfrac{1}{2}$.   25. −5.
26. 3.   28. 6.   29. 23.   30. 6.   31. $\tfrac{4}{5}$.   32. $\tfrac{1}{3}$.
33. −1.   34. −$\tfrac{4}{5}$.   35. −$\tfrac{1}{3}$.   36. 1.   37. $2\tfrac{1}{3}$.   38. −1.
39. 2.   40. 2.   41. −$\tfrac{7}{10}$.   42. −5.   43. 3.   44. $\tfrac{4}{5}$.
45. −2.   47. −1.   48. $\tfrac{4}{15}$.   49. $\tfrac{3}{5}$.   50. $\tfrac{1}{5}$.

EXERCISE 87. Pages 189–191.

1. 32, 24.   2. Base, 13 ft.; altitude, 5 ft.; area, 65 sq. ft.
3. $25.   4. 27, 18.   5. $1\tfrac{3}{4}$.   6. A, 24 yrs.; B, 64 yrs.
7. Oklahoma, 1907; Washington, 1889.   8. 79.   9. 48.
10. $\tfrac{5}{11}$.   11. 69°.   12. 18 at 50¢ per dozen; 36 at 75¢ per dozen.
13. Engine, $18,700; sleeper, $19,000; parlor car, $15,500.
14. $2300 at 5%; $700 at 6%.   15. Wyoming, 1890; Maine, 1820.
16. $\tfrac{22}{15}$.   17. $2150 at 5%; $1800 at 4%.   18. $\tfrac{3}{8}$.   19. 30°.   20. 1.

EXERCISE 88. Page 192.

5. $3\tfrac{3}{4}$ da.   6. $3\tfrac{3}{5}$ da.   7. $1\tfrac{1}{5}$ hr.
8. 9 hr. 36 min.   9. 6 hr.   10. $22\tfrac{1}{2}$ da.

EXERCISE 89. Pages 193-194.

1. 120 lb.
2. 8 ft. from the fulcrum.
3. 5 ft. from A.
4. $2\frac{2}{5}$ ft.
5. 7 ft. from the fulcrum.
6. On the left side, 7 ft. from the fulcrum.

EXERCISE 90. Pages 196-197.

4. a. $(r + 5)$ mi. per hour;
   b. slow train, $\frac{100}{r}$ hr.; fast train, $\frac{100}{r+5}$ hr.
5. a. $\frac{50}{r}$ hr., $\frac{250}{3r}$ hr.; b. $\frac{250}{3r} = \frac{50}{r} + 1$.
6. a. Slow train, $\frac{100}{t}$ mi. per hour; fast train, $\frac{150}{t}$ mi. per hour.
   b. $\frac{150}{t} = \frac{100}{t} + 20$.
7. Slow train, 15 mi. per hour; fast train, 45 mi. per hour.
8. 12 mi. per hour.
9. Freight train, 15 mi. per hour.; passenger train, 35 mi. per hour.
10. 40 mi. per hour.
11. a. Downstream, 8 mi. per hour. b. Upstream, 2 mi. per hour.
12. a. 3 hr.; b. 12 hr.; c. 15 hr.
13. a. $\frac{d}{8}$ hr.; b. $\frac{d}{2}$ hr.; c. $\frac{d}{8} + \frac{d}{2} = 5.$; d. 8 mi.
14. 12 mi.
15. $21\frac{3}{5}$ mi.

EXERCISE 91. Pages 198-200.

1. 20.
2. 21 yr.
3. Width, 36 ft.; length, 60 ft.
4. 30°, 15°, 60°, 75°, **180°**.
5. 33°, 67°, 80°.
6. A, 32 mi.; B, 25 mi.
7. Shaft, 500 ft.; pyramid, 55 ft.
8. Slow train, 27 mi. per hour; fast train, 45 mi. per hour.
9. 10, 12, 14.
10. 10 da.
11. $4\frac{1}{2}$ mi. per hour.
12. A, 31 yr.; B, **12 yr.**
13. $10,600.

ANSWERS

14. Slow train, 30 mi. per hour; fast train, 45 mi. per hour.
15. 6 hr.
16. $630 at $4\tfrac{1}{2}\%$; $810 at $3\tfrac{1}{2}\%$
17. 3 mi. per hour.
18. 3.5.
19. 2.65.
20. .90013.

EXERCISE 92. Pages 201–202.

1. $7a$.
2. $2b$.
3. $\dfrac{2a}{3b}$.
4. $\dfrac{3s}{2r}$.
5. c.
6. $a-b$.
7. $r+s$.
8. $c^2 - cd + d^2$.
9. $\dfrac{m-1}{m}$.
10. $m^2 - mn + n^2$.
11. $2b + a$.
12. $a-1$.
13. $2m$.
14. $-a$.
15. $\dfrac{10m}{3n}$.
16. $12(a-b)$.
17. $m+n$.
18. $\dfrac{2}{n}$.
19. $a+b$.
20. $\dfrac{1}{a-b}$.
21. $-2a$.
22. $-\dfrac{2a}{3b}$.
23. $\dfrac{2a^2}{2a-b}$.
24. $\dfrac{b^2}{a}$.
25. $\dfrac{a}{2}$.

EXERCISE 93. Pages 204–205.

1. a. $\dfrac{A}{b}$; b. $\dfrac{A}{a}$.
2. a. $\dfrac{2A}{b}$; b. $\dfrac{2A}{a}$.
3. $\dfrac{C}{2\pi}$.
4. a. $\dfrac{V}{lh}$; b. $\dfrac{V}{lw}$.
5. a. $\dfrac{3V}{h}$; b. $\dfrac{3V}{b}$.
6. $C = \tfrac{5}{9}(F - 32)$.
7. a. 330; b. 20; c. $\dfrac{2A}{b+c}$; d. $\dfrac{2A - ac}{a}$.
8. a. $P = \dfrac{100A}{100 + rt}$; b. $t = \dfrac{100(A-P)}{Pr}$.
9. a. $\dfrac{aT - 1}{a}$; b. $\dfrac{1}{T-t}$.
10. a. $m(g-f)$; b. $\dfrac{mg - T}{m}$; c. $\dfrac{T}{g-f}$.
11. a. $\dfrac{Mu}{v-u}$; b. $\dfrac{m(v-u)}{u}$.
12. a. $\dfrac{Cb}{Kb + C}$; b. $\dfrac{aC}{C - Ka}$.
13. a. $\dfrac{sa + c}{s+1}$; b. $\dfrac{sb - c + b}{s}$.
14. a. $\dfrac{273(h-k)}{k}$; b. $\dfrac{273h}{273 + t}$.

15. a. $lMt + M$; b. $\dfrac{L}{lt+1}$. 16. a. 89.78^+; b. $\dfrac{w(600\,d^2 + l^2)}{3000\,d^2}$.

17. a. $.34_+$; b. $\dfrac{ad^2}{p-d}$. 18. a. $\dfrac{nE}{nR+r}$; b. $\dfrac{Cr}{E-CR}$; c. $\dfrac{n(E-CR)}{C}$.

19. a. 585.93^+; b. $\dfrac{mv^2}{Fg}$; c. $\dfrac{Fgr}{v^2}$.

20. a. 120; b. $\dfrac{fg}{q-f}$; c. $\dfrac{fp}{p-f}$.

EXERCISE 94. Pages 206-208.

1. Mississippi, 3000 mi.; St. Lawrence, 2200 mi.; Yukon, 2100 mi.; Arkansas, 2000 mi.; San Francisco, 1400 mi.; Columbia, 1200 mi.

2. Corn cracked, 28 oz.; corn meal, 20 oz.; oats, 16 oz.; oats ground, 12 oz.; wheat, 30 oz.; cottonseed meal, 20 oz.

3.
AB 5.	1.	10.	40.	3.
CD 8.5	1.7	17.	68.	5.1
EF 3.	.6	6.	24.	1.8
GH 1.	.2	2.	8.	.6
ZW 5.	1.	10.	40.	3.
MN 4.	.8	8.	32.	2.4
XY 2.5	.5	5.	20.	1.5

EXERCISE 95. Pages 210-211.

2. $7:30, 16°$; $8:30, 19°$; $11:30, 20.5°$; $2:30, 9°$; $5:30, -5°$.

6. $B, 1:12$; $C, 1:30$; $D, 1:48$; $E, 2:24$; $G, 3:30$; $H, 4:06$; $I, 4:30$.

8. $33.

EXERCISE 96. Pages 212-213.

1. $A, +2$; $B, -4$; $C, -3$; $D, +6$.
2. $A, +5$; $B, +2$; $C, -2$; $D, -5$.
3. $E, (+5, +2.5)$; $F, (-2.5, +3)$; $G, (-3.5, -4.5)$; $H, (+4.5, -3)$.

5. A parallelogram; point $(+6, 3.5)$.
6. A hexagon; point $(5.5, -5)$.

EXERCISE 97. Page 214.

1. $B (5, -6)$; yes. $C, (1, 2)$; yes. $D, (-2, 8)$; yes.
2. They do not. 3. A straight line. 4. They do.
5. A straight line. 6. They do.

ANSWERS

EXERCISE 99. Pages 219-220.

1. $(7, -2)$.
2. $(3, 1)$.
3. $(2, 5)$.
4. $(-2, 3)$.
5. Dependent.
6. $(4, -5.)$
7. Dependent.
8. $(-2, -3)$.
9. They have a common solution; $(3, 4)$.
10. They do not have a common solution.

EXERCISE 100. Page 220.

3. Simultaneous; $(6, -2)$.
5. Simultaneous; $(-3, 2)$.

EXERCISE 101. Page 224.

1. $x = 3$; $y = 2$.
2. $a = 2$; $b = -3$.
3. $s = 1$; $r = -4$.
4. $m = 2$; $n = 3$.
5. $c = 3$; $d = -5$.
6. $a = -3$; $b = 2$.
7. $x = -\frac{3}{4}$; $y = \frac{3}{4}$.
8. $s = 6$; $t = -2$.
9. $p = -1$; $q = -3$.
10. $r = -\frac{5}{2}$; $y = -\frac{3}{2}$.
11. $c = 5$; $t = -4\frac{1}{3}$.
12. $x = 3$; $y = 2$.
13. $x = -\frac{6}{5}$; $y = \frac{4}{5}$.
14. $v = \frac{1}{2}$; $g = \frac{1}{3}$.
15. $x = \frac{1}{4}$; $y = \frac{1}{6}$.
16. $x = 5$; $y = -3$.
17. $x = 4$; $y = -2$.
18. $r = 3$; $s = 11$.
19. $m = 2$; $n = -\frac{1}{2}$.
20. $a = -4$; $b = 10$.

EXERCISE 102. Page 226.

1. $m = 3$; $n = 4$.
2. $r = -4$; $s = -1$.
3. $x = 2$; $y = -1$.
4. $x = -1$; $y = 3$.
5. $x = 1$; $y = 2$.
6. $p = 5$; $q = -7$.
7. $m = -5$; $n = \frac{1}{2}$.
8. $x = 2$; $y = 6$.
9. $x = 1$; $y = \frac{1}{3}$.
10. $r = 3$; $t = -7$.
11. $p = \frac{7}{4}$; $q = \frac{8}{5}$.
12. $x = -3$; $w = -\frac{4}{3}$.
13. $A = -2$; $B = 2$.
14. $M = 5$; $N = -2$.
15. $p = \frac{1}{4}$; $q = 1$.
16. $x = \frac{3}{2}$; $y = \frac{2}{3}$.
17. $c = \frac{2}{3}$; $d = -\frac{3}{2}$.
18. $e = -3$; $f = -2$.
19. $g = -2$; $k = \frac{1}{2}$.
20. $r = 4$; $s = -5$.

22 ALGEBRA

EXERCISE 103. Pages 227-228.

1. $x = 6$; $y = -10$.
2. $p = 12$; $q = -12$.
3. $m = 1$; $y = -2$.
4. $r = 6$; $s = 2$.
5. $t = \frac{2}{3}$; $w = -\frac{1}{2}$.
6. $r = 18$; $t = 6$.
7. $c = -1$; $d = 5$.
8. $x = 4$; $y = -3$.
9. $m = -3$; $n = 5$.
10. $a = -8$; $b = 5$.
11. $x = -1$; $y = -5$.
12. $x = -6$; $y = -3$.
13. $m = 3$; $n = -5$.
14. $r = 4$; $s = -5$.
15. $p = 10$; $w = 7$.
16. $x = 5$; $y = -4$.
17. $a = \frac{1}{2}$; $b = -2$.

EXERCISE 104. Pages 229-230.

1. $a = -3$; $b = 5$.
2. $c = 4$; $d = -6$.
3. $p = \frac{3}{4}$; $q = -\frac{2}{3}$.
4. $x = \frac{1}{3}$; $y = \frac{1}{2}$.
5. $r = \frac{1}{2}$; $s = -\frac{1}{3}$.
6. $w = -5$; $v = 2$.
7. $A = \frac{2}{3}$; $B = \frac{3}{4}$.
8. $r = \frac{2}{5}$; $t = -\frac{3}{7}$.
9. $x = -6$; $y = -2$.
10. $x = 3$; $y = 4$.

EXERCISE 105. Pages 231-236.

1. 24, 35.
2. 12, 20.
3. $\frac{10}{9}$.
4. $\frac{15}{19}$.
5. Anthracite, $4.50; bituminous, $2.60.
6. A, 24 yr.; B, 40 yr.
7. 15, 26.
8. Tower, 510 ft.; statue, 37 ft.
9. $\frac{9}{16}$.
10. Length, 486 ft.; width, 470 ft.
11. Base, 40 in.; equal sides, 50 in.
12. A, 35 yr.; B, 27 yr.
13. Yale, 1700; Princeton, 1746.
14. Short side, 15 in.; long side, 25 in.
15. Oxford, 872; Harvard, 1636.
16. First weight, 15 lb.; second weight, 20 lb.
17. 7, 5.
18. $\frac{2}{3}$, $\frac{4}{5}$.
19. 13 dimes, 21 quarters.
20. A, 68 yr.; B, 18 yr.
21. Length, 21 ft.; width, 17 ft.
22. Length, 85 ft.; width, 64 ft.
23. First weight, $61\frac{1}{4}$ lb.; second weight, 95 lb.
24. John, 70 lb.; James, 80 lb.
25. Crew, 10 mi. per hour in still water; current, 2 mi. per hour.

ANSWERS

26. Distance, 72 mi.; current, 3 mi. per hour.

27. Distance, 8 mi.; crew, 4 mi. per hour in still water.

28. Slow train, 25 mi. per hour; express train, 40 mi. per hour.

29. Length, 75 ft.; width, 54 ft.

30. Fore-wheel, 9 ft.; hind-wheel, 15 ft.

31. $1500 at 6%; $1000 at $4\frac{1}{2}$%.   **32.** $2000 at 5%; $3000 at 6%.

33. $1200 at 4%; $500 at 5%.   **34.** $800, 6 yr.; $300, 10 yr.

35. $105°, 75°$.   **36.** $35°, 13.5°, 131.5°$.

37. Ordinary train, 37 mi. per hour; fast train, 55.5 mi. per hour.

38. A, 14 da.; B, 10.5 da.   **39.** A, 12 da.; B, 18 da.

40. First man, $15,000 at $4\frac{1}{2}$%; second man, $18,000 at $3\frac{1}{2}$%; third man, $13,000 at $5\frac{1}{2}$%.

EXERCISE 106. Pages 237–238.

6. 84.   **7.** 72.   **8.** 97.   **9.** 83.   **10.** 59.

EXERCISE 107. Pages 239–241.

1. $x = \dfrac{35a + 24b}{23}; \; y = \dfrac{14a - 18b}{23}.$

2. $x = \dfrac{6a + 5b}{2a + 3b}; \; y = \dfrac{-8}{2a + 3b}.$ **3.** $x = \dfrac{np - mq}{4p - m}; \; y = \dfrac{4q - n}{4p - m}.$

4. $x = \dfrac{2b + c}{5a}; \; y = \dfrac{b - 2c}{5}.$ **5.** $x = \dfrac{dp - en}{dm - cn}; \; y = \dfrac{em - cp}{dm - cn}.$

6. $x = a + b; \; y = 2a.$ **7.** $x = -2a; \; y = b.$

8. $x = \dfrac{3b}{2}; \; y = -\dfrac{a}{2}.$ **9.** $x = 2a; \; y = a - b.$

10. $x = c - d; \; y = 2c + d.$ **11.** $x = \dfrac{1}{a}; \; y = \dfrac{1}{b}.$

12. $x = s; \; y = -r.$ **13.** $x = -\dfrac{m + n}{m}; \; y = -\dfrac{m + n}{n}.$

14. $x = \dfrac{b - a^2}{1 - ab}; \; y = \dfrac{a - b^2}{1 - ab}.$ **15.** $\dfrac{m + n}{2}; \dfrac{m - n}{2}.$

16. Larger, $\dfrac{cd}{1 + d}$; smaller, $\dfrac{c}{1 + d}$.   **17.** Larger, $\dfrac{rs + t}{1 + s}$; smaller, $\dfrac{r - t}{1 + s}$.

18. A, $\dfrac{4k}{10 - k}$; B, $\dfrac{4k}{k - 6}$.

24 ALGEBRA

19. Tens' digit, $\dfrac{ab-a}{9+b}$; units' digit, $\dfrac{10\,a}{9+b}$.

20. $\dfrac{3\,b-4\,a}{2\,b-3\,a}$.

21. First, $\dfrac{ac+d}{a+b}$; second, $\dfrac{bc-d}{a+b}$.

22. Greater, $\dfrac{a^2-b^2}{ac-bd}$; less, $\dfrac{a^2-b^2}{bc-ad}$.

23. $T=\dfrac{mng}{m+n}$; $f=\dfrac{mg}{m+n}$.

24. $T=\dfrac{2\,mng}{m+n}$; $f=\dfrac{(m-n)g}{m+n}$.

EXERCISE 108. Pages 242–243.

1. $a=-4$; $b=-5$; $c=-6$.
2. $x=-1$; $y=-2$; $z=2$.
3. $m=2$; $n=5$; $p=-1$.
4. $r=2$; $s=-3$; $t=5$.
5. $r=4$; $t=-3$; $x=-5$.
6. $A=\tfrac{1}{2}$; $B=3$; $C=-2$.
7. $x=\tfrac{1}{2}$; $y=\tfrac{1}{3}$; $z=\tfrac{1}{4}$.
8. $x=-\tfrac{3}{2}$; $y=\tfrac{3}{13}$; $z=-\tfrac{3}{10}$.
9. $x=\dfrac{5\,b-a-3\,c}{6}$; $y=\dfrac{a+b-3\,c}{6}$; $z=\dfrac{a-b+c}{2}$.
10. $x=\dfrac{-2}{b+c}$; $y=\dfrac{-2}{a+c}$; $z=\dfrac{-2}{a+b}$.
11. A, 60°; B, 40°; C, 80°.
12. a, 80 in.; b, 50 in.; c, 45 in.
13. a, 84 in.; b, 63 in.; c, 72 in.
14. Atlantic, 35,000,000 sq. mi.; Pacific, 71,000,000 sq. mi.; Indian, 28,000,000 sq. mi.
15. Water, 1 cup; sugar, $2\tfrac{1}{2}$ cups; glucose, $\tfrac{1}{3}$ cup.
17. 896.
18. A, 15 days; B, 30 days; C, 60 days.

EXERCISE 109. Page 245.

16. ± 56.
17. $\pm 54\,x^2 y$.
18. $\pm 65\,ab$.
19. $\pm 75\,m^2 n^3$.
20. $\pm 72\,r^2 s$.
21. $\pm 105\,xy^2 z$.

EXERCISE 110. Pages 246–247.

4. $\pm(2\,x^2+x+1)$.
5. $\pm(a^2-3\,a+1)$.
6. $\pm(3\,x^2-4\,x-2)$.
7. $\pm(3\,a^2-5\,a+4)$.
8. $\pm(5\,x^2-2\,xy-3\,y^2)$.
9. $\pm(2\,a^3+3\,a^2-1)$.

10. $\pm (4\,m^2 + mx^2 - 3\,x^4)$.
11. $\pm (1 - x + x^2 - x^3)$.
12. $\pm (x^3 - 2\,xa^2 + 5\,a^3)$.
13. $\pm (3\,x + 5\,y - 4\,z)$.
14. $\pm (a - b - c)$.
15. $\pm (3\,a^2 - 2\,ab - 5\,b^2)$.
16. $\pm (2\,x^2 + 5\,x - 7)$.
17. $\pm (7\,m^2 - mn - 4\,n^2)$.
18. $\pm \left(m + 4 - \dfrac{2}{m}\right)$.
19. $\pm \left(x - \dfrac{y}{2} - \dfrac{3\,y^2}{2x}\right)$.
20. $\pm \left(\dfrac{4}{3} + \dfrac{x}{a} - \dfrac{2\,x^2}{a^2}\right)$.

EXERCISE 111. Page 250.

1. ± 39.
2. ± 67.
3. ± 75.
4. ± 94.
5. ± 153.
6. ± 234.
7. ± 417.
8. ± 205.
9. ± 21.5.
10. ± 3.14.
11. ± 3.46.
12. ± 4.23.

EXERCISE 112. Page 250.

1. ± 1.732.
2. ± 2.236.
3. ± 2.449.
4. ± 2.645.
5. ± 3.162.
6. ± 3.316.
7. ± 3.605.
8. ± 3.741.
9. ± 3.872.
10. ± 4.123.
11. ± 4.358.
12. ± 4.582.

EXERCISE 113. Page 251.

1. ± 1.000.
2. ± 1.414.
3. ± 1.732.
4. ± 2.000.
5. ± 2.236.
6. ± 2.449.
7. ± 2.645.
8. ± 2.828.
9. ± 3.000.
10. ± 3.162.
11. ± 3.316.
12. ± 3.464.
13. ± 3.605.
14. ± 3.741.
15. ± 3.872.
16. ± 4.000.
17. ± 4.123.
18. ± 4.242.
19. ± 4.358.
20. ± 4.472.
21. ± 4.582.
22. ± 4.690.
23. ± 4.795.
24. ± 4.898.
25. ± 5.000.
26. ± 5.099.
27. ± 5.196.
28. ± 5.291.
29. ± 5.385.
30. ± 5.477.
31. ± 5.567.
32. ± 5.656.
33. ± 5.744.
34. ± 5.830.
35. ± 5.916.
36. ± 6.000.
37. ± 6.082.
38. ± 6.164.
39. ± 6.245.
40. ± 6.324.
41. ± 6.403.
42. ± 6.480.
43. ± 6.557.
44. ± 6.633.
45. ± 6.708.
46. ± 6.782.
47. ± 6.855.
48. ± 6.928.
49. ± 7.000.
50. ± 7.071.

EXERCISE 114. Page 252.

1. $\pm \frac{1}{2}\sqrt{3}$, or $\pm .866$.
2. $\pm \frac{1}{3}\sqrt{5}$, or $\pm .745$.
3. $\pm \frac{1}{4}\sqrt{7}$, or $\pm .661$.
4. $\pm \frac{1}{3}\sqrt{3}$, or $\pm .577$.
5. $\pm \frac{1}{2}\sqrt{2}$, or $\pm .707$.
6. $\pm \frac{1}{2}\sqrt{10}$, or $\pm .632$.
7. $\pm \frac{1}{7}\sqrt{21}$, or $\pm .654$.
8. $\pm \frac{1}{4}\sqrt{10}$, or $\pm .790$.
9. $\pm \frac{1}{6}\sqrt{30}$, or $\pm .912$.
10. $\pm \frac{1}{7}\sqrt{28}$, or $\pm .755$.
11. $\pm \frac{1}{5}\sqrt{45}$, or ± 1.341.
12. $\pm \frac{1}{10}\sqrt{30}$, or $\pm .547$.
13. $\pm \frac{1}{11}\sqrt{77}$, or $\pm .797$.
14. $\pm \frac{1}{6}\sqrt{10}$, or $\pm .527$.
15. $\pm \frac{1}{9}\sqrt{6}$, or $\pm .272$.

EXERCISE 115. Page 253.

1. $7\sqrt{3}$, or 12.124.
2. $4\sqrt{2}$, or 5.656.
3. $2\sqrt{5}$, or 4.472.
4. $5\sqrt{3}$, or 8.660.
5. $5\sqrt{7}$, or 13.225.
6. $4\sqrt{2}$, or 5.656.
7. $\frac{7}{3}\sqrt{3}$, or 4.041.
8. $\frac{3}{10}\sqrt{10}$, or $.948$.
9. $\frac{1}{3}(3\sqrt{6} + \sqrt{3})$, or 1.008.
10. $-\frac{7}{4}\sqrt{6}$, or -4.285.
11. $\frac{1}{3}(2 + \sqrt{5})$, or 1.412.
12. $\frac{1}{2}(1 - \sqrt{3})$, or $-.366$.
13. $\frac{1}{5}(3 + \sqrt{2})$, or $.882$.
14. $\frac{1}{7}(\sqrt{2} - 1)$, or $.059$.
15. $-\frac{3}{11}$, or $-.272$.
16. $\frac{2}{3}(1 + \sqrt{3}$, or 1.821.
17. $\frac{1}{6}(\sqrt{6} - 5)$, or $-.425$.
18. $\frac{1}{7}(\sqrt{14} - 3)$, or $.105$.
19. $\frac{1}{8}(-3 + 2\sqrt{10})$, or $.415$.
20. $\frac{1}{5}(3 - \sqrt{95})$, or -1.349.

EXERCISE 116. Pages 255-256.

1. ± 5.
2. ± 4.
3. ± 6.
4. ± 2.
5. $\pm \sqrt{3}$, or ± 1.732.
6. $\pm \sqrt{15}$, or ± 3.872.
7. $\pm \frac{1}{3}\sqrt{7}$, or $\pm .881$.
8. $\pm \frac{2}{11}\sqrt{11}$, or $\pm .603$.
9. $\pm \frac{2}{3}\sqrt{3}$, or ± 1.154.
10. $\pm \sqrt{6}$, or ± 2.449.
11. ± 2.
12. $\pm \sqrt{11}$, or ± 3.316.
13. ± 8.
14. $\pm \frac{1}{2}$.
16. $\pm \sqrt{m - a^2}$.
17. $\pm \frac{1}{2}\sqrt{2(c-a)}$.
18. $\pm \frac{1}{a}\sqrt{am}$.
19. $\pm \frac{d}{2c}\sqrt{2c}$.
20. $\pm \frac{1}{h}\sqrt{2ch}$.
21. $\pm \frac{1}{3m}\sqrt{3m(n+p)}$.

ANSWERS

EXERCISE 117. Pages 257-258.

1. $27+$ ft.   2. 37.4 ft.   3. 21.5 in. and 64.5 in.   4. $4.1\,a$.
5. $a.\ \pm\sqrt{b^2-c^2};\ b.\ \pm\sqrt{b^2-a^2}$.   6. 12.   7. 48.   8. $2.8\,a$.
9. 8.6.   10. $a.\ .8\,s;\ .4\,s^2$.   11. 254.5 sq. in.   12. 117.7 ft.
13. $a.\ \dfrac{1}{22}\sqrt{154\,A};\ b.\ \dfrac{1}{\pi}\sqrt{\pi A}$.   14. 1021.4 cu. ft.   15. $\dfrac{1}{2}\sqrt{69}$.
16. $\dfrac{1}{\pi h}\sqrt{\pi Vh}$.   17. $\dfrac{1}{2\pi}\sqrt{\pi S}$.   18. $\dfrac{1}{\pi h}\sqrt{3\pi Vh}$.
19. $a.\ 144$ ft.; $b.\ 400$ ft.   20. 7.5 sec.   21. 5.8 sec.   22. $\dfrac{1}{g}\sqrt{2\,gs}$.
23. $\dfrac{1}{m}\sqrt{fmr}$.

EXERCISE 118. Page 259.

1. $8, -3$.   2. $3, -2.5$.   3. $-4, -2.5$.   4. $1.25, -\tfrac{2}{3}$.
5. $0, 1.4$.   6. $0, 5\tfrac{1}{3}$.   7. $-a, \dfrac{a}{2}$.   8. $\dfrac{-m}{4}, \dfrac{-3\,m}{2}$.
9. $\tfrac{5}{2}k, -\tfrac{2}{3}k$.   10. $5\,p, \tfrac{3}{5}p$.   11. $5, -3.5$.   12. $-2, \tfrac{5}{6}$.
13. $\tfrac{1}{3}, \tfrac{3}{4}$.   14. $-10, -1.6$.   15. $0, -5$.   16. $5, 5\tfrac{1}{3}$.
17. $10, 5$.   18. $2, 13$.   19. $-3, 2.8$.   20. $-7, 1.5$.

EXERCISE 119. Page 262.

1. -3.   2. 3.5.   3. $4, -4$.   4. $4, -3$.   5. $6, 1$.   6. $-5, -1$.

EXERCISE 120. Pages 265-266.

1. $5, -1$.   2. $3, -11$.   3. $9, -3$.   4. $-4, -6$.   5. $5, -3$.
6. $2 \pm 2\sqrt{2}$; or $4.828, -.828$.   7. $-3 \pm \sqrt{10}$; or $.162, -6.162$.
8. $1 \pm \sqrt{2}$; or $2.414, -.414$.   9. $4 \pm 2\sqrt{5}$; or $8.472, -.472$.
10. $5 \pm \sqrt{30}$; or $10.477, -.477$.   11. $-4, -1$.   12. $5, 2$.
13. $2, 1$.   14. $-6, 5$.   15. $10, 3$.   16. $6, -1$.
17. $\dfrac{-9 \pm 5\sqrt{5}}{2}$; or $1.090, -10.090$.   18. $\dfrac{15 \pm \sqrt{161}}{2}$; or $13.844, 1.156$.
20. $2, -\tfrac{2}{5}$.   21. $2, -\tfrac{4}{5}$.   22. $\dfrac{-3 \pm \sqrt{58}}{7}$; or $.659, -1.516$.
23. $1, -\tfrac{2}{3}$.   24. $1, -\tfrac{2}{5}$.   25. $\dfrac{5 \pm \sqrt{473}}{8}$; or $3.343, -2.093$.
26. $1, -\tfrac{1}{3}$.   27. $\tfrac{5}{3}, -1$.   28. $\tfrac{3}{5}, -1$.   29. $\tfrac{3}{2}, \tfrac{1}{2}$.   30. $\tfrac{7}{3}, -1$.

31. $-\frac{3}{2}, 3$.

32. $\dfrac{-3 \pm \sqrt{29}}{10}$; or $-.838, .238$.

33. $\dfrac{5 \pm \sqrt{265}}{12}$; or $1.773, -.939$.

34. $-\frac{3}{5}, \frac{1}{5}$.

35. $\dfrac{1 \pm \sqrt{2}}{2}$; or $1.207, -.207$.

36. $-6 \pm \sqrt{42}$; or $.480, -12.480$.

37. $-1, \frac{7}{5}$.

38. $\dfrac{1 \pm \sqrt{41}}{2}$; $3.701, -2.701$.

39. $-1, \frac{4}{5}$.

40. $\dfrac{5 \pm \sqrt{67}}{3}$; or $4.395, -1.061$.

41. $\dfrac{8 \pm \sqrt{94}}{3}$; or $5.898, -.565$.

42. $\frac{2}{3}, -\frac{6}{5}$.

43. $3 \pm \sqrt{3}$; or $4.732, 1.268$.

44. $6, 8$.

45. $\dfrac{4 \pm \sqrt{13}}{3}$; or $2.535, .131$.

EXERCISE 121. Page 267.

1. $-a \pm \sqrt{a^2 + 3}$.
2. $-a \pm \sqrt{a^2 - b}$.
3. $-2 \pm \sqrt{4 + c}$.
4. $\dfrac{-3 \pm \sqrt{9 - 4m}}{2}$.
5. $\dfrac{-3 \pm \sqrt{8n + 9}}{4}$.
6. $\dfrac{-2a \pm \sqrt{4a^2 - 2b}}{2}$.
7. $\dfrac{-3a \pm \sqrt{16t + 9a^2}}{2}$.
8. $1, -(2m + 1)$.
9. $2a \pm 3b$.
10. $\dfrac{-1 \pm \sqrt{1 - a}}{a}$.
11. $\dfrac{-2t \pm \sqrt{4t^2 + 5r}}{r}$.
12. $\dfrac{-d \pm \sqrt{d^2 - cp}}{c}$.
13. $x = \dfrac{-m \pm \sqrt{m^2 - 4n}}{2}$.
14. $\dfrac{-b \pm \sqrt{b^2 - 4ac}}{2a}$.

EXERCISE 122. Page 269.

1. $1, \frac{3}{4}$.
2. $-\frac{5}{3}, -\frac{1}{2}$.
3. $12, -6$.
4. $10, -3$.
5. $\frac{11}{3}, -3$.
6. $\dfrac{-5 \pm \sqrt{13}}{6}$; or, $-1.434, -.232$.
7. $\dfrac{5 \pm \sqrt{5}}{10}$; or, $.723, .276$.
8. $\dfrac{11 \pm \sqrt{73}}{12}$; or, $1.628, .204$.
9. $\dfrac{3 \pm \sqrt{17}}{4}$; or, $1.780, -.280$.
10. $\dfrac{-1 \pm \sqrt{5}}{2}$; or, $.618, -1.618$.

11. $2 \pm \sqrt{2}$; or, 3.414, .586.
12. $2, \frac{1}{8}$.
13. $\frac{2}{5}, -2$.
14. $\frac{-8 \pm \sqrt{37}}{9}$; or, $-.213, -1.564$.
15. $\frac{5}{3}, -\frac{1}{5}$.
16. $3, -\frac{3}{2}$.
17. $\frac{-1 \pm \sqrt{145}}{6}$; or, $-2.173, 1.840$.
18. $\frac{5 \pm \sqrt{19}}{2}$; or, 4.679, .321.
19. $\frac{2 \pm \sqrt{19}}{5}$; or, $1.271, -.471$.

EXERCISE 123. Pages 270-272.

1. $-6, \frac{1}{4}$.
2. $-3, 1\frac{7}{5}$.
3. $-6, 5$.
4. $6 \pm \sqrt{3}$; or 7.732, 4.268.
5. $\frac{-5 \pm \sqrt{181}}{6}$; or, $-3.075, 1.408$.
6. $3, -\frac{4}{5}$.
7. $5 \pm \sqrt{30}$; or, $10.477, -.477$.
8. $1, -\frac{2}{3}$.
9. $\frac{5 \pm 5\sqrt{5}}{2}$; or, $8.090, -3.090$.
10. $\frac{1}{4}, \frac{1}{2}$.
11. $\frac{5 \pm \sqrt{29}}{2}$; or, $5.192, -.192$.
12. $-1\frac{9}{8}, 3$.
13. $-3, -4$.
14. $-1, 4$.
15. $-3, \frac{5}{7}$.
16. $2, 1\frac{5}{4}$.
17. -1.
18. $\frac{-11 \pm \sqrt{329}}{4}$; or, $1.784, -7.284$.
19. $-\frac{1}{9}, -\frac{1}{8}$.
20. $-\frac{2}{7}$.
22. $5c, c$.
23. $\frac{r(1 \pm \sqrt{7})}{3}$.
24. $p \pm \sqrt{p^2 - c^2}$.
25. $\frac{p \pm \sqrt{p^2 - 4c^2 + 4d^2}}{2}$.
26. $\frac{-a \pm \sqrt{a^2 + 2gs}}{g}$.
27. $1, 2P - 1$.
28. $a, -1$.
29. $-a, -b$.
30. $1, -\frac{2b}{a}$.
31. $\frac{3n}{m}$; or, $-2n$.

ALGEBRA

EXERCISE 124. Pages 272-275.

1. $1, -\frac{3}{4}$.
2. $-2, \frac{5}{3}$.
3. $17, 18; -18, -17$.
4. $4, 5, 6; -6, -5, -4$.
5. $18, 19; -19, -18$.
6. $\frac{2}{3}; \frac{3}{4}$.
7. Width, 17 ft.; length, 21 ft.
8. $\frac{8}{5}$.
9. Length, 220 ft.; width, 130 ft.
10. Altitude, 7 in.; base, 18 in.
11. Altitude, 32 ft.; base, 18 ft.
12. Altitude, 49 ft.; base, 25 ft.
13. Altitude, 125 ft.; base, 30 ft.
14. Altitude, 63 ft.; base, 27 ft.
15. Altitude, 12 ft.; base, 16 ft.
16. Altitude, 24 ft.; base, 10 ft.
17. 15 in., 15 in., 5 in.
18. 21 mi. per hour.
19. 30 mi. per hour.
20. 6 mi. per hour.
21. 20 mi. per hour.
22. Large pipe, 3 hr.; small pipe, 6 hr.
23. 3 mi. per hour.
24. 10 ft.
25. 15 rd.
26. $\frac{3}{11}$; or, $\frac{-15}{-7}$.
27. Inside city, 10 mi. per hour; outside city, 25 mi. per hour.
28. $\frac{2}{4}$.
29. Bicyclist, 8 mi. per hour; automobilist, 20 mi. per hour.
30. Fore wheel, 12 ft.; hind wheel, 16 ft.

EXERCISE 125. Page 276.

1. $\pm 7i$.
2. $\pm 6i$.
3. $\pm 10i$.
4. $\pm 9ai$.
5. $\pm 5i$.
6. $\pm 8i$.
7. $\pm 12i$.
8. $\pm 11abi$.
9. $\pm \frac{1}{2}i$.
10. $\pm \frac{2}{3}i$.
11. $\pm \frac{4}{5}i$.
12. $\pm \frac{3}{7}i$.
13. $\pm i\sqrt{3}$.
14. $\pm 4i\sqrt{2}$.
15. $\pm 3i\sqrt{2}$.
16. $\pm 6i\sqrt{2}$.
17. $\pm i\sqrt{5}$.
18. $\pm 3i\sqrt{3}$.
19. $\pm 2i\sqrt{3}$.
20. $\pm 2i\sqrt{7}$.
22. $\pm \frac{i\sqrt{2}}{3}$.
23. $\pm \frac{i\sqrt{3}}{2}$.
24. $\pm \frac{i\sqrt{5}}{6}$.
25. $\pm \frac{2i\sqrt{2}}{3}$.
26. $\pm \frac{5i\sqrt{3}}{2}$.
27. $\pm \frac{2i\sqrt{5}}{7}$.
28. $\pm \frac{4i\sqrt{2}}{5}$.
29. $\pm \frac{5i\sqrt{5}}{8}$.
30. $\pm \frac{3i\sqrt{7}}{10}$.

EXERCISE 126. Pages 277-278.

2. $9i$.
3. $-6i$.
4. i.
5. $23i$.
6. 0.
7. $7i$.
8. $2ai$.
9. $6xi$.
10. $4i\sqrt{3}$.
11. $i\sqrt{2}$.
12. $5i\sqrt{5}$.
13. $4i\sqrt{7}$.
14. $-2i\sqrt{6}$.
15. $i\sqrt{11}$.
17. $\frac{1 \pm i\sqrt{3}}{2}$

ANSWERS 31

18. $\dfrac{2 \pm 2i}{3}$. 19. $\dfrac{3 \pm i\sqrt{5}}{4}$. 20. $\dfrac{3 \pm 2i\sqrt{7}}{5}$. 21. $\dfrac{7 \pm 3i\sqrt{3}}{10}$.

22. $\dfrac{6 \pm 5i\sqrt{3}}{13}$.

EXERCISE 127. Page 279.

1. $-1 \pm i\sqrt{2}$.
2. $\dfrac{-3 \pm i\sqrt{7}}{2}$.
3. $\dfrac{1 \pm i\sqrt{15}}{4}$.
4. $\dfrac{1 \pm i\sqrt{14}}{3}$.
5. $\dfrac{7 \pm i\sqrt{11}}{10}$.
6. $\dfrac{9 \pm i\sqrt{79}}{16}$.
7. $\dfrac{15 \pm i\sqrt{39}}{22}$.
8. $\dfrac{3 \pm i\sqrt{31}}{4}$.
9. $\dfrac{-9 \pm i\sqrt{39}}{6}$.
10. $\dfrac{-5 \pm i\sqrt{51}}{2}$.
11. $\dfrac{-5 \pm i\sqrt{29}}{9}$.
12. $\dfrac{(5 \pm i\sqrt{31})a}{4}$.
13. $\dfrac{(2 \pm i\sqrt{2})w}{3}$.
14. $\dfrac{(7 \pm i\sqrt{11})t}{10}$.

EXERCISE 128. Pages 281–282.

1. $a^2 + 2ab + b^2 - 25$.
2. $m^2 + 2mn + n^2 - 4p^2$.
3. $100 - r^2 - 2rs - s^2$.
4. $9p^2 - c^2 - 2cd - d^2$.
5. $c^2 + 4cd + 4d^2 - 121a^2$.
6. $a^2 - 2ab + b^2 - c^2$.
7. $x^2 - 2xy + y^2 - z^2$.
8. $a^4 - a^2 + 2a - 1$.
9. $a^4 + a^2b^2 + b^4$.
10. $a^2 - 4b^2 + 12bc - 9c^2$.
11. $9x^2 - 16y^2 - 16yz - 4z^2$.
12. $x^4 - 5x^2 + 4$.
13. $a^2 + 2ar + r^2 - c^2 + 2cd - d^2$
14. $a^2 - 2ab + b^2 - m^2 - 2mn - n^2$
15. $4x^2 - 4xy + y^2 - z^2 - 2zw - w^2$
17. $m^2 + 2mn + n^2 - 9m - 9n + 20$
18. $x^2 - 2xy + y^2 + 2x - 2y - 48$
19. $6x^2 - 5xy - 5xz + y^2 + 2yz + z^2$
20. $x^2 + 6xy + 9y^2 + 5xz + 15yz - 150z^2$.
21. $r^2 + 4rs + 4s^2 + 4rt + 8st - 21t^2$.
22. $12p^2 - 31pq - 31pr + 20q^2 + 40qr + 20r^2$.
23. $x^4 + 4x^3 - 8x - 5$.
24. $a^2 + 2ab + b^2 - 10a - 10b + 25$
25. $36 + 12m - 12n + m^2 - 2mn + n^2$.
26. $4a^2 - 4ac - 4ad + c^2 + 2cd + d^2$.
27. $a^2 + 2ab + b^2 + 2ac + 2bc + c^2$.
28. $a^2 + 6ab + 9b^2 - 2ac - 6bc + c^2$.
29. $a^2 - 2ab + b^2 + 2ac - 2ad - 2bc + 2bd + c^2 - 2cd + d^2$.
30. $4r^2 + 4rs + s^2 - 4rt - 2st + 4rx + 2sx + t^2 - 2tx + x^2$.
31. $9a^2 - 6ab + b^2 + 12ac - 4bc - 6ad + 2bd + 4c^2 - 4cd + d^2$.

ALGEBRA

EXERCISE 129. Pages 282-283.

1. $\{a+b+c\}\{a+b-c\}$.
2. $\{m-n+x\}\{m-n-x\}$.
3. $\{x+y+z\}\{x-y-z\}$.
4. $\{m+n-p\}\{m-n+p\}$.
5. $\{7x-y\}\{7x-3y\}$.
6. $\{a+b+20\}\{a+b+3\}$.
7. $\{x-y+9\}\{x-y-7\}$.
8. $\{x+y-9\}\{x+y+4\}$.
9. $\{r+s+5t\}\{r+s-t\}$.
10. $\{p-q+10r\}\{p-q-2r\}$.
11. $(x+2)^2(x-1)(x-3)$.
12. $\{3m-3n-2\}^2$.
13. $\{x-y+m-n\}\{x-y-m+n\}$.
14. $(a-1)^4$.
15. $(n+1)^2(n-1)^2$.
16. $(x+2)^2(x+1)^2$.
17. $(3a+2)^2(3a-2)^2$.
18. $(a^2+7a+24)(a^2+7a-4)$.
19. $(m+n+16)(m+n-9)$.
20. $(x+3)(x-2)(x+4)(x-3)$.
21. $(x+y-z)(x^2+2xy+y^2+xz+yz+z^2)$.
22. $(r+s+2t)(r^2+2rs+s^2-2rt-2st+4t^2)$.
23. $2n(3m^2+n^2)$.
24. $(2a+1)(a^2+a+1)$.
25. $-(a+2b)(7a^2+10ab+4b^2)$.
26. $2x(x^2+3y^2)$.
27. $-(3x^4+3x^2+1)$.
28. $(2m+n)(13m^2-5mn+n^2)$.
29. $(a-3b)(7a^2+3ab+3b^2)$.
30. $18y(x^2+3y^2)$.

EXERCISE 130. Pages 283-284.

1. $\{a-b+c\}\{a-b-c\}$.
2. $\{m+n+p\}\{m+n-p\}$.
3. $\{a+x+y\}\{a-x-y\}$.
4. $\{x+y-z\}\{x-y+z\}$.
5. $\{a+b+2\}\{a+b-2\}$.
6. $\{1+m-n\}\{1-m+n\}$.
7. $\{3a-4b+2c\}\{3a-4b-2c\}$.
8. $\{4x+2y-5z\}\{4x-2y+5z\}$.
9. $\{m-2n+x\}\{m-2n-x\}$.
10. $\{2a+b+3\}\{2a-b-3\}$.
11. $\{5x+y+3z\}\{5x+y-3z\}$.
12. $\{a-b+c-d\}\{a-b-c+d\}$.
13. $\{a+x+b-y\}\{a+x-b+y\}$.
14. $\{x-m+y+n\}\{x-m-y-n\}$.
15. $\{x+y+a+b\}\{x+y-a-b\}$.
16. $\{2a+b+3c-2\}\{2a+b-3c+2\}$.
17. $\{x-4y+z+6\}\{x-4y-z-6\}$.
18. $\{m-5a+3n-b\}\{m-5a-3n+b\}$.
19. $\{2a-3b+c-d\}\{2a-3b-c+d\}$.
20. $\{3x^2-z+2x+5y\}\{3x^2-z-2x-5y\}$.

EXERCISE 131. Page 285.

1. $\{x^2 + x + 1\}\{x^2 - x + 1\}$.
2. $\{a^2 + am + m^2\}\{a^2 - am + m^2\}$.
3. $\{c^2 + 2c + 5\}\{c^2 - 2c + 5\}$.
4. $\{y^2 + 3y + 6\}\{y^2 - 3y + 6\}$.
5. $\{1 + 2t + 3t^2\}\{1 - 2t + 3t^2\}$.
6. $\{1 + 3r + 4r^2\}\{1 - 3r + 4r^2\}$.
7. $\{x^2 + 4xy + 2y^2\}\{x^2 - 4xy + 2y^2\}$.
8. $\{3m^2 + 5m + 1\}\{3m^2 - 5m + 1\}$.
9. $\{2y^2 + 6y + 1\}\{2y^2 - 6y + 1\}$.
10. $\{5x^2y^2 + xy - 1\}\{5x^2y^2 - xy - 1\}$
11. $\{2a^2 + ab + 3b^2\}\{2a^2 - ab + 3b^3\}$.
12. $\{3m^2 + 4mn + 5n^2\}\{3m^2 - 4mn + 5n^2\}$.
13. $\{2r^2 + 2rt - 7t^2\}\{2r^2 - 2rt - 7t^2\}$.
14. $\{3m^2n^4 + 5mn^2 + 4\}\{3m^2n^4 - 5mn^2 + 4\}$.
15. $\{2p^4 + 2p^2r - 5r^2\}\{2p^4 - 2p^2r - 5r^2\}$.
16. $\{3a^2 + 5ab + 7b^2\}\{3a^2 - 5ab + 7b^2\}$.
17. $\{2x^2 + 3xy^2 + 4y^4\}\{2x^2 - 3xy^2 + 4y^4\}$.
18. $\{3t^2 + tx - 5x^2\}\{3t^2 - tx - 5x^2\}$.
19. $\{4m^2n^2 + 5mn + 5\}\{4m^2n^2 - 5mn + 5\}$.
20. $\{5p^2 + 6py + 7y^2\}\{5p^2 - 6py + 7y^2\}$.
21. $\{x^2 + 2x + 2\}\{x^2 - 2x + 2\}$.
22. $\{y^2 + 4y + 8\}\{y^2 - 4y + 8\}$.
23. $\{x^2 + 2xy + 2y^2\}\{x^2 - 2xy + 2y^2\}$.
24. $\{2x^4 + 2x^2 + 1\}\{2x^4 - 2x^2 + 1\}$.

EXERCISE 132. Page 286.

1. $(2a - 3)(x + y)$.
2. $(5m + 2n)(r + s)$.
3. $(3p - r)(2x - y)$.
4. $(8 - m)(t + w)$.
5. $(a - d)(b + c)$.
6. $(a + m)(b + n)$.
7. $(a + b)(x - y)$.
8. $(a - b)(c - d)$.
9. $(a^2 + 1)(a + 1)$.
10. $(x^2 - 1)(4x - 5)$.
11. $(1 - 2a)(1 + 2a)(2 + 3a)$.
12. $(3x^2 + 1)(x + 2)$.
13. $(5x - 1)(2m - 3n)$.
14. $(ax - by)(a^2 + bc)$.
15. $(ac + bd)(ab - cd)$.
16. $(6a^2 - 11)(5a - 2)$.
17. $(8 + 3x^2)(7 - 4x)$.
18. $(a + 3b)(3x - y)$.
19. $(x^2 - 4y)(4x + y^2)$.
20. $(r + s)(t - n)$.
21. $(a + b - c)(r + s)$.
22. $(a + b)(x + y - z)$.
23. $(m + p)(a - b - c)$.
24. $(x^2 + y^2 - z^2)(x + y)$.
25. $(2a - 3b + c)(x - y)$.

EXERCISE 133. Pages 288-289.

1. $a^3 - a^2b + ab^2 - b^3$.
2. $a^3 + a^2b + ab^2 + b^3$.
3. $x^4 + x^3y + x^2y^2 + xy^3 + y^4$.
4. $m^4 + m^3 + m^2 + m + 1$.
5. $a^5b^5 - a^4b^4c + a^3b^3c^2 - a^2b^2c^3 + abc^4 - c^5$.
6. $a^6 + a^4b^2 + a^2b^4 + b^6$.
7. $x^4 - x^3z^3 + x^2z^6 - xz^9 + z^{12}$.
8. $1 - a + a^2 - a^3 + a^4$.
9. $16 + 8a + 4a^2 + 2a^3 + a^4$.
10. $m^6 + m^5n + m^4n^2 + m^3n^3 + m^2n^4 + mn^5 + n^6$.
11. $1 - 2a + 4a^2 - 8a^3$.
12. $27x^3 - 9x^2y + 3xy^2 - y^3$.
13. $8 + 4x + 2x^2 + x^3$.
14. $a^4 + 3a^3x + 9a^2x^2 + 27ax^3 + 81x^4$.
15. $27c^3 - 18c^2d + 12cd^2 - 8d^3$.
16. $(3x - 2y)(9x^2 + 6xy + 4y^2)$.
17. $(x^2 + y^2)(x + y)(x - y)$.
18. $(x - y^2)(x^4 + x^3y^2 + x^2y^4 + xy^6 + y^8)$.
19. $(2 - m)(16 + 8m + 4m^2 + 2m^3 + m^4)$.
20. $(rs - y)(r^2s^2 + rsy + y^2)(rs + y)(r^2s^2 - rsy + y^2)$.
21. $(a + b)(a^6 - a^5b + a^4b^2 - a^3b^3 + a^2b^4 - ab^5 + b^6)$.
22. $(2 + r)(16 - 8r + 4r^2 - 2r^3 + r^4)$.
23. Not factorable.
24. $(x^2 + y^2)(x^4 - x^2y^2 + y^4)$.
25. $(x + y)(x^4 - x^3y + x^2y^2 - xy^3 + y^4)(x - y)(x^4 + x^3y + x^2y^2 + xy^3 + y^4)$.
26. Not factorable.
27. $(m - 3)(m^4 + 3m^3 + 9m^2 + 27m + 81)$.
28. $(2 - x)(4 + 2x + x^2)(2 + x)(4 - 2x + x^2)$.
29. $(x^4 + 16)(x^2 + 4)(x + 2)(x - 2)$.
30. $(2a + 3b)(16a^4 - 24a^3b + 36a^2b^2 - 54ab^3 + 81b^4)$.

EXERCISE 134. Page 290.

1. $-4; -6$.
2. $310; -150$.
3. $-6; 26$.
4. $5; -100$.
5. $126; 16$.

ANSWERS

EXERCISE 135. Page 291.

1. Quotient: $x^2 - x + 1$.
   Remainder: -4.
2. Quotient: $2x^2 - 6x + 12$.
   Remainder: -27.
3. Quotient: $y^2 + 2y + 1$.
   Remainder: 12.
4. Quotient: $z^3 + 3z^2 + 9z - 18$.
   Remainder: 11.
5. Quotient: $t^4 + 2t^3 + 4t^2 + 8t + 16$.
   Remainder: 0.
6. Quotient: $3m^3 + 9m^2 + 2m + 6$.
   Remainder: 0.
7. Quotient: $4a^2 - 2a + 10$.
   Remainder: 0.
8. Quotient: $6c^3 - 3c^2 + 9c + 1$.
   Remainder: 2.
9. Quotient: $3x^2 + 7mx + 5m^2$.
   Remainder: 0.
10. Quotient: $4x^3 - 8bx^2 + b^2x - 2b^3$.
    Remainder: 0.

EXERCISE 136. Page 293.

1. $(x+3)(x-2)$.
2. $(x+1)(x-2)(x-1)$.
3. $(x+1)(x+2)(x-2)$.
4. $(x-1)(x-2)(x-3)$.
5. $(x-1)(x-3)(x+3)$.
6. $(y-1)(2y^2 + 3y + 3)$.
7. $(z+1)(z^2 - 3z + 3)$.
8. $(r+2)(r^2 + 2r + 2)$.
9. $(t-1)(t+1)(t^2 + t - 1)$.
10. $(m-1)(m-3)(m-2)(m+1)$.
11. $(x-m)(x^2 + 2mx + 2m^2)$.
12. $(x-p)(3x^2 + 3px + 4p^2)$.
13. $(x+r)(x^2 - 6rx + 6r^2)$.
14. $(x-t)(x+2t)(x+2t)$.
15. $(x-c)(x+c)(x-3c)(x+2c)$.

EXERCISE 137. Pages 293-295.

1. $(ab + cd)(ac - bd)$.
2. $\{a+b+c\}\{a-b-c\}$.
3. $4a^2b^2(a+b)(a^2 - ab + b^2)$.
4. $(x^2 + y^2)(x + y)$.
5. $(1+a^4)(1+a^2)(1+a)(1-a)$.
6. $(3a - 7b)(5c + 6d)$.
7. $(x-1)(x+3)(x+2)$.
8. $3ab^2(a-b)(a^4 + a^3b + a^2b^2 + ab^3 + b^4)$.
9. $\{a^2 + 2a - 9\}\{a^2 - 2a - 9\}$.

ALGEBRA

10. $(x+1)(x-2)(x^2+x+2)$.
11. $(x-6)(x+1)(x-4)(x-1)$.
12. $(4x^2+2xy-9y^2)(4x^2-2xy-9y^2)$.
13. $(a-1)^2(a^2+a+1)^2$.
14. $(3m+3n-2)^2$.
15. $\{2x+y^2\}\{16x^4-8x^3y^2+4x^2y^4-2xy^6+y^8\}$.
16. $(a+1)(a-3)(a+1)$.
17. $\{3x+5y+4z\}\{3x+5y-4z\}$.
18. $(a-x)(a^2+ax+x^2)(b+y)(b^2-by+y^2)$.
19. $\{m^2+25\}\{m+5\}\{m-5\}$.
20. $\{a-2\}\{a^2+2a+4\}\{a+1\}\{a^2-a+1\}$.
21. $(2-m)(64+32m+16m^2+8m^3+4m^4+2m^5+m^6)$.
22. $2bc\{a+b+c\}\{a-b-c\}$.
23. $(x+1)^2(x^4-x^3+x^2-x+1)^2$.
24. $(a^2+2)(a-5)$.
25. $(a-1)(a-4)(a^2+a+2)$.
26. $(a+1)(a^4-a^3+a^2-a+1)(a-1)(a^4+a^3+a^2+a+1)$.
27. $(a^4+1)(a+1)(a-1)$.
28. $(x^2+1)(x+1)(x-1)(x+1)(x^2-x+1)$.
29. $\{x+y-z\}\{x-y+z\}\{x+y+z\}\{x-y-z\}$.
30. $(a+b)(a^2-3ab+b^2)$.
31. H. C. F. $= a-7$.
    L. C. M. $= (a-7)(3a^2-1)(a+13)$.
32. H. C. F. $= a-b$.
    L. C. M. $= (a-b)(c+d)(a-5b)$.
33. H. C. F. $= a+b-c$.
    L. C. M. $= (a+b+c)(a+b-c)(a-b+c)$.
34. H. C. F. $= m(m-2)$.
    L. C. M. $= m(m+2)(m-2)(m+11)(2m^2-3)$.
35. H. C. F. $= 3a-b$.
    L. C. M. $= (3a-b)^2(9a^2+3ab+b^2)(a^2+b)$.
36. H. C. F. $= 2m-n$.
    L. C. M. $= (2m+n)^2(2m-n)^2(x+y)(4m^2+n^2)$.
37. H. C. F. $= a-x$.
    L. C. M. $= (a-x)^2(a+x)(3a^2+5x^2)$.

ANSWERS

38. H. C. F. $= x - 1$.
L. C. M. $= (x+2)(x-1)(x^2+x+2)$.

39. H. C. F. $= x - 2$.
L. C. M. $= (x-2)(x^2+x+1)(x+3)$.

40. H. C. F. $= x^2 - a^2$.
L. C. M. $= (x^2-a^2)(x+3a)(x+2a)$.

41. $\dfrac{x+y+z}{x+y-z}$.

42. $\dfrac{2m-5}{3m+4}$.

43. $\dfrac{x-y}{a+b}$.

44. $\dfrac{b-a}{d+2c}$.

45. $\dfrac{(x+y-z)^2}{(x-y-z)^2}$.

46. $(a+b)(a-b-c)$.

47. $\dfrac{a+b+c}{a-b+c}$.

48. 1.

50. $-a$; b.

51. $-(m+n)$; $m+n$.

52. $\dfrac{b}{a}$; c.

53. -3; $\dfrac{2d}{a}$.

54. $\dfrac{p}{3n}$; $-\dfrac{m}{a}$.

55. $-\dfrac{e}{d}$; $-\dfrac{c}{a}$.

EXERCISE 138. Page 296.

1. $+1$; -1; $+5$; -5.

2. $+3$; -3; $+1.414$; -1.414.

3. $+4$; -4; $+\sqrt{-1}$; $-\sqrt{-1}$.

4. $+2$; -2; $+\frac{1}{2}$; $-\frac{1}{2}$.

5. $+\frac{2}{3}$; $-\frac{2}{3}$; $\sqrt{-2}$; $-\sqrt{-2}$.

6. 1; 2; -3.

7. $+3$; -3; -2.

8. -1; 4; -3.

9. -2; 5; -3.

10. $\dfrac{-1+\sqrt{5}}{2}$, or $.61+$;
$\dfrac{-1-\sqrt{5}}{2}$, or $-1.61+$.
2.

11. -2; $1+\sqrt{2}$, or 2.414; $1-\sqrt{2}$, or $-.414$.

12. 1; $\dfrac{-1+\sqrt{-3}}{2}$; $\dfrac{-1-\sqrt{-3}}{2}$.

13. 2; $-1+\sqrt{-3}$; $-1-\sqrt{-3}$.

14. 5; $\sqrt{-1}$; $-\sqrt{-1}$.

15. 1; -2; 2; $2\sqrt{-1}$; $-2\sqrt{-1}$.

16. -2; 3; $\sqrt{-1}$; $-\sqrt{-1}$.

17. n; $-n$; m; $-m$.

18. c; $-c$; $-\dfrac{b}{a}$.

19. a; $\dfrac{-a+a\sqrt{3}}{2}$; $\dfrac{-a-a\sqrt{3}}{2}$.

20. $r\sqrt{-1}$; $-r\sqrt{-1}$; r; $-r$.

EXERCISE 139. Page 300.

1. Circle of radius 6.

2. Parabola, with y axis as axis.

3. Parabola, with y axis as axis.

ALGEBRA

4. Ellipse, with axes 12 and 6.
5. Hyperbola with axes 12 and 6.
6. Hyperbola, with x and y axes as asymptotes.
7. Circle with radius $\sqrt{55}$.
8. Ellipse with axes 4 and 8.

EXERCISE 140. Page 303.

1. $x=6, y=8$;
   $x=-8, y=-6$.
2. $x=3, y=5$;
   $x=-\frac{5}{2}; y=-6$.
3. $x=0, y=-3$;
   $x=4, y=5$.
4. $x=-7, y=1$;
   $x=1, y=-7$.
5. $x=7, y=-1$;
   $x=1, y=-7$;
   $x=-1, y=7$;
   $x=-7, y=1$.
6. $x=2, y=4$;
   $x=2, y=-4$;
   $x=-2, y=4$;
   $x=-2, y=-4$.
7. $x=4, y=0$;
   $x=-5, y=3$;
   $x=-5, y=-3$.
8. $x=2, y=2\sqrt{5}$;
   $x=2, y=-2\sqrt{5}$;
   $x=-2, y=2\sqrt{5}$;
   $x=-2, y=-2\sqrt{5}$.
9. An ellipse and three parabolas.

EXERCISE 141. Page 305.

1. $a=7, b=8$;
   $a=-8, b=-7$.
2. $x=2, y=3$;
   $x=10, y=-13$.
3. $x=-4, y=-3$;
   $x=\frac{2}{3}; y=-1\frac{3}{9}$.
4. $m=10, n=17$;
   $m=-3, n=4$.
5. $x=6, y=-9$;
   $x=-9, y=6$.
6. $x=6, y=9$;
   $x=-9, y=-6$.
7. $x=-10, y=1$;
   $x=1, y=-10$.
8. $x=5, y=-7$;
   $x=-7, y=5$.
9. $x=2, y=\frac{1}{2}$;
   $x=\frac{1}{2}, y=2$.
10. $c=\frac{2}{3}, d=-2$;
    $c=4, d=-7$.
11. $a=-4, b=3$;
    $a=\frac{4}{11}, b=-\frac{27}{11}$.
12. $x=-a, y=-(a+1)$;
    $x=a+1; y=a$.
13. $x=a-b, y=a+b$;
    $x=a+b, y=a-b$.
14. $a=6, b=10$;
    $a=10, b=6$.
15. $x=-3, y=\frac{4}{3}$;
    $x=8, y=16$.
16. $r=-\frac{36}{7}, t=-\frac{12}{7}$.
    $r=4, t=12$.

EXERCISE 142. Page 307.

1. $c=3, d=-\frac{7}{2}$;
   $c=-3, d=\frac{7}{2}$;
   $c=5, d=-\frac{1}{2}$;
   $c=-5, d=\frac{1}{2}$.
2. $x=\frac{1}{2}, y=-3$;
   $x=-\frac{1}{2}, y=3$;
   $x=\sqrt{2}, y=\sqrt{2}$;
   $x=-\sqrt{2}, y=-\sqrt{2}$.

ANSWERS

3. $m = \tfrac{1}{3}$, $n = -2$;
$m = -\tfrac{1}{3}$, $n = 2$;
$m = \tfrac{5}{9}\sqrt{3}$, $n = \tfrac{1}{3}\sqrt{3}$;
$m = -\tfrac{5}{9}\sqrt{3}$, $n = -\tfrac{1}{3}\sqrt{3}$.

4. $h = 10$, $r = 5$;
$h = -10$, $r = -5$;
$h = \tfrac{5}{2}\sqrt{2}$, $r = -\tfrac{15}{2}\sqrt{2}$;
$h = -\tfrac{5}{2}\sqrt{2}$, $r = \tfrac{15}{2}\sqrt{2}$.

5. $x = 2$, $y = -5$;
$x = -2$, $y = 5$;
$x = \tfrac{3}{2}\sqrt{2}$, $y = -\tfrac{7}{2}\sqrt{2}$;
$x = -\tfrac{3}{2}\sqrt{2}$, $y = \tfrac{7}{2}\sqrt{2}$.

6. $a = 3$, $b = 6$;
$a = -3$, $b = -6$;
$a = 4\sqrt{3}$, $b = -5\sqrt{3}$;
$a = -4\sqrt{3}$, $b = 5\sqrt{3}$.

7. $x = 2$, $y = -1$;
$x = -2$, $y = 1$;
$x = \tfrac{5}{13}\sqrt{-13}$, $y = \tfrac{3}{13}\sqrt{-13}$;
$x = -\tfrac{5}{13}\sqrt{-13}$, $y = -\tfrac{3}{13}\sqrt{-13}$.

8. $x = 4$, $y = 1$;
$x = -4$, $y = -1$;
$x = \tfrac{7}{3}\sqrt{2}$, $y = -\tfrac{4}{3}\sqrt{2}$;
$x = -\tfrac{7}{3}\sqrt{2}$, $y = \tfrac{4}{3}\sqrt{2}$.

9. $x = 2\sqrt{2}$, $y = -\sqrt{2}$;
$x = -2\sqrt{2}$, $y = \sqrt{2}$;
$x = \sqrt{19}$, $y = \tfrac{3}{5}\sqrt{19}$;
$x = -\sqrt{19}$, $y = -\tfrac{3}{5}\sqrt{19}$.

10. $m = 6$, $n = -4$;
$m = -6$, $n = 4$;
$m = \tfrac{14}{3}\sqrt{-3}$, $n = \tfrac{16}{3}\sqrt{-3}$;
$m = -\tfrac{14}{3}\sqrt{-3}$, $n = -\tfrac{16}{3}\sqrt{-3}$.

EXERCISE 143. Pages 308–309.

1. $x = 9$, $y = 5$.

2. $x = 4$, $y = 2$;
$x = 4$, $y = -2$;
$x = -4$, $y = 2$;
$x = -4$, $y = -2$.

3. $x = 5$, $y = -2$;
$x = 2$, $y = -5$.

4. $x = -3$, $y = -4$;
$x = 4$, $y = 3$.

5. $x = -1$, $y = -6$;
$x = -6$, $y = -1$.

6. $a = -7$, $b = 2$;
$a = 2$, $b = -7$.

7. $m = 2$, $n = 5$;
$m = -5$, $n = -2$.

8. $c = \tfrac{5}{3}$, $d = -3$;
$c = -1$, $d = 5$.

9. $x = 2$, $y = 4$;
$x = 4$, $y = 2$.

10. $x = 8$, $y = -2$;
$x = -2$, $y = 8$.

11. $x = -2$, $y = -5$;
$x = 5$, $y = 2$.

12. $x = 3$, $y = -1$;
$x = -3$, $y = -3$.

13. $x = -8$, $y = -4$;
$x = 2$, $y = 1$.

14. $x = 3a$, $y = -a$;
$x = -a$, $y = 3a$.

15. $f = \tfrac{1}{4}$, $g = \tfrac{1}{3}$;
$f = \tfrac{1}{3}$, $g = \tfrac{1}{4}$.

EXERCISE 144. Pages 310–311.

1. $x=6, y=2$;
   $x=-6, y=-2$;
   $x=2, y=6$;
   $x=-2, y=-6$.

2. $A=-\frac{5}{2}, B=16$;
   $A=8, B=-5$;
   $A=\frac{3}{2}, B=8$;
   $A=4, B=3$.

3. $w=3, t=1$;
   $w=3, t=-1$;
   $w=-3, t=1$;
   $w=-3, t=-1$.

4. $m=\frac{3}{5}, p=-\frac{4}{5}$;
   $m=-\frac{3}{5}, p=\frac{4}{5}$;
   $m=\frac{4}{5}, p=-\frac{3}{5}$;
   $m=-\frac{4}{5}, p=\frac{3}{5}$.

5. $x=3, y=5$;
   $x=3, y=-5$;
   $x=-3, y=5$;
   $x=-3, y=-5$.

6. $x=\frac{4}{3}, v=\frac{19}{6}$;
   $x=-3, v=1$;
   $x=-\frac{4}{3}, v=-\frac{19}{6}$;
   $x=3, v=-1$.

7. $r=-5, t=-6$.

8. $c=8, d=-11$;
   $c=11, d=-8$.

9. $x=3, y=9$;
   $x=9, y=3$.

10. $p=2, s=-1$;
    $p=-2, s=1$;
    $p=\sqrt{-1}, s=2\sqrt{-1}$;
    $p=-\sqrt{-1}, s=-2\sqrt{-1}$.

11. $a=5, b=4$;
    $a=5, b=-4$;
    $a=-4, b=\frac{1}{2}\sqrt{46}$;
    $a=-4, b=-\frac{1}{2}\sqrt{46}$.

12. $x=a+1, y=a-1$;
    $x=a-1, y=a+1$.

13. $m=6, n=3$;
    $m=-6, n=3$;
    $m=6, n=-3$;
    $m=-6, n=-3$.

14. $x=-a, y=-(a+1)$;
    $x=a+1, y=a$.

15. $t=2, v=-2$;
    $t=-2, v=2$;
    $t=16\sqrt{-1}, v=-6\sqrt{-1}$;
    $t=-16\sqrt{-1}, v=6\sqrt{-1}$.

16. $x=-\frac{7}{5}, y=\frac{1}{5}$;
    $x=4, y=2$.

17. $p=375, r=4$.

18. $m=-6, v=25$;
    $m=-25, v=6$.

19. $x=2a, y=-a$;
    $x=-a, y=2a$.

20. $x=a, y=a-b$;
    $x=a, y=-a+b$;
    $x=-a, y=a-b$;
    $x=-a, y=-a+b$.

21. $x=2a-b, y=a+2b$;
    $x=2a-b, y=-(a+2b)$;
    $x=-(2a-b), y=a+2b$;
    $x=-(2a-b), y=-(a+2b)$.

22. $x=2\sqrt{3}, y=2\sqrt{2}$;
    $x=-2\sqrt{3}, y=2\sqrt{2}$;
    $x=2\sqrt{3}, y=-2\sqrt{2}$;
    $x=-2\sqrt{3}, y=-2\sqrt{2}$.

23. $r=0, s=-\frac{1}{2}$;
    $r=5, s=2$.

24. $x=6, y=2\sqrt{5}$;
    $x=6, y=-2\sqrt{5}$;
    $x=-5, y=3$;
    $x=-5, y=-3$.

25. $x=3, y=1$;
    $x=-3, y=-1$;
    $x=1, y=3$;
    $x=-1, y=-3$.

ANSWERS

26. $a = 3, b = 2$;
    $a = -3, b = -2$;
    $a = 2, b = 3$;
    $a = -2, b = -3$.

27. $x = -1, y = 2$;
    $x = 2, y = -1$.

28. $m = 0, n = 0$;
    $m = -\frac{27}{4}, n = \frac{9}{4}$;
    $m = \frac{27}{2}, n = \frac{9}{2}$.

29. $x = 0, y = 0$;
    $x = 2, y = 2$;
    $x = -\sqrt{2}, y = 2 + \sqrt{2}$;
    $x = \sqrt{2}, y = 2 - \sqrt{2}$.

30. $x = 2a, y = 2b$;
    $x = -a, y = -b$.

31. $x = 12, y = -\frac{1}{12}$;
    $x = 2, y = -3$.

32. $m = \frac{7}{2}, n = \frac{9}{2}$;
    $m = -\frac{7}{2}, n = \frac{9}{2}$;
    $m = \frac{7}{2}, n = -\frac{9}{2}$;
    $m = -\frac{7}{2}, n = -\frac{9}{2}$.

33. $m = -1, n = -3$;
    $m = 3, n = 1$;
    $m = -1, n = 2$;
    $m = -2, n = 1$.

34. $a = 5, b = 1$;
    $a = -5, b = -1$;
    $a = \frac{3}{5}\sqrt{-10}, b = -\frac{3}{5}\sqrt{-10}$;
    $a = -\frac{3}{5}\sqrt{-10}, b = \frac{3}{5}\sqrt{-10}$.

35. $x = 4, y = 3$;
    $x = -4, y = -3$;
    $x = \frac{1}{2}\sqrt{-5}, y = -\frac{1}{5}\sqrt{-5}$;
    $x = -\frac{1}{2}\sqrt{-5}, y = \frac{1}{5}\sqrt{-5}$.

36. $t = 2, w = -1$;
    $t = -2, w = 1$;
    $t = \frac{5}{13}\sqrt{-13}, w = \frac{3}{13}\sqrt{-13}$;
    $t = -\frac{5}{13}\sqrt{-13}, w = -\frac{3}{13}\sqrt{-13}$.

37. $x = 4, y = -3$;
    $x = 3, y = -4$;
    $x = -6 + \sqrt{43}, y = 6 + \sqrt{43}$;
    $x = -6 - \sqrt{43}, y = 6 - \sqrt{43}$.

38. $x = 2, y = -5$;
    $x = -\frac{10}{3}, y = -21$;
    $x = \dfrac{5 + \sqrt{193}}{4}, y = \dfrac{63 + 3\sqrt{193}}{4}$;
    $x = \dfrac{5 - \sqrt{193}}{4}, y = \dfrac{63 - 3\sqrt{193}}{4}$.

EXERCISE 145. Pages 311–314.

1. 7, 8. 2. 5, 14; -14, -5. 3. 9, 16; -19.5, -12.5.

4. 5, 3; -5, -3; -3i, 5i; 3i, -5i.

5. 4, 6; -6, -4.

6. 7, 5; -5, -7.

7. 3, -2.

8. 4, 8; $-\frac{8}{3}, \frac{4}{3}$.

9. $\frac{5}{8}$, or $\dfrac{-9}{22}$.

10. 35.   11. 73.   12. 32.

13. Width, 12 rd.; length, 18 rd.
14. Base, 6 ft., and altitude, 8 ft.; or base, 8 ft., and altitude, 6 ft.
15. Base, 2 in., and altitude, 6 in.; or base, 6 in., and altitude, 2 in.
16. Length, 30 rd., and width, 12 rd.; or length, 60 rd., and width, 6 rd.
17. Side of square, 6 ft.; base of rectangle, 13 ft.
18. Width, 7 rd.; length, 10 rd.
19. 7 rd., and 5 rd.; or $8\frac{1}{2}$ rd., and $2\frac{3}{5}$ rd.
20. A, 10 days; B, 15 days.
22. 25°; 30°.
21. 4 in.; 8 in.
23. 70°; 110°.
24. Passenger, 50 mi. an hour, and freight, 40 mi. an hour; or passenger, 35 mi. an hour; and freight, 25 mi. an hour.
25. Rate of crew, 6 mi. an hour, and rate of stream, 3 mi. an hour; or rate of crew, $2\frac{2}{3}$ mi. an hour, and rate of stream, $\frac{3}{5}$ mi. an hour.

EXERCISE 146. Pages 316–317.

1. Sum, -7; product, 6.
2. Sum, 1; product, 12.
3. Sum, $\frac{1}{3}$; product, -2.
4. Sum, $\frac{1}{3}$; product, $\frac{1}{4}$.
5. Sum, $\frac{2}{7}$; product, $-\frac{1}{3}$.
6. Sum, $-\frac{1}{6}$; product, $-\frac{2}{3}$.
7. Sum, $-\frac{3}{2}p$; product, $-\frac{5}{2}p^2$.
8. Sum, $-\frac{4}{7}t$; product, $\frac{3}{2}t^2$.
10. -3.
11. $-\frac{6}{7}$.
12. $-\frac{8}{3}$.
13. $1\frac{1}{3}k$.
14. $\frac{1}{4}p$.
16. 9.
17. 13.
18. -15.
19. $\frac{9}{4}$.
20. $\frac{25}{12}$.

EXERCISE 147. Page 317.

1. $x^2 - 5x + 6 = 0$.
2. $x^2 + 9x + 18 = 0$.
3. $x^2 + 3x - 54 = 0$.
4. $x^2 - 7x - 60 = 0$.
5. $2x^2 - 7x + 6 = 0$.
6. $3x^2 - 2x - 1 = 0$.
7. $8x^2 - 10x + 3 = 0$.
8. $x^2 + 2mx - 15m^2 = 0$.
9. $5x^2 - 17tx - 12t^2 = 0$.
10. $28x^2 - cx - 15c^2 = 0$.
11. $x^3 - 19x + 30 = 0$.
12. $x^2 - 2ax + a^2 - 9m^2 = 0$.
13. $x^2 - 4ax + 4a^2 - b^2 = 0$.
14. $x^2 - 6x + 4 = 0$.
15. $x^2 - 4x - 14 = 0$.

ANSWERS

EXERCISE 148. Page 319.

1. Real, rational, unequal.
2. Real, rational, equal.
3. Real, rational, unequal.
4. Real, irrational, unequal.
5. Imaginary.
6. Real, irrational, unequal.
7. Imaginary.
8. Real, irrational, unequal.
9. Imaginary.
10. Real, rational, unequal.
11. Real, rational, unequal.
12. Real, rational, unequal.

EXERCISE 149. Pages 321–322.

1. x^{11}.
2. m^{23}.
3. y^{n+5}.
4. m^{3a}.
5. a^{5n}.
6. b^{r+3}.
7. c^{n+1}.
8. d^{3r+1}.
9. z^{2r}.
10. t^{2n+1}.
11. w^{2m}.
12. g^{n+1}.
13. x^2.
14. x^4.
15. y^{4n}.
16. m^{2c}.
17. a^{3n}.
18. b^{r+2}.
19. c^{n+2}.
20. d^{r+3}.
21. z^2.
22. t^8.
23. w^{2n}.
24. $g^{2n-2r+1}$.
25. x^{24}.
26. y^{35}.
27. m^{32}.
28. $-a^{25}b^{15}$.
29. $y^{20}z^8w^4$.
30. $m^{15}n^{10}p^{20}$.
31. a^{3n}.
32. b^{2m}.
33. $-c^{3n}d^{3m}$.
34. $x^{4m}y^{3m}$.
35. $r^{2t}s^{6t}$.
36. $x^{mr}y^{nr}$.
37. $\dfrac{x^8}{y^{12}}$.
38. $\dfrac{m^{5p}}{n^{3p}}$.
39. $\dfrac{a^{5p}}{b^{6p}}$.
40. $\dfrac{r^{2n}}{s^{2m}}$.
41. $-\dfrac{x^{3a}}{y^{3b}}$.
42. $\dfrac{a^{4n}}{b^{6n}}$.
43. $\dfrac{a^{nr}}{b^{mr}}$.
44. $\dfrac{x^{ac}}{y^{bc}}$.
45. $\dfrac{r^{2kn}}{t^{3km}}$.

EXERCISE 150. Page 323.

1. 2.
2. -3.
3. -2.
4. $3\,a$.
5. $3\,b$.
6. m^5n^2.
7. $\dfrac{x^2}{y^3}$.
8. $-\dfrac{m^3}{n^4}$.
9. $\dfrac{x^3}{y^2}$.
10. $-\dfrac{t}{w^2}$.
11. $2\,ab$.
12. $5\,a^2b$.
13. $-3\,m^2n^3$.
14. $-2\,mn^2$.
15. $3\,y^2z$.
16. $-b^3cd^2$.
17. $\dfrac{m}{3}$.
18. $\dfrac{2\,a}{x^2}$.
19. $-\dfrac{3\,m^3}{2\,n}$.
20. $\dfrac{xy^2z}{r^2s^4}$.
21. a^m.
22. a^r.
23. b^nc^2.
24. $-x^ty^{2s}$.
25. $a^{2r}b^3$.
26. a^2b^3.
27. $\dfrac{x^m}{2\,y^2}$.
28. $\dfrac{2\,x^m}{y^{2r}}$.
29. $\dfrac{a^3}{b^7}$.
30. $\dfrac{x^n}{y^p}$.

EXERCISE 151. Page 324.

1. $\sqrt{4}$; 2.
2. $\sqrt[3]{27}$; 3.
3. $\sqrt[3]{-8}$; -2.
4. $\sqrt[5]{32}$; 2.
5. $\sqrt[4]{81}$; 3.
6. $\sqrt[6]{64}$; 2.
7. $\sqrt[3]{-125}$; -5.
8. $\sqrt[4]{256}$; 4.
9. $\sqrt[3]{-1000}$; -10.
10. $\sqrt[3]{x^6}$; x^2.
11. $\sqrt[6]{y^{12}}$; y^2.
12. $\sqrt[5]{z^{10}}$; z^2.
13. $\sqrt[3]{-64\,x^3y^3}$; $-4xy$.
14. $\sqrt[5]{32\,a^5b^{20}}$; $2ab^4$.
15. $\sqrt[4]{81\,x^8y^4}$; $3x^2y$.
16. $\sqrt[3]{2^2}$.
17. $\sqrt[4]{4^3}$.
18. $\sqrt{5^3}$.
19. $\sqrt{4\,x}$.
20. $4\sqrt{x}$.
21. $3\sqrt{y^3}$.
22. $2\,a\sqrt[3]{b^2}$.
23. $\sqrt[3]{(2\,ab)^2}$.
24. $\sqrt[5]{m^4}\cdot\sqrt[4]{n^5}$.
25. $8\sqrt[6]{a}\sqrt[5]{b^3}$.
26. $a^{\frac{3}{5}}$.
27. $x^{\frac{5}{6}}$.
28. $(2\,a)^{\frac{1}{3}}$.
29. $2\,a^{\frac{1}{3}}$.
30. $m^{\frac{5}{7}}$.
31. $b^{\frac{7}{8}}c^{\frac{1}{4}}$.
32. $2\,n^{\frac{2}{3}}$.
33. $4\,y^{\frac{3}{5}}$.
34. $3\,x^{\frac{4}{5}}y$.
35. $a^2b^{\frac{2}{3}}$.

EXERCISE 152. Page 325.

1. $\frac{1}{3^2}$; $\frac{1}{9}$.
2. $\frac{1}{2^3}$; $\frac{1}{8}$.
3. $\frac{1}{3^3}$; $\frac{1}{27}$.
4. 7^0; 1.
5. $\frac{1}{3}\cdot\frac{1}{2^4}$; $\frac{1}{48}$.
6. $\frac{1}{4^2}$; $\frac{1}{16}$.
7. $\frac{9}{6^2}$; $\frac{1}{4}$.
8. $\frac{100}{5^2}$; 4.
9. $\frac{64}{4^3}$; 1.
10. $\frac{1}{\sqrt{16}}$; $\frac{1}{4}$.
11. $\frac{1}{\sqrt[3]{-27}}$; $-\frac{1}{3}$.
12. $\frac{1}{\sqrt[4]{81}}$; $\frac{1}{3}$.
13. $\frac{1}{\sqrt[6]{64}}$; $\frac{1}{2}$.
14. $\frac{1}{\sqrt[3]{-125}}$; $-\frac{1}{5}$.
15. $\frac{1}{\sqrt[5]{-32}}$; $-\frac{1}{2}$.
16. $\frac{a^2}{b^5}$.
17. $\frac{1}{8\,a^8}$.
18. $\frac{2}{a^3}$.
19. $\frac{b^4}{9\,a^2}$.
20. $\frac{3\,b^4}{a^2}$.
21. $\frac{m^5}{4\,n^4}$.
22. $\frac{4}{a^6b^3}$.
23. $\frac{8\,a^3}{9\,b^2}$.

ANSWERS

EXERCISE 153. Page 326.

1. $\dfrac{z}{x^4y^3}$.

2. $2\,ab^3$.

3. $\dfrac{x^2y^5}{2}$.

4. $\dfrac{8\,x^2y^3}{5}$.

5. $\dfrac{6\,m^4p^2}{7\,n^3}$.

6. $\dfrac{3\,b^2c^2}{2\,a^3d^4}$.

7. $\dfrac{8\,a^{\frac{3}{4}}y^{\frac{1}{2}}}{x^3b^9}$.

8. $\dfrac{5\,a^4c^{\frac{2}{3}}}{6\,b^{\frac{3}{5}}d^5}$.

9. $3\,x^6y^{-2}$.

10. $b^{\frac{1}{3}}c^{-4}$.

11. $2\,a^2b^5c^5$.

12. $d^{-3}mn^{-6}$.

13. $7\,x^{-7}yz^{-\frac{1}{6}}$.

14. $a^{-\frac{2}{5}}b^4c^{-\frac{3}{5}}$.

15. $4\,a^{\frac{3}{4}}b^3c^2d^{-\frac{1}{4}}$.

16. $2\,a^{\frac{6}{7}}b^{-5}m^{\frac{9}{8}}n^{\frac{5}{3}}$.

EXERCISE 154. Pages 327–329.

2. a. r^8; r^{12}; r^5s^{-4}; $r^{10}s^2$; r^2s^{-6}; $r^{n+5}s^m$.
   b. r^{-3}; r; $r^{-6}s^{-4}$; $r^{-1}s^2$; $r^{-9}s^{-6}$; $r^{n-6}s^m$.
   c. r^3s^3; r^7s^3; s^{-1}; r^5s^5; $r^{-3}s^{-3}$; r^ns^{m+3}.
   d. r^5s^3; r^9s^3; r^2s^{-1}; r^7s^5; $r^{-1}s^{-3}$; $r^{n+2}s^{m+3}$.
   e. $r^{-1}s^{-5}$; r^3s^{-5}; $r^{-4}s^{-9}$; rs^{-3}; $r^{-7}s^{-11}$; $r^{n-4}s^{m-5}$.

3. a. x; $x^{\frac{7}{4}}$; $x^{\frac{1}{2}}y^{\frac{2}{3}}$; $x^{\frac{5}{6}}y^{\frac{1}{6}}$; $x^{a+\frac{1}{2}}y^b$.
   b. $x^{\frac{5}{6}}$; $x^{\frac{7}{12}}$; $x^{\frac{1}{3}}y^{\frac{2}{3}}$; $xy^{\frac{1}{6}}$; $x^{a+\frac{1}{3}}y^b$.
   c. $x^{\frac{1}{2}}y^{\frac{2}{3}}$; $x^{\frac{1}{4}}y^{\frac{1}{3}}$; $y^{\frac{1}{3}}$; $x^{\frac{1}{3}}y^{\frac{5}{6}}$; $x^ay^{b+\frac{2}{3}}$.
   d. $x^{\frac{3}{4}}y^{\frac{1}{6}}$; $x^{\frac{1}{2}}y^{\frac{1}{6}}$; $x^{\frac{1}{4}}y^{\frac{5}{6}}$; $x^{\frac{1}{12}}y^{\frac{1}{3}}$; $x^{a+\frac{1}{4}}y^{b+\frac{1}{6}}$.

4. a. $m^{\frac{2}{3}}$; $mn^{-\frac{1}{4}}$; $m^{\frac{6}{5}}n^{-\frac{1}{10}}$; $m^{\frac{1}{2}}n^{\frac{1}{3}}$; $m^{\frac{5}{6}}n^{-\frac{3}{4}}$.
   b. $m^{\frac{1}{6}}$; $m^{\frac{1}{2}}n^{-\frac{1}{4}}$; $m^{\frac{7}{10}}n^{-\frac{1}{10}}$; $m^0n^{\frac{1}{3}}$; $m^{\frac{1}{3}}n^{-\frac{3}{4}}$.
   c. $m^{-\frac{1}{3}}n^{-\frac{1}{4}}$; $n^{-\frac{1}{2}}$; $m^{\frac{1}{5}}n^{-\frac{7}{20}}$; $m^{-\frac{1}{2}}n^{\frac{1}{12}}$; $m^{-\frac{1}{6}}n^{-1}$.
   d. $m^{-\frac{4}{3}}n^2$; $m^{-1}n^{\frac{7}{4}}$; $m^{-\frac{4}{5}}n^{\frac{19}{10}}$; $m^{-\frac{3}{2}}n^{\frac{7}{3}}$; $m^{-\frac{7}{6}}n^{\frac{5}{4}}$.

5. $a - b$.

6. $8\,a^{-2} - 18\,a^{-1} - 47 - 15\,a$.

7. $x^{-3} - 16$.

8. $x^{\frac{2}{3}} + x^{\frac{1}{3}}y^{\frac{1}{3}} + y^{\frac{2}{3}}$.

9. $a^{-1} - b$.

10. $x^{-\frac{2}{3}} - 2\,x^{-\frac{1}{3}}y^{-\frac{1}{3}} + y^{-\frac{2}{3}}$.

11. $r^{2n} - 2\,r^ns^m + s^{2m}$.

12. $x + 7\,x^{\frac{1}{2}} - 78$.

13. $r^3 - 2\,r^{\frac{3}{2}}s^{\frac{5}{2}} + s^5$.

14. $a^{\frac{6}{5}} - a^{\frac{3}{5}}b^{-1} - 56\,b^{-2}$.

16.
   a. t^7; t^{-15}; t^{a-3}; $t^{-2\frac{1}{2}}$; $t^{-3\frac{1}{4}}$; $t^{-\frac{2}{3}}$.
   b. t^{14}; t^{-8}; t^{a+4}; $t^{4\frac{1}{2}}$; $t^{3\frac{3}{4}}$; $t^{6\frac{1}{2}}$.
   c. $t^{9\frac{1}{2}}$; $t^{-12\frac{1}{2}}$; $t^{a-\frac{1}{2}}$; 1; $t^{-\frac{3}{4}}$; t^2.
   d. $t^{10\frac{1}{3}}$; $t^{-11\frac{2}{3}}$; $t^{a+\frac{1}{3}}$; $t^{\frac{5}{6}}$; $t^{\frac{1}{12}}$; $t^{2\frac{5}{6}}$.

17.
   a. $c^{-6}d^3$; $c^{x-1}d^5$; $c^{-\frac{5}{6}}d^{-\frac{3}{4}}$; $c^{1\frac{1}{4}}d^{2\frac{1}{2}}$.
   b. $c^{-3}d^5$; $c^{x+2}d^7$; $c^{2\frac{1}{6}}d^{\frac{2}{3}}$; $c^{4\frac{1}{4}}d^{4\frac{1}{2}}$.

18. $a + a^2 + a^3$.

19. $2x^{-4} + 3x^{-2} + 6$.

20. $a^{3\frac{1}{2}} + a^{2\frac{1}{2}} + a^{1\frac{1}{2}} + a^{\frac{1}{2}}$.

21. $a^{\frac{4}{3}} - a^{\frac{2}{3}}b^{\frac{2}{3}} + 3b^{\frac{4}{3}}$.

22. $a^{\frac{1}{2}} - 1$.

23. $a^{\frac{1}{2}} - 2a^{\frac{1}{4}} + 1$.

24.
   a. x^{12}; y^{-24}; $z^{1\frac{2}{5}}$; r^{-1}; $t^{4.8}$.
   b. x^{-18}; y^{36}; $z^{-1\frac{8}{5}}$; $r^{\frac{3}{2}}$; $t^{-7.2}$.
   c. x^3; y^{-6}; $z^{\frac{3}{5}}$; $r^{-\frac{1}{4}}$; $t^{1.2}$.
   d. x^{-2}; y^4; $z^{-\frac{2}{5}}$; $r^{\frac{1}{6}}$; $t^{-.8}$.
   e. x^{-9}; y^{18}; $z^{-\frac{9}{5}}$; $r^{\frac{3}{4}}$; $t^{-3.6}$.

27.
   a. a^4b^{-6}; $m^{-6}p$; $x^{-\frac{3}{2}}y^{-\frac{3}{4}}$; $r^{-2a}s^{-2b}$.
   b. $a^{-8}b^{12}$; $m^{12}p^{-2}$; $x^3y^{\frac{3}{2}}$; $r^{4a}s^{4b}$.
   c. $a^{\frac{1}{3}}b^{-\frac{1}{2}}$; $m^{-\frac{1}{2}}p^{\frac{1}{12}}$; $x^{-\frac{1}{8}}y^{-\frac{1}{16}}$; $r^{-\frac{a}{6}}s^{-\frac{b}{6}}$.
   d. $a^{-\frac{2}{3}}b$; $mp^{-\frac{1}{6}}$; $x^{\frac{1}{4}}y^{\frac{1}{8}}$; $r^{\frac{a}{3}}s^{\frac{b}{3}}$.

29. 125.
30. 243.
31. 128.
32. 27.
33. 343.
34. 9.
35. $128x^7$.
36. $27x^3$.
37. $32m^5$.
38. -128.
39. $32x^5y^{10}$.
40. 625.
41. $16a^2b^4$.
42. $-8m^3$.
43. $64x^8y^6$.
44. 32.

46.
   a. $10^{2.75}$; $10^{3.23}$; $10^{4.47}$; $10^{10.32}$; $10^{10.86}$.
   b. $10^{3.75}$; $10^{4.23}$; $10^{5.47}$; $10^{11.32}$; $10^{11.86}$.
   c. 10^3; $10^{3.48}$; $10^{4.72}$; $10^{10.57}$; $10^{11.11}$.

47. The exponent is increased by 1.
The exponent is increased by 2.

48.
   a. $10^{.75}$; $10^{1.23}$; $10^{2.47}$; $10^{8.32}$; $10^{8.86}$.
   b. $10^{-.25}$; $10^{.23}$; $10^{1.47}$; $10^{7.32}$; $10^{7.86}$.
   c. $10^{.50}$; $10^{.98}$; $10^{2.22}$; $10^{8.07}$; $10^{8.61}$.

49. a^{-6m}.

50. a^{n^2-2n}.

ANSWERS

EXERCISE 155. Page 331.

1. $\sqrt{5} = 2.23+$.
2. $\sqrt{10} = 3.16+$.
3. $\sqrt{2} = 1.41+$.
4. $\sqrt{6} = 2.44+$.
5. $\sqrt{3} = 1.73+$.
6. $\sqrt{7} = 2.64+$.
7. $\sqrt{2} = 1.41+$.
8. $\sqrt{3} = 1.73+$.
9. $\sqrt{2} = 1.41+$.
10. $\sqrt[3]{7}$.
11. $\sqrt[4]{5}$.
12. $\sqrt[5]{3}$.
13. $\sqrt{2} = 1.41+$.
14. $\sqrt[7]{2}$.
15. $\sqrt[5]{6}$.
16. $\sqrt[6]{10}$.
17. $\sqrt[3]{3}$.
18. $\sqrt{11\,ab}$.
19. $\sqrt{5\,xy}$.
20. $\sqrt{2\,m}$.
21. $\sqrt{3\,w}$.
22. $\sqrt[4]{2\,x^3m^2}$.
23. $\sqrt{3\,a^2x}$.
24. $\sqrt[3]{4\,ax^2}$.

EXERCISE 156. Page 332.

1. $2\sqrt{7} = 5.29+$.
2. $2\sqrt{3} = 3.464+$.
3. $4\sqrt{5} = 8.944+$.
4. $3\sqrt{7} = 7.935+$.
5. $7\sqrt{2} = 9.898+$.
6. $4\sqrt{6} = 9.796+$.
7. $4\sqrt{7} = 10.580+$.
8. $6\sqrt{3} = 10.392+$.
9. $5\sqrt{5} = 11.180+$.
10. $3\,a\sqrt{11}$.
11. $2\,xy^2\sqrt{15}$.
12. $10\,mn\sqrt{2\,m}$.
13. $2\,a\sqrt[3]{5}$.
14. $3\sqrt[3]{2\,m}$.
15. $5\,x^2\sqrt[3]{3}$.
16. $3\,a\sqrt[3]{4\,a^2}$.
17. $4\,y\sqrt[3]{2\,xy}$.
18. $5\,mn\sqrt[3]{9\,n}$.
19. $3\sqrt[4]{2}$.
20. $2\,ab^2\sqrt[4]{4\,a^2b}$.
21. $2\,ac\sqrt[5]{2\,ac^2}$.
22. $3\,np\sqrt[5]{n}$.
23. $2\,x\sqrt[6]{2\,y^5}$.
24. $2\,y\sqrt[7]{x^3y}$.
25. $(a - 2\,b)\sqrt{a + 2\,b}$.
26. $(3\,a - 2\,b)\sqrt{3\,ab}$.
27. $(x + 3)\sqrt{5\,x}$.
28. $(x - 3)\sqrt{(x + 2)(x + 5)}$.

30. $\dfrac{\sqrt[3]{2}}{3\,m^2}$.
31. $\dfrac{\sqrt[3]{4\,a^2}}{5}$.
32. $\dfrac{\sqrt[4]{7\,m}}{2\,a}$.
33. $\dfrac{\sqrt[4]{5\,y}}{3\,x}$.
34. $\dfrac{\sqrt[5]{3\,d}}{2\,c}$.
35. $\dfrac{\sqrt[5]{5\,rs}}{xy^2}$.
36. $\dfrac{\sqrt[6]{3\,y^2}}{2\,x}$.
37. $\dfrac{\sqrt[7]{5}}{2\,mn^2}$.

EXERCISE 157. Page 333.

1. $\tfrac{1}{3}\sqrt{6} = .816+$.
2. $\tfrac{1}{5}\sqrt{35} = 1.183+$.
3. $\tfrac{1}{3}\sqrt{15} = 1.290+$.
4. $\tfrac{1}{2}\sqrt{10} = 1.581+$.
5. $\tfrac{1}{11}\sqrt{33} = .522+$.
6. $\dfrac{1}{6\,a}\sqrt{15\,a}$.
7. $\dfrac{3\,a}{4\,b}\sqrt{2\,b}$.
8. $\dfrac{m}{10\,n}\sqrt{65\,m}$.
9. $\tfrac{1}{2}\sqrt[3]{2}$.
10. $\tfrac{1}{2}\sqrt[3]{12}$.
11. $\tfrac{1}{5}\sqrt[3]{50}$.
12. $\dfrac{1}{2\,a}\sqrt[3]{28\,a^2}$.

13. $\dfrac{b}{3}\sqrt[3]{15\,c}.$

14. $\dfrac{2\,ac}{5}\sqrt[3]{5\,c}.$

15. $\dfrac{x}{4\,y}\sqrt[3]{20\,y}.$

16. $\tfrac{1}{2}\sqrt[4]{2}.$

17. $\tfrac{1}{3}\sqrt[4]{6}.$

18. $\tfrac{1}{4}\sqrt[4]{12}.$

19. $\dfrac{1}{5\,b}\sqrt[4]{5\,ab^3}.$

20. $\dfrac{1}{3\,n}\sqrt[4]{45\,m^3 n}.$

21. $\dfrac{1}{2\,cd}\sqrt[4]{11a^3 d}.$

22. $\tfrac{1}{3}\sqrt[5]{9}.$

23. $\tfrac{1}{2}\sqrt[5]{6\,a}.$

24. $\dfrac{1}{5\,b}\sqrt[5]{100\,b^2}.$

25. $\dfrac{a}{2\,c}\sqrt[6]{12\,bc}.$

26. $\dfrac{1}{2\,m}\sqrt[7]{28\,m^4 n^4}.$

27. $\dfrac{1}{a-b}\sqrt{a^2-b^2}.$

28. $\dfrac{a}{2}\sqrt{3}.$

EXERCISE 158. Page 334.

1. $\sqrt{50}.$
2. $\sqrt{192}.$
3. $\sqrt[3]{320}.$
4. $\sqrt[3]{500}.$
5. $\sqrt[4]{80}.$
6. $\sqrt[5]{486}.$
7. $\sqrt{128\,a^3}.$
8. $\sqrt{294\,x^7}.$
9. $\sqrt[3]{135\,a^5 b^3}.$
10. $\sqrt[3]{x^{11}y^{10}}.$
11. $\sqrt[4]{162\,m^9}.$
12. $\sqrt[5]{224\,a^8}.$
13. $\sqrt{1-a^2}.$
14. $\sqrt{x^2-1}.$
15. $\sqrt{\dfrac{a-b}{a+b}}.$
16. $\sqrt{\dfrac{(x-1)^2}{x^2+1}}.$

EXERCISE 159. Pages 334–335.

1. $3\sqrt{2}=4.242+.$
2. $14\sqrt{5}=31.304+.$
3. $\sqrt{6}=2.449+.$
4. $5\sqrt[3]{2}.$
5. $3\sqrt[3]{3\,m}.$
6. $3\sqrt[3]{x^2}+2\sqrt[3]{3\,x^2}.$
7. $-\sqrt[4]{2}.$
8. $\sqrt[5]{2}.$
9. $3\sqrt[6]{3}.$
10. $0.$
11. $4\,x\sqrt{6\,x}.$
12. $\tfrac{11}{4}\sqrt{2}=3.888+.$
13. $\tfrac{7}{9}\sqrt{6}=1.904+.$
14. $\tfrac{1}{2}\sqrt[3]{6}.$
15. $\tfrac{9}{20}\sqrt{10}=1.422+.$
16. $\left(\dfrac{a+b^2}{2}\right)\sqrt[4]{2}.$
17. $\sqrt[5]{m}+\tfrac{1}{2}\sqrt[5]{2\,m}.$
18. $\left(m+\dfrac{1}{m}\right)\sqrt[6]{2\,m}.$
19. $\dfrac{1}{a}\sqrt[7]{3\,a^2}-\dfrac{1}{b}\sqrt[7]{a^2 b^3}.$
20. $\dfrac{2}{a-b}\sqrt{a^2-b^2}.$

EXERCISE 160. Page 336.

1. $\sqrt[6]{27}\,;\ \sqrt[6]{25}.$
2. $\sqrt[10]{32}\,;\ \sqrt[10]{9}.$
3. $\sqrt[15]{a^{10}b^5}\,;\ \sqrt[15]{a^{12}b^9}.$
4. $\sqrt[14]{128}\,;\ \sqrt[14]{144}.$
5. $\sqrt[12]{256}\,;\ \sqrt[12]{216}.$
6. $\sqrt[20]{x^{10}y^{10}}\,;\ \sqrt[20]{y^5 z^5}\,;\ \sqrt[20]{x^4 z^4}.$
7. $\sqrt[12]{16\,a^4}\,;\ \sqrt[12]{8\,b^3}\,;\ \sqrt[12]{36\,c^2}.$
8. $\sqrt[18]{64}\,;\ \sqrt[18]{512}\,;\ \sqrt[18]{169}.$
9. $\sqrt[12]{(1-x)^3}\,;\ \sqrt[12]{(1+x)^2}.$
10. $\sqrt[24]{(a+b)^3}\,;\ \sqrt[24]{(a-b)^4}.$
11. $\sqrt[3]{2}$ is less than $\sqrt[4]{3}.$
12. $\sqrt[3]{11}$ is less than $\sqrt{5}.$
13. $\sqrt[5]{10}$ is less than $\sqrt[3]{4}.$
14. $\sqrt[5]{15}$ is less than $\sqrt{3}.$

ANSWERS

15. $\sqrt[4]{7}$ is less than $\sqrt[3]{5}$, and $\sqrt[3]{5}$ is less than $\sqrt{3}$.
16. $\sqrt[6]{175}$ is less than $\sqrt[3]{14}$, and $\sqrt[3]{14}$ is less than $\sqrt{6}$.

EXERCISE 161. Pages 336-337.

1. $2\sqrt{5} = 4.472+$.
2. 6.
3. $7\sqrt{2} = 9.898+$.
4. $5\sqrt{3} = 8.66+$.
5. $6\sqrt{7} = 15.87+$.
6. $30\sqrt{2} = 42.42+$.
7. 30.
8. 27.
9. 50.
10. $56\sqrt{7} = 148.12+$.
11. $30\,x\sqrt{2}$.
12. $18\,m\sqrt{5\,m}$.
13. $\sqrt{x^2 - 1}$.
14. $x - 5$.
15. $9(x+2)$.
17. 22.
18. $4a^2 - b$.
19. $-53 - \sqrt{3}$.
20. $3 + 16\sqrt{3}$.
21. $26 - 17\sqrt{2}$.
22. $21 + 8\sqrt{5}$.
23. $67 - 12\sqrt{7}$.
24. -47.
25. -13.
26. $a - b$.
27. $x + 2 + 2\sqrt{x+1}$.
28. $a + 13 - 8\sqrt{a-3}$
29. $2x + 5 - 2\sqrt{x(x+5)}$.
30. $2x - 2\sqrt{x^2 - 1}$.

EXERCISE 162. Page 338.

1. 2.
2. $6\sqrt[3]{2}$.
3. $15\,x\sqrt[3]{x}$.
4. $3\sqrt[4]{3}$.
5. $6\sqrt[5]{3}$.
6. $2\,x\sqrt[6]{3\,x}$.
7. $6\,xy\sqrt[7]{y}$.
8. $\sqrt[6]{a^5}$.
9. $\sqrt[6]{b^5}$.
10. $m\sqrt[4]{m}$.
11. $\sqrt[6]{2^5}$.
12. $2\sqrt{5}$.
13. $3\,a\sqrt[6]{375\,a}$.
14. $\sqrt[6]{32\,c^5}$.
15. $5\,mn\sqrt[9]{6}$.

EXERCISE 163. Page 339.

1. 2.
2. $\sqrt{2} = 1.414+$.
3. $\sqrt{3} = 1.732+$.
4. $3\sqrt{3} = 5.196+$.
5. 4.
6. 2.
7. $3\,b$.
8. $3\sqrt{3\,r}$.
9. $4\,c^2d\sqrt{6\,c}$.
10. $5\sqrt{3} = 8.66+$.
11. $22\sqrt{x}$.
12. $\frac{1}{2}\sqrt{10} = 1.581+$.
13. $\frac{1}{3}\sqrt{15} = 1.290+$.
14. $\frac{2}{7}\sqrt{21} = 1.309+$.
15. $\frac{1}{5}\sqrt{55} = 1.483+$.
16. 5.
17. $3 + 5\sqrt{3} = 11.66+$.
18. $\frac{2}{3}(\sqrt{6} + \sqrt{30}) = 5.284+$.
19. $\frac{3}{2}\sqrt{10} - 4\sqrt{3} = -2.185+$.

ALGEBRA

20. 3.
21. $\sqrt[3]{9}$.
22. $\frac{1}{3}\sqrt[5]{162\,a}$.
23. $2m\sqrt{2}$.
24. $\frac{1}{c}\sqrt[3]{5\,a^2c^7}$.
25. $\frac{2}{y}\sqrt[7]{2\,y^6}$.
26. $\frac{3\,b}{y}\sqrt{y}$.
27. $\frac{3\,m}{b}\sqrt[5]{b}$.
28. $\sqrt[m]{5\,r^2}$.
29. $\sqrt[n]{x}$.

EXERCISE 164. Page 340.

1. $\sqrt[3]{4}$.
2. $\sqrt[4]{27}$.
3. $\tfrac{1}{2}\sqrt[3]{36}$.
4. $\sqrt{5}$.
5. $\sqrt[5]{a^4}$.
6. $\sqrt[6]{2}$.
7. $\sqrt[4]{3}$.
8. 1.
9. $\sqrt[4]{2\,x}$.
10. $\sqrt[6]{18\,a}$.
11. $\tfrac{1}{2}\sqrt[10]{3\cdot 2^9}$.
12. $3\sqrt[6]{x^3y}$.
13. $\sqrt[6]{5}$.
14. $\sqrt[3]{4}$.
15. $\frac{1}{y}\sqrt[15]{4\,x^7y^{14}}$.

EXERCISE 165. Page 341.

1. $\dfrac{3(3-\sqrt{5})}{2} = 1.146^{+}$.
2. $\dfrac{\sqrt{6}+2}{2} = 2.224^{+}$.
3. $3+\sqrt{5} = 5.236^{+}$.
4. $\dfrac{5(\sqrt{3}+4)}{-13} = -2.204^{+}$.
5. $\tfrac{6}{11}(2\sqrt{5}-3) = .802^{+}$.
6. $\dfrac{1+\sqrt{3}}{2} = 1.366^{+}$.
7. $\dfrac{2-\sqrt{2}}{2} = .293^{+}$.
8. $\dfrac{a+b^2+2\,b\sqrt{a}}{a-b^2}$.
9. $\dfrac{x+y-2\sqrt{xy}}{x-y}$.
10. $\dfrac{7-2\sqrt{10}}{3} = .225^{+}$.
11. $\dfrac{6+5\sqrt{2}}{14} = .933^{+}$.
12. $-\dfrac{11+8\sqrt{2}}{3} = -7.437^{+}$.
13. $\dfrac{x-4-\sqrt{x-2}}{x-6}$.
14. $\dfrac{b-2a-2\sqrt{a(a-b)}}{b}$.
15. $\dfrac{1-\sqrt{1-a^2}}{a}$.

EXERCISE 166. Page 342.

1. $\sqrt{5} = 2.236^{+}$.
2. 2.
3. $4\sqrt[8]{32}$.
4. $\sqrt{6} = 2.449^{+}$.
5. $4\sqrt[3]{4}$.
6. $32\,a^5b\sqrt[3]{b^2}$.
7. $a\sqrt[3]{7\,a}$.
8. $5\sqrt{2\,xy}$.
9. $3\sqrt[6]{3}$.
10. $50\,m^3\sqrt[5]{3\,m}$.
11. $\sqrt[7]{(3\,a-2)^8}$.
12. $2\,y\sqrt[4]{3\,x^3y}$.

ANSWERS

13. $\sqrt{2} = 1.414+$
14. $\sqrt{3} = 1.732+$.
15. $\sqrt[3]{5}$.
16. $\sqrt[6]{2\,a}$.
17. $\sqrt[5]{7}$.
18. $\sqrt[8]{10}$.
19. $\sqrt[20]{2\,xy^3}$.
20. $\sqrt[12]{9\,a^7}$.
21. $\sqrt[4]{x-3}$.

EXERCISE 167. Page 343.

1. $\pm(\sqrt{7}+2)$.
2. $\pm(3-2\sqrt{2})$.
3. $\pm(\sqrt{6}-\sqrt{5})$.
4. $\pm(\sqrt{5}-\sqrt{3})$.
5. $\pm(2+\sqrt{2})$.
6. $\pm(\sqrt{5}-1)$.
7. $\pm(\sqrt{6}-\sqrt{3})$.
8. $\pm(\sqrt{6}+\sqrt{2})$.
9. $\pm(\sqrt{11}-3)$.

EXERCISE 168. Page 344.

1. -6.
2. -6.
3. $-3\sqrt{2}$.
4. $-5\sqrt{3}$.
5. $-12\,a^2$.
6. -18.
7. -40.
8. $-abc$.
9. $-mn\sqrt{rs}$.
10. $\sqrt{ab}$.
11. 5.
12. 14.
13. $37+21\,i\sqrt{6}$.
14. $102-2\,i\sqrt{3}$.
15. 4.
16. $11-8\,i\sqrt{5}$.
17. x^2+y.
18. $\dfrac{-1-i\sqrt{3}}{2}$.
19. $\dfrac{-1+i\sqrt{3}}{2}$.
20. 1.

EXERCISE 169. Page 345.

1. $\sqrt{5}$.
2. 2.
3. $-i\sqrt{7}$.
4. $-3\,i$.
5. $\dfrac{1}{c}\sqrt{ac}$.
6. $\dfrac{\sqrt{a}}{a}$.
7. 10.
8. 9.
9. $3\,a\sqrt{3}$.
10. $2\sqrt{2\,x}$.
11. $\dfrac{1+i\sqrt{3}}{2}$.
12. i.
13. $\dfrac{40\,i\sqrt{6}-71}{121}$.
14. $\dfrac{-32\,i\sqrt{3}-15}{21}$.

EXERCISE 170. Page 346.

2. $r_1 = \dfrac{1+\sqrt{5}}{2};\ r_2 = \dfrac{1-\sqrt{5}}{2}$.
3. $r_1 = 1+\sqrt{3};\ r_2 = 1-\sqrt{3}$.
4. $r_1 = \dfrac{3+\sqrt{5}}{2};\ r_2 = \dfrac{3-\sqrt{5}}{2}$.

52 ALGEBRA

5. $r_1 = \dfrac{-1+\sqrt{-3}}{2}$; $r_2 = \dfrac{-1-\sqrt{-3}}{2}$.

6. $r_1 = -1$; $r_2 = \dfrac{1+\sqrt{-3}}{2}$; $r_3 = \dfrac{1-\sqrt{-3}}{2}$.

7. $r_1 = 2$; $r_2 = -1+\sqrt{-3}$; $r_3 = -1-\sqrt{-3}$.

8. $c = \frac{1}{2}\sqrt{2}$; $t = 1$; $S = \sqrt{2}$; $C = \sqrt{2}$; $T = 1$.

9. $c = \frac{1}{2}$; $t = \sqrt{3}$; $S = 2$; $C = \frac{2}{3}\sqrt{3}$; $T = \frac{1}{3}\sqrt{3}$.

10.
(a) $(x+\sqrt{2})(x-\sqrt{2})$;
(b) $(x+\sqrt{5})(x-\sqrt{5})$;
(c) $(x+3i)(x-3i)$;
(d) $(x+i\sqrt{2})(x-i\sqrt{2})$;
(e) $(x+2i)(x-2i)$;
(f) $(x\sqrt{3}-2)(x\sqrt{3}+2)$;
(g) $(x\sqrt{5}+3)(x\sqrt{5}-3)$;
(h) $(x\sqrt{2}+\sqrt{5})(x\sqrt{2}-\sqrt{5})$;
(i) $(x\sqrt{a}+\sqrt{b})(x\sqrt{a}-\sqrt{b})$.

EXERCISE 171. Pages 348-349.

1. 3.
2. -6.
3. $\frac{2}{3}$.
4. 16.
5. $\frac{25}{36}$.
6. $\frac{1}{6}$.
7. -2.
8. $\frac{1}{2}$.
9. $\frac{27}{4}$.
10. $\frac{3}{16}$.
11. $\frac{5}{4}a$.
12. $\frac{5}{12}$.

13. 6. (-6 does not satisfy the equation.)
14. 3. ($\frac{1}{7}$ does not satisfy.)
15. -1. (7 does not satisfy.)
16. 2. (26 does not satisfy.)
17. -7; -4.
18. 1. ($-\frac{21}{3}$ is not a root.)
19. $\frac{3}{2}$. (0 is not a root.)
20. -3; -4.
21. $-\frac{18}{5}$. ($\frac{3}{5}$ is not a root.)
22. $(3a+b)^2$. ($-(3a-b)^2$ is not a root.)
23. 0; $\dfrac{4a}{5}$.
24. No roots.
25. $2a$. ($42a$ is not a root.)
26. (a) $l = \dfrac{gt^2}{\pi^2}$. (b) $g = \dfrac{l\pi^2}{t^2}$.
27. (a) $g = \dfrac{V^2}{2s}$. (b) $s = \dfrac{V^2}{2g}$.

EXERCISE 172. Page 353.

1. 2. 3. 4. 5. 1. 7. 0. 9. 2. 11. 2. 13. 5. 15. 1. 17. 4
2. 3. 4. 0. 6. 2. 8. 4. 10. 5. 12. 6. 14. 3. 16. 2. 18. 6

ANSWERS

EXERCISE 173. Page 353.

1. −2.   3. −4.   5. −5.   7. −1.   9. 2.   11. 4.   13. 3
2. −3.   4. −2.   6. −2.   8. −1.   10. 0.   12. 1.

EXERCISE 174. Page 354.

1. 8 − 10.   4. 8 − 10.   7. 9 − 10.   10. 9 − 10.   13. 6 − 10.
2. 7 − 10.   5. 5 − 10.   8. 9 − 10.   11. 5 − 10.
3. 6 − 10.   6. 8 − 10.   9. 7 − 10.   12. 8 − 10.

EXERCISE 175. Page 355.

1. 2.3711.   5. 1.8573.   9. 1.7497.   13. 7.6675 − 10
2. 2.8859.   6. .9031.   10. .8938.   14. 3.9390.
3. 2.9258.   7. .5051.   11. 9.9657 − 10.   15. 4.3927.
4. 2.9542.   8. 2.7924.   12. 8.5132 − 10.   16. 1.7832.

EXERCISE 176. Page 359.

1. 21.   3. 9.   5. 5.   7. 8.   9. 14
2. 17.   4. 8.   6. 13.   8. 6.   10. 8.
11. 2.5126.   16. 1.5073.   21. 2.5147.   26. .4971.
12. 2.4202.   17. .2063.   22. 2.3861.   27. .0192.
13. 2.8956.   18. .9010.   23. 1.7974.   28. 9.3567 − 10.
14. 2.6922.   19. 9.9275 − 10.   24. 2.9052.   29. 8.8025 − 10.
15. 2.8472.   20. 8.7304 − 10.   25. .7961.   30. 7.6087 − 10.

EXERCISE 177. Page 360.

1. 411.   4. 900.   7. 55.   10. .631.
2. 21.7.   5. 8490.   8. 50400.   11. .0345.
3. 4980.   6. 6.55.   9. 7.75.   12. .00259.

EXERCISE 178. Page 361.

1. 64.257.   6. 7.488.   11. 344.25.
2. 2272.63.   7. .8143.   12. .50375.
3. 461.22.   8. .0642.   13. 291.33.
4. 5.06125.   9. .00385.   14. 1456.66.
5. 356.76.   10. .01994.   15. 853.166.

EXERCISE 179. Pages 362-363.

1. 1.3222.
2. 1.6232.
3. 1.5562.
4. 2.1003.
5. 2.1070.
6. 2.4013.
7. 2.5104.
8. 2.5774.
9. 2.2252.
11. 903.4.
12. 163.62.
13. 105.48.
14. 1033.33.
15. 25088.
16. 1004.41.
17. 18969.5.
18. 824.33.
19. 37766.6.
21. .07378.
22. .01381.
23. 4.89.
24. .31185.
25. .000106.
26. .00005.

EXERCISE 180. Page 364.

1. .3680.
2. .6690.
3. .1091.
4. .2340.
5. .2589.
6. .4192.
7. .0670.
8. 9.8172 − 10.
9. 5.3125.
10. 4.53.
11. 3.02.
12. 1.56.
13. 95.625.
14. 217.5.
15. 2742.
16. .329.
17. .110.
18. .215.
19. .0065.
20. .101.
21. 242.16.
22. 1.007.
23. 8.788.
24. .000009.
25. .00353.

EXERCISE 181. Pages 365-366.

1. 3.3397.
2. 1.5050.
3. 3.3804.
4. 4.2939.
5. .4407.
6. .2112.
7. .1556.
8. .3820.
9. 55237.5.
10. 8.55.
11. 1.85.
12. 1.77.
13. 1017.9.
14. 3691.6.
15. 144.
16. 523.75.
17. .542.
18. 92.06
19. 1.98.
20. .402.

21. (a) 9177.5.　(b) 6990.
22. (a) 7240.　(b) 998.2.
23. (a) $248.64.　(b) $464.10.
24. (a) $369.75.　(b) $125.48.
25. 42 bbl. (about).

EXERCISE 182. Page 367.

1. An A. P.　Diff. = 3.
Next two terms: 16, 19.

2. Not an A. P.

3. An A. P.　Diff. = − 3.
Next two terms: − 2, − 5.

4. An A. P.　Diff. = − 5.
Next two terms: 5, 0.

5. An A. P.　Diff. = .75.
Next two terms: 5.5, 6.25.

6. An A. P.　Diff. = 2.5 m.
Next two terms: 12.5 m, 15 m.

7. An A. P.　Diff. = − 2.5 p.
Next two terms: − 3.5 p, − 6 p.

8. An A. P.　Diff. = .06.
Next two terms: 1.24, 1.30.

ANSWERS

9. An A. P. Diff. $= b$.
   Next two terms: $a+4b$, $a+5b$.
10. An A. P. Diff. $r - 2s$.
    Next two terms: $8r$, $9r - 2s$.
11. 15, 21, 27, 33, 39.
12. 25, 17, 9, 1, -7.
13. 7.5, 11, 14.5, 18, 21.5.
14. x, $x-4$, $x-8$, $x-12$, $x-16$.
15. a, $a+d$, $a+2d$, $a+3d$, $a+4d$.

EXERCISE 183. Pages 368–369.

1. 69 ; 117.
2. -40 ; -80.
3. -67 ; -157.
4. $9\frac{1}{2}$; 27.
5. 1.55 ; 2.30.
6. 27.
7. 27.
8. 41.
9. 35.
10. 21.
11. 2.
12. 8.
13. $\frac{1}{2}$.
14. -10.
15. 61.
16. $10.95 ; $11.20.

EXERCISE 184. Page 370.

1. 3, 7, 11, 15, 19.
2. -10, -4, 2, 8, 14, 20.
3. 3, 5.5, 8, 10.5, 13, 15.5, 18, 20.5, 23, 25.5, 28.
4. $\frac{1}{2}$, $1\frac{1}{4}$, 2, $2\frac{3}{4}$, $3\frac{1}{2}$, $4\frac{1}{4}$, 5.
5. $-\frac{5}{4}$, $-1\frac{7}{8}$, $-2\frac{1}{2}$, $-3\frac{1}{8}$, $-3\frac{3}{4}$, $-4\frac{3}{8}$, -5.
6. 11.
7. $2\sqrt{2}$.
8. x.
9. $\dfrac{a+b}{2}$.
10. $\dfrac{s-r}{3}$.
11. $\dfrac{p-m}{k+1}$.

EXERCISE 185. Pages 371–373.

1. 432.
2. -630.
3. -264.
4. $13.30.
5. 330.
6. 620.
7. 36.
8. $\frac{2}{5}$.
9. 5050.
10. 2550.
11. 2500.
12. 15750.
13. Salary, 10th yr., $810.
    Total earnings, $5850.
14. $1330.
15. 325.
16. $990.
17. $323.25.
18. $19D$; $(2t-1)D$.
19. $25D$; $100D$; t^2D.
20. 209.04 ft. ; $16.08(2t-1)$ ft.
21. 402 ft. ; $16.08 t^2$ ft.
22. $S = \frac{1}{2}gt^2$.

EXERCISE 186. Pages 374–375.

1. $a = 1$; $S = 540$.
2. $d = 3$; $S = 552$.
3. $n = 35$; $d = \frac{1}{4}$.
4. $n = 22$; $S = \frac{1}{2}$.
5. $a = -3$; $l = 5$.
6. $d = \frac{3}{8}$; $l = 6$.
7. $n = 13$; $d = -\frac{3}{4}$.
8. $n = 15$, $l = -3$;
   $n = 6$, $l = \frac{15}{4}$.

ALGEBRA

9. $d = \dfrac{l-a}{n-1}$.

10. $n = \dfrac{l-a+d}{d}$.

11. $l = \dfrac{2S - na}{n}$.

12. $a = \dfrac{2S - nd(n-1)}{2n}$.

13. $a = l - (n-1)d$.
    $S = \dfrac{n}{2}\{2l - (n-1)d\}$.

14. -50.

15. 31.

16. $\frac{5}{2}$.

17. $10, 2, -6, -14$.

18. $-6, -2, 2, 6, 10$;
    $21, \frac{84}{7}, \frac{41}{7}, -\frac{12}{7}, -\frac{65}{7}$.

19. $-3, 7, 17$; $-3, -9\frac{2}{5}, -15\frac{4}{5}$.

20. $-5, 4, 13$.

EXERCISE 187. Pages 375–376.

1. $r = 2$.
   64, and 128.

2. Not a G. P.

3. $r = \frac{1}{3}$.
   3, and 1.

4. $r = -3$.
   -162, and 486.

5. $r = \frac{1}{2}$.
   $\dfrac{5m}{8}$, and $\dfrac{5m}{16}$.

6. $r = 2x$.
   $24x^4$, and $48x^5$.

7. Not a G. P.

8. $r = (1+r)$.
   $(1+r)^4$, and $(1+r)^5$.

9. $r = \dfrac{1}{m}$.
   $\dfrac{1}{m^4}$, and $\dfrac{1}{m^5}$.

10. $r = \dfrac{1}{5x}$.
    $\dfrac{2}{25x^4}$, and $\dfrac{2}{125x^5}$.

11. $-5, 10, -20, 40, -80$.

12. $100, 20, 4, \frac{4}{5}, \frac{4}{25}$.

13. $\frac{1}{3}, \frac{2}{3}, \frac{4}{3}, \frac{8}{3}, \frac{16}{3}$.

14. $\frac{1}{2}x, \frac{1}{6}x, \frac{1}{18}x, \frac{1}{54}x, \frac{1}{162}x$.

15. a, ar, ar^2, ar^3, ar^4.

EXERCISE 188. Pages 376–377.

1. 243. 2. $\frac{128}{243}$. 3. -1250. 4. $\frac{3}{256}$. 5. 1280. 6. $4x^8$.

7. $(1+r)^{10}$. 8. $\dfrac{1}{2^{14}}$; $\dfrac{1}{2^{k-1}}$. 9. $\dfrac{m^{13}}{3^{12}}$; $\dfrac{m^{n+1}}{3^n}$.

10. 8. 11. 6. 12. 6. 13. $\frac{1}{2}$. 14. 3. 15. 2.

EXERCISE 189. Page 378.

1. $3, 9, 27, 81, 243, 729$.

2. $2, 4, 8, 16, 32, 64, 128$; or
   $2, -4, 8, -16, 32, -64, 128$.

3. $\frac{1}{9}, \frac{1}{3}, 1, 3$.

4. $8, 16, 32$; or $8, -16, 32$.

5. $3t, \dfrac{1}{2}, \dfrac{1}{12t}$; or
   $3t, -\dfrac{1}{2}, \dfrac{1}{12t}$.

ANSWERS 57

6. $2x, 4x^3, 8x^5$; or
$2x, -4x^3, 8x^5$.

7. $\dfrac{m}{x}, 1, \dfrac{x}{m}$; or $\dfrac{m}{x}, -1, \dfrac{x}{m}$.

8. $a, \sqrt{ab}, b$; or $a, -\sqrt{ab}, b$.

9. $3, 3\sqrt{2}, 6, 6\sqrt{2}, 12$;
$3, -3\sqrt{2}, 6, -6\sqrt{2}, 12$;
$3, 3\sqrt{-2}, -6, -6\sqrt{-2}, 12$; or
$3, -3\sqrt{-2}, -6, 6\sqrt{-2}, 12$.

10. $a, \sqrt[3]{a^2b}, \sqrt[3]{ab^2}, b$.

EXERCISE 190. Page 379.

1. 1275.
2. $47\frac{1}{4}$.
3. 2735.
4. $\frac{547}{18}$.
5. -1042.
6. $\dfrac{3m(1-m^{30})}{1-m^2}$.
7. $\dfrac{1-m^{20}}{1-m^2}$.
8. $\dfrac{(1+r)^{15}-1}{r}$.
9. 2046.
10. 88,572.
11. $4118.
12. 1984.
13. $6553.55.

EXERCISE 191. Page 381.

1. 9.
2. 2.
3. $21\frac{1}{3}$.
4. $5\frac{5}{9}$.
5. $1\frac{1}{9}$.
6. $2x$.
7. $\frac{10}{9}a$.
8. $\frac{5}{6}$.
9. -5.
10. $\frac{9}{104}$.
12. $\frac{1}{3}$.
13. $\frac{7}{9}$.
14. $\frac{8}{15}$.
15. $\frac{29}{45}$.
16. $\frac{7}{33}$.
17. $\frac{5}{33}$.

EXERCISE 192. Pages 383–384.

1. $x^4 + 4x^3y + 6x^2y^2 + 4xy^3 + y^4$.
2. $m^5 - 5m^4n + 10m^3n^2 - 10m^2n^3 + 5mn^4 - n^5$.
3. $c^4 + 4c^3 + 6c^2 + 4c + 1$.
4. $r^5 - 10r^4 + 40r^3 - 80r^2 + 80r - 32$.
5. $m^6 + 6m^5n + 15m^4n^2 + 20m^3n^3 + 15m^2n^4 + 6mn^5 + n^6$.
6. $a^8 - 4a^6b^2 + 6a^4b^4 - 4a^2b^6 + b^8$.
7. $32a^5 + 80a^4 + 80a^3 + 40a^2 + 10a + 1$.
8. $a^4 - 12a^3b + 54a^2b^2 - 108ab^3 + 81b^4$.
9. $1 + 6x^2 + 15x^4 + 20x^6 + 15x^8 + 6x^{10} + x^{12}$.
10. $1 - 8x + 28x^2 - 56x^3 + 70x^4 - 56x^5 + 28x^6 - 8x^7 + x^8$.
11. $a^5 - \frac{5}{2}a^4 + \frac{5}{2}a^3 - \frac{5}{4}a^2 + \frac{5}{16}a - \frac{1}{32}$.
12. $\frac{1}{81} + \frac{4}{27}x + \frac{2}{3}x^2 + \frac{4}{3}x^3 + x^4$.
13. $64m^{12} - 192m^{10} + 240m^8 - 160m^6 + 60m^4 - 12m^2 + 1$.

14. $a^8 + 4a^6b^2c + 6a^4b^4c^2 + 4a^2b^6c^3 + b^8c^4$.
15. $243 + 405x^3 + 270x^6 + 90x^9 + 15x^{12} + x^{15}$.
16. $a^{15} - 45a^{14} + 945a^{13} - \cdots$.
17. $m^{40} + 40m^{38}n + 760m^{36}n^2 + \cdots$.
18. $a^{16} - 8a^{15} + 30a^{14} \cdots$.
19. $a^{20} - 10a^{18}b^3 + 45a^{16}b^6 \cdots$.
20. $x^{36} + 36x^{33}y^5 + 594x^{30}y^{10} \cdots$.
21. $m^{22} - 44m^{20}n^2 + 880m^{18}n^4 \cdots$.
22. $\dfrac{1}{a^7} + \dfrac{7}{a^6b} + \dfrac{21}{a^5b^2} \cdots$.
23. $\dfrac{1}{a^6} - \dfrac{6}{a^4} + \dfrac{15}{a^2} \cdots$.
24. $\dfrac{a^8}{b^8} + 8\dfrac{a^6}{b^6} + 28\dfrac{a^4}{b^4} \cdots$.
25. $a^{-5} + 5a^{-4}b^{-2} + 10a^{-3}b^{-4} \cdots$.
26. $a^{\frac{7}{2}} - 7a^3b^{\frac{1}{3}} + 21a^{\frac{5}{2}}b^{\frac{2}{3}} \cdots$.
27. $8 - 24\sqrt{6} + 180 \cdots$.
28. $a^n + na^{n-1}x + \dfrac{n(n-1)}{1 \cdot 2}a^{n-2}x^2 + \dfrac{n(n-1)(n-2)}{1 \cdot 2 \cdot 3}a^{n-3}x^3 \cdots$.

EXERCISE 193. Page 385.

1. $56a^5x^3$.
2. $165m^3n^8$.
3. $2016g^5$.
4. $-11440q^7x^9$.
5. $-792m^{10}n^{21}$.
6. $61236a^{15}x^{25}$.
7. $\frac{5005}{64}c^9$.
8. $210 \cdot 64 \cdot 81 \cdot x^{12}$.
9. $-792x^{7m}y^{5n}$.
10. $\dfrac{5005a^9}{b^3}$.
11. $-220\dfrac{x^{15}}{y^3}$.
12. $-1716 \cdot 128\, x^{-6}y^{\frac{7}{2}}$.

EXERCISE 194. Pages 386–387.

10. 27, 36.
11. 25, 11.
12. 93.5 ft.
13. 22, 33, 44.
14. 270 acres, and 450 acres.
15. $200, $300, $500.

EXERCISE 195. Pages 387–388.

1. $\frac{5}{3}$.
2. $\frac{20}{3}$.
3. $\frac{35}{16}$.
4. 8.
5. -5.5.
6. -2.
7. $\dfrac{ac}{b}$.
8. $\dfrac{3ac}{2b}$.
9. $\dfrac{rt}{s}$.
10. $\dfrac{cp}{m}$.
11. $\dfrac{ab}{a+b}$.
12. $\dfrac{mn}{n-a}$.

… ANSWERS

EXERCISE 196. Pages 388–389.

1. 10.
2. $\frac{8}{5}$.
3. 6.
4. 8.
5. $\frac{bc}{3a}$.
6. y^2.
7. ± 30.
8. $\pm \frac{1}{5}\sqrt{35}$.
9. $\pm a\sqrt{2}$.
10. $\pm 6\,mn\sqrt{mn}$.
11. $\pm(a-3)$.
12. $\pm(x^2+xy+y^2)$.
13. $138\frac{8}{9}$.
14. $\frac{27}{175}$.
15. $\frac{a}{2}$.
16. $\frac{3n^3}{4}$.
17. $\frac{a-3}{a+3}$.
18. $\frac{9y^2}{10x}$.
19. $\frac{1}{2}$.
20. $\pm\dfrac{x-y}{a-b}$.

EXERCISE 197. Pages 392–393.

1. a. $\dfrac{4}{3}=\dfrac{20}{15}$; b. $\dfrac{5}{2}=\dfrac{x}{m}$; c. $\dfrac{b}{a}=\dfrac{y}{x}$.

2. a. $\dfrac{3}{15}=\dfrac{4}{20}$; b. $\dfrac{2}{m}=\dfrac{5}{x}$; c. $\dfrac{a}{x}=\dfrac{b}{y}$.

3. a. $\dfrac{7}{4}=\dfrac{35}{20}$; b. $\dfrac{7}{5}=\dfrac{m+x}{x}$; c. $\dfrac{a+b}{b}=\dfrac{x+y}{y}$.

4. a. $\dfrac{-1}{4}=\dfrac{-5}{20}$; b. $\dfrac{-3}{5}=\dfrac{m-x}{x}$; c. $\dfrac{a-b}{b}=\dfrac{x-y}{y}$.

5. a. $\dfrac{b+a}{a}=\dfrac{x+y}{x}$; b. $\dfrac{a-x}{x}=\dfrac{b-y}{y}$; c. $\dfrac{a+b}{x+y}=\dfrac{b}{y}$; d. $\dfrac{b}{a-b}=\dfrac{y}{x-y}$.

EXERCISE 198. Pages 393–394.

5. $4\frac{4}{7}$.
6. $5\frac{5}{6}$.
7. $AE = EC$.
8. AE, $21\frac{3}{7}$; EC, $8\frac{4}{7}$.
11. 60 ft.
12. 105 ft.
13. 887 ft.

EXERCISE 199. Pages 397–399.

1. $A \propto ba$; $A = kab$.
2. $A \propto d^2$; $A = kd^2$.
3. $V \propto lwh$; $V = klwh$.
4. $d \propto n^2$; $d = kn^2$.
5. $I \propto Prt$; $I = kPrt$.
6. $r = \dfrac{k}{t}$.
7. $r = \dfrac{k}{c}$.
8. $w = \dfrac{k}{d^2}$.
9. $c = \dfrac{ks}{n}$.
10. $v = kar^2$.
12. 72.
13. $y = \frac{5}{8}x^3$.
14. $\frac{1}{3}$.
15. -18.
16. 576 ft.
17. $375.
18. $6400.
19. 150.
20. 64.

ALGEBRA

EXERCISE 200. Page 400.

1. $2x+1$.
2. $1-4a$.
3. $3m^2+1$.
4. $2t^2-5$.
5. $\dfrac{a}{2}-\dfrac{b}{3}$

EXERCISE 201. Page 402.

1. $c+d$.
2. $r-s$.
3. a^2+4b.
4. $3m+5n$.
5. x^2-2x-1.
6. $2a^2+3a+1$.
7. $2y^2+y-2$.
8. a^2-3a-2.

EXERCISE 202. Page 404.

1. 27.
2. 53.
3. 3.9.
4. 136.
5. 9.5.
6. 3.59.
7. 57.2.
8. 7.63.
9. 92.4.

EXERCISE 203. Page 405.

1-5. See answers to examples 21-25 of Exercise 35.
6-10. See answers to examples 21-25 of Exercise 46.

EXERCISE 204. Pages 409-410.

1. $x-3$.
2. $x-2$.
3. $2m^2-m+1$.
4. $y(x+3)$.
5. $4x-3y$.
6. n^2+3n-2.
7. $3a^3+4a^2-a-2$.
8. $3b^2-b-1$.
9. $3a^2+ax-2x^2$.
10. $x-2$.

EXERCISE 205. Page 410.

1. H.C.F. $=3a-1$.
   L.C.M. $=(a-4)(3a^2+14a-5)$.
2. H.C.F. $=2a+3b$.
   L.C.M. $=(3a+8b)(12a^2+16ab-3b^2)$.
3. H.C.F. $=m-3$.
   L.C.M. $=(12m+15)(4m^3-11m^2-6m+9)$.
4. H.C.F. $=a^2-4a-3$.
   L.C.M. $=(2a+3)(3a^3-14a^2-a+6)$.
5. H.C.F. $=2x^2-x+1$.
   L.C.M. $=(3x-2)(4x^4-5x^2+4x-3)$.

ANSWERS

EXERCISE 206. Page 415.

1. ∞.
2. ∞.
3. 0.
4. $\frac{2}{5}$.
5. 0.
6. ∞.
7. ∞.
8. 0.
9. 2.
10. 0.
11. -4.
12. ∞.
13. 0.
14. $\frac{5}{3}$.
15. $-\frac{1}{5}$.
16. 1.
17. $x = \infty$.
    $y = \infty$.
18. $x = -\infty$.
    $y = \infty$.

EXERCISE 207. Page 416.

1. $-1; 1; 3$.
2. $-2; 1; 5$.
3. $-3; 0; 2$.
4. $-3; -1; 1; 3$.
5. $-1; -\sqrt{10}; \sqrt{10}$.
6. $1; -2\sqrt{2}; 2\sqrt{2}$.

EXERCISE 208. Page 417.

1. -8.
2. -41.
3. 48.
4. 13.
5. -36.
6. $3a - 8c$.
7. $2mr + 2np$.
8. $15ae - 8cd$.
9. $\begin{vmatrix} m & y \\ x & n \end{vmatrix}$.
10. $\begin{vmatrix} 2a & d \\ c & b \end{vmatrix}$.
11. $\begin{vmatrix} 3 & 7 \\ 2 & 11 \end{vmatrix}$.
12. $\begin{vmatrix} 2c & 1 \\ 5d & 3 \end{vmatrix}$.
13. $\begin{vmatrix} c & -q \\ p & d \end{vmatrix}$.
14. $\begin{vmatrix} 3m & -2s \\ r & n \end{vmatrix}$.

EXERCISE 209. Page 419.

1-10. See answers to examples 1-10 respectively of Exercise 101, Page 224.

EXERCISE 210. Page 420.

1. 12.
2. 20.
3. -154.
5. $x = 7; y = 8; z = -9$.
6. $x = -3; y = -4; z = 1.5$.
7. $a = 3; b = 4; c = -5$.
8. $x = -2; y = -3; z = 1$.
9. $x = -1\frac{1}{7}; y = \frac{4}{3}; z = -\frac{2}{3}$.
10. $x = -\frac{8}{5}; y = \frac{1}{5}; z = -\frac{2}{5}$.

R. + J. = R. J.